SEQUENCE SPACES AND SERIES

PURE AND APPLIED MATHEMATICS

A Program of Monographs, Textbooks, and Lecture Notes

Contributions to *Lecture Notes in Pure and Applied Mathematics* are reproduced by direct photography of the author's typewritten manuscript. Potential authors are advised to submit preliminary manuscripts for review purposes. After acceptance, the author is responsible for preparing the final manuscript in camera-ready form, suitable for direct reproduction. Marcel Dekker, Inc. will furnish instructions to authors and special typing paper. Sample pages are reviewed and returned with our suggestions to assure quality control and the most attractive rendering of your manuscript. The publisher will also be happy to supervise and assist in all stages of the preparation of your camera-ready manuscript.

LECTURE NOTES
IN PURE AND APPLIED MATHEMATICS

1. *N. Jacobson,* Exceptional Lie Algebras
2. *L.-Å. Lindahl and F. Poulsen,* Thin Sets in Harmonic Analysis
3. *I. Satake,* Classification Theory of Semi-Simple Algebraic Groups
4. *F. Hirzebruch, W. D. Newmann, and S. S. Koh,* Differentiable Manifolds and Quadratic Forms *(out of print)*
5. *I. Chavel,* Riemannian Symmetric Spaces of Rank One
6. *R. B. Burckel,* Characterization of C(X) Among Its Subalgebras
7. *B. R. McDonald, A. R. Magid, and K. C. Smith,* Ring Theory: Proceedings of the Oklahoma Conference
8. *Y.-T. Siu,* Techniques of Extension of Analytic Objects
9. *S. R. Caradus, W. E. Pfaffenberger, and B. Yood,* Calkin Algebras and Algebras of Operators on Banach Spaces
10. *E. O. Roxin, P.-T. Liu, and R. L. Sternberg,* Differential Games and Control Theory
11. *M. Orzech and C. Small,* The Brauer Group of Commutative Rings
12. *S. Thomeier,* Topology and Its Applications
13. *J. M. López and K. A. Ross,* Sidon Sets
14. *W. W. Comfort and S. Negrepontis,* Continuous Pseudometrics
15. *K. McKennon and J. M. Robertson,* Locally Convex Spaces
16. *M. Carmeli and S. Malin,* Representations of the Rotation and Lorentz Groups: An Introduction
17. *G. B. Seligman,* Rational Methods in Lie Algebras
18. *D. G. de Figueiredo,* Functional Analysis: Proceedings of the Brazilian Mathematical Society Symposium
19. *L. Cesari, R. Kannan, and J. D. Schuur,* Nonlinear Functional Analysis and Differential Equations: Proceedings of the Michigan State University Conference
20. *J. J. Schäffer,* Geometry of Spheres in Normed Spaces
21. *K. Yano and M. Kon,* Anti-Invariant Submanifolds
22. *W. V. Vasconcelos,* The Rings of Dimension Two
23. *R. E. Chandler,* Hausdorff Compactifications
24. *S. P. Franklin and B. V. S. Thomas,* Topology: Proceedings of the Memphis State University Conference
25. *S. K. Jain,* Ring Theory: Proceedings of the Ohio University Conference
26. *B. R. McDonald and R. A. Morris,* Ring Theory II: Proceedings of the Second Oklahoma Conference
27. *R. B. Mura and A. Rhemtulla,* Orderable Groups
28. *J. R. Graef,* Stability of Dynamical Systems: Theory and Applications
29. *H.-C. Wang,* Homogeneous Banach Algebras
30. *E. O. Roxin, P.-T. Liu, and R. L. Sternberg,* Differential Games and Control Theory II
31. *R. D. Porter,* Introduction to Fibre Bundles
32. *M. Altman,* Contractors and Contractor Directions Theory and Applications
33. *J. S. Golan,* Decomposition and Dimension in Module Categories
34. *G. Fairweather,* Finite Element Galerkin Methods for Differential Equations
35. *J. D. Sally,* Numbers of Generators of Ideals in Local Rings
36. *S. S. Miller,* Complex Analysis: Proceedings of the S.U.N.Y. Brockport Conference
37. *R. Gordon,* Representation Theory of Algebras: Proceedings of the Philadelphia Conference
38. *M. Goto and F. D. Grosshans,* Semisimple Lie Algebras
39. *A. I. Arruda, N. C. A. da Costa, and R. Chuaqui,* Mathematical Logic: Proceedings of the First Brazilian Conference
40. *F. Van Oystaeyen,* Ring Theory: Proceedings of the 1977 Antwerp Conference

41. *F. Van Oystaeyen and A. Verschoren,* Reflectors and Localization: Application to Sheaf Theory
42. *M. Satyanarayana,* Positively Ordered Semigroups
43. *D. L. Russell,* Mathematics of Finite-Dimensional Control Systems
44. *P.-T. Liu and E. Roxin,* Differential Games and Control Theory III: Proceedings of the Third Kingston Conference, Part A
45. *A. Geramita and J. Seberry,* Orthogonal Designs: Quadratic Forms and Hadamard Matrices
46. *J. Cigler, V. Losert, and P. Michor,* Banach Modules and Functors on Categories of Banach Spaces
47. *P.-T. Liu and J. G. Sutinen,* Control Theory in Mathematical Economics: Proceedings of the Third Kingston Conference, Part B
48. *C. Byrnes,* Partial Differential Equations and Geometry
49. *G. Klambauer,* Problems and Propositions in Analysis
50. *J. Knopfmacher,* Analytic Arithmetic of Algebraic Function Fields
51. *F. Van Oystaeyen,* Ring Theory: Proceedings of the 1978 Antwerp Conference
52. *B. Kedem,* Binary Time Series
53. *J. Barros-Neto and R. A. Artino,* Hypoelliptic Boundary-Value Problems
54. *R. L. Sternberg, A. J. Kalinowski, and J. S. Papadakis,* Nonlinear Partial Differential Equations in Engineering and Applied Science
55. *B. R. McDonald,* Ring Theory and Algebra III: Proceedings of The Third Oklahoma Conference
56. *J. S. Golan,* Structure Sheaves over a Noncommutative Ring
57. *T. V. Narayana, J. G. Williams, and R. M. Mathsen,* Combinatorics, Representation Theory and Statistical Methods in Groups: YOUNG DAY Proceedings
58. *T. A. Burton,* Modeling and Differential Equations in Biology
59. *K. H. Kim and F. W. Roush,* Introduction to Mathematical Consensus Theory
60. *J. Banas and K. Goebel,* Measures of Noncompactness in Banach Spaces
61. *O. A. Nielsen,* Direct Integral Theory
62. *J. E. Smith, G. O. Kenny, and R. N. Ball,* Ordered Groups: Proceedings of the Boise State Conference
63. *J. Cronin,* Mathematics of Cell Electrophysiology
64. *J. W. Brewer,* Power Series Over Commutative Rings (in press)
65. *P. K. Kamthan and M. Gupta,* Sequence Spaces and Series

Other Volumes in Preparation

SEQUENCE SPACES AND SERIES

P. K. Kamthan
Indian Institute of Technology
Kanpur, India

Manjul Gupta
Indian Institute of Technology
Kanpur, India

MARCEL DEKKER, INC. New York and Basel

Library of Congress Cataloging in Publication Data

Kamthan, P. K. [date]
Sequence spaces and series.

(Lecture notes in pure and applied mathematics ; 65)
Includes bibliographical references and indexes.
1. Sequence spaces. 2. Series, Infinite.
3. Convergence. I. Gupta, Manjul [date] joint author. II. Title
QA322.K35 515.7'3 80-29517
ISBN 0-8247-1224-2

MARCEL DEKKER, INC.
270 Madison Avenue, New York, New York 10016

Current printing (last digit):
10 9 8 7 6 5 4 3 2 1

PRINTED IN THE UNITED STATES OF AMERICA

To

G. Köthe

the creator of modern sequence space theory

and

our parents

for their lasting encouragement

PREFACE

The present monograph is a result of a research project which was begun almost a decade ago with the intention of knitting together many theorems on the Schauder basis theory in locally convex spaces. After much discussion, we realized that a useful treatment of the Schauder basis theory could best be presented after a very systematic study of the theory of topological sequence spaces and series.

In attempting to fulfill this objective, we rediscovered the wide applicability of sequence spaces and series to several other branches of functional analysis, e.g., the theory of functions, summability theory, the theory of locally convex spaces, nuclear spaces, and matrix transformations. It was this background that prompted us a couple of years ago to undertake a smaller project on sequence spaces and series with partial support from the then Educational Development Centre, Indian Institute of Technology, Kanpur. The results are contained in a set of mimeographed notes (1975-1976).

Since the appearance of the first typed draft, the material of the present book has undergone substantial enlargement and enormous revision.

Though there are available a few books dealing partially with sequence spaces and series, the overlap between this book and other texts on related topics is very small. Indeed, an advanced and up-to-date treatment of the duality theory displayed by distinct pairs of sequence spaces, the past ten years' research in several topological aspects of new and classical sequence spaces, and the advances in the convergence theory of series in topological vector spaces are among the important features of this monograph, which we hope will bridge the wide gap between the available literature and further developments in this direction. We do not claim here an exhaustive treatment of the subject matter, but we have attempted to make this small treatise profitable to the community of research workers in various branches of functional analysis. At the same time, we have also taken care to ensure that a good part of this book is accessible to graduate students who have had a first course in the theory of topological vector spaces.

Except for Chapter 1, almost every section of the text provides sufficient motivation to give beginners an insight into the subject matter. To deepen understanding of a particular topic, many exercises with possible hints for solutions have been added from Chapter 2 on, along with a large number of definitions, propositions, and theorems. In addition, examples and counterexamples are included throughout Chapters 2 through 4 to enable the reader to appreciate the scope and limits of related results.

All definitions, examples, exercises, propositions, theorems, and corollaries, and a few relevant equations of each Chapter x (x = 1, 2, 3, or 4) are double-numbered by section; for instance, Exercise u.v of Chapter x is an exercise from Section u having the serial number v relative to all preceding results of this section; and if this exercise is referred to in another Chapter $y \neq x$, it is cited as Exercise x.u.v. On the other hand, a result within the same Chapter x is indicated merely by the number of that result; that is, no mention of x is made. The symbol □ at the end of a proof indicates its completion.

Chapters 1 through 4 are organized as follows. Chapter 1, which contains results from the theory of topological vector spaces and a brief description of nuclear spaces (all results being given without proof), will facilitate the reading of the material of subsequent chapters. Although most of the results of Chapter 1 are to be found in one of the standard texts referred to in the introductory remarks of that chapter, with some trimming and pruning here and there, there are many propositions which have been taken from recent papers and theses mentioned appropriately therein. For the sake of notation and terminology, the reader is urged to glance at the first few pages of Chapter 1, which is indeed a prelude to the rest of the book.

Chapter 2 is substantially devoted to very basic material in the theory of sequence spaces, and in fact lays the foundation of numerous preliminary ideas on the natural structures and topologies as well as the duality theory of sequence spaces. Theorem 8.3, which deals with the Mackey convergence of the Nth section of a sequence and is due originally to Köthe, is one of the fundamental results of this chapter. It also contains a table of 17 different sequence spaces, exhibiting their α-, β-, γ-, and topological duals.

Chapter 3 is concerned primarily with a number of notions on the convergence of infinite series together with their interrelationships and applications to linear operators in the most general setting of topological vector spaces. The results of this chapter not only find application in this book but are also useful in the study of several branches of analysis and functional analysis dealing with the different modes of convergence of infinite series.

Chapter 4, which is mainly concerned with some advanced topics in sequence spaces, reflects a wide spectrum of recent investigations, revealing in particular their applications in inclusion maps theory, matrix transformations, the nuclearity of spaces, the Schauder basis theory, and the theory of summability domains. It also presents the duality theory between a sequence space and its β-dual, a few generalizations of results of Chapter 2, and an introduction to structure theorems on Lorentz and Orlicz sequence spaces.

An overall picture of the project referred to at the beginning of this note includes future publications on (i) bases in topological vector spaces and applications; (ii) decompositions of topological vector spaces; and (iii) Schauder bases, ε-entropy, and nuclearity, of which (i) and (ii) are nearing their final drafts and the last one is now being written. The present monograph will undoubtedly serve as an introduction to the later ones.

We are extremely grateful to our family and friends whose moral support through many difficulties we had to face in compiling this monograph (including obtaining financial support for the purchase of many items that one normally needs to prepare a typed draft) always encouraged us toward the completion of this project.

It is indeed our pleasure to record our gratitude to Professor G. Bennett, U.S.A., who obliged us many times with his prompt solutions of some problems in Chapter 4. We are also grateful to Professors T. Husain, Canada, and G. Köthe, West Germany, for a few solutions of problems in Chapters 1 and 2, and we extend our thanks further to Professor Husain, who made available a part of his National Research Council grant to one of us to visit McMaster University in 1974, where a portion of the original draft of our planned project was completed. We gratefully acknowledge the kindly advice rendered by Professors A. Pełczynski, Poland, and I. Singer, Romania, during the writing of the manuscript.

We deeply appreciate the kind words and suggestions of Professors C. Besaga, Poland, N. De Grande-De Kimpe, Belgium, E. Dubinsky, U.S.A.,

D. J. H. Garling, England, B. S. Mitiagin, U.S.S.R., and A. Pietsch, East Germany, regarding portions of this monograph. Thanks are also due to our students J. Patterson and M. A. Sofi for their help in preparing the index. We further acknowledge Sofi's pointing out a number of oversights in the final draft of the manuscript.

Finally, we shall consider ourselves amply rewarded if this work could serve students and scholars alike in the spirit in which it was initiated, and we shall be grateful to receive any useful comments toward the improvement of this monograph.

Indian Institute of Technology
Kanpur

P. K. Kamthan
Manjul Gupta

CONTENTS

Chapter 1

PREREQUISITES

1. INTRODUCTION

The theory of sequence spaces and series presented in subsequent chapters depends essentially upon various results from topological vector spaces and their ramifications.

Therefore, as a prelude to our basic work, keeping in view the readers' need for ready references, we list here almost all those important results from the theory of topological vector spaces we are going to make ample use of in the next three chapters. However, this is by no means an exhaustive treatment of the subject matter. These results were gathered from several monographs, research papers, and standard texts; see, for example, Refs. 20, 21, 36, 48, 63, 76, 92, 93, 132, 134, 140, 204, 207, 221, 225, 227, 245, and 264, and many other research papers and theses cited throughout the chapter. All results are stated without proof and can be found in at least one of the sources mentioned above; we leave to the reader to find the corresponding proofs in the references. In case a particular result is not to be found in any of the standard texts, the corresponding reference is given either before or after the statement. Finally, we assume the reader's familiarity with the basic facts from algebra, measure theory, and topology.

2. TOPOLOGICAL VECTOR SPACES

The following notation will be used throughout the sequel.

$\mathbb{R}$ = set of all real numbers

$\mathbb{C}$ = set of all complex numbers

$\mathbb{N}$ = set of all positive integers

$\mathbb{R}_+$ = set of all positive real numbers

$\mathbb{R}^+$ = $\mathbb{R}_+ \cup \{0\}$

$\mathbb{K}$ = $\mathbb{R}$ or $\mathbb{C}$ equipped with its usual topology

X = a nontrivial vector space over $\mathbb{K}$

Vector addition between any two elements x and y in X and scalar multiplication between α in $\mathbb{K}$ and x in X are respectively written as $x + y$ and αx. For any two sets A and B contained in X and any α in $\mathbb{K}$, we use the notation $A + B$, αA, and $A \sim B$ to mean respectively the following sets: $\{x + y : x \in A, y \in B\}$, $\{\alpha x : x \in A\}$ and $\{x : x \in A, x \notin B\}$. In case we wish to emphasize a certain property P of the vector space X, we write X as (X,P); also, for any subset A of X, we use the *symbol* sp{A} to mean the *linear hull* or the *space generated* by A. A *sequence* (resp. *net*) in X will be denoted by $\{x_n\}$ (resp. $\{x_\alpha\}$, where the α's belong to a directed set Λ); we shall frequently use the notation

$n \geq k$ (resp. $\alpha \geq \beta$) or $\forall n \geq k$ (resp. $\alpha \geq \beta$)

interchangeably, to mean all integers in $\mathbb{N}$ (resp. all members in Λ) which are greater than and equal to k in $\mathbb{N}$ (resp. β in Λ).

DEFINITION 2.1 An arbitrary subset A of X is said to be (i) *absorbing* if for each x in X there exists an α in $\mathbb{K}$ with $x \in \alpha A$; (ii) *balanced* if $\lambda A \subset A$ for all λ with $|\lambda| \leq 1$; (iii) *convex* if for each pair $x,y \in A$, $\{\alpha x + (1 - \alpha)y : 0 \leq \alpha \leq 1\} \subset A$; and (iv) *absolutely convex* if A is balanced and convex. Further, the smallest convex (resp. absolutely convex) set containing a given subset A of X is termed as the *convex* (resp. *absolutely convex* or *balanced convex*) *hull* of A and is denoted by con(A) [resp. $\Gamma(A)$]. For sets A and B in X, the notation $A \prec B$ means that B absorbs A, i.e., $A \subset \alpha B$ for some α in $\mathbb{K}$.

DEFINITION 2.2 A vector space X equipped with a topology T, which we usually write as (X,T), is called a *topological vector space* (abbreviated TVS) if the operations

(TV_1) $(x,y) \to x + y$ from $X \times X \to X$

(TV_2) $(\alpha,x) \to \alpha x$ from $\mathbb{K} \times X \to X$

are jointly continuous, where $X \times X$ and $\mathbb{K} \times X$ are equipped with their usual product topologies. A topology T on X such that (X,T) becomes a TVS is referred to as a *linear* or *vector topology* on X.

PROPOSITION 2.3 A vector space X equipped with a topology T is a TVS if and only if there exists a *filter base* or a *fundamental neighborhood system* $\mathcal{B}$ (at the origin of X) consisting of subsets of X such that

(FN_1) Each u in $\mathcal{B}$ is absorbing and balanced.

(FN_2) For each u in $\mathcal{B}$ there corresponds a v in $\mathcal{B}$ with $v + v \subset u$.

Remark: Proposition 2.3 is still valid if (FN_1) is replaced by

(FN_1)' Each u in $\mathcal{B}$ is absorbing, balanced, and T-closed.

From now on, the letter $\mathcal{B}$ (or $\mathcal{B}_T$ in case we wish to emphasize the underlying topology T) will stand for a neighborhood system at the origin of a TVS (X,T) with $\mathcal{B}$ satisfying (FN_1)' and (FN_2).

If the family $\mathcal{B}$ in Proposition 2.3 satisfies the conditions (FN_2) and

(FN_1)" Each u in $\mathcal{B}$ is absorbing, balanced, and convex

the corresponding linear topology T on X is called a *locally convex topology* and the space (X,T) is said to be a *locally convex topological vector space* (abbreviated l.c. TVS).

DEFINITION 2.4 For any absorbing and balanced set u of a vector space X, the function $p \equiv p_u: X \to \mathbb{R}^+$ defined by $p_u(x) = \inf \{\alpha : \alpha > 0,\ x \in \alpha u\}$, is called the *Minkowski functional* or the *gauge* associated with u. The function p_u associated with an absorbing and a balanced set u is also called a *pseudonorm* on X. A function $p: X \times \Lambda \to \mathbb{R}^+$, where $\Lambda = (\Lambda, \geq)$ is some directed set, is called a *pseudonorm function* if the following conditions are satisfied:

(PN_1) $p(x,d) \geq 0$, $\forall x \in X$, $d \in \Lambda$.

(PN_2) $p(\alpha x,d) = |\alpha| p(x,d)$, $\forall \alpha \in \mathbb{K}$, $x \in X$, $d \in \Lambda$.

(PN_3) For each $d \in \Lambda$, there corresponds an $e \in \Lambda$ such that

$$p(x + y,d) \leq p(x,e) + p(y,e) \qquad \forall x,y \in X$$

(PN_4) If $d \geq e$, then $p(x,d) \geq p(x,e)$, $\forall x \in X$.

Following Ref. 97, p. 630, we have

PROPOSITION 2.5 Every pseudonorm function p on X gives rise to a unique linear topology T_p on X. Conversely, to every linear topology T on X there corresponds a pseudonorm function p on X such that T is equivalent to T_p, which we express as $T = T_p$ or $T \approx T_p$.

Remark: The topology T of a TVS X is Hausdorff if and only if for each $x \neq 0$, there exists $\alpha \in \Lambda$ with $p(x,\alpha) \neq 0$.

Another equivalent notion of the linear topology is contained in

DEFINITION 2.6 A function $q : X \to \mathbf{R}^+$ is called an F-*seminorm*, provided

($F\text{-}SN_1$) $q(x) \geq 0$, $\forall x \in X$, $q(0) = 0$.

($F\text{-}SN_2$) $q(x + y) \leq q(x) + q(y)$, $\forall x,y \in X$.

($F\text{-}SN_3$) $q(\lambda x) \leq q(x)$ whenever $|\lambda| \leq 1$, $x \in X$.

($F\text{-}SN_4$) $q(\alpha_n x) \to 0$ whenever $\alpha_n \to 0$ and $x \in X$.

If in addition q also satisfies the condition

($F\text{-}SN_5$) $q(x) = 0 \Rightarrow x = 0$

then q is called an F-*norm* on X.

PROPOSITION 2.7 A vector space X equipped with a topology T is a TVS if and only if there exists a family D of F-seminorms on X generating a unique topology equivalent to T; also, T is Hausdorff if and only if for x in X, $x \neq 0$, we have $q(x) \neq 0$ for some q in D.

An important note: In what follows we shall regard the topology T of a TVS (X,T) as having been generated either by a family of pseudonorms (that is, a pseudonorm function) or by a family of F-seminorms, and in each case we *shall denote this family by the letter* D (or D_T, in case the underlying topology T is to be emphasized). In case (X,T) is an l.c. TVS, D is then the family of seminorms (cf. Definition 4.1).

DEFINITION 2.8 A subset B of a TVS (X,T) is called *bounded* (resp. *totally bounded* or *precompact*) if to every u in $\mathcal{B}$, there corresponds $\lambda \in \mathbb{R}_+$ (resp. a finite family $\{x_1, \ldots, x_n\}$ in B) such that

$$B \subset \lambda u \qquad (\text{resp. } \cup\{x_i + u : 1 \leq i \leq n\})$$

The smallest balanced, T-closed, and convex subset of a TVS (X,T) containing a set $A \subset X$ will be denoted by $\langle A \rangle$.

PROPOSITION 2.9 Let (X,T) be a Hausdorff TVS. Then a totally bounded subset B of X is bounded and the T-closure $\bar{B}$ of B is totally bounded. Further, $A \subset X$ is bounded if and only if $\varepsilon_n x_n \to 0$ in (X,T) whenever $x_n \in A$, $\varepsilon_n \in \mathbb{K}$ $(n \geq 1)$, with $\varepsilon_n \to 0$ as $n \to \infty$; also, for a bounded subset A of X, $\varepsilon_n x \to 0$ uniformly in $x \in A$ for any sequence $\{\varepsilon_n\}$ from $\mathbb{K}$ with $\varepsilon_n \to 0$. In an l.c. TVS (X,T), $\Gamma(B)$ is totally bounded for any totally bounded subset B of X.

DEFINITION 2.10 Let $\{x_\alpha\}$ (resp. $\{x_n\}$) be a net (resp. a sequence) in a TVS (X,T). Then (i) $\{x_\alpha\}$ (resp. $\{x_n\}$) is said to be a *Cauchy net* (resp. *Cauchy sequence*) provided for each $\varepsilon > 0$ and $p \in D$ there exists $\mu \in \Lambda$ (resp. $N \in \mathbb{N}$) such that $p(x_\alpha - x_\beta) < \varepsilon$ for all $\alpha, \beta \geq \mu$ [resp. $p(x_n - x_m) < \varepsilon$ for all $m,n \geq N$]. (X,T) is said to be (ii) *complete* (resp. *sequentially complete* or *semicomplete*) if every Cauchy net $\{x_\alpha\}$ (resp. Cauchy sequence $\{x_n\}$) converges in (X,T) and it is said to be *quasicomplete* if every closed and bounded set in X is complete. Further $\{x_n\}$ is said to be (iii) T-*null* (resp. T-*regular*) if for every (resp. for some) $u \in \mathcal{B}$, $x_n \in u$ eventually (resp. $x_n \notin u$, $n \geq 1$). Finally, (X,T) is said to be (iv) T-*separable* (resp. ω-*separable*) if there exists a countable set A (resp. a subspace Y with dimension $\aleph_0$) such that $\bar{A} = X$ (resp. $\bar{Y} = X$).

Note: Convergence of a net $\{x_\alpha\}$ in a TVS (X,T) to $x \in X$ will henceforth be written

$$T\text{-}\lim_\alpha x_\alpha = x \qquad \text{or} \qquad x_\alpha \xrightarrow{\alpha} x(T)$$

Occasionally we will drop the index α above the notation $\to$ and the letter T provided it does not lead to any confusion regarding the choice of the directed set or the particular topology used in the limiting process. Further, if we wish to emphasize the completeness, etc., of a TVS relative to a particular topology T we do so by expressing it as T-completeness, etc.

Remark: It is clear that

$$\text{completeness} \Rightarrow \text{quasicompleteness} \Rightarrow \text{sequential completeness}$$

However, the reverse implications are not necessarily true; see Ref. 140, p. 58, and Ref. 134, p. 210.

It is easy to see that ω-separability of a TVS (X,T) implies separability but the converse is not true (cf. Ref. 105 and Ref. 125, Chapter 1, Example 5.9).

Next we have (Ref. 261, p. 343):

PROPOSITION 2.11 Two Hausdorff vector topologies T_1 and T_2 on a vector space X have the same convergent sequences in X if and only if they have the same Cauchy sequences in X; hence (X,T_1) is sequentially complete if and only if (X,T_2) is sequentially complete provided T_1 and T_2 have the same convergent sequences in X.

DEFINITION 2.12 A set B in a TVS (X,T) is called (i) *compact* if every net in B has at least one adherent point belonging to B; (ii) *relatively compact* if $\bar{B}$ is compact; (iii) *countably compact* if every sequence $\{x_n\}$ in B has at least an adherent point in B; and (iv) *sequentially compact* if every sequence $\{x_n\} \subset B$ has a subsequence $\{x_{n_k}\}$ which is convergent to a point of B.

PROPOSITION 2.13 (i) A subset B of a TVS X is compact if and only if B is totally bounded and complete, and (ii) in a quasicomplete l.c. TVS X, the hull $\langle A \rangle$ of a compact set A is compact.

THEOREM 2.14 A Hausdorff TVS X is finite dimensional if and only if there exists $u \in \mathcal{B}$ such that u is totally bounded.

PROPOSITION 2.15 Let a vector space X be equipped with two Hausdorff linear topologies T_1 and T_2 with $T_1 \subset T_2$. Suppose the members of $\mathcal{B}_{T_2}$ are T_1-complete. Then (X,T_2) is complete (Ref. 92, p. 207).

3. CONTINUITY OF LINEAR MAPS

Let us begin with

DEFINITION 3.1 Let (X,T) and (Y,T_1) be two TVS. A family H of linear maps $R: (X,T) \to (Y,T_1)$ is said to be an *equicontinuous* family if to each $p \in D_{T_1}$, there exist $M \in \mathbb{R}_+$ and $q \in D_T$ such that

$$p(R(x)) \le Mq(x) \qquad \forall x \in X,\ R \in H$$

An arbitrary $f \in H$ such that (i) f is 1-1 and onto Y (i.e., f is a *bijective linear map* from X onto Y), and f and f^{-1} are continuous, is called a *topological isomorphism*, and (ii) f is 1-1 (i.e., f is *injective*) and continuous is called a *topological homomorphism* if f is a topological isomorphism from X onto f[X]. If X = Y in the definition of a topological isomorphism, f is called an *automorphism*.

DEFINITION 3.2 Let X be a TVS. If $\hat{X}$ is a complete TVS and R is a topological isomorphism of X into $\hat{X}$ such that $\overline{R[X]} = \hat{X}$, then $\hat{X}$ (together with R) is called a *completion* of X.

THEOREM 3.3 Each TVS X can be mapped by a topological isomorphism onto a subspace Y of a complete TVS $\hat{X}$ with $\bar{Y} = \hat{X}$.

DEFINITION 3.4 A linear operator P from X into itself is called a *projection* if P(P(x)) = P(x) for every x in X.

PROPOSITION 3.5 (i) If the graph of a projection P on a TVS X is closed, then P[X] is also closed. (ii) For any projection P on X,

$$X = \ker(P) \oplus P[X]$$

where $\ker(P) = \{x : x \in X,\ P(x) = 0\}$. Also, for any subspace Y of X there exists a projection P of X with Y = P[X].

THEOREM 3.6 (*Extension Theorem*) Let R be a continuous linear map from a subset A of a TVS X into a complete TVS Y which is also Hausdorff; then there exists a unique continuous linear map $\hat{R}$ from $\bar{A}$ into Y such that $\hat{R}(x) = R(x)$ for $x \in A$.

Projective, Quotient, and Direct Sum Topologies

An important concept of a linear topology is contained in

DEFINITION 3.7 Let Φ be a family of linear maps from a vector space X into a collection of TVS. The topology *generated* by $\{f^{-1}[u] : f \in \Phi$, u is a neighborhood in the range space of f$\}$, that is, the collection of arbitrary unions of arbitrary finite intersections of the family of such subsets of X, is called the *weak linear topology* on X *generated* by Φ or the *projective topology*, and is usually denoted by $\sigma(X,\Phi)$. If Φ is *total* or *separating* on X (i.e., $f(x) = 0$ for each f in Φ implies $x = 0$), the resulting projective topology is *Hausdorff*. If each TVS is replaced by an l.c. TVS, the corresponding projective topology on X is *locally convex*. If

$$X = \prod_{\alpha\in\Lambda} X_\alpha$$

is the usual product space where each X_α is a TVS then the *linear product topology* on X is the topology $\sigma(X,\Phi)$ with $\Phi = \{P_\alpha : \alpha \in \Lambda\}$, P_α being the usual projection from X onto X_α.

PROPOSITION 3.8 Let X, X_α, and P_α be as defined above. Then the weak topology on X is just the product of the weak topologies on the X_α's, in the sense of Def. 7.1. Further, a subset B of X is (weakly) relatively compact if and only if each $P_\alpha[B]$ is (weakly) relatively compact in X_α.

PROPOSITION 3.9 Let (X,T) be an l.c. TVS and Y be a vector space equipped with the projective topology S defined by a separating family $\Phi = \{f_\alpha : \alpha \in \Lambda\}$ of linear maps from Y into a collection of l.c. TVS $\{Y_\alpha : \alpha \in \Lambda\}$; then the linear map $F: X \to Y$ is T-S continuous if and only if $f_\alpha \circ F$ is continuous from X into Y_α for each $\alpha \in \Lambda$.

PROPOSITION 3.10 Let Y be a vector space equipped with the projective topology S defined by a separating family $\Phi = \{f_\alpha : \alpha \in \Lambda\}$ of linear maps from Y into a collection of l.c. TVS $\{Y_\alpha : \alpha \in \Lambda\}$. Then Y is topologically isomorphic to a subspace Z of $\Pi\{Y_\alpha : \alpha \in \Lambda\}$ under the map F, where $F(y) = (f_\alpha(y) : \alpha \in \Lambda)$.

Concerning the dual of a space relative to a projective topology we have (Ref. 76, p. 79).

THEOREM 3.11 Let X be a vector space equipped with the projective topology S defined by a separating family $\Phi = \{f_\alpha : \alpha \in \Lambda\}$ of linear maps from X into a collection of l.c. TVS $\{X_\alpha : \alpha \in \Lambda\}$. Then X*, the topological dual of (X,S), is given by

$$X^* = \{f : f \in X', f = \sum_{i\in\sigma} g_i \circ f_{\alpha_i}\}$$

where X' is the algebraic dual of X, σ is a finite subset of Λ, and $g_i \in X^*_{\alpha_i}$, $i \in \sigma$.

There is another closely associated notion of *projective equicontinuous topology* contained in (cf. Refs. 168, 169).

LEMMA 3.12 Let $\{R_\alpha : \alpha \in \Lambda\}$ be a family of linear maps from a vector space X into a TVS (Y,T) such that $\{R_\alpha(x) : \alpha \in \Lambda\}$ is T-bounded for each $x \in X$. Then there exists a weakest linear topology S on X such that $\{R_\alpha\}$ is S-T equicontinuous; also, S is generated by $D_S = \{p^* : p \in D_T\}$, where

$$p^*(x) = \sup_\alpha p(R_\alpha(x)) \qquad x \in X$$

Further, if (Y,T) is Hausdorff, then (X,S) is Hausdorff if and only if $R_\alpha(x) = 0$ for each $\alpha \in \Lambda$ implies $x = 0$.

After McArthur and Retherford [170] we also have

LEMMA 3.13 Let F be a set, (X,T) a TVS, A_n and A transformations from F into X. Then A maps a subset E of F into a precompact subset A[E] of X provided

(i) $A_n[E]$ is precompact for each $n \geq 1$.
(ii) $\lim_{n\to\infty} A_n(x) = A(x)$ uniformly in $x \in E$.

For the proof of the following, one may consult Wilansky [264, p. 189] or Woods [269, p. 25].

LEMMA 3.14 Let $\{S_\alpha\}$ be an equicontinuous net of operators from a TVS (X,T) into itself. Then the set $Y = \{x : x \in X, \lim_\alpha S_\alpha(x) = x\}$ is a closed subspace of X.

DEFINITION 3.15 Let $\{S_\alpha : \alpha \in \Lambda\}$ be a family of linear maps $S_\alpha : X_\alpha \to X$, where $\{X_\alpha : \alpha \in \Lambda\}$ is a family of TVS and X is a vector space; then the strongest linear topology T on X such that each S_α is continuous on X_α is called the *final linear topology* on X (relative to $\{S_\alpha\}$).

Let X be a TVS and M a subspace of X. Consider the quotient space X/M and the natural canonical map ϕ (or ϕ_M) from X onto X/M, $\phi(x) = \hat{x}$, $\hat{x}$ being the equivalence class in X/M with its representative element x. The *quotient topology* on X/M is the final linear topology on this space relative to ϕ; moreover, if for each $p \in D$ we define

$$\hat{p}(\hat{x}) = \inf \{p(y) : y \in \hat{x}\} \qquad \hat{x} \in X/M$$

the quotient topology on X/M is generated by $\hat{D} = \{\hat{p} : p \in D\}$. It is rather straightforward to verify that the quotient map ϕ is also an open map; thus ϕ is a linear, continuous, open, and onto map from X to X/M, where X/M is equipped with the quotient topology.

DEFINITION 3.16 A continuous linear map f from a TVS (X,T) into a TVS (Y,T_1) is called a *strict morphism* if the map $\bar{f}$ given by $f = \bar{f} \circ \phi$ where ϕ is the canonical map from X onto the quotient space X/ker(f), is a topological homomorphism.

PROPOSITION 3.17 Let X, Y, and f be as in Definition 3.16. Then the following are equivalent:

(i) f is a strict morphism.

(ii) f maps every neighborhood of 0 in X onto a neighborhood of 0 in f[X].

(iii) f maps every open set of X onto an open set of f[X].

Let there be a family of TVS $\{X_\alpha : \alpha \in \Lambda\}$ over the same field $\mathbb{K}$. Let us consider the two situations (a) when each X_α is a subspace of a given TVS X and their union spans X and (b) when (a) is not necessarily true. In case (a), when each $x \in X$ can be uniquely represented as

$$x = \Sigma_\alpha x_\alpha$$

where only finitely many terms of the sum are nonzero, we say that X is the (algebraic) *internal direct sum* of the X_α's and write

$$X = \oplus_\alpha X_\alpha$$

In case (b) we consider the subspace F of $X = \Pi_\alpha X_\alpha$ consisting of those elements having finitely many nonzero coordinates. We call F the (algebraic) *external direct sum* of the X_α's and designate F again by $\oplus_\alpha X_\alpha$. (The spaces X_α of which we are considering the internal direct sum can also be considered relative to their external direct sum.) In either of these direct sums there is a natural map I_β from X_β into $\oplus_\alpha X_\alpha$ defined by $I_\beta(x_\beta) = x_\beta \in X_\beta$ or $I_\beta(x_\beta) = \Sigma_\alpha y_\alpha \in \oplus_\alpha X_\alpha$, where $y_\alpha = 0$, $\alpha \neq \beta$, and $y_\beta = x_\beta$, according as we consider the internal direct sum or external direct sum, respectively, of the X_α's.

DEFINITION 3.18 The strongest linear topology (final linear topology) T on the internal (resp. external) direct sum $\oplus_\alpha X_\alpha$ of the TVS X_α relative to which the maps I_α are continuous is termed the *internal* (resp. *external*) *direct sum topology*, and the corresponding pair $(\oplus_\alpha X_\alpha, T)$ is called the *internal* (resp. *external*) *topological direct sum* of the TVS X_α.

Note: In the future we shall drop the word internal or external before direct sums and the context will make clear which type of sum we are considering.

We recall that a set A in a topological space X is called a set of *first category* in X if $A = \bigcup\{A_n : n \in \mathbb{N}\}$ where each A_n is *nowhere dense* in X (i.e., the interior of the set $\bar{A} = \emptyset$). A set A which is not of first category is said to be of *second category*. A topological space X that cannot be expressed as the countable union of nowhere dense subsets of itself is called a *Baire space*; a complete metric space is a Baire space.

Either of the following Theorems 3.19 and 3.20 is usually called the *Banach-Steinhaus theorem.*

THEOREM 3.19 Let H be a family of continuous linear maps from a TVS X into another TVS Y. Assume that X contains a set A which is of second category such that $\{R(x) : R \in H\}$ is bounded in Y for each $x \in A$. Then H is equicontinuous.

THEOREM 3.20 Let H be a sequence of continuous linear maps $\{R_n\}$ from a TVS (X,T) into a TVS (Y,T_1) such that

$$\lim_n R_n(x) = R(x)$$

for x in a set of second category in X. Then R is continuous and

$$\lim_n R_n(x) = R(x)$$

uniformly over any totally bounded subset of X.

Next, we have

THEOREM 3.21 Let X be an F-space (see Definition 4.4) and Y a TVS. Suppose $\{R_n\}$is a sequence of continuous linear maps from X into Y such that $\{R_n(x)\}$ is bounded and $\{R_n(x)\}$ is Cauchy in Y, respectively, for $x \in X$ and $x \in Z$ where $\bar{Z} = X$. Then $\{R_n(x)\}$ is Cauchy in Y for each $x \in X$.

4. TYPES OF TVS

Broadly speaking, we can divide topological vector spaces into the following classes: (i) metrizable spaces or linear metric spaces; (ii) locally bounded spaces; (iii) locally convex spaces; (iv) normed spaces; and, of course, spaces which are just TVS without having any of the properties (i) to (iv).

DEFINITION 4.1 (i) A metric or a semimetric ρ on a vector space X is said to be *invariant* if $\rho(x + z, y + z) = \rho(x,y)$ for all x, y, z in X; a function $q: X \to \mathbf{R}_+$ satisfying the conditions (SN_1) $q(x) \geq 0$, (SN_2) $q(\alpha x) = |\alpha| q(x)$, and (SN_3) $q(x + y) \leq q(x) + q(y)$ where $\alpha \in \mathbb{K}$ and $x,y \in X$ is called a *seminorm* on the vector space X, and if q satisfies the additional condition that $q(x) = 0$ implies $x = 0$, then q is called a *norm*; (ii) a set B in a TVS X is called a *barrel* if it is absorbing, balanced, convex, and closed in X.

DEFINITIONS 4.2 A TVS (X,T) is said to be

(i) *Semimetrizable* if $\mathcal{B}$ consists of a countable number of 0-neighborhoods
(ii) *Locally bounded* if there exists a bounded member of $\mathcal{B}$
(iii) *Locally convex* if each member of $\mathcal{B}$ contains a convex neighborhood of the origin in X (cf. remarks following Proposition 2.3)
(iv) *Normed* (or *seminormed*) if T is given by a norm (seminorm).

An Important Note: Since we shall deal with Hausdorff spaces, from now on we shall consider only *Hausdorff* TVS and consequently we shall not qualify any of the functions generating a particular topology by the prefix "semi."

One can see that many results of this chapter are valid even for non-Hausdorff TVS.

Let us mention here that the property of a TVS X being any of the four types mentioned above is also possessed by its completion X (cf. Theorem 3.3). Henceforth, we shall abbreviate metrizable, locally bounded, locally convex, and normed TVS, respectively, as (X,ρ), l.b. TVS, l.c. TVS, and $(X,\|\cdot\|)$, where ρ and $\|\cdot\|$ are respectively the corresponding metric and norm on X. Also, whenever $\mathcal{B}$ refers to an l.c. TVS (X,T) we shall understand that its members are barrels; further, if a TVS (X,T) is an l.c. TVS we shall take the corresponding family D as that consisting of (all) seminorms $\{p_\alpha\}$ generating the topology T.

PROPOSITION 4.3 A TVS (X,T) is metrizable if and only if T is generated by an invariant metric ρ on X; that is, $T \approx T_\rho$, ρ being an invariant metric on X.

DEFINITION 4.4 A TVS (X,T) with $T \approx T_q$, q being an F-norm on X, is termed an F*-*space*, and if in addition (X,T_q) is complete, X is called an F-*space*. An F-space (X,T) which is also locally convex is called a *Fréchet space*.

PROPOSITION 4.5 Let (X,T) be a TVS. Then X is metrizable if and only if $T = T_q$, q being an F-norm on X.

PROPOSITION 4.6 The topology T of a Fréchet space (X,T) can be given by an invariant metric ρ resulting from an F-norm q [i.e., $\rho(x,y) = q(x - y)$] with

$$q(x) = \sum_{n\geq 1} \frac{1}{2^n} \frac{p_n(x)}{1 + p_n(x)} \qquad x \in X \text{ (Fréchet combination)}$$

where $\{p_n\}$ is a sequence of T-continuous seminorms generating the topology T.

DEFINITION 4.7 A norm $\|\cdot\|_p$ is called p-*homogeneous* if the homogeneous property in the corresponding function is replaced by

$$\|\lambda x\|_p = |\lambda|^p \|x\|_p \qquad p \in \mathbb{R}_+$$

DEFINITION 4.8 A set A in a vector space X is said to be *starlike* if $\lambda A \subset A$ for all λ with $0 \le \lambda < 1$; for a starlike set A the *modulus of concavity* c(A) is given by

$$c(A) = \inf \{\lambda : \lambda > 0 \text{ and } A + A \subset \lambda A\}$$

The number $c(X) = \inf\{c(u) : u \text{ is balanced, bounded, and open in a TVS } X\}$ is called the *concavity module* of X and we write $p_X = \log_{10} c(X)/\log_{10} 2$.

The following is due to Rolewicz [205, p. 472].

PROPOSITION 4.9 Let (X,T) be a locally bounded space. For each p, $0 < p < p_X$, there is a p-homogeneous F-norm which generates the topology T.

The following is usually referred to as the *Kolmogorov theorem*.

THEOREM 4.10 A TVS X is normed if and only if X is locally bounded and locally convex.

Lohman and Stiles prove (Ref. 158, p. 237)

PROPOSITION 4.11 Let (X,T) be a separable TVS and Y be a semimetrizable linear subspace of X. Then Y is also separable.

In general topological spaces, we have (Ref. 264, p. 164)

PROPOSITION 4.12 A compact semimetric space is separable.

We quote from Ref. 47, pp. 175 and 191:

PROPOSITION 4.13 The product of a countable family of separable topological spaces is separable, and the product of a countable family of metrizable spaces is metrizable.

5. MORE RESULTS ON CONTINUITY AND EQUICONTINUITY

We start with the *closed graph theorem*.

THEOREM 5.1 Let R be a linear operator from a TVS (X,T) into an F-space (Y,T_1). Suppose that

(i) The graph of R is closed in the product space $X \times Y$.

(ii) For each neighborhood u of 0 in Y, the set $\overline{R^{-1}(u)}$ is a neighborhood of 0 in X.

Then R is continuous. Also we have

(iii) If (X,T) is metrizable and $x_n \to 0$ in X implies that $\{R(x_n)\}$ is bounded in Y, then R is continuous.

THEOREM 5.2 A continuous bijective linear map from an F-space X onto a TVS Y of second category is a topological isomorphism. Further, a continuous linear map R from an F-space X into another F-space Y is either a topological homomorphism or has an image R[X] which is of first category in $\overline{R[X]}$. R is a topological homomorphism if and only if R[X] is closed.

Note: The second part of the above theorem is usually referred to as the *Banach-Schauder theorem.*

PROPOSITION 5.3 Let R be a linear map from a TVS (X,T) into another TVS (Y,T_1). If for each $p \in D_T$ there exist $q \in D_{T_1}$ and $m \in \mathbb{R}^+$ with $mp(x) \leq q(R(x))$, $x \in X$, then R is 1-1 and R^{-1} is continuous.

The following is a stronger variation of the well-known *open mapping theorem.*

THEOREM 5.4 Let R be a continuous linear map from an F-space X into a TVS Y. If R[X] is of second category in Y then R maps X onto Y, Y is an F-space, and R is an open map.

The *principle of uniform boundedness* is contained in

THEOREM 5.5 Let H be a family of continuous linear maps from a TVS X into an l.c. TVS Y. Let $A \subset X$ be balanced, convex, bounded, sequentially closed, and sequentially complete, and assume that $\{R(x) : R \in H\}$ is bounded in Y for each $x \in A$. Then H is uniformly bounded on A.

A better conclusion is contained in

THEOREM 5.6 Let (X,T) be a TVS in which each barrel is a T-neighborhood of 0 in X and let H be a family of continuous linear maps from X into an l.c. TVS (Y,T_1) such that $\{R(x) : R \in H\}$ is T_1-bounded for each $x \in X$. Then H is T-T_1 equicontinuous.

The above result is known as the *barrel theorem*.

6. LOCALLY CONVEX SPACES

The importance of l.c. TVS lies in the richness of their topological duals, a fact exhibited by the well-known *Hahn-Banach theorem*, namely

THEOREM 6.1 Let (X,p) be a seminormed space and Y be a subspace of X. Suppose f is a linear functional on Y such that $|f(y)| \leq p(y)$ for all $y \in Y$. Then there exists a continuous linear functional $\tilde{f}$ on X such that $\tilde{f}(y) = f(y)$ for $y \in Y$, and $|\tilde{f}(x)| \leq p(x)$ for each $x \in X$.

PROPOSITION 6.2 Let Y be a closed subspace of an l.c. TVS X and x_0 be a point of X such that $x_0 \notin Y$. Then there exists a continuous linear functional f on X such that $f(x_0) = 1$ and $f(y) = 0$ for every $y \in Y$.

Note: If X is a TVS, we write X^* and X', respectively, for the *topological dual* and the *algebraic dual* of X. From the preceding results $X^* \supsetneq \{0\}$ for any nontrivial l.c. TVS X (i.e., $X \supsetneq \{0\}$): however, this fact is not necessarily valid for l.b. TVS. Let us also recall that a maximal subspace H of a vector space X is called a *hyperplane*, and a *closed* (an *open*) half space of X is given by $\{x : R\ell\ f(x) \leq \alpha\}(\{x : R\ell\ f(x) < \alpha\})$ where $f \in X'$ and $\alpha \in \mathbb{R}$. The *restriction* of a map f on X to its subspace Y shall be denoted henceforth by f_Y or $f|Y$. If X is a TVS and Y a subspace of X, the *annihilator* of Y is the subspace $Y^\perp$ of X^* defined by $\{f : f \in X^*, f(y) = 0 \text{ for every } y \in Y\}$.

PROPOSITION 6.3 Let $A,B \subset X$, an l.c. TVS, where $A \cap B \neq \emptyset$, $A,B \neq \emptyset$, A is compact, and B is balanced and closed. Then there exists an $f \in X^*$ such that $\sup \{|f(x)| : x \in B\} < \inf \{|f(y)| : y \in A\}$.

PROPOSITION 6.4 Let X be a TVS and Y be a subspace of X. Then $(X/Y)^*$ is isomorphic to $Y^\perp$, and if X is an l.c. TVS then $X^*/Y^\perp$ is isomorphic to Y^*; in the second case the isomorphism R is given by $R(\hat{f}) = \hat{f}_Y$.

The next two results we quote are from Ref. 227, p. 37.

PROPOSITION 6.5 Let (X,T) be an l.c. TVS. Then a set $A \subset X$ is T-closed and convex if and only if A is the intersection of a family of closed half spaces.

PROPOSITION 6.6 Let (X,T) be an l.c. TVS and Y be a T-closed subspace of X; then Y is the intersection of all T-closed hyperplanes containing Y.

The final discussion of this section is concerned with inductive limits.

DEFINITIONS 6.7 Let $\{X_\alpha : \alpha \in \Lambda\}$ be a family of l.c. TVS and R_α be a linear map from X_α into a vector space X. Assume that $X = \cup\{R_\alpha[X_\alpha] : \alpha \in \Lambda\}$. The finest locally convex topology T on X such that each R_α is continuous on X is called the *inductive limit topology* of X and (X,T) is called the *inductive limit* of X_α. If $\Lambda = \mathbb{N}$ then (X,T) is called the *generalized inductive limit* of $X_n (n \in \mathbb{N})$, and the topology T is called the *generalized inductive limit topology*.

Remark: If $\mathcal{B}_\alpha$ is a base of balanced convex neighborhoods for the topology of X_α, $\alpha \in \Lambda$, then the neighborhood system for the inductive limit topology T on X is also given by the collection of balanced convex hulls of the sets of form $\cup\{R_\alpha[v_\alpha] : \alpha \in \Lambda\}$, $v_\alpha \in \mathcal{B}_\alpha$ (cf. Ref. 204, p. 79).

PROPOSITION 6.8 Let (X,T) be the generalized inductive limit of $\{(X_n,T_n)\}$, $X_n \subset X_{n+1}$, $n \in \mathbb{N}$, with respect to injective maps $I_n: X_n \to X$. Suppose that the topology S_n on X_n induced by T_{n+1} is equivalent to T_n for $n \geq 1$. Then T induces on each X_n the topology T_n.

DEFINITION 6.9 If the generalized inductive limit topology T on $X = \cup\{X_n : n \geq 1\}$ with respect to injective maps $I_n: X_n \to X$ induces on each X_n the topology equivalent to its original locally convex topology T_n, then T is called the *strict inductive limit topology* and the pair (X,T) is called the *strict inductive limit* of $\{X_n\}$.

The following result is essentially due to Dieudonné and Schwartz [42, p. 70].

THEOREM 6.10 Let (X,T) be the strict inductive limit of the l.c. TVS $\{(X_n,T_n)\}$. Assume that X_n is T_{n+1}-closed in X_{n+1} $(n \geq 1)$. Then a set $B \subset X$ is T-bounded in X if and only if $B \subset X_N$ and B is T_N-bounded for some $N \in \mathbb{N}$; also, (X,T) is complete if and only if for every Cauchy net $\{x_\alpha\}$ in X_n relative to the induced topology τ_n on X_n from T there exists $p \in \mathbb{N}$, $p \geq n$, such that $\{x_\alpha\}$ is convergent in (X_p,τ_p), and in turn it follows that (X,T) is complete if and only if each (X_n,T_n) is complete.

DEFINITION 6.11 A (generalized) strict inductive limit (X,T) of Fréchet spaces (X_n,T_n) is called a *(generalized) LF-space*.

7. DUALITY

The so-called duality theory of vector spaces plays a central role in clarifying the topological structure of locally convex spaces. We shall have occasion to compare these properties with their counterparts in F*-spaces. It is convenient to start with

DEFINITION 7.1 Let X and Y be two vector spaces over the same field $\mathbb{K}$. Then X and Y are said to form a dual system $\langle X,Y\rangle$ provided there exists a bilinear functional $B: X \times Y \to \mathbb{K}$ such that for each x in X, $x \neq 0$ (resp. $y \in Y$, $y \neq 0$), there corresponds y in Y (resp. x in X) such that $B(x,y) \neq 0$. In a dual system $\langle X,Y\rangle$, X (resp. Y) can be thought of as a subspace of Y' (resp. X') through the *canonical map* Ψ (resp. Φ) given by $\Psi(x) = B(x,\cdot)$ [resp. $\Phi(y) = B(\cdot,y)$]. The natural locally convex topology $\sigma(X,Y)$ on X [resp. $\sigma(Y,X)$ on Y] generated by the family of seminorms $\{p_y : y \in Y\}$ where $p_y(x) = |B(x,y)|$, $x \in X$ [resp. $\{q_x : x \in X\}$ where $q_x(y) = |B(x,y)|$, $y \in Y$], is called the *weak topology* on X (resp. Y). Also, for $\langle X,Y\rangle$, the *polar* A° of an arbitrary set $A \subset X$ is the set $\{y : y \in Y \text{ with } |B(x,y)| \leq 1 \text{ for all } x \in A\}$. The polar of A° for a set $A \subset X$ is known as the *bipolar* of A and is written as $A^{\circ\circ}$.

PROPOSITION 7.2 Let $\langle X,Y\rangle$ be a dual system. For a nonempty subset $A \subset X$, $A^{\circ\circ}$ [i.e., $(A^\circ)^\circ$] is the smallest balanced, convex, and $\sigma(X,Y)$-closed set containing A.

DEFINITION 7.3 For any dual system $\langle X,Y\rangle$, a locally convex topology T on X (resp. Y) is said to be *compatible* with $\langle X,Y\rangle$ if X^* (resp. Y^*) relative to the topology T is Y (resp. X).

PROPOSITION 7.4 In a dual system $\langle X,Y\rangle$ the closed convex sets of X (resp. Y) are the same for all locally convex topologies on X (resp. Y) compatible with $\langle X,Y\rangle$.

DEFINITION 7.5 Let $\langle X,Y\rangle$ be a dual system and $\mathcal{S}$ be a family of $\sigma(X,Y)$-bounded sets of X. The locally convex topology on Y generated by $\{A^\circ : A \in \mathcal{S}\}$ or, equivalently, by the family $\{q_A : A \in \mathcal{S}\}$ of seminorms on Y where

$$q_A(y) = \sup \{|B(x,y)| : x \in A\}$$

is called the *$\mathcal{S}$-topology* or the *polar topology* on Y. If

(i) $\mathcal{S}$ is the family of all finite subsets of X.

(ii) $\mathcal{S}$ is the family of all $\sigma(X,Y)$-bounded subsets of X.

(iii) $\mathcal{S}$ is the family of all balanced, convex, and $\sigma(X,Y)$-compact subsets of X.

then the corresponding $\mathcal{S}$-topology on Y is called the *weak*, *strong*, and the *Mackey topology*, and they are respectively denoted by $\sigma(Y,X)$, $\beta(Y,X)$, and $\tau(Y,X)$; (iv) if $\mathcal{S}$ denotes the family of all $\beta(Y,X)$-bounded sets, the corresponding $\mathcal{S}$-topology on X is denoted by $\beta^*(X,Y)$ and is termed the *strong star topology*; and (v) if $\mathcal{S}$ is the collection of all $\sigma(Y,X)$-compact subsets of Y, the corresponding $\mathcal{S}$-topology shall be denoted by $\delta(X,Y)$.

PROPOSITION 7.6 (i) A subset $M \subset X^*$, X being a TVS with topology T, is T-equicontinuous if and only if $M \subset u^\circ$ for some $u \in \mathcal{B}$; and (ii) if (X,T) is an l.c. TVS then T is equivalent to the $\mathcal{S}$-topology where $\mathcal{S}$ is the family of all equicontinuous subsets of X^*, and we have

$$\beta(X,X^*) \supset \beta^*(X,X^*) \supset \tau(X,X^*) \supset T$$

PROPOSITION 7.7 Let (X,T) be an l.c. TVS. If $\{x_\alpha\}$ is a T-Cauchy net in X and if $x \in X$ is a $\sigma(X,X^*)$-cluster point of $\{x_\alpha\}$ then $T\text{-}\lim_\alpha x_\alpha = x$. Hence a weakly (sequentially) complete l.c. TVS is (sequentially) complete.

PROPOSITION 7.8 Let $\langle X,Y \rangle$ be a dual system and T an S-topology on X. If $\{x_n\}$ is a T-Cauchy sequence in X such that $x_n \to x$ in $\sigma(X,Y)$ for some x in X, then $x_n \to x$ in T.

We recall

DEFINITION 7.9 A set $F \subset X$ is said to be *finite dimensional* if there exists a finite set $E \subset F$ consisting of linearly independent elements such that $F \subset sp\{E\}$.

A similar version of the first part of the following result is given in Ref. 32, p. 19; see also Ref. 134, p. 161; the second part is to be found in Ref. 204, p. 50.

PROPOSITION 7.10 Let $\langle X,Y \rangle$ be a dual system. (i) A subset $B \subset Y$ is $\sigma(X,Y)$-equicontinuous if and only if B is finite dimensional and $\sigma(Y,X)$-bounded; and (ii) each $\sigma(X,Y)$-bounded subset of X is $\sigma(X,Y)$-precompact.

The following is given in Ref. 130, p. 76.

PROPOSITION 7.11 Consider a dual system $\langle X,Y \rangle$. Suppose H is a family of $\sigma(X,Y)$-continuous linear maps from X into itself such that for $x \in X$, $\{R(x) : R \in H\}$ is $\beta(X,Y)$-bounded. Then H is $\beta(X,Y)$-equicontinuous.

The next result is known as the *Alaoglu-Bourbaki theorem*.

THEOREM 7.12 For each 0-neighborhood u in a TVS (X,T) the set $u^\circ \subset X^*$ is $\sigma(X^*,X)$-compact.

The following is proved in Ref. 140, p. 249.

PROPOSITION 7.13 Let (X,T) be a sequentially complete l.c. TVS and $\{x_n\}$ be a sequence in X such that $x_n \to 0$ in $\sigma(X,X^*)$. Then the bipolar B of the sequence $\{x_n\}$ is $\sigma(X,X^*)$-compact and

$$B = \left\{x : x = \sum_{n=1}^{\infty} \alpha_n x_n \text{ with } \sum_{n=1}^{\infty} |\alpha_n| \le 1\right\}$$

The *Mackey-Arens theorem* is contained in

THEOREM 7.14 Let $\langle X,Y\rangle$ be a dual system. A locally convex topology T on X (resp. Y) is compatible with $\langle X,Y\rangle$ if and only if T is an $\mathcal{S}$-topology where $\mathcal{S}$ is some collection of balanced, convex, and $\sigma(Y,X)$-compact [resp. $\sigma(X,Y)$-compact] subsets of Y (resp. X) with $\cup\{A : A \in \mathcal{S}\} = Y$ (resp. X); also, T is compatible if and only if $\sigma(X,Y) \subset T \subset \tau(X,Y)$ [resp. $\sigma(Y,X) \subset T \subset \tau(Y,X)$].

Now we have the so-called *Banach-Mackey* and *Mackey theorems*, respectively.

THEOREM 7.15 An arbitrary balanced, convex, bounded, and complete subset A of an l.c. TVS X is absorbed by each barrel in X.

THEOREM 7.16 Let $\langle X,Y\rangle$ be a dual system. Then bounded sets in X (resp. Y) are the same for all locally convex topologies compatible with $\langle X,Y\rangle$.

DEFINITION 7.17 A set B in a TVS X is called *bornivorous* if every bounded subset of X is absorbed by B.

THEOREM 7.18 Let X be an l.c. TVS. A set $B \subset X^*$ is $\beta(X^*,X)$-bounded if and only if B is absorbed by A° where A is some bornivorous barrel in X; further, if X is quasicomplete, then each $\sigma(X^*,X)$-bounded subset of X^* is $\beta(X^*,X)$-bounded.

The following is given in Ref. 263, p. 476 and Ref. 13, p. 200.

PROPOSITION 7.19 (i) Let Y be a subspace of an l.c. TVS (X,T). If X^* is $\beta(X^*,X)$-separable, then Y^* is $\beta(Y^*,Y)$-separable. (ii) If $\{X_i : i \ge 1\}$ is a sequence of l.c. TVS such that each X_i^* is $\beta(X_i^*,X_i)$-separable, then the dual X^* of $X = \Pi_{i\ge 1} X_i$ is $\beta(X^*,X)$-separable.

PROPOSITION 7.20 Let <X,Y> be a dual system. Then $\sigma(X,Y)$ is metrizable (normable) if and only if Y is of countable (finite) dimension.

After Mackey [161, p. 192] we have

DEFINITION 7.21 A dual system <X,Y> is called an M-*system* if each $\sigma(Y,X)$-bounded set in Y is $\beta(Y,X)$-bounded.

One has (for instance, see Ref. 81)

PROPOSITION 7.22 Let <X,Y> be an M-dual system. Then every $\sigma(X,Y)$-bounded set in X is $\beta(X,Y)$-bounded.

8. BARRELED AND BORNOLOGICAL SPACES

Barreled spaces and their offshoots together with bornological spaces reveal a fine structure of locally convex spaces close to the inner structure of Banach spaces.

DEFINITION 8.1 An l.c. TVS (X,T) is said to be (i) *barreled* if every barrel in X is a neighborhood of 0; (ii) *infrabarreled* if every bornivorous barrel in X is a neighborhood of 0; σ-*barreled* (σ-*infrabarreled* or σ-*quasibarreled*) if every countable $\sigma(X^*,X)$-bounded [$\beta(X^*,X)$-bounded] subset of X* is equicontinuous; (iv) *sequentially barreled* if every $\sigma(X^*,X)$-convergent sequence in X* is equicontinuous; (v) *bornological* if every balanced, convex, and bornivorous subset of X is a neighborhood of 0; and (vi) a *Mackey space* if $T \approx \tau(X,X^*)$.

PROPOSITION 8.2 An F-space is a Baire space, and therefore a Fréchet space is barreled.

Often useful is

THEOREM 8.3 (i) An l.c. TVS (X,T) is barreled if and only if every $\sigma(X^*,X)$-bounded subset of X* is equicontinuous. Thus for a barreled l.c. TVS (X,T), the following subsets of X* are the same: equicontinuous subsets, $\sigma(X^*,X)$-relatively compact subsets, $\beta(X^*,X)$-bounded subsets, and

$\sigma(X^*,X)$-bounded subsets. Therefore, an l.c. TVS (X,T) is barreled if and only if $T \approx \beta(X,X^*)$. Also, the completion $(\hat{X},\hat{T})$ of a barreled space (X,T) is barreled. (ii) A Mackey space $(X,\tau(X,X^*))$ is barreled if and only if every $\sigma(X^*,X)$-bounded set is $\sigma(X^*,X)$-relatively compact.

PROPOSITION 8.4 (i) An l.c. TVS X is barreled if and only if every pointwise bounded set of continuous seminorms on X is equicontinuous; further, if X is barreled then the pointwise limit of a sequence of continuous seminorms on X is a continuous seminorm, and (ii) a subspace Y with codimension $\aleph_0$ of a metrizable barreled space X is also barreled (see Ref. 9, p. 275).

PROPOSITION 8.5 Let (X,T) be an l.c. TVS. Then every convex and $\sigma(X^*,X)$-relatively compact subset of X^* is $\beta(X^*,X)$-bounded; moreover, every $\beta(X^*,X)$-bounded subset of X^* is equicontinuous if and only if (X,T) is infrabarreled, that is, (X,T) is infrabarreled if and only if $T \approx \beta^*(X,X^*)$.

THEOREM 8.6 Let X be a barreled space and $\mathcal{S}$ be a collection of bounded subsets that cover X. Then X^* equipped with the $\mathcal{S}$-topology is quasi-complete.

PROPOSITION 8.7 (i) Each infrabarreled space is Mackey. (ii) An l.c. TVS (X,T) is bornological if $\mathcal{B}$ consists of a countable number of sets; also, an l.c. TVS X is bornological if and only if it is a Mackey space and each $f \in X'$ transforming bounded sets of X into bounded sets of $\mathbb{K}$ belongs to X^*. A bornological space is always infrabarreled, and a complete bornological space is always barreled. (iii) For a bornological space X, the space $(X^*,\beta(X^*,X))$ is always complete.

Results on F-spaces

Let us start with (cf. Ref. 233)

PROPOSITION 8.8 Let (X,q) be an F-space having a nontrivial dual X^* and $v_n = \text{con}\{x : x \in X, q(x) < 1/n\}$, $n \geq 1$. Then the sequence $\{v_n\}$ is a base for a 0-neighborhood system for $(X,\tau(X,X^*))$ and $\tau(X,X^*)$ is weaker than T_q; moreover $\tau(X,X^*)$ is metrizable.

Also we have (Ref. 233, p. 13):

PROPOSITION 8.9 Let (X,T) be an F-space. Then the following statements are equivalent:

(i) X is not locally convex.

(ii) $\tau(X,X^*) \subsetneq T$.

(iii) $(X,\tau(X,X^*))$ is not complete.

The following two results are taken from Ref. 68.

PROPOSITION 8.10 Let $\langle X,Y \rangle$ be a dual system such that $\sigma(X,Y) \neq \tau(X,Y)$. Then there is a nonconvex linear topology T on X with $\sigma(X,Y) \subsetneq T \subsetneq \tau(X,Y)$.

PROPOSITION 8.11 Let X and Y be in duality. Then $\sigma(X,Y) \approx \tau(X,Y)$ if and only if $(\hat{X},\hat{\tau}(X,Y)) = Y'$.

Next, we have

DEFINITION 8.12 Let a vector space X be equipped with two linear topologies ρ and τ. We say that τ is *ρ-polar* if there exists a $\mathcal{B}_\tau$ consisting of ρ-closed sets.

After Kalton [109], we have

PROPOSITION 8.13 If τ is ρ-polar, then τ is generated by a collection of F-seminorms $\{\eta_\alpha : \alpha \in I\}$,

$$\eta_\alpha(x) = \sup\{\lambda(x) : \lambda \in \Lambda_\alpha\}$$

where each Λ_α is a collection of ρ-continuous F-seminorms. If τ is metrizable, τ is generated by one such F-norm.

PROPOSITION 8.14 Let (X,τ) be an F-space and let $\rho \subsetneq \tau$ be a linear topology on X. Then

(i) If the net $x_\alpha \to 0$ in ρ but $\not\to 0$ in τ, then there are linear topologies λ and μ on X such that (a) $\rho \subset \lambda \subsetneq \mu \subset \tau$; (b) μ is metrizable and λ-polar; (c) $x_\alpha \to 0$ in λ but $x_\alpha \not\to 0$ in μ.

(ii) If u is in $\mathcal{B}_\tau$ but is not in $\mathcal{B}_\rho$, then there are linear topologies λ and μ satisfying (a), (b) above and (c)' $u \in \mathcal{B}_\mu$ but

$u \notin \mathcal{B}_\lambda$.

(iii) If τ is locally bounded, then there is a linear topology μ with $\mu \subsetneq \tau$, and τ is μ-polar.

PROPOSITION 8.15 Let X be a finite dimensional space and suppose M is a balanced closed subset of X. If $M \cap Y$ is bounded for every one-dimensional subspace Y of X, then M is bounded in X.

9. REFLEXIVE AND MONTEL SPACES

For a TVS X with dual X*, define for each $x \in X$ the linear functional $\tilde{x}$ on X* by $\tilde{x}(f) = f(x)$, $f \in X^*$. Clearly $\tilde{x}$ is continuous on $(X^*, \beta(X^*,X))$. Let X** denote the topological dual of $(X^*, \beta(X^*,X))$, where X is an l.c. TVS. (The space X** is also called the *bidual* of X.) It is clear that $\tilde{x} \in X^{**}$ and the map ψ: $X \to X^{**}$ given by $x \to \tilde{x}$ is a 1-1 linear map. ψ is also called the *canonical embedding* of X into X** (algebraic). The vector spaces X* and X** form a dual system $\langle X^*, X^{**}\rangle$, which gives rise to a natural locally convex $\mathcal{S}$-topology on X**, called the *epsilon topology* $\varepsilon(X^{**},X^*)$ corresponding to the family $\mathcal{S}$ of all equicontinuous subsets of X*. We now pass on to

DEFINITION 9.1 An l.c. TVS (X,T) is said to be (i) *semireflexive* if the map ψ is an onto map; (ii) *reflexive* if the map ψ: $(X,T) \to (X^{**}, \beta(X^{**},X^*))$ is a topological isomorphism; (iii) *semi-Montel* if every bounded subset of X is relatively compact, and (iv) *Montel* if it is semi-Montel and infrabarreled.

PROPOSITION 9.2 An l.c. TVS X is semireflexive if and only if any of the following three conditions holds:

(i) Every bounded, $\sigma(X,X^*)$-closed subset of X is $\sigma(X,X^*)$-compact.

(ii) $(X,\sigma(X,X^*))$ is quasicomplete.

(iii) Every convex subset of X* which is $\beta(X^*,X)$-closed is also $\sigma(X^*,X)$-closed.

PROPOSITION 9.3 An l.c. TVS X is reflexive if and only if it is semireflexive and infrabarreled.

PROPOSITION 9.4 Let (X,T) be a semi-Montel space. Then the following are true:

(i) On a bounded subset B of X, the topologies induced by T and $\sigma(X,X^*)$ are the same.

(ii) If $x_n \to x$ in $\sigma(X,X^*)$, then $x_n \to x$ in T, where $\{x_n\} \subset X$ and $x \in X$.

(iii) Let $\{x_\varepsilon\}_{0<\varepsilon<\alpha}$ be a family of elements of X which converges to a point $x \in X$ in the topology $\sigma(X,X^*)$ as $\varepsilon \to 0$. Then $\{x_\varepsilon\}$ converges to x in the topology T.

PROPOSITION 9.5 (i) For an l.c. TVS X, the following diagram holds:

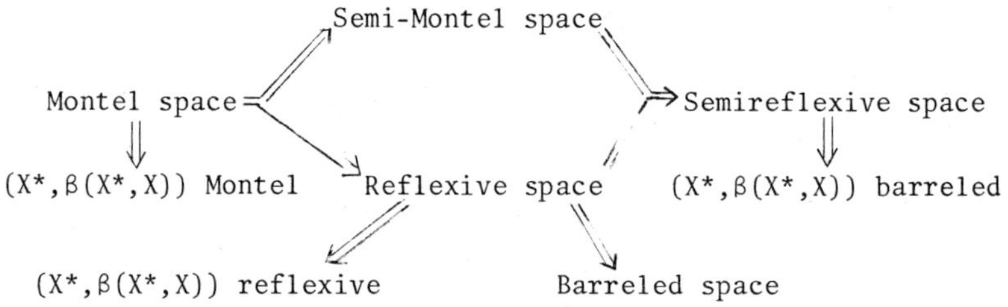

(ii) Let (X,T) be a quasicomplete Mackey space. If $(X^*,\beta(X^*,X))$ is semireflexive, then (X,T) is reflexive (cf. Ref. 140, p. 303).

Next, we have (Ref. 107, p. 403)

PROPOSITION 9.6 Let X be an l.c. TVS which is $\sigma(X^{**},X^*)$-sequentially dense in X^{**}. Assume that Y is a weakly sequentially complete l.c. TVS and the map $f: X \to Y$ is continuous. Then f maps bounded sets into weakly relatively compact sets.

10. PROPERTIES OF A TVS AND ITS DUAL

We shall have occasion to make use of

DEFINITION 10.1 A TVS (X,T) is said to have (i) the t-*property* if for each absorbing set A of X there exists a T-open set G such that $G \subset \bar{A}$; (ii) the *Banach-Steinhaus property* (BSP) if every $\sigma(X^*,X)$-bounded subset of X^* is $\beta(X^*,X)$-bounded (such a space is called a W-*space* or a *Banach-*

Steinhaus space); (iii) the *Hahn-Banach extension property* (HBEP) if every continuous linear functional on a closed subspace of X has a continuous linear extension on X; (iv) the S-*property* if $(X^*, \sigma(X^*,X))$ is sequentially complete (such a space is called an S-*space*); (v) the C-*property* if every $\sigma(X^*,X)$-bounded subset of X^* is $\sigma(X^*,X)$-relatively compact (such a space is called a C-*space*); (vi) the ω-*property* if there exists a sequence $\{p_n\} \subset D_T$ for which $p_n(x) = 0$, $n \geq 1$, is equivalent to $x = 0$ where $x \in X$. Further, (vii) a barreled space is said to have *property* P if the range of the canonical embedding of X into X^{**} is $\sigma(X^{**},X^*)$-dense in X^{**} (such a space is called a P-*space*); and (viii) for any sequence $\{\lambda_n\} \subset \mathbb{R}$, a TVS X is said to have *property* $P(\lambda_n)$ if for any $u \in \mathcal{B}$ there exists v such that $\lambda_1 v + \cdots + \lambda_n v + \cdots \subset u$ (such a space is called a $P(\lambda_n)$-*space*).

A direct consequence of Theorem 8.6 is the first part of the following result; for the second part see Ref. 40, Corollary 4a.

PROPOSITION 10.2 Each barreled space is an S-, a C-, a W-, and a σ-barreled space (and hence a sequentially barreled space). Conversely, if (X,T) is σ-barreled and T-separable, then (X,T) is barreled.

Note: For examples of the above properties other than those from sequence spaces, one may look into Ref. 149.

The next result is referred to as the *Banach-Steinhaus closure theorem*.

THEOREM 10.3 Let X be a TVS with the t-property, Y a TVS, and $\{f_n\}$ a pointwise bounded sequence of continuous linear maps from X to Y. Let

$$\lim_{n\to\infty} f_n(x) = f(x) \qquad x \in X$$

Then f is continuous and linear.

Now we have (cf. Ref. 261)

THEOREM 10.4 Let X be an l.c. TVS. Then X is a W-space if and only if any of the following conditions is satisfied:

(i) Each barrel in X is bornivorous.

(ii) Each $\sigma(X^*,X)$-bounded sequence in X^* is $\beta(X^*,X)$-bounded.

(iii) For each bounded subset A of X and each $\sigma(X^*,X)$-bounded subset B of X^*, $\sup\{|f(x)| : x \in A, f \in B\} < \infty$.

(iv) Each pointwise bounded family of operators from X into an arbitrary l.c. TVS is uniformly bounded on bounded sets.

From Proposition 8.5, there follows

PROPOSITION 10.5 An l.c. TVS X is barreled if and only if X is infrabarreled and a W-space; an l.c. TVS X is a W-space if and only if X and $(X,\beta(X,X^*))$ have the same bounded sets.

A consequence of Proposition 7.22 is

PROPOSITION 10.6 An l.c. TVS X is a W-space if and only if $(X^*,\sigma(X^*,X))$ is a W-space.

We recall the following device due to Grothendieck for getting normed spaces out of a TVS X. Let A be a nonempty balanced convex subset of an l.c. TVS X; then

$$\mathrm{sp}\,\{A\} = \cup\{nA : n \geq 1\}$$

and we denote it by X_A. Let q_A represent the Minkowski functional of A. If A is also bounded, then (X_A,q_A) is a normed space, and if in addition to this A is sequentially complete, then (X_A,q_A) is a Banach space (Ref. 21, p. 207, and Ref. 269, p. 10).

PROPOSITION 10.7 Let X be a sequentially complete l.c. TVS. Then X is a W-space, and in turn it follows that (i) if X is barreled and S is a collection of $\sigma(X,X^*)$-bounded sets such that S covers X, then X^* equipped with the S-topology is a W-space; (ii) if X is bornological, then $(X^*,\beta(X^*,X))$ is a W-space; (iii) if X is semireflexive, then $(X^*,\beta(X^*,X))$ is a W-space; and (iv) if X is an S-space, X is a W-space.

PROPOSITION 10.8 Let X be an F^*-space and Y a subspace of X. Then every continuous linear functional on Y has a continuous linear extension to X if and only if $\tau(Y,Y^*)$ is the restriction of $\tau(X,X^*)$ to Y.

For the proof see Ref. 233, p. 7.

DEFINITION 10.9 Let (X,T) be a TVS with topological dual X^*. By X^+ we mean the space of all $f \in X'$ such that f is *sequentially continuous*, and by X^b we understand the space of all $f \in X'$ such that f is *bounded*. If $X^* = X^+$, (X,T) is called a *Mazur space*. If $X^* = X^b$, then (X,T) is called *semibornological*. Further, a set $K \subset X'$ is called *T-limited* if for every T-null sequence $\{x_n\}$ in X,

$$\lim_{n\to\infty} \sup\{|g(x_n)| : g \in K\} = 0$$

Remark: Let $\mathcal{B}^+$ denote the family of all balanced convex subsets B of an l.c. TVS (X,T) satisfying the condition: For every T-null sequence $\{x_n\}$ in X, $\{x_n\}$ is eventually in B. Then $\mathcal{B}^+$ generates a locally convex Hausdorff topology T^+ which is the finest locally convex Hausdorff topology on X with the same convergent sequences as T; also, $(X,T^+)^* = X^+$ (cf. Ref. 261, p. 342).

For the first and the second part of the next result, see Ref. 87, p. 223, and Ref. 137, p. 83, respectively.

PROPOSITION 10.10 For each Mazur space X, the space $(X^*,\beta(X^*,X))$ is complete, while if X is Mazur and semibornological, then $(X^*,\sigma(X^*,X))$ is barreled.

After Knowles and Cook [137] we have

PROPOSITION 10.11 For an l.c. TVS (X,T), the following conditions are equivalent:

(i) Each $\sigma(X,X^*)$-bounded set is finite dimensional.

(ii) $\sigma(X^*,X) = \beta(X^*,X)$.

(iii) $X^+ = X^b = X'$.

(iv) $(X^*,\sigma(X^*,X))$ is barreled.

Note: We can replace X^* by Y in the above result provided $\langle X,Y\rangle$ is a dual system.

Sequential Barreledness and Completeness

Following Kalton [107] and Webb [261] we have

PROPOSITION 10.12 Each sequentially barreled space is a W-space; if (X,T) is a sequentially complete l.c. TVS, then $(X^*,\tau(X^*,X))$ is sequentially barreled; conversely, if X is a metrizable l.c. TVS such that $(X^*,\tau(X^*,X))$ is sequentially barreled, then X is complete.

PROPOSITION 10.13 (i) If (X,T) is sequentially complete with $T = \tau(X,X^+)$, then (X,T) is sequentially barreled; if (X,T) is sequentially barreled and a Mazur space, then X is an S-space. Indeed, if (X,T) is a l.c. TVS and $T = \tau(X,X^+)$, then (X,T) is sequentially barreled if and only if X is an S-space. (ii) A Mackey Mazur space (X,T) is sequentially barreled if and only if every weakly bounded subset of X is strongly bounded.

PROPOSITION 10.14 Let (X,T) be a Mackey space such that X is $\beta(X,X^*)$-separable and is an S-space. Then X is barreled.

Other Forms of the Closed Graph Theorem

Let us begin with a class of l.c. TVS for which the open mapping theorem is true.

DEFINITION 10.15 An l.c. TVS (X,T) is called a *Pták* or *fully complete* space if each linear subspace F of X* is $\sigma(X^*,X)$-closed whenever $F \cap M$ is $\sigma(X^*,X)$-closed, for any balanced, convex, $\sigma(X^*,X)$-closed, equicontinuous subset M of X*.

PROPOSITION 10.16 Every Fréchet space is Pták and every Pták space is complete; also, a closed subspace of a Pták space is a Pták space, and the dual $(X^*,\beta(X^*,X))$ of a reflexive Fréchet space X is a Pták space.

After Robertson and Robertson [204] we have

THEOREM 10.17 A linear map $f: X \to Y$, where X is barreled and Y is Pták, is continuous provided the graph of f is closed in $X \times Y$.

Kalton's closed graph theorem (Ref. 107, p. 403) is as follows.

THEOREM 10.18 Let (X,T) be a Mackey space and Y a separable Fréchet space. If the graph of a linear map $f: X \to Y$ is closed, then f is continuous.

Earlier Mahowald proved (cf. Ref. 162)

THEOREM 10.19 An l.c. TVS X is barreled if and only if for every Banach space Y the condition "Any linear map f from X into Y that has a closed graph is continuous" is true.

Theorems 10.17 and 10.19 result in (Ref. 18, p. 512)

PROPOSITION 10.20 Let X be a Banach (resp. Fréchet) space and X_0 a dense linear subspace of X. Then the following statements are equivalent:

(i) X_0 is barreled.

(ii) If Y is a Banach (resp. Fréchet) space and $f: Y \to X$ is a continuous linear map with $X_0 \subset f[Y]$, then $f[Y] = X$.

Sequential, Bounded, and Precompact Topologies

Of particular interest are the following topologies (Refs. 134 and 261) contained in

DEFINITION 10.21 (i) The *topology* T^+ is the finest locally convex topology on X (a TVS with topology T) with the same convergent sequences as the initial topology T; and (ii) the *topology* T^b (resp. T^p) is the finest locally convex topology on X with the same bounded (resp. precompact) sets as the initial topology T. The topology T^b is also called the *bound topology derived from* T or the *associated bornological topology*.

Remarks: Clearly, $X^* \subset X^+ \subset X^b \subset X'$ and $T \subset T^+ \subset T^b$. Also $(X,T^+)^* = X^+ = (X,T^+)^+$ and $(X,T^b)^* = X^b$ (cf. Ref. 261, p. 344). The space (X,T) is bornological if $T = T^b$, in which case $T = T^+$. A neighborhood system $\mathcal{B}^+$ at 0 for the topology T^+ consists of all balanced, convex sets B of (X,T) which satisfy the condition: For every T-null sequence $\{x_n\}$ in X, $\{x_n\}$ is eventually in B. For the topology T^b, the family of all balanced, convex, and bornivorous subsets of X is a neighborhood system at 0. The collection $\mathcal{B}^p$ of all balanced, convex subsets V of X satisfying the condition: For every T-precompact subset P of X, there exists a finite number of points $x_1, x_2, \ldots, x_n$ in P such that

$$P \subset \bigcup_{i=1}^{n} (x_i + V)$$

forms a base at 0 for T^p. For further details, we refer to Ref. 261 and Ref. 134, Sec. 19.

The following result, being fundamental for T-limited sets, is useful for the *external construction* of T^+.

PROPOSITION 10.22 Let (X,T) be an l.c. TVS and K a T-limited subset of X'. Then

(i) $K \subset X'$.
(ii) K is $\beta(X^+,X)$-bounded in X^+.
(iii) $K^{\circ\circ}$ is T-limited, where $K^\circ \subset X$ and $K^{\circ\circ} \subset X'$.

Following Ref. 261 we have

PROPOSITION 10.23 (i) T^+ is the topology of uniform convergence on the T-limited subsets of X^+; (ii) T^+ is the finest locally convex topology on X with the same Cauchy sequences as T; and (iii) a subset K of X^+ is T-limited if and only if every T-Cauchy sequence in X is uniformly T-Cauchy on K.

PROPOSITION 10.24 For an l.c. TVS (X,T), $(X,T^p)^* = X^b$ and $T \subset T^p \subset T^b$.

Šmulian's SB-*Spaces*

These spaces were considered by Webb [261], who called them (K)-spaces.

DEFINITION 10.25 A dual pair <X,Y> of vector spaces X and Y is said to satisfy *Šmulian's condition* if every $\sigma(X,Y)$-compact subset of X is $\sigma(X,Y)$-sequentially compact; and (ii) an l.c. TVS (X,T) is called a Šmulian's SB (SSB)-space if it is sequentially barreled and the dual pair <X*,X> satisfies Šmulian's condition.

Concerning convergent sequences and precompact sets in SSB-spaces we have (Ref. 261)

PROPOSITION 10.26 Let (X,T) be an SSB-space. Then

(i) A subset A of X is T-precompact if and only if it is $\sigma(X,X^*)$-bounded.

(ii) Every bounded subset of X is precompact if and only if in X^* the topologies $\sigma(X^*,X)$ and $\beta(X^*,X)$ have the same convergent sequences.

(iii) Every T-precompact subset of X is $\tau(X,X^*)$-precompact.

(iv) T and $\tau(X,X^*)$ coincide on the T-precompact subsets of X.

(v) T and $\tau(X,X^*)$ have the same convergent sequences in X.

PROPOSITION 10.27 Let $\langle X,Y\rangle$ be a dual pair of vector spaces such that $(X,\tau(X,Y))$ and $(Y,\tau(Y,X))$ are both SSB-spaces. Then the following statements are equivalent:

(i) The topologies $\sigma(X,Y)$ and $\tau(X,Y)$ on X have the same convergent sequences.

(ii) The topologies $\sigma(Y,X)$ and $\tau(Y,X)$ on Y have the same convergent sequences.

(iii) For every $\sigma(X,Y)$-null sequence $\{x_n\}$ in X and every $\sigma(Y,X)$-null sequence $\{y_n\}$ in Y, we have $\langle x_n,y_n\rangle \to 0$.

If in addition $(X,\tau(X,Y))$ and $(Y,\tau(Y,X))$ are quasicomplete, the above conditions are equivalent to

(iv) Every $\sigma(X,Y)$-compact subset of X is $\tau(X,Y)$-compact.

(v) Every $\sigma(Y,X)$-compact subset of Y is $\tau(Y,X)$-compact.

A Condition for Reflexivity

An l.c. TVS (X,T) is semireflexive if and only if $\sigma(X^*,X) = \sigma(X^*,X^{**})$. Replacing this condition by a weaker condition, namely, $[\sigma(X^*,X)]^+ = [\sigma(X^*,X^{**})]^+$, or equivalently, $\sigma(X^*,X)$- and $\sigma(X^*,X^{**})$-convergent sequences are the same in X^*, Webb [261] proves

PROPOSITION 10.28 Let (X,T) be a separable complete l.c. TVS for which $[\sigma(X^*,X)]^+ = [\sigma(X^*,X^{**})]^+$. Then (X,T) is semireflexive.

Other simple applications of this condition are (cf. Ref. 261):

PROPOSITION 10.29 If (X,T) is an l.c. TVS for which $T = \tau(X,X^+)$ and $[\sigma(X^*,X)]^+ = [\sigma(X^*,X^{**})]^+$, then (X,T) is sequentially barreled.

PROPOSITION 10.30 If (X,T) is a separable metrizable space for which $[\sigma(X^*,X)]^+ = [\sigma(X^*,X^{**})]^+$, then $X^{**} = \hat{X}$.

11. OTHER USEFUL TOPOLOGIES

We begin with

DEFINITION 11.1 Let (X,T) be an l.c. TVS. Suppose S is the family of all precompact (balanced, convex, and compact subsets) of X; then the corresponding S-topology on X^* is denoted by $\lambda(X^*,X)[\kappa(X^*,X)]$. Let S be the family of all balanced, convex, and $\kappa(X^*,X)$-compact subsets of X^*; then the corresponding S-topology on X is denoted by $\gamma(X,X^*)$.

DEFINITION 11.2 Let X be an l.c. TVS. The finest topology (finest locally convex topology) on X^* which induces on every equicontinuous subset of X^* the same topology as $\sigma(X^*,X)$ is denoted by $\nu(X^*,X)[\mu(X^*,X)]$.

Remark: As pointed out by Kōmura [138], the topology $\nu(X^*,X)$ is not necessarily a linear topology on X^*. Clearly one has

$$\sigma(X^*,X) \subset \kappa(X^*,X) \subset \lambda(X^*,X) \subset \mu(X^*,X) \subset \nu(X^*,X)$$

For the proof of the next result, see Ref. 201, p. 64.

PROPOSITION 11.3 Let X be a metrizable l.c. TVS. Then (i) for each set A consisting of a sequence of points from X converging to 0, the set $\langle A\rangle$ is precompact, and (ii) every precompact set B is contained in $\langle A\rangle$ for some A consisting of points of a sequence from X converging to 0.

There follows now

PROPOSITION 11.4 Let (X,T) be an l.c. TVS. If X is (i) metrizable, then $\lambda(X^*,X) = \nu(X^*,X)$; and (ii) quasicomplete (complete), then $\lambda(X^*,X) = \kappa(X^*,X)[\lambda(X^*,X) = \mu(X^*,X)]$.

The preceding result leads to the well-known *Krein-Šmulian theorem*, namely

THEOREM 11.5 Let X be a Fréchet space. A convex set $B \subset X^*$ is $\sigma(X^*,X)$-closed if and only if for every balanced, convex, $\sigma(X^*,X)$-closed equicontinuous subset M of X^*, the set $B \cap M$ is $\sigma(X^*,X)$-closed.

The next result is known as the *Grothendieck completion theorem*.

THEOREM 11.6 Let (X,T) be an l.c. TVS and $\mathcal{S}$ be a family of subsets of X which are balanced, convex, T-closed, and bounded such that

$$X = \cup\{A : A \in \mathcal{S}\}$$

Suppose F is the vector subspace of X' consisting of those f for which $f|A$ is continuous on A for each $A \in \mathcal{S}$. Denote by S the $\mathcal{S}$-topology on X^*. Then F is the completion of (X^*,S).

The following is known as the *Grothendieck precompactness theorem* (Ref. 76, p. 93; Ref. 16, p. 563):

THEOREM 11.7 For a dual pair $\langle X,Y\rangle$ of vector spaces, let $\mathcal{S}_1$ and $\mathcal{S}_2$ be the collections of $\sigma(X,Y)$- and $\sigma(Y,X)$-bounded subsets of X and Y, respectively, such that $\cup\{A : A \in \mathcal{S}_1\}$ spans X and $\cup\{B : B \in \mathcal{S}_2\}$ spans Y. Then the following conditions are equivalent:

(i) Each $A \in \mathcal{S}_1$ is precompact in the $\mathcal{S}_2$-topology.

(ii) Each $B \in \mathcal{S}_2$ is precompact in the $\mathcal{S}_1$-topology.

The following two results are known respectively as the *theorems of Eberlein* and *Krein*.

THEOREM 11.8 Let (X,T) be an l.c. TVS and B be a subset of X whose closed convex hull A is complete or $\tau(X,X^*)$-complete. Then A is weakly relatively compact if and only if A is weakly relatively sequentially compact.

THEOREM 11.9 Let (X,T) be an l.c. TVS and $B \subset X$ be $\sigma(X,X^*)$-compact. If A denotes either the T-closed convex hull or the T-closed balanced convex hull of B, then A is $\sigma(X,X^*)$-compact if and only if A is $\tau(X,X^*)$-complete.

12. ADJOINTS OF LINEAR MAPS

If R is a linear map from a vector space X into another vector space Y, there exists a unique linear map R' from Y' into X' defined by $\langle R(x), y'\rangle = \langle x, R'(y')\rangle$ for every $x \in X$ and $y' \in Y'$. We call R' the *adjoint* of R. If X and Y are TVS and R defined above is continuous, then $R'[Y^*] \subset X^*$ and we write R^* for the restriction of R' on Y^*. In general we have

PROPOSITION 12.1 Let $\langle X_1, Y_1\rangle$ and $\langle X_2, Y_2\rangle$ be dual pairs and R a linear map from X_1 into X_2. Then $R'[Y_2] \subset Y_1$ if and only if R is $\sigma(X_1,Y_1)$-$\sigma(X_2,Y_2)$ continuous.

PROPOSITION 12.2 Let (X,T) and (Y,S) be two l.c. TVS and f be a T-S continuous linear map from X into Y. Then f is also $\sigma(X,X^*)$-$\sigma(Y,Y^*)$ continuous.

PROPOSITION 12.3 Let (X,T_1) and (Y,T_2) be two l.c. TVS. If the linear map $R: X \to Y$ is T_1-T_2 continuous then $R^*: Y^* \to X^*$ is $\sigma(Y^*,Y)$-$\sigma(X^*,X)$, or $\kappa(Y^*,Y)$-$\kappa(X^*,X)$, or $\lambda(Y^*,Y)$-$\lambda(X^*,X)$ continuous; also, if the linear map R is $\sigma(X,X^*)$-$\sigma(Y,Y^*)$ continuous then R is $\tau(X,X^*)$-T_2 continuous. Therefore R is $\sigma(X,X^*)$-$\sigma(Y,Y^*)$ continuous if and only if R is $\tau(X,X^*)$-$\tau(Y,Y^*)$ continuous.

13. NUCLEARITY AND APPROXIMATIVE DIMENSION

We now collect the necessary material to be used in the last chapter of this book. The basic sources are Refs. 39, 45, 62, 73, 173, 190, 207, 225, 226, 235, and 247 (cf. also Ref. 118 for further references and history).

DEFINITION 13.1 Let X be a vector space. Suppose A and B are subsets of X with $A \prec B$. Let

$$\delta(A,B;L) = \inf\{\delta \geq 0 : A \subset \delta B + L\}$$

L being a subspace of X. If $\mathcal{L}_n$ denotes the family of all subspaces L_n of X with $\dim(L_n) \leq n$, the number δ_n defined by

$$\delta_n(A,B) = \inf\{\delta(A,B;L) : L \in \mathcal{L}_n\}$$

is called the *(Kolmogorov)* nth *diameter* of A relative to B.

Note: When X is a normed space, denote by U the closed unit ball of X. For any bounded subset A of X we abbreviate $\delta_n(A,U)$ as $\delta_n(A)$.

It is clear that for any two subsets A and B of a vector space X with $A \prec B$, $\delta_n(A,B)$ is the infimum of all positive numbers δ such that there is a linear subspace L of X with $\dim L \le n$ for which

$$A \subset \delta B + L$$

The following properties of nth diameters are to be found in Refs. 190, 226, and 247.

PROPOSITION 13.2 Let (X,T) be an l.c. TVS and $A \subset X$. Then

(i) $\delta_0(A,U) \ge \delta_1(A,U) \ge \cdots \ge \delta_n(A,U) \ge \cdots \ge 0$.
(ii) $\delta_n(\lambda A,\mu U) = \lambda\mu^{-1}\delta_n(A,U)$ for $\lambda,\mu \in \mathbb{K}$.
(iii) $\delta_n(A^*,U^*) \le \delta_n(A;U)$ for $A^* \subset A, U \subset U^* \in \mathcal{B}$.
(iv) $\delta_{m+n}(W,U) \le \delta_m(W,V)\delta_n(V,U)$, $W \prec V \prec U$, where $U,V,W \in \mathcal{B}$.

The following result characterizes precompact subsets in an l.c. TVS (X,T); cf. Ref. 247, p. 54 (cf. also Ref. 190, p. 146).

PROPOSITION 13.3 A bounded subset B of an l.c. TVS (X,T) is T-precompact if and only if for each $U \in \mathcal{B}$, $\delta_n(B,U) \to 0$ as $n \to \infty$.

The following result (Ref. 144) is usually referred to as the *Krasnoselski-Krein-Milman lemma*.

LEMMA 13.4 Let L and M be subspaces of a normed space $(X,\|\cdot\|)$, with $\dim(M) < \infty$ and $\dim(L) > \dim(M)$. Then there exists an x in L such that

$$\|x\| = \inf\{\|x - y\| : y \in M\} = 1$$

One can deduce the following (Ref. 190, p. 145, and Ref. 247, p. 58):

PROPOSITION 13.5 Let A be a bounded subset of a normed space $(X,\|\cdot\|)$ and $U = \{x : x \in X, \|x\| \le 1\}$. Let L be an $(n + 1)$-dimensional subspace of X. Suppose $\alpha \ge 0$ satisfies the relation

$$\alpha(U \cap L) \subset A$$

Then $\delta_n(A) \equiv \delta_n(A,U) \geq \alpha$.

It is easy to prove the following (cf. Ref. 247, p. 57):

PROPOSITION 13.6 Let X be a vector space containing two sets A and B with $A \prec B$. Let Y be another vector space and F be a linear operator from X to Y. Then

$$\delta_n(F[A],F[B]) \leq \delta_n(A,B)$$

DEFINITION 13.7 The *diametrical approximative dimension* $\Delta(X)$ of an l.c. TVS (X,T) is the collection of all sequences $\{\lambda_n\}$ with the following property: Given any $U \in \mathcal{B}$ there exists $V \in \mathcal{B}$ with $V \prec U$ and $\lim_{n\to\infty} \lambda_n\delta_n(V,U) = 0$.

Note: For several results on $\Delta(X)$, see Refs. 195 and 247.

DEFINITION 13.8 A linear operator T from an l.c. TVS X into another l.c. TVS Y is said to be *precompact* (resp. *compact* or *completely continuous*) provided T[A] is precompact (resp. relatively compact) in Y for each bounded subset A of X.

Note: The operator T: X → Y such that T[u] is precompact (resp. relatively compact) for some $u \in \mathcal{B}_X$ is sometimes also called precompact (resp. compact).

The following is the generalized form of *Schauder's theorem* (Ref. 134, p. 208):

PROPOSITION 13.9 Let (X,R) and (Y,S) be two l.c. TVS and T a $\sigma(X,X^*)$-$\sigma(Y,Y^*)$ continuous linear map from X into Y. Assume X* has its strong topology $\beta(X^*,X)$. Then T is precompact if and only if T* maps equicontinuous sets into precompact sets.

DEFINITION 13.10 A linear operator T from a Banach space X into another Banach space Y is called *λ-nuclear* for a sequence space λ, provided there exist a sequence $\{\lambda_n\} \in \lambda$, sequences $\{f_n\} \subset X^*$ and $\{y_n\} \subset Y$, with the property that $\{f_n\}$ is $\beta(X^*,X)$-bounded and $\{g(y_n)\} \in \lambda^\times$ (Köthe dual of λ; cf. Chapter 2, Section 2) for each $g \in Y^*$ such that

$$T(x) = \sum_{n=1}^{\infty} \lambda_n \langle x, f_n \rangle y_n$$

where the convergence of the infinite series is taken relative to the topology on Y.

Remarks: If $\lambda = \ell^1$, the corresponding λ-nuclear map is usually referred to as a *nuclear map* and has been extensively studied in Refs. 190 and 140; for the general case we refer to Ref. 45 (cf. also Refs. 259 and 260 for properties of λ-nuclear operators). In the special case when $\lambda = \ell_\phi$ with

$$\ell_\phi = \{\{x_n\} : \sum_{n\geq 1} \phi(|x_n|) < \infty\}$$

the corresponding λ-nuclear operator is called *ϕ-nuclear*, where $\phi: \mathbb{R}^+ \to \mathbb{R}^+$ is continuous, strictly increasing, subadditive, and $\phi(0) = 0$. For a rigorous treatment of these operators, we refer to Ref. 210.

DEFINITION 13.11 Let X and Y be two normed spaces. A linear operator $T: X \to Y$ is said to be *absolutely λ-summing* for a sequence space λ provided for each sequence $\{x_n\}$ in X with $\{\langle x_n, f \rangle\} \in \lambda$, $f \in X^*$, the sequence $\{\|T(x_n)\|\} \in \lambda$.

The above definition is given in Ref. 192, which also contains several results on absolutely λ-summing operators, including their characterization; earlier Pietsch [191] studied these operators (called p-*absolutely summing operators*) extensively when $\lambda = \ell^p$.

Note: The above definition can be generalized to locally convex spaces. An extension of p-absolutely summing operators to (p,q)-*absolutely summing operators*, which we may further generalize to (λ,μ)-*absolutely summing operators* is due to Mitiagin and Pelczynski [174]. In the sequel we shall not need all these generalized concepts.

The following characterization is due to Terzioğlu [249].

THEOREM 13.12 A linear operator T from a Banach space X into a Banach space Y is compact if and only if there exists a sequence $\{f_n\} \subset X^*$ with $f_n \to 0$ in $\beta(X^*,X)$ and

$$\|T(x)\| \le \sup_n |\langle x, f_n\rangle| \qquad \forall x \text{ in } X$$

Nuclear and Schwartz Spaces

Let (X,T) be an l.c. TVS. For each $u \in \mathcal{B}$, consider $p_u \in D_T$ and let

$$N_u = \{x : x \in X, p_u(x) = 0\} = \text{kernel of } p_u$$

Suppose $X_u = X/N_u$, and equip X_u with the usual quotient norm $\hat{p}_u$, where

$$\hat{p}_u(x_u) = \inf\{p_u(x + y) : y \in N_u\} \qquad x_u = x + N_u$$

Let $v \in \mathcal{B}$ with $v \prec u$; then $p_u \le p_v$, that is, $N_v \subset N_u$. Thus there exists a canonical embedding $K_u^v: X_v \to X_u$ with $K_u^v(x_v) = x_u$. Clearly K_u^v is a continuous linear operator. If $\hat{X}_u$ denotes the completion of the normed space X_u, the map K_u^v can be uniquely extended from $\hat{X}_v$ to $\hat{X}_u$ and we denote this extension by $\hat{K}_u^v$.

DEFINITION 13.13 An l.c. TVS (X,T) is called λ-*nuclear* (resp. *Schwartz*) if for each $u \in \mathcal{B}$ there exists $v \in \mathcal{B}$ with $v \prec u$ such that $\hat{K}_u^v$ is λ-nuclear (resp. precompact). If $\lambda = \ell_\phi$, the ℓ_ϕ-nuclear space is called a ϕ-*nuclear space* (when $\ell_\phi = \ell^1$, the corresponding space is called just *nuclear*).

In most of the cases we shall be interested in results on nuclear spaces, and one can always look for generalization to λ-nuclear spaces wherever they are possible.

The following result contains a comparative characterization of nuclear and Schwartz spaces (Ref. 190, p. 71, and Ref. 248, p. 237).

THEOREM 13.14 An l.c. TVS (X,T) is a nuclear (resp. Schwartz) space if and only if for each $u \in \mathcal{B}$ there exist $v \in \mathcal{B}$ and a sequence $\{f_n\}$ in X^* with $\{p_{v^\circ}(f_n)\} \in \ell^1$ (resp. c_0) and such that

$$p_u(x) \le \sum_{n=1}^{\infty} |\langle x, f_n\rangle| \quad (\text{resp. } \sup_n |\langle x, f_n\rangle|)$$

is valid for each x in X.

The following is from Ref. 226, p. 14, and Ref. 247, p. 75.

THEOREM 13.15 For an l.c. TVS (X,T) the following statements are equivalent:

(i) (X,T) is nuclear.

(ii) There exists $\alpha > 0$ such that for each $u \in \mathcal{B}$ one can find $v \in \mathcal{B}$ with $v \prec u$ and

$$\sum_{n=0}^{\infty} [\delta_n(v,u)]^{\alpha} < \infty$$

(iii) For every $\beta > 0$ and $u \in \mathcal{B}$ there exists $v \in \mathcal{B}$ such that $v \prec u$ and

$$\sum_{n=0}^{\infty} [\delta_n(v,u)]^{\beta} < \infty$$

(iv) $\{(n + 1)^{\alpha}\} \in \Delta(X)$ for some $\alpha > 0$.

(v) $\{(n + 1)^{\beta}\} \in \Delta(X)$ for each $\beta > 0$.

Concerning Schwartz spaces we have (Ref. 51, p. 20, and Ref. 247, p. 73)

THEOREM 13.16 Let (X,T) be an l.c. TVS. Then the following statements are equivalent:

(i) (X,T) is a Schwartz space.

(ii) For every $u \in \mathcal{B}$ there exists $v \in \mathcal{B}$ with $v \prec u$ and

$$\lim_{n\to\infty} \delta_n(v,u) = 0$$

(iii) $\ell^{\infty} \subset \Delta(X)$.

(iv) $c_0 \neq \Delta(X)$.

Concerning ϕ-nuclearity we have the following analog (Ref. 210, p. 151, 154; and Ref. 211, p. 279):

THEOREM 13.17 Let (X,T) be an l.c. TVS. Then the following are equivalent:

(i) (X,T) is ϕ-nuclear.

(ii) For each $u \in \mathcal{B}$ there exists $v \in \mathcal{B}$ such that $v \prec u$ and

$$\sum_{n=0}^{\infty} \phi(\delta_n(v,u)) < \infty$$

(iii) For each $p > 0$ and each $u \in \mathcal{B}$ there exists $v \in \mathcal{B}$ with $v \prec u$ and such that

$$\sum_{n=0}^{\infty} \phi([\delta_n(v,u)]^p) < \infty$$

(iv) For each $u \in \mathcal{B}$ there exist $v \in \mathcal{B}$, $v \prec u$, and a sequence $\{f_n\} \subset X^*$ with $\{p_{v^\circ}(f_n)\} \in \ell_\phi$ such that

$$p_u(x) \leq \sum_{n\geq 1} |\langle x, f_n\rangle| \qquad \forall x \text{ in } X$$

Finally, we quote from Pietsch [190] the following:

PROPOSITION 13.18 The topological product of arbitrarily many nuclear spaces is nuclear.

14. TWO-NORM SPACES

Motivated by an earlier paper of Fichtenholz, Alexiewicz [2] introduced the concept of a two-norm space, which is closely related to the theory of Saks spaces developed simultaneously by Orlicz [180] (cf. also Ref. 181). The notion of Saks spaces goes back to two earlier papers of Saks [222,223]. Besides having applications in the theory of summability (Ref. 182), the theory of two-norm spaces as developed by Alexiewicz and Semandeni (cf. Refs. 1-5) also finds application in the study of sequence spaces (cf. Ref. 31, Chapter 4, and Ref. 265) and in the theory of Schauder bases and decompositions in Banach spaces (cf. Refs. 242-244). In this section we give just a few elementary concepts of this theory, which we shall need in a subsequent chapter. By a *two-norm space* we mean a vector space X equipped with two norms $\|\cdot\|_1$ and $\|\cdot\|_2$, where the homogeneity property of either of the norms may be overlooked in general, and we denote the structure of a two-norm space by X_s, that is, $X_s = (X, \|\cdot\|_1, \|\cdot\|_2)$.

DEFINITION 14.1 (i) A space X_s is said to satisfy the *property* (n_0) if the norm $\|\cdot\|_1$ is finer than $\|\cdot\|_2$; (ii) in X_s a sequence $\{x_n\}$ is said to be *γ-convergent to* x (resp. *γ-Cauchy*) if $\sup_{n\geq 1} \|x_n\|_1 < \infty$ and also $\lim_{n\to\infty}\|x_n - x\|_2 = 0$ (resp. $\lim_{m,n\to\infty}\|x_n - x_m\|_2 = 0$); (iii) X_s is said to be γ-*complete* if every γ-Cauchy sequence is γ-convergent in X; and (iv) X_s is called *quasinormal* if there is a constant $C(X_s) \geq 1$ such that for any γ-convergent sequence $\{x_n\}$ to x in X, we have

$$\|x\|_1 \leq C(X_s) \liminf_n \|x_n\|_1$$

Note: From now on we shall abbreviate the statement "$\{x_n\}$ is γ-convergent to x" as "$x_n \to x$ (γ)."

The smallest constant $C(X_s)$ is called the *constant of quasinormality* of X_s. If $C(X_s) = 1$, X_s is called γ-*normal*.

Concerning the dual of X_s, we have

DEFINITION 14.2 A linear functional f on X is called a γ-*linear functional on* X_s if $f(x_n) \to f(x)$ whenever $x_n \to x$ (γ). The collection of all γ-linear functionals on X_s is the *space* $A(X_s)$, which we call the γ-*dual* of X_s.

If $(X_j^*, \|\cdot\|_j^*) = (X, \|\cdot\|_j)^*$, j = 1, 2, where $\|\cdot\|_j^*$ is the dual norm on X_j^* defined by $\|\cdot\|_j$, we have (Ref. 182, p. 57)

PROPOSITION 14.3 Let a two-norm space X_s satisfy the property (n_0). Then $X_2^* \subset A(X_s)$ and $A(X_s)$ is a closed subspace of X_1^*.

Note: If $A(X_s) = X_1^*$, the space X_s is called *saturated*.

Alexiewicz and Semadeni [5] prove

PROPOSITION 14.4 If X_s is quasinormal and satisfies the property (n_0), then $(X_2^*, \|\cdot\|_1^*)$ is dense in $(A(X_s), \|\cdot\|_1^*)$.

PROPOSITION 14.5 If X_s is quasinormal and satisfies the property (n_0), then $A(X_s) = X_2^*$ if and only if the norms $\|\cdot\|_1$ and $\|\cdot\|_2$ are equivalent.

γ-reflexivity

Let $(X,\|\cdot\|_1,\|\cdot\|_2) = X_s$ be a two-norm space, $(X_j^*,\|\cdot\|_j^*) = (X_j,\|\cdot\|_j)^*$ and $(X_j^{**},\|\cdot\|_j^{**}) = (X_j^*,\|\cdot\|_j^*)^*$, $j = 1, 2$, where $\|\cdot\|_j^*$ and $\|\cdot\|_j^{**}$ are respectively the dual and bidual norms to $\|\cdot\|_j$. If X_s satisfies the property (n_0), then $(X_2^*,\|\cdot\|_2^*,\|\cdot\|_1^*) = X_{2s}^*$ also satisfies (n_0), and it is a γ-complete, γ-normal, two-norm space (cf. Ref. 4, p. 278). The space X_{2s}^* is called the *γ-conjugate space* to X_s. If $X_{21}^{**} = (X_2^*,\|\cdot\|_1^*)^*$, then $(X_{21}^{**},\|\cdot\|_{12}^{**},\|\cdot\|_2^{**}) = X_{21s}^{**}$, where $\|\cdot\|_{12}^{**}$ is defined on X_{21}^{**} by $\|\cdot\|_1^*|X_2^*$, is a two-norm space γ-conjugate to X_{2s}^* and is known as the *second γ-conjugate space* to X_s. The *γ-canonical embedding* J_γ is then defined from X_s to X_{21s}^{**} as follows:

$$J_\gamma(x)(f) = f(x) \qquad \forall f \in X_2^*$$

where $x \in X$.

We now have (Ref. 4, p. 278)

PROPOSITION 14.6 Let X_s be γ-normal. Then $(A(X_s),\|\cdot\|_1^*)^* = (X_{21}^{**},\|\cdot\|_{12}^{**})$.

The following is shown in Ref. 5, p. 119:

PROPOSITION 14.7 Let X_s satisfy the property (n_0). Then J_γ is a γ-topological isomorphism if and only if X_s is quasinormal.

Next, we have (Ref. 4, p. 279)

PROPOSITION 14.8 Let the property (n_0) be true for X_s. Then J_γ is a γ-isometry (i.e., $\|x\|_1 = \|J(x)\|_{12}^{**}$, $\|x\|_2 = \|J(x)\|_2^{**}$) if and only if X_s is γ-normal.

Finally, we come to the following natural definition of γ-reflexivity.

DEFINITION 14.9 A two-norm space X_s is called *γ-reflexive* if it is γ-normal and J_γ maps X onto X_{21}^{**}.

Chapter 2

SEQUENCE SPACES

1. INTRODUCTION

In several branches of analysis, for instance, the structural theory of topological vector spaces, Schauder basis theory, summability theory, and the theory of functions, the study of sequence spaces (SS) occupies a very prominent position. The impact and importance of this study can be appreciated when one sees the construction of numerous examples of locally convex spaces obtained as a consequence of the dual structure displayed by several pairs of distinct sequence spaces, thus reflecting in depth the distinguishing structural features of the spaces in question. Besides, these distinct sequence spaces endowed with different polar topologies provide an excellent source to vector space pathologists for the introduction on locally convex spaces to several new and penetrating notions implicit in the theory of Banach spaces. Apart from this, the theory of SS is a powerful tool for obtaining positive results concerning Schauder bases and their associated types, which we shall take up in a forthcoming monograph (Ref. 125). Thanks to an ever increasing interest in recent times, the theory of SS has made remarkable advances in enveloping summability theory via unified techniques effecting matrix transformations from one sequence space into another.

Thus we have several important applications of the theory of sequence spaces and therefore we attempt to present a systematic treatment of this subject matter in such a way so as to cover almost the entire spectrum of analysis and functional analysis outlined in the foregoing paragraph. Standard references for our work are Cooke [34], Köthe [140], Köthe and Toeplitz [143], Zeller [270,272], and many other papers and theses quoted in subsequent sections. Essentially we restrict our attention to two different aspects of the theory in this chapter, namely (i) the salient features of sequence spaces and (ii) duality results for pairs of distinct sequence spaces. The presentation is intended to be especially useful in the study of the Schauder basis and summability theories.

Finally, let us make a few remarks concerning related fields of investigation where there is a lot yet to be achieved. One of these is the theory of vector-valued sequence spaces as developed relative to specific scalar-valued sequence spaces, and we refer the reader to the original work of De Grande-De Kimpe [37], Pietsch [189,190], and Rosier [212,213]. The other direction of interest is the theory of vector-valued sequence spaces based on the duality structure of two vector spaces and its applications to Schauder decompositions, which we plan to discuss in a forthcoming work (Ref. 131); for instance, one may consult Gregory [65-67], Gupta, Kamthan, and Rao [82-84], Leonard [148], Pietsch [189], Phoung-Các [187,188], Rao [199], and Zelonka [273]. The scope of the present monograph does not, however, allow us to consider either of these two subjects here.

2. BASIC DEFINITIONS AND RESULTS

The primary aim of this section is to collect all the basic definitions and results on sequence spaces of which we shall make frequent use in the rest of this work without further reference.

We denote by ω the family of *all* sequences $\{x_n\}$ with $x_n \in \mathbb{K}$, $n \geq 1$. The family ω under the usual pointwise addition and scalar multiplication becomes a vector space over $\mathbb{K}$. Any subspace λ of ω will henceforth be referred to as a *sequence space* and we shall generally assume that λ is a nontrivial vector space of ω. An arbitrary member $\{x_n\}$ of ω shall be sometimes *denoted by* x only. For x in ω, we write $|x|$ *to mean* $\{|x_i|\}$. The multiplication between two sequences x and y is also defined pointwise, i.e., $xy = \{x_i y_i\}$. A *sequence algebra* is a subspace λ of ω such that λ is closed under multiplication. The following notation is reserved for the sequences e^n, $n \geq 1$, and e, defined below:

$$e^n_m = \begin{cases} 0 & \text{if } m \neq n \\ 1 & \text{if } m = n \end{cases}$$

e^n_m being the mth coordinate of e^n, and $e = \{1, 1, 1, \ldots\}$.

e is usually referred to as the *unity* of ω while each e^n is occasionally called a *unit vector* of ω (the sequence e^n is just termed the nth *unit vector* of ω). A commonly used sequence space is ϕ, defined as

$$\phi = \text{sp}\,\{e^n : n \geq 1\}$$

ϕ is the well-known *sequence space of finitely nonzero sequences from* $\mathbb{K}$.

An extremely useful concept in the theory of Schauder bases as well as in summability theory is that of the nth *section* of an element $x \in \omega$. More generally we introduce it as follows. If $M \subset \mathbb{N}$, the linear map $S_M: \omega \to \omega$ is defined by the relation

$$(S_M(x))_i = \begin{cases} x_i & \text{if } i \in M \\ 0 & \text{if } i \notin M \end{cases}$$

If $M = \{1, 2, \ldots, n\}$, we write S_n for S_M. The element $S_n(x)$ is called the nth *section* of $x \in \omega$; sometimes we also use the symbol $x^{(n)}$ for $S_n(x)$. It is clear that

$$S_n(x) \text{ or } x^{(n)} = \{x_1, x_2, \ldots, x_n, 0, 0, \ldots\}$$
$$= \sum_{i=1}^{n} x_i e^i$$

where $x_1, x_2, \ldots$ are coordinates of x.

For a subsequence J of $\mathbb{N}$ and a sequence space λ, we define λ_J by

$$\lambda_J = \{\{x_i\} : \text{there is a } \{y_i\} \in \lambda \text{ with } x_i = y_{n_i},\ \forall n_i \in J\}$$

and call λ_J the *J-stepspace* or *J-sectional subspace* of λ. If $x_J \in \lambda_J$, then the *canonical preimage* of x_J is the sequence $\bar{x}_J$ which agrees with x_J on the indices in J and is zero elsewhere. The *canonical preimage* of λ_J is the space $\bar{\lambda}_J$ containing the canonical preimages of the elements of λ_J. If J_1 and J_2 are disjoint subsequences of $\mathbb{N}$ whose union is $\mathbb{N}$, we say that λ_{J_1} and λ_{J_2} are *complementary stepspaces*.

Note: For several results on λ_J, see Definition 8.7 onward.

The set of all *permutations* of $\mathbb{N}$ (i.e., one-one and onto maps of $\mathbb{N}$) will be denoted by Π.

DEFINITION 2.1 Let λ be a sequence space. Then λ is called

(i) *Symmetric* if $x_\sigma \equiv \{x_{\sigma(i)}\} \in \lambda$ whenever $x \in \lambda$ and $\sigma \in \Pi$.

(ii) *Normal* or *solid* if $y \in \lambda$ whenever $|y_i| \le |x_i|$, $i \ge 1$, for some $x \in \lambda$.

(iii) *Monotone* provided λ contains the canonical preimages of all its stepspaces.

Below we present a number of examples of sequence spaces; a few should be already familiar to the reader. In what follows we abbreviate the infinite sum notation $\Sigma_{i=1}^{\infty}$ as $\Sigma_{i\ge 1}$.

$$c_0 = \{x : x \in \omega,\ \lim_n x_n = 0\}$$

$$c = \{x : x \in \omega,\ \lim_n x_n \text{ exists in } \mathbb{K}\}$$

$$\ell^p = \{x : x \in \omega,\ \Sigma_{i\ge 1} |x_i|^p < \infty\},\ 0 < p < \infty$$

$$\ell^\infty \text{ or } m = \{x : x \in \omega,\ \sup_n |x_n| < \infty\}$$

$$m_0 = \text{sp}\,\{A\}, \text{ where } A \text{ is the set of all sequences of zeros and ones}$$

$$k = \{x : x \in \omega,\ x_{i+1} = x_i,\ i \ge i_0, \text{ for some } i_0 \in \mathbb{N}\}$$

$$a = \{x : x \in \omega,\ x_{i+1} = -x_i,\ i \ge i_0, \text{ for some } i_0 \in \mathbb{N}\}$$

$$\delta = \{x : x \in \omega,\ \lim_n |x_n|^{1/n} = 0\}$$

$$d = \{x : x \in \omega,\ \sup_n |x_n|^{1/n} < \infty\}$$

$$\Pi_r = \{x : x \in \omega,\ \lim_n |x_n|^{1/n} \le r^{-1}\},\ r \in \mathbb{R}^+$$

$$d_{1/r} = \{x : x \in \omega,\ \lim\sup_n |x_n|^{1/n} < r\},\ r \in \mathbb{R}^+$$

$$cs = \{x : x \in \omega,\ \lim_n \Sigma_{i=1}^{n} x_i \text{ exists}\}$$

$$bv = \{x : x \in \omega,\ \lim_n \Sigma_{i=1}^{n} |x_{i+1} - x_i| \text{ exists}\}$$

$$bv_0 = \{x : x \in bv \text{ such that } \lim_n x_n = 0\}$$

$$bs = \{x : x \in \omega,\ \sup_n |\Sigma_{i=1}^{n} x_i| < \infty\}$$

$$as = \{x : x \in \omega,\ \lim_{n\to\infty} \Sigma_{i=1}^{n} (-1)^i x_i \text{ exists}\}$$

Another sequence space that will be of much use in the formulation of counterexamples is constructed as follows. Let $\mathcal{O}$ stand for all sequences $x = \{x_i\}$ in ω such that

$$x_i = 0 \text{ or } 1 \qquad \text{and} \qquad \frac{1}{n}\sum_{i=1}^{n} x_i \to 0 \text{ as } n \to \infty$$

For any sequence space λ, let us define the subset λ_0 of ω by

$$\lambda_0 = \{\alpha x : \alpha \in \mathcal{O},\ x \in \lambda\}$$

Remarks: Let us note that if λ is monotone then λ_0 is a sequence space with $\phi \subset \lambda_0 \subset \lambda$. It is clear that if $x \in \lambda_0$ and $\alpha \in \mathbb{K}$ then $\alpha x \in \lambda_0$. Let us take $z^1, z^2 \in \lambda_0$. Then $z^1 = au$, $z^2 = bv$, where $a,b \in \mathcal{O}$ and $u,v \in \lambda$. Consider the subsets J_i $(i = 1, 2, 3, 4)$ of $\mathbb{N}$ such that

$$\begin{array}{llll} a_i \neq 0 & \text{and} & b_i = 0 & \text{for } i \in J_1 \\ a_i = 0 & \text{and} & b_i \neq 0 & \text{for } i \in J_2 \\ a_i \neq 0 & \text{and} & b_i \neq 0 & \text{for } i \in J_3 \\ a_i = 0 = b_i & & \text{for } i \in J_4 & \end{array}$$

Note that $J_i \cap J_j \neq \emptyset$, $i = j$, and $\mathbb{N} = J_1 \cup J_2 \cup J_3 \cup J_4$. Write $y = u + v$. Then $y \in \lambda$, and also $\bar{u}_{J_1}$, $\bar{v}_{J_2}$, $\bar{y}_{J_3} \in \lambda$, since λ is monotone. Thus $x \equiv \bar{u}_{J_1} + \bar{v}_{J_2} + \bar{y}_{J_3} \in \lambda$. Define a sequence $d = \{d_i\} \in \omega$ such that

$$d_i = \begin{cases} 1 & i \in J_1 \cup J_2 \cup J_3 \\ 0 & i \in J_4 \end{cases}$$

One easily verifies that $z^1 + z^2 = dx$. Here $d \in \mathcal{O}$ since

$$\frac{1}{n}\sum_{i=1}^{n} d_i \leq \frac{1}{n}\left(\sum_{i=1}^{n} a_i + \sum_{i=1}^{n} b_i\right)$$

Thus $z^1 + z^2 \in \lambda_0$. Let us observe further that if λ is normal, then λ_0 is also normal.

Note: For sequence spaces λ and μ, we write $\lambda\mu$ for $\{xy : x \in \lambda,\ y \in \mu\}$.

EXERCISE 2.2 Show that the sequence space m_0 is monotone but not normal. Also prove that a sequence space λ is normal if and only if $\ell^\infty\lambda \subset \lambda$.

PROPOSITION 2.3 Let λ be a sequence space. Then

(i) λ is monotone if and only if $m_0\lambda \subset \lambda$.

(ii) λ is normal if and only if $y \in \lambda$ whenever $|y_n| = |x_n|$, $n \geq 1$, for some $x \in \lambda$.

Proof. (1) Assume first that $m_0\lambda \subset \lambda$. Let $\bar{\lambda}_J$ be the canonical preimage of an arbitrary stepspace λ_J of λ. If $\{x_i\} \in \bar{\lambda}_J$, then there is a $\{y_i\} \in \lambda$ such that $x_i = y_i$ for $i \in J$ and $x_i = 0$ for $i \in \mathbb{N} \sim J$. Define $\{m_i\} \in m_0$ by

$$m_i = \begin{cases} 1 & i \in J \\ 0 & i \in \mathbb{N} \sim J \end{cases}$$

Then $\{x_i\} = \{m_i\}\{y_i\}$ and so $\{x_i\} \in \lambda$, that is, $\bar{\lambda}_J \subset \lambda$.

Conversely, let $\bar{\lambda}_J \subset \lambda$ for each subsequence J of $\mathbb{N}$ and suppose $\{z_i\} = \{m_i\}\{y_i\}$ where $\{m_i\} \in m_0$ and $\{y_i\} \in \lambda$. Now the m_i's are distinct for a finite number of indices, say $i_1, \ldots, i_n$; let $\alpha^1, \ldots, \alpha^p$ denote the scalars assumed by $\{m_i\}$ repeatedly over the respective subsequences $J_1, \ldots, J_p$ of $\mathbb{N}$. Then

$$\{z_i\} = \sum_{i=1}^{p} \alpha_i S_{J_i}(\{y_n\}) + \sum_{k=1}^{n} m_{i_k} y_{i_k} e^{i_k}$$

where $S_{J_i}(\{y_n\}) \in \bar{\lambda}_{J_i}$. Hence $\{z_i\} \in \lambda$, that is, $m_0\lambda \in \lambda$.

(ii) We need prove the "if" part only. Let therefore $x \in \lambda$ and $u \in \omega$ be such that $|u_n| \leq |x_n|$ for $n \geq 1$. Suppose $x_n = \xi_n + i\eta_n$ $(i = \sqrt{-1})$; $\xi_n, \eta_n \in \mathbb{R}$, $n \geq 1$. Then $\bar{x} = \{\bar{x}_n\} \in \lambda$ where $\bar{x}_n = \xi_n - i\eta_n$. Let $u_n = v_n + iw_n$; then $v_n^2 + w_n^2 \leq \xi_n^2 + \eta_n^2$. We can determine z_n $(n \geq 1)$ from $\mathbb{R}$ so that $v_n^2 + z_n^2 = \xi_n^2 + \eta_n^2$. Put $\zeta = \{v_n + iz_n\}$. Then $|\zeta_n| = |x_n|$, $n \geq 1$, and thus $\zeta \in \lambda$. Consequently $v = \{v_n\} \in \lambda$, since $(1/2)(\zeta + \bar{\zeta}) = \{v_n\}$. Determine t_n $(n \geq 1)$ from $\mathbb{R}$ so that $t_n^2 + w_n^2 = \xi_n^2 + \eta_n^2$. If $s = \{t_n + iw_n\}$, then $|s_n| = |x_n|$, $n \geq 1$, and so $s \in \lambda$. Since $(1/2i)(s - \bar{s}) = \{w_n\}$ we see that $\{w_n\} \in \lambda$. Therefore $u \in \lambda$. □

Duals

The only sequence space whose algebraic dual behaves nicely (e.g., whose elements are sequences) is the space ϕ; its algebraic dual is ω. Thus from the point of view of the duality theory, the study of sequence spaces is much more profitable when we consider them equipped with linear topologies. However, in such cases it is rather cumbersome to obtain their topological duals. Even if we are successful in finding these topological duals, we would like to deal with only those duals whose members are representable as sequences; indeed, such situations present not much difficulty in the analysis. Köthe and Toeplitz [143] were the first to recognize the problem, and to resolve it they introduced a kind of dual (namely, the α-dual) which turns out to be the same as the topological dual in quite many familiar and useful examples of sequence spaces endowed with their natural linear metrics. In the same paper (Ref. 143, p. 427), they also introduced another kind of dual (namely, the β-dual; cf. also Ref. 29 where it is called the g-dual by Chillingworth) which together with the given sequence space forms a nice dual system. A still more general notion of a dual was later introduced by Garling [56]. From the point of view of the duality structure, this last notion of a dual is not very important. For symmetric sequence spaces there is another notion of a dual, called a δ-dual, due to Garling [57] and Ruckle [217].

Our purpose in this subsection is to present certain basic definitions and results concerning these several duals.

DEFINITION 2.4 Let λ be a sequence space and define

(i) $\lambda^\alpha = \{x : x \in \omega, \Sigma_{i\geq 1} |x_i y_i| < \infty, \forall y \in \lambda\}$

(ii) $\lambda^\beta = \{x : x \in \omega, |\Sigma_{i\geq 1} x_i y_i| < \infty, \forall y \in \lambda\}$

(iii) $\lambda^\gamma = \{x : x \in \omega, \sup_n |\Sigma_{i=1}^n x_i y_i| < \infty, \forall y \in \lambda\}$

(iv) $\lambda^\delta = \{x : x \in \omega, \Sigma_{i\geq 1} |x_i y_{\rho(i)}| < \infty, \forall y \in \lambda \text{ and } \rho \in \Pi\}$

Then λ^α, λ^β, λ^γ, and λ^δ are called the α-, β-, γ-, and δ-*dual*, respectively.

Remarks: λ^α, λ^β, λ^γ, and λ^δ are sequence spaces, and $\phi \subset \lambda^\delta \subset \lambda^\alpha \subset \lambda^\beta \subset \lambda^\gamma$. In the literature λ^α is frequently denoted by $\lambda^\times$, which we shall also adopt after a few preliminaries.

Let us observe that $\lambda^\alpha = \{x : xy \in \ell^1, \forall y \in \lambda\}$ and $\lambda^\beta = \{x : xy \in cs, \forall y \in \lambda\}$, Replacing ℓ^1 and cs by a "sum sequence space" (see Ref. 218, p. 865), Ruckle [219] developed a more general theory than the α- and β-duals of sequence spaces.

EXERCISE 2.5 Let $\zeta = \alpha, \beta, \gamma$, or δ. Show that

(i) If $\lambda \subset \mu$, then $\mu^\zeta \subset \lambda^\zeta$.

(ii) If $\lambda = \cup\{\lambda_i : i \in I\}$, then $\lambda^\zeta = \cap\{\lambda_i^\zeta : i \in I\}$, I being an index set; see Ref. 56.

For any sequence space λ we denote $(\lambda^\zeta)^\eta$ by $\lambda^{\zeta\eta}$, where $\zeta,\eta = \alpha, \beta, \gamma$, or δ. It is clear that $\lambda \subset \lambda^{\zeta\zeta}$ where $\zeta = \alpha, \beta, \gamma$, or δ. Accordingly we have

DEFINITION 2.6 For a sequence space λ, if $\lambda = \lambda^{\zeta\zeta}$ then λ is called a *ζ-space*, $\zeta = \alpha, \beta, \gamma$, or δ. In particular, an α-space is called a *Köthe space* or a *perfect sequence space*.

Next we have (Ref. 15, p. 55; Ref. 56, p. 964; Ref. 217):

PROPOSITION 2.7 Let λ be a sequence space. If λ is monotone, then $\lambda^\alpha = \lambda^\beta$, and if λ is normal, then $\lambda^\alpha = \lambda^\gamma$. Further, if λ is symmetric, $\lambda^\alpha = \lambda^\delta$.

Proof. Let $x \in \lambda^\beta$ and so $x \in (m_0\lambda)^\beta$. Thus $\Sigma_{i\geq 1} \alpha_i x_i y_i$ converges for each $\alpha \in m_0$ and $y \in \lambda$; in particular, the series $\Sigma_{i\geq 1} x_i y_i$ is subseries convergent and thus $\Sigma_{i\geq 1} |x_i y_i| < \infty$ for each $y \in \lambda$. Hence $x \in \lambda^\alpha \Rightarrow \lambda^\beta \subset \lambda^\alpha$.

For the second part, let $x \in \lambda^\gamma$. Then

$$\sup_n \left|\sum_{i=1}^n x_i y_i\right| < \infty \qquad \forall y \in \lambda$$

Observe that $\{(\bar{x}_i \bar{y}_i / x_i y_i) y_i\} \in \lambda$ for any $y \in \lambda$. Hence $\Sigma_{i\geq 1} |x_i y_i| < \infty$ for each $y \in \lambda$, so that $x \in \lambda^\alpha$.

Finally, let λ be symmetric and $x \in \lambda^\alpha$. For each $y \in \lambda$ and any $\sigma \in \Pi$, $y_{\sigma^{-1}} \in \lambda$, so that

$$\sum_{i\geq 1} |x_i y_{\sigma^{-1}(i)}| = \sum_{j\geq 1} |x_{\sigma(j)} y_j| < \infty$$

and thus x belongs to λ^δ.

The reverse inclusions have been observed earlier. □

The discussion concerning δ-duals and symmetric sequence spaces is postponed to a later subsection; in the meantime let us consider a few examples of α-, β-, and γ-duals. In what follows we write an α-dual as $\lambda^{\times}$, which seems to be more conventional (by the way, $\lambda^{\times}$ is also called the *cross* or the *Köthe dual* of the sequence space λ).

PROPOSITION 2.8 Let λ be a sequence space. Then $\lambda^{\zeta} = \lambda^{\zeta\zeta\zeta}$, where $\zeta = \alpha$, β, or γ; in particular, $\lambda^{\times}$ is a Köthe space, λ^{β} is a β-space and λ^{γ} is a γ-space. Also we have

$$\text{Perfectness (of } \lambda) \Longrightarrow \text{normality (of } \lambda) \Longrightarrow \text{monotonocity (of } \lambda)$$

Further we have

(i) $\omega^{\times} = \phi$, $\phi^{\times} = \omega$.

(ii) $(\ell^1)^{\times} = \ell^{\infty}$, $(\ell^{\infty})^{\times} = \ell^1$.

(iii) $\delta^{\times} = d$, $d^{\times} = \delta$.

(iv) $c_0^{\times} = c^{\times} = \ell^1$, $k^{\times} = \ell^1$.

(v) k and c are not monotone and hence not normal.

(vi) c_0 is normal but not perfect.

(vii) m_0 is monotone but not normal.

Proof. Up to (i) the proofs seem to be rather straightforward and so we omit them. For (ii) it is sufficient to establish the inclusions

$$(\ell^1)^{\times} \subset \ell^{\infty} \qquad \text{and} \qquad (\ell^{\infty})^{\times} \subset \ell^1$$

Let, therefore, $x \in (\ell^1)^{\times}$ and $x \notin \ell^{\infty}$. Hence there exists a strictly increasing sequence $\{n_i\} \subset \mathbb{N}$ with $|x_{n_i}| > i^3$. If

$$y_n = \begin{cases} i^{-2} & n = n_i;\ i \geq 1 \\ 0 & n \neq n_i \end{cases}$$

then $\{y_n\} \in \ell^1$ but $\Sigma_{i\geq 1} |x_i y_i| = \infty$. Thus $x \notin (\ell^1)^{\times}$ and so $(\ell^1)^{\times} \subset \ell^{\infty}$.

Since $e \in \ell^{\infty}$, it follows that $(\ell^{\infty})^{\times} \subset \ell^1$.

(iii) Let $x \in d$. There exists $M > 0$ with $|x_i| \leq M^i$, $i \geq 1$. One may choose $\varepsilon > 0$ such that $\varepsilon M < 1$. If $y \in \delta$ we have $|y_i| \leq \varepsilon^i$ for

$i \geq i_0 \equiv i_0(\varepsilon)$. Therefore $\Sigma_{i\geq 1} |x_i y_i| < \infty$, yielding

$$d \subset \delta^{\times}$$

On the other hand, let $x \in \delta^{\times}$ but $x \notin d$. Hence

$$|x_{n_i}| > i^{2n_i} \qquad i \geq 1, \text{ where } n_i < n_{i+1}$$

If

$$y_n = \begin{cases} i^{-n_i} & n = n_i \\ 0 & n \neq n_i \end{cases}$$

then $\{y_n\} \in \delta$ but $\Sigma_{i\geq 1} |x_i y_i| = \infty$. Thus $x \notin \delta^{\times}$, a contradiction. Therefore, $\delta^{\times} \subset d$ and we find that $\delta^{\times} = d$. Similarly we can prove that $\delta = d^{\times}$.

(iv) The proof here is rather obvious and so is omitted.

(v) Observe that $\{1, 0, 1, 0, \ldots\} \notin k$ or c.

(vi) This makes use of (iv).

(vii) We find here that $\{1/n\} \notin m_0$ although $1/n \leq 1$ for $n \geq 1$, and $\{1, 1, \ldots\} \in m_0$. □

COROLLARY 2.9 The spaces ϕ, ω, ℓ^1, ℓ^{∞}, d, and δ are all perfect.

EXERCISE 2.10 (i) Show that

$$(\ell^p)^{\times} = \ell^q \qquad 1 < p,q < \infty, \text{ with } \frac{1}{p} + \frac{1}{q} = 1$$

and hence prove that each ℓ^p $(1 \leq p < \infty)$ is perfect.

(ii) Prove that

$$\Pi_r^{\times} = d_{1/r} \qquad \text{and} \qquad d_r^{\times} = \Pi_{1/r} \qquad r > 0$$

and therefore each of the spaces Π_r and $d_{1/r}$ is perfect.

Next we have a set of nonperfect spaces (i.e., spaces that are not Köthe) in

PROPOSITION 2.11 We have

(i) $(cs)^{\times} = (bv)^{\times} = (bv_0)^{\times} = (bs)^{\times} = \ell^1$.

(ii) $(cs)^{\beta} = bv$, $(bv)^{\beta} = cs$, $(bv_0)^{\beta} = bs$, $(bs)^{\beta} = bv_0$.

(iii) $(cs)^\gamma = bv$, $(bv)^\gamma = bs$, $(bv_0)^\gamma = bs$, $(bs)^\gamma = bv$.

Proof. (i) Most of the proofs can be obtained along lines similar to those adopted in the proof of Proposition 2.8, i.e., based on contradiction methods. For instance, to prove that $(cs)^\times \subset \ell^1$, let $x \in (cs)^\times$ but $x \notin \ell^1$. Thus to every positive integer k we find an odd n_k in $\mathbb{N}$ with $n_k < n_{k+1}$ and

$$\sum_{i=n_k+1}^{n_{k+1}} |x_i| > 2^k \qquad k = 1, 2, \ldots$$

Define

$$y_i = \begin{cases} (-1)^i 2^{-k/2} & n_k < i \le n_{k+1},\ k \ge 1 \\ 0 & \text{elsewhere} \end{cases}$$

Then $\{y_i\} \in cs$ and $\Sigma_{i\ge1} |x_i y_i| = \infty$. This contradicts the fact that $x \in (cs)^\times$, and so $(cs)^\times \subset \ell^1$. As $cs \subset c_0$, we have $\ell^1 = c_0^\times \subset (cs)^\times$. Therefore $(cs)^\times = \ell^1$.

(ii) We prove here $(cs)^\beta = bv$; the other statements can be disposed of similarly. To show $(cs)^\beta \subset bv$, consider $y \in (cs)^\beta$ and $z \in c_0$. Then the sequence $\{\omega_n\}$ defined by $\omega_n = z_n - z_{n-1}$, $n \ge 1$, where $z_0 = 0$, belongs to cs. Therefore, the series $\Sigma_{n\ge1} \omega_n y_n$ converges. But

$$\sum_{i=1}^{n} (z_i - z_{i-1})y_i = \sum_{i=1}^{n-1} z_i(y_i - y_{i+1}) + z_n y_n$$

and $\{y_n\} \in (cs)^\beta \subset \ell^\infty$ (indeed, $cs \supset \ell^1$) imply that

$$\sum_{i=1}^{\infty} (z_i - z_{i-1})y_i = \sum_{i=1}^{\infty} z_i(y_i - y_{i-1})$$

Hence $\{y_i - y_{i+1}\} \in (c_0)^\beta = c_0^\times = \ell^1$, i.e., $y \in bv$. To prove the other inclusion, let us take $y \in bv$. Then $\{y_i - y_{i+1}\} \in \ell^1$. Further, if $x \in cs$, the sequence $\{\omega_n\}$, $\omega_n = \Sigma_{i=1}^n x_i$, $n \ge 1$, is an element of c. As $c^\times = \ell^1$, the series $\Sigma_{i\ge1} \omega_i(y_i - y_{i+1})$ is absolutely convergent. Also for integers $n,m \in \mathbb{N}$ with $n > m$, we have

$$\left|\sum_{i=m}^{n} (\omega_i - \omega_{i-1})y_i\right| \le \left|\sum_{i=m}^{n-1} \omega_i(y_i - y_{i+1})\right| + |\omega_n y_n - \omega_{m-1} y_m|$$

As $\{\omega_n\} \in c$ and $\{y_n\} \in bv \subset c$, the right-hand side of the above inequality converges to zero as $m,n \to \infty$. Hence the series $\Sigma_{i=1}^{\infty} (\omega_i - \omega_{i-1})y_i$ or $\Sigma_{i=1}^{\infty} x_i y_i$ converges and so $bv \subset (cs)^{\beta}$. Thus $(cs)^{\beta} = bv$.

(iii) To prove $(cs)^{\gamma} = bv$, we need show that $(cs)^{\gamma} \subset bv$, as the other inclusion follows from the preceding part. Let $y \in (cs)^{\gamma}$ and $z \in c_0$. Then for the sequence $\{\omega_n\}$ in cs, defined as $\omega_n = z_n - z_{n-1}$, $n \ge 1$, $z_0 = 0$, we can find a constant $K > 0$ such that

$$\left|\sum_{i=1}^{n} \omega_i y_i\right| \le K \qquad \text{for all } n \ge 1$$

Since $\{z_n\} \in c_0$ and $\{y_n\} \in (cs)^{\gamma} \subset \ell^{\infty}$, there exists a constant M such that $|z_n y_n| \le M$ for all $n \ge 1$. Now proceeding as in the first part of the preceding proof, we get for all $n \ge 1$,

$$\left|\sum_{i=1}^{n} z_i(y_i - y_{i+1})\right| \le \left|\sum_{i=1}^{n+1} (z_i - z_{i-1})y_i\right| + |z_{n+1}y_{n+1}|$$
$$\le K + M$$

Hence $\{y_i - y_{i+1}\} \in (c_0)^{\gamma} = c_0^{\times} = \ell^1$. Therefore $(cs)^{\gamma} = bv$. The other proofs are left as simple exercises. □

PROPOSITION 2.12 We have

(i) $m_0^{\times} = m_0^{\beta} = m_0^{\gamma} = \ell^1$.

(ii) $k^{\times} = \ell^1$, $k^{\beta} = cs$, $k^{\gamma} = bs$.

Proof. (i) It is sufficient to prove that $m_0^{\gamma} \subset \ell^1$. Let $y \in m_0^{\gamma}$ and suppose that each $y_i \in \mathbf{R}$. Choose $J \subset \mathbf{N}$ such that $y_i < 0$ for $i \in J$. Then

$$\sum_{i=1}^{n} |y_i| = \sum_{J\cap[1,n]} (-y_i) + \sum_{J_1\cap[1,n]} y_i < \infty \qquad J_1 = \mathbf{N} \sim J$$

since $\bar{e}_J$ and $\bar{e}_{J_1}$ belong to m_0. Thus $y \in \ell^1$. The general case follows by breaking up each y_i into its real and imaginary parts.

(ii) In view of Proposition 2.8, we need show that $k^{\beta} = cs$ and $k^{\gamma} = bs$.

Since $k \subset bv$, we get $cs \subset k^{\beta}$. The inclusion $k^{\beta} \subset cs$ is clearly true and so $k^{\beta} = cs$. The equality $k^{\gamma} = bs$ follows similarly. □

Note: For a functional analytic proof of $m_0^\gamma = \ell^1$, see the remark following the proof of Proposition 7.21.

3. TOPOLOGY ON SEQUENCE SPACES

One of the easiest and natural ways in which a sequence space λ can be endowed with a linear topology, or more specifically, with a locally convex topology, is to consider the duality structure of λ with either $\lambda^\times$ or λ^β and then determine various polar topologies. This discussion, which is the central theme of this chapter, will be taken up in later sections. In the meantime, let us explore the salient features of the linear topological sequence spaces we are going to study.

Before we demonstrate the importance and usefulness of the linear topology with which we are going to equip λ, let us assume from now on that *any sequence space we discuss contains* ϕ, a fact which is of paramount importance, at least in the Schauder basis theory. If we look into the duals of many sequence spaces discussed in the preceding paragraphs, we find that the e^i's belong to all of them. The same is true for the topological duals of most of the sequence spaces endowed with their natural metrics, in which case these duals coincide either with the α- or β-duals (observe that each e^i is also regarded here as a functional on λ since $\langle x, e^i \rangle = x_i$, $x \in \lambda$). This fact has an important role in the Schauder basis theory as well as in the theory of summability. Accordingly we have

DEFINITION 3.1 A sequence space λ with a linear topology is called a K-*space* provided each of the maps P_i: $\lambda \to \mathbb{K}$, $P_i(x) = x_i$ is continuous, $i \geq 1$.

Note: It will be assumed from now on that ω *is always endowed* with its natural locally convex (indeed, Fréchet) topology generated by the sequence $\{p_n\}$ of seminorms on ω, where $p_n(x) = |x_n|$, $n \geq 1$.

EXERCISE 3.2 Show that a sequence space λ equipped with a linear topology is a K-space if and only if the identity map I: $\lambda \to \omega$ is continuous.

DEFINITION 3.3 A K-space λ is called a *Fréchet* K-*space* (resp. an FK-, a BK-*space*) provided λ is an F-space (resp. a Fréchet, a Banach space).

Of several considerations that force us to introduce the concept of an AK-space and a few other related definitions, the one which will most concern us is the idea of a Schauder base. We have made a running reference to this notion earlier, and formally it is given in

DEFINITION 3.4 A sequence $\{x_n\}$ contained in a TVS (X,T) is called a *base* or *basis* for this space if each x in X can be uniquely expressed as

$$x = T\text{-}\lim_{n\to\infty} \sum_{i=1}^{n} \alpha_i x_i \tag{*}$$

The uniquely determined sequence $\{\alpha_n\}$ of scalars is usually referred to as the *sequence of associated coordinate functionals* (s.a.c.f.). Indeed, each α_n in (*) above determines a linear functional on X, i.e., $\alpha_n \equiv f_n(x)$ where $f_n \in X'$ for $n \geq 1$. Thus if we want to emphasize the s.a.c.f. attached to a base $\{x_n\}$ we would unambiguously write $\{x_n\}$ as $\{x_n;f_n\}$. A base $\{x_n;f_n\}$ for a TVS (X,T) is a *Schauder base* provided $\{f_n\} \subset X^*$.

Remark: It is easily verified that an l.c. TVS (X,T) possessing a Schauder base $\{x_n;f_n\}$ is separable. Indeed, the set $\{\Sigma_{i=1}^{n} r_i x_i : n \in \mathbb{N}$ and the r_i's are rationals$\}$ is a countable T-dense subset of X.

As remarked earlier, a detailed discussion of the basis concept, including its motivation, theory, applications, and numerous examples and counterexamples, will be carried out in our forthcoming work; meanwhile, let us grant that the existence of a base or a Schauder base in a TVS X is itself of vast importance from the point of view of representation theory, and has far-reaching effects on the structure of X. The sequence $\{e^n\}$, apart from being a Hamel base for ϕ, presents a very simple structure in itself. We should therefore be interested to know if $\{e^n\}$ is a Schauder base for a sequence space equipped with a linear topology, and for that reason it will be advantageous to confine our attention to K-spaces. Therefore we have the following (Ref. 58).

DEFINITION 3.5 Let (λ,T) be a K-space. An element $x \in \lambda$ is said to have the *property* AK (resp. SAK) provided

$$x^{(n)} = \sum_{i=1}^{n} x_i e^i \to x \qquad \text{in } T \text{ [resp. } \sigma(\lambda,\lambda^*)]$$

to have the *property* AD if $x \in \bar{\phi}$ (the T-closure of ϕ), and to have the *property* BS if $\{S_n(x) : n \geq 1\}$ is T-bounded. A K-space λ is called an AK (resp. an AD, a BS)-*space* if each x in λ has the property AK (resp. AD, BS); if each x in λ has the property SAK, λ is called an SAK-*space*. We write S_λ (resp. W_λ) for the collection of all those points of λ having the property AK (resp. SAK). If (λ,T) is a sequence space with a linear topology T, we *write* λ_c for $\bar{\phi}$, the closure of ϕ in (λ,T), and use the *symbol* λ_s for the *space* $\{\{f(e^i)\} : f \in \lambda^*\}$.

We have (Ref. 219, p. 239)

PROPOSITION 3.6 Let (λ,T) be an l.c. TVS which is also a sequence space. Then $\lambda_s = (\lambda_c)_s$, and $(\lambda_c)_s$ is algebraically isomorphic to $\lambda_c^* \equiv (\lambda_c)^*$ under the map ψ: $\lambda_c^* \to \lambda_s$, $\psi(f) = \{f(e^i)\}$.

Proof. It is clear that $\lambda_s \subset (\lambda_c)_s$. For the reverse inclusion, we need observe from the Hahn-Banach theorem that if $g \in \lambda_c^*$ then g can be extended to $\hat{g} \in \lambda^*$ such that $g(e^i) = \hat{g}(e^i)$, $i \geq 1$. For the second part, observe that if $\psi(f) = 0$, $f \in \lambda_c^*$, then $f(e^i) = 0$ for $i \geq 1$, and so $f(x) = 0$ for $x \in \phi$. Consequently $f(y) = 0$ for $y \in \lambda_c$, that is, $f = 0$. Thus ψ is one-to-one. □

COROLLARY 3.7 Let (λ,T) be as in Proposition 3.6. Then we have:

(i) If (λ,T) is an AD-space, then λ^* can be identified with λ_s.

(ii) If (λ,T) is an AK-space, then λ^* and λ_s are algebraically isomorphic and $\lambda^* \subset \lambda^\beta$.

Proof. Indeed, for (i) let us observe that $\lambda_c = \lambda$. For (ii), let us note that the AK-property implies the AD-property; thus a part of the result follows from (i). Let $f \in \lambda^*$. Let $x \in \lambda$ be arbitrary. Then

$$x = \sum_{i\geq 1} x_i e^i \Longrightarrow f(x) = \sum_{i\geq 1} x_i f(e^i)$$

Hence $\{f(e^i)\} \in \lambda^\beta$ and so $\lambda_s \subset \lambda^\beta$. □

EXERCISE 3.8 (i) Let (λ,T) be an AK-space, and T a linear topology. Then each $f \in \lambda^*$ (resp. λ^+) can be identified with $\{f(e^i)\}$, and $\lambda^* \subset \lambda^+ \subset \lambda^\beta$. [Hint: Show that the map $\psi: \lambda^* \to \lambda_s$, $\psi(f) = \{f(e^i)\}$, is injective and a similar argument for λ^+.] (ii) If (λ,T) is a barreled K-space, show that for y in λ, the map $x \to \Sigma_{i\geq 1} x_i y_i$ is continuous. [Hint: Proceed as in Proposition 3.9.]

Next, we have (Ref. 56, p. 965)

PROPOSITION 3.9 If (λ,T) is a barreled AK-space, then $\lambda^* = \lambda^\beta$.

Proof. Let $y \in \lambda^\beta$ and define $f_n \in \lambda^*$ by $f_n(x) = \Sigma_{i=1}^n x_i y_i$. Since $\{f_n\}$ is pointwise bounded, it follows from Theorem 1.10.3 that $f_y \in \lambda^*$, where

$$f_y(x) = \sum_{i\geq 1} x_i y_i$$

But $f_y = \{f_y(e^i)\}$ [cf. Corollary 3.7(ii)] and so $\{y_i\} = \{f_y(e^i)\} \in \lambda^*$. Therefore $\lambda^\beta \subset \lambda^*$. Now make use of Exercise 3.8. □

The spaces ω and ϕ form a dual system $\langle\omega,\phi\rangle$, the related bilinear functional $\langle\cdot,\cdot\rangle$ being given by

$$\langle x,y\rangle = \sum_{i\in\sigma} x_i y_i \qquad x \in \omega,\ y \in \phi$$

where $\sigma \in \Phi$, the family of all finite subsets of $\mathbb{N}$. It is easily seen that the usual topology on ω (cf. the note following Definition 3.1) is nothing but the weak topology $\sigma(\omega,\phi)$. The restriction of $\sigma(\omega,\phi)$ to any sequence subspace λ, written sometimes as $\sigma(\omega,\phi)|\lambda$, is called the *topology of coordinatewise convergence* on λ. Observe that the topology of a K-space is finer than its topology of coordinatewise convergence.

The following fundamental result characterizes compact subsets of a sequence space equipped with a linear topology, and generalizes an earlier result of Köthe [140]. This is given in Ref. 58, p. 1010, and since its proof runs on lines parallel to that in Ref. 140, p. 415, we omit it.

THEOREM 3.10 Let (λ,T) be a sequence space which is also a TVS such that T is finer than the topology of coordinatewise convergence on λ. If M is a subset of λ, the following statements are equivalent:

(i) M is T-compact.

(ii) M is T-sequentially compact.

(iii) M is T-countably compact.

(iv) M is compact in the topology of coordinatewise convergence, and T and the topology of coordinate convergence give rise to the same convergent sequences in M.

The following "relative" form of Theorem 3.10 is essentially due to Fremlin [54] and its proof is practically the same as that of the preceding theorem. Indeed we have (Ref. 58)

THEOREM 3.11 Let (λ,T) be a sequence space which is also a TVS, with T being finer than the topology of coordinatewise convergence. For a subset M of λ, the following are equivalent:

(i) M is T-relatively compact.

(ii) M is T-relatively sequentially compact [i.e., any sequence in M has a subsequence converging in (λ,T)].

(iii) M is T-relatively countably compact (i.e., each sequence in M has a T-adherent point in λ).

(iv) M is coordinatewise bounded, and any sequence of points of M convergent coordinatewise in ω converges to a point of λ in the topology T.

PROPOSITION 3.12 If (λ,T) is a barreled AK-space, then $\lambda^\beta = \lambda^\gamma$.

Proof. Let S_n^* denote the operator from λ^γ into itself defined by

$$S_n^*(y) = \sum_{i=1}^{n} y_i e^i \qquad y \in \lambda^\gamma$$

Suppose $y \in \lambda^\gamma$; then $\{S_n^*(y)\} \subset \lambda^\beta$ and $\{S_n^*(y)\}$ is $\sigma(\lambda^\beta,\lambda)$-bounded, since for each $x \in \lambda$,

$$\sup_n \left| \sum_{i=1}^{n} y_i x_i \right| < \infty$$

Using Proposition 3.9 we find that $\{S_n^*(y)\}$ is $\sigma(\lambda^*,\lambda)$-bounded, and therefore $\{S_n^*(y)\}$ is $\sigma(\lambda^*,\lambda)$-relatively compact [since (λ,T) is barreled; cf. Theorem 1.8.3]. By the same proposition it follows that $\{S_n^*(y)\}$ is $\sigma(\lambda^\beta,\lambda)$-relative compact. By Theorem 3.11, there exists a subsequence $\{S_{n_k}^*(y)\}$ which converges to an element y_0 in $(\lambda^\beta,\sigma(\lambda^\beta,\lambda))$. Thus $\{S_{n_k}^*(y)\}$

converges coordinatewise to y_0. Hence $y = y_0 \in \lambda^\beta$, that is, $\lambda^\beta = \lambda^\gamma$. □

DEFINITION 3.13 A K-space (λ,T) is called *locally P-invariant* if the set $P = \{S_n : n \geq 1\}$ is equicontinuous.

Then we have (Ref. 58)

PROPOSITION 3.14 Let (λ,T) be a locally convex locally P-invariant K-space. Then an element of λ has the property AK if and only if it has the property AD.

Proof. Suppose $x_0 \in \lambda$ has the property AD. Choose $p \in D$ and $\varepsilon > 0$ arbitrarily. There exists $q_1 \in D$ such that

$$p(S_n(x)) \leq q_1(x) \qquad \forall n \geq 1,\ x \in \lambda$$

Suppose $q = \max\{p,q_1\}$. There exists $y \in \phi$ with $q(x_0 - y) \leq \varepsilon/2$. Also, we can find an integer N such that $S_n(y) = y$ for all $n \geq N$. Therefore for $n \geq N$,

$$\begin{aligned} p(x_0 - S_n(x_0)) &\leq p(x_0 - y) + p(S_n(y - x_0)) \\ &\leq q(x_0 - y) + q_1(y - x_0) \leq \varepsilon \end{aligned}$$

and we obtain the result. In the other direction the result is trivial. □

EXERCISE 3.15 Prove Proposition 3.14 when T is a linear topology instead of a locally convex topology.

EXERCISE 3.16 Let (λ,T) be a locally P-invariant AK-space. Then T is also generated by $\{\sup_n p(S_n(x)) : p \in D\}$, D being the associated family of pseudonorms generating the topology T.

K-spaces Relative to α-, β-, and γ-duals

As mentioned in the beginning of this section, there is a natural way of defining K-space topologies by considering dual pairs of sequence spaces. For a given sequence space λ, let μ denote a subspace of λ^β with $\phi \subset \mu$. Then λ and μ form a dual system under the bilinear functional $\langle x,y \rangle$, where

$$\langle x,y\rangle = \sum_{i\geq 1} x_i y_i \qquad x \in \lambda,\ y \in \mu$$

Thus we can talk about several S-topologies on λ (as well as on μ). However, the topologies on λ which interest us most at the moment are $\sigma(\lambda,\mu)$ and $\tau(\lambda,\mu)$. Indeed we have

PROPOSITION 3.17 Let T be any (Hausdorff) locally convex topology on λ compatible with the dual structure $\langle\lambda,\mu\rangle$ where λ and μ are as defined above; then (λ,T) is a K-space. In particular, $(\lambda,\sigma(\lambda,\mu))$ and $(\lambda,\tau(\lambda,\mu))$ are K-spaces.

Proof. Observe that e^i can be identified with P_i, $i \geq 1$. Since $e^i \in \mu$, $i \geq 1$, the result follows. □

EXERCISE 3.18 Show that $\sigma(\omega,\phi)|\ell^1$ is strictly smaller (coarser) than $\sigma(\ell^1,\ell^\infty)$. [Hint: $e^n \to 0$ in $\sigma(\omega,\phi)|\ell^1$ but $q_e(e^n) = 1$, $n \geq 1$, where q_e is defined by 3.20.]

PROPOSITION 3.19 Let λ and μ be as in Proposition 3.17. Then $(\lambda,\sigma(\lambda,\mu))$ is an AK-space. In particular, $\{e^n;e^n\}$ is a Schauder base for $(\lambda,\sigma(\lambda,\mu))$.

Proof. If $x \in \lambda$ and $y \in \mu$ then

$$\langle x^{(n)},y\rangle = \left\langle \sum_{i=1}^{n} x_i e^i, y\right\rangle = \sum_{i=1}^{n} x_i y_i$$

$$\Longrightarrow \langle x^{(n)} - x,y\rangle = \sum_{i\geq n+1} x_i y_i \to 0 \qquad \text{as } n \to \infty$$

Since $(\lambda,\sigma(\lambda,\mu))$ is already a K-space, we are done. □

Note: In discussing the dual system $\langle\lambda,\mu\rangle$, it will be advantageous to confine our attention to the cases when $\mu = \lambda^\times$ and λ^β. In this situation, the seminorms that give rise to the topologies $\sigma(\lambda,\lambda^\times)$ and $\sigma(\lambda,\lambda^\beta)$ on λ shall be denoted by $q_y(\cdot)$, where $y \in \lambda^\times$ (resp. λ^β) and

$$q_y(x) = \left|\sum_{i\geq 1} x_i y_i\right| \tag{3.20}$$

Later on (cf. Theorem 8.3) we will prove a result stronger than Proposition 3.19.

There is another locally convex topology derived in a natural fashion from the dual system $\langle\lambda,\lambda^\times\rangle$. To be precise we have

DEFINITION 3.21 Consider the dual system $\langle\lambda,\lambda^\times\rangle$. Suppose μ is a subspace of $\lambda^\times$, $\phi \subset \mu$. For each $y \in \mu$, define the seminorm p_y on λ by

$$p_y(x) = \sum_{i\geq 1} |x_i y_i| \qquad x \in \lambda \tag{3.22}$$

The locally convex topology generated by $\{p_y : y \in \mu\}$ is called the *normal* or *solid* or *Köthe topology* on λ and we shall denote it by $\eta(\lambda,\mu)$.

Remark: A seminorm p on a normal sequence space λ is said to be *absolutely monotone* if $p(x) \leq p(y)$ for $x,y \in \lambda$ with $|x| \leq |y|$. A locally convex topology T on a normal sequence space λ is called *locally normal* or *locally solid* provided T is generated by a family of absolutely monotone seminorms. It follows therefore that the normal topology of a normal sequence space is locally normal. Further, it is not difficult to verify that the members of $\mathcal{B}_T$ can also be chosen to be normal.

It is clear that $\sigma(\lambda,\mu) \subset \eta(\lambda,\mu)$. In the next section we will discuss several other properties of the topology η. Meanwhile, we have

PROPOSITION 3.23 Let λ,μ be as in the preceding definition. Then $(\lambda,\eta(\lambda,\mu))$ is an AK-space. In particular, $\{e^n;e^n\}$ is a Schauder base for $(\lambda,\eta(\lambda,\mu))$.

Proof. Use Proposition 3.17, the result $\sigma(\lambda,\mu) \subset \eta(\lambda,\mu)$, and the inequality

$$p_y(x^{(n)} - x) \leq \sum_{i\geq n+1} |x_i y_i|$$

valid for all $n \geq 1$. □

Before we proceed, let us examine the following natural problem. As before let us consider the dual system $\langle\lambda,\mu\rangle$ where $\mu \subset \lambda^\beta$. Then each S_n is $\sigma(\lambda,\mu)$-$\sigma(\lambda,\mu)$ continuous and it is natural to inquire about the equicontinuity of $\{S_n\}$ on $(\lambda,\sigma(\lambda,\mu))$; that is, we would like to examine the P-invariance of $(\lambda,\sigma(\lambda,\mu))$. A complete answer to this problem is provided in

PROPOSITION 3.24 Let λ and μ be as above. Then $(\lambda,\sigma(\lambda,\mu))$ is locally P-invariant if and only if $\mu = \phi$.

Proof. Suppose first that $\mu = \phi$. Choose an arbitrary element $y \in \lambda^{\times}$ with $y = \{y_1, y_2, \ldots, y_L, 0, 0, \ldots\}$. Then for any integer $n \geq 1$ and $x \in \lambda$,

$$q_y(S_n(x)) \leq L \max\{q_{y_i e^i}(x) : 1 \leq i \leq L\}$$

which in turn guarantees the locally P-invariant character of the space $(\lambda,\sigma(\lambda,\mu))$.

Let now the space $(\lambda,\sigma(\lambda,\mu))$ be locally P-invariant. Then for $y \in \mu$, the sequence $\{y \circ S_n\}$ of functionals on λ is $\sigma(\lambda,\mu)$-equicontinuous. Consequently, by Proposition 1.7.10, $\{y \circ S_n\}$ is finite dimensional. Hence there exist $k_1, k_2, \ldots, k_p \in \mathbb{N}$ with $k_1 \leq k_2 \leq \cdots \leq k_p$ such that $\{y \circ S_{k_1}, \ldots, y \circ S_{k_p}\}$ is linearly independent and $\{y \circ S_n\} \subset \text{sp}\,\{y \circ S_{k_1}, \ldots, y \circ S_{k_p}\}$. Thus for each $x \in \lambda$,

$$(y \circ S_n)(x) = \sum_{i=1}^{p} \alpha_i^n (y \circ S_{k_i})(x)$$

or

$$y(x^{(n)}) = \sum_{i=1}^{p} \alpha_i^n y(x^{(k_i)})$$

where α_i^n $(i = 1, \ldots, p)$ are constants depending upon n. Therefore, for $j > k_p$, $y((e^j)^{(n)}) = 0$, i.e., $y_j = 0$. Hence $y \in \phi$. □

Now we consider a different type of topology on a sequence space λ resulting from its γ-dual λ^{γ} and follow Garling [56].

DEFINITION 3.25 Let λ be a sequence space and λ^{γ} be its γ-dual. Suppose μ is a subspace of λ^{γ} with $\phi \subset \mu$. The topology on λ generated by the collection $\{r_y\}$ of seminorms, where for $y \in \mu$,

$$r_y(x) = \sup_n \left| \sum_{i=1}^{n} x_i y_i \right| \qquad x \in \lambda$$

is called the *weak γ-dual topology* and is denoted by $\sigma\gamma(\lambda,\mu)$.

We have (Ref. 56, p. 973)

PROPOSITION 3.26 $(\lambda, \sigma\gamma(\lambda,\mu))$ is an AK-space if and only if $\mu \subset \lambda^\beta$.

Proof. Let $\mu \subset \lambda^\beta$. Hence we have also the topology $\sigma(\lambda,\mu)$ on λ. Since for each $x \in \lambda$, $y \in \mu$, $q_y(x) \le r_y(x)$, we obtain $\sigma(\lambda,\mu) \subset \sigma\gamma(\lambda,\mu)$. Therefore, Proposition 3.17 implies that $(\lambda,\sigma\gamma(\lambda,\mu))$ is a K-space. It is now straightforward to verify that for any x in λ and $y \in \mu$, $r_y(x^{(n)} - x) \to 0$ as $n \to \infty$. In the other direction, let $(\lambda,\sigma\gamma(\lambda,\mu))$ be an AK-space but $\mu \not\subset \lambda^\beta$. Hence there exist x in λ and y in μ such that $\Sigma_{i\ge1} x_i y_i$ is not convergent; consequently,

$$r_y(x^{(n)} - x) = \sup_{m>n} \left| \sum_{i=n+1}^{m} x_i y_i \right|$$

does not tend to zero as $n \to \infty$ and so x does not have the AK-property. □

Spaces of the Form λ_A, μ_A, and ν_A

In this subsection we describe methods of constructing sequence spaces which can be topologized in a fairly natural way so as to become K-spaces; we follow Ref. 56 once again for this discussion.

Let A be a family of coordinatewise bounded subsets [i.e., $\sigma(\omega,\phi)$-bounded subsets] of ω directed by inclusion such that

i) $\cup\{A : A \in A\} \supset \phi$.

ii) $\alpha A \in A$ whenever $\alpha \in \mathbb{K}$ and $A \in A$.

DEFINITION 3.27 With the above definition of A, we introduce

(i) $\lambda_A = \{x : x \in \omega$ and $r_A(x) \equiv \sup_{y\in A, n\ge1} |\Sigma_{i=1}^n x_i y_i| < \infty$, for each A in $A\}$.

(ii) $\mu_A = \{x : x \in \omega$, $\Sigma_{i\ge1} x_i y_i$ converges for each y in $\cup\{A : A \in A\}$ and $q_A(x) \equiv \sup_{y\in A} |\Sigma_{i\ge1} x_i y_i| < \infty$ for each A in $A\}$.

(iii) $\nu_A = \lambda_A \cap \mu_A$.

The spaces λ_A and μ_A can be topologized respectively by the families $\{r_A : A \in A\}$ and $\{q_A : A \in A\}$ so that these spaces become l.c. TVS's and we shall denote these topologies respectively by $\tau\gamma_A$ and τ_A. The topologies induced by $\tau\gamma_A$ and τ_A on ν_A will again be denoted by $\tau\gamma_A$ and τ_A.

PROPOSITION 3.28 The spaces $(\lambda_A, \tau\gamma_A)$ and (μ_A, τ_A) are Hausdorff l.c. TVS's and are K-spaces.

Proof. Since $\{e^i\} \in A$ for $i \geq 1$, the result follows directly from the definition of these topologies. □

Let now λ, μ be as in Definition 3.25 and observe that $\mu \subset \lambda^\gamma$ is equivalent to $\lambda \subset \mu^\gamma$. Suppose A is the collection of all finite subsets of μ. Then

$$(\lambda_A, \tau\gamma_A) = (\mu^\gamma, \sigma\gamma(\mu^\gamma, \mu))$$
$$(\mu_A, \tau_A) = (\mu^\beta, \sigma(\mu^\beta, \mu))$$
$$(\nu_A, \tau\gamma_A) = (\mu^\beta, \sigma\gamma(\mu^\beta, \mu))$$
$$\sigma\gamma(\lambda, \mu) = \sigma\gamma(\mu^\gamma, \mu)|\lambda$$

Sequence Spaces: Natural Metrics and Duals

Below we provide a table containing more or less all important sequence spaces together with their natural linear metrics, which we are going to make ample use of in our subsequent work. This table also contains the different duals of the spaces.

EXERCISE 3.30 Show that cs with its norm defined above is an AK-BK space and is isometrically isomorphic to c under the map ψ, where

$$(\psi(x))_n = \sum_{i=1}^{n} x_i$$

Prove also that $(cs)^* = bv$.

EXERCISE 3.31 Show that $bv \subset c$ and is a BK-BS space but is not AD. Also prove that bv is a Banach algebra relative to pointwise multiplication. If U is the unit ball of bv, show that UU = U.

EXPERCISE 3.32 Prove that the space bv_0 is an AK-space and is a maximal closed subspace of bv, and $(bv_0)^* = bs$.

EXERCISE 3.33 Show that bs is a BK-BS space but is not AD and the map $\psi: bs \to \ell^\infty$ (defined above) is an isometric isomorphism.

TABLE 3.29 *Note:* In this table, the symbol ≈ stands for "congruent to" or "isometrically isomorphic to."

No.	Sequence space	Norm or paranorm ($\|\cdot\|$ or $\lvert\cdot\rvert$)	Topological dual	α-dual	β-dual	γ-dual
1	c_0	$\|x\|_\infty = \sup\{\lvert x_n\rvert : n \ge 1\}$	ℓ^1	ℓ^1	ℓ^1	ℓ^1
2	$c = c_0 \oplus \text{sp}\,\{e\}$	$\|x\|_\infty = \sup\{\lvert x_n\rvert : n \ge 1\}$	$\approx \ell^1$ or $\ell^1 \oplus \mathbb{K}$	ℓ^1	ℓ^1	ℓ^1
3	ℓ^p $(1 < p < \infty)$	$\|x\|_p = \left\{\sum_{i\ge1} \lvert x_i\rvert^p\right\}^{1/p}$	ℓ^q where $\frac{1}{p} + \frac{1}{q} = 1$	ℓ^q	ℓ^q	ℓ^q
4	ℓ^∞	$\|x\|_\infty = \sup\{\lvert x_n\rvert : n \ge 1\}$	$\approx \text{ba}(\mathbb{N}, \Phi_\infty)$ (cf. Theorem 7.22)	ℓ^1	ℓ^1	ℓ^1
5	ℓ^1	$\|x\|_1 = \sum_{i\ge1} \lvert x_i\rvert$	ℓ^∞	ℓ^∞	ℓ^∞	ℓ^∞
6	ℓ^p $(0 < p < 1)$	$\lvert x\rvert_p = \sum_{i\ge1} \lvert x_i\rvert^p$	ℓ^∞	ℓ^∞	ℓ^∞	ℓ^∞
7	m_0	$\|x\|_\infty = \sup\{\lvert x_n\rvert : n \ge 1\}$	$\text{ba}(N, \Phi_\infty)$	ℓ^1	ℓ^1	ℓ^1
8	$k = \phi \oplus \text{sp}\,\{e\}$	$\|x\|_\infty = \sup\{\lvert x_n\rvert : n \ge 1\}$	$\ell^1 \approx \ell^1 \oplus \mathbb{K}$	ℓ^1	cs	bs
9	$a = \phi \oplus \text{sp}\,\{e_a\}$, $e_a = \{1, -1, \ldots\}$	$\|x\|_\infty = \sup\{\lvert x_n\rvert : n \ge 1\}$	$\ell^1 \approx \ell^1 \oplus \mathbb{K}$	ℓ^1	as	--
10	δ	$\lvert x\rvert_\delta = \sup\{\lvert x_n\rvert^{1/n} : n \ge 1\}$	d	d	d	d
11†	d	--	--	δ	δ	δ

12	Π_r	$\lvert x\rvert_r = \sum_{n\geq 1} \frac{1}{2^n} \frac{\rho_n(x)}{1 + \rho_n(x)}$	$d_{1/r}$	$d_{1/r}$	$d_{1/r}$	$d_{1/r}$
13[†]	$d_{1/r}$	--	--	Π_r	Π_r	Π_r
14	cs	$\lVert x\rVert_{cs} = \sup_n \left\lvert \sum_{i=1}^{n} x_i \right\rvert$	bv	ℓ^1	bv	bv
15	$bv = bv_0 \oplus sp\,\{e\}$	$\lVert x\rVert_{bv} = \sum_{n\geq 1} \lvert x_{n+1} - x_n\rvert + \lim_{n\to\infty} \lvert x_n\rvert$	$bs \oplus \mathbb{K} \approx bs \times \mathbb{K}$	ℓ^1	cs	bs
16	bv_0	$\lVert x\rVert_{bv_0} = \sum_{n\geq 1} \lvert x_{n+1} - x_n\rvert$	bs	ℓ^1	bs	bs
17	bs	$\lVert x\rVert_{bs} = \sup_n \left\lvert \sum_{i=1}^{n} x_i \right\rvert$	$ba(N, \Phi_\infty)$	ℓ^1	bv_0	bv

[†]The natural metrics on these spaces do not lead to linear topologies; for further discussion, see Ref. 98.

Construction of Abstract BK-topologies

To obtain an AK-BK space, we have to deal first with the construction of a BK-space. In this direction Ruckle [215] introduced a norm on ω, which is indeed the abstraction of norms on ω, giving rise to several distinct BK-spaces, such as c_0, c, ℓ^p, ℓ^∞, bv, bs, and many others; in fact, we have

DEFINITION 3.34 A *proper sequential norm* (p.s.n.) is a function $N: \omega \to \mathbb{R}^*$ (extended real number system) such that

(i) N is a norm.
(ii) $0 < \inf_n N(e^n) \le \sup_n N(e^n) < \infty$.
(iii) $N(x) = \sup_n N(x^{(n)})$.

Note: A function N satisfying (i) and (iii) is called a *sequential norm* (s.n.).

EXERCISE 3.35 For any $x \in \omega$, show that

$$\frac{1}{2} k_N \sup_n |x_n| \le N(x) \le K_N \sup_n \sum_{i=1}^{n} |x_i|$$

where

$$K_N = \sup_n N(e^n) \qquad k_n = \inf_n N(e^n)$$

Next we have (Ref. 215, p. 1283)

PROPOSITION 3.36 Let N be a p.s.n. Then $S_N = \{x : x \in \omega, N(x) < \infty\}$ equipped with N is a BK-space such that $\lambda_N = [e^n] = \overline{sp}\,\{e^n\}$ is a closed AK-BK subspace of S_N.

Proof. By Exercise 3.35, the space (S_N, N) is clearly a K-space, and it also follows that if $\{x^n\}$ is an N-Cauchy sequence in S_N then $\lim_{n\to\infty} x_i^n$ exists for each $i \ge 1$, say, x_i. Let $x = \{x_i\}$; then

$$N((x - x^n)^{(k)}) \to 0 \qquad \text{for each } k \ge 1$$

(cf. right-hand inequality in Exercise 3.35). If $\varepsilon > 0$ is given, choose n_0 such that

$$N(x^m - x^n) < \varepsilon \qquad \forall m,n \geq n_0$$

$$\Longrightarrow \quad N((x^m - x^n)^{(k)}) < \varepsilon \qquad \forall m,n \geq n_0,\ k \geq 1 \quad \text{[cf. (iii)]}$$

Following the usual procedure, we then find that

$$N((x^{n_0} - x)^{(k)}) < \varepsilon \qquad \forall k \geq 1$$

and it follows that

$$N((x^n - x)^{(k)}) < \varepsilon \qquad \forall n \geq n_0,\ k \geq 1$$

$$\Longrightarrow \quad N(x^n - x) \leq \varepsilon \qquad \forall n \geq n_0$$

Consequently $N(x) < \infty$ and $N(x^n - x) \to 0$ as $n \to \infty$. Thus (S_N, N) is a BK-space.

Finally, we have

$$N\left(\sum_{i=1}^{m} \alpha_i e^i\right) \leq N\left(\sum_{i=1}^{n} \alpha_i e^i\right)$$

which forces $\{e^n\}$ to be a Schauder base for λ_N (cf. Ref. 81, Theorem 3.2; Ref. 123, p. 54; Ref. 164, p. 57; Ref. 236, p. 58: Ref. 264, p. 211--a proof of this statement will appear in Chapter 1 of Ref. 125). Hence λ_N is an AK-BK space. □

Remarks: According to (ii) and (iii), the sequence space (S_N, N) is a regular BS-space (Definition 4.5.1) for which $\{e^n\}$ is bounded. If $(\lambda, \|\cdot\|)$ is any AK-BK space such that λ is also regular and BS, then the p.s.n. N defined by

$$N(x) = \sup_n \left\| \sum_{i=1}^{n} x_i e^i \right\|$$

is equivalent to $\|\cdot\|$.

Note: For nontrivial examples of proper sequential norms related to Schauder bases in Banach spaces, we once again refer to Ref. 215, p. 1284.

Ruckle [215] has also introduced two types of proper sequential norms which are ultimately useful in studying unconditional and symmetric bases in Banach spaces--a topic which we shall study in detail in Chapter 2 of

Ref. 125. These notions are contained in

DEFINITION 3.37 Let N be a p.s.n. on ω. Then N is (i) *balanced* if $N(x) = \sup\{N(\{\alpha_i x_i\}) : \{\alpha_i\} \subset \mathbb{K};\ |\alpha_i| \leq 1,\ i \geq 1\}$ for each $x \in \omega$; and (ii) *symmetric* if $N(x) = N(x_\sigma)$ for each permutation σ of $\mathbb{N}$.

A balanced p.s.n. can always be generated by a p.s.n. satisfying a comparatively less restrictive condition than that in Definition 3.37(i); indeed we have (Ref. 215)

PROPOSITION 3.38 Let N be a p.s.n. such that $N(\alpha x) < \infty$ for each $\alpha \in \ell^\infty$ whenever $N(x) < \infty$. Then there exists a balanced p.s.n. M such that $S_M = S_N$.

Proof. Consider S_N. For each $x \in S_N$, define the linear operator $R_x : \ell^\infty \to S_N$ by $R_x(\alpha) = \alpha x$. By the closed graph theorem (cf. also Proposition 4.3.2) the operator R_x is continuous, and so

$$N(R_x[A]) < \infty \qquad A = \{\alpha : \alpha \in \ell^\infty,\ \|\alpha\|_\infty \leq 1\}$$

Hence we may define $M(x)$, $x \in S_N$, by

$$M(x) = \sup\{N(\alpha x) : \alpha \in A\}$$

Clearly

$$M(x) = \sup\{N(R_x(\alpha)) : \|\alpha\|_\infty \leq 1\}$$

Thus one easily proves that M is a balanced p.s.n. The other part, namely, $S_M = S_N$, is left as an exercise. □

EXERCISE 3.39 Let $\{N_\alpha\}$ be a family of p.s.n.'s and $K > 0$ be such that $\sup_\alpha N_\alpha(e^i) < K$ for each $i \geq 1$. Then $\sup_\alpha N_\alpha$ is a p.s.n. Further, if each N_α is balanced (symmetric), then $\sup_\alpha N_\alpha$ is also balanced (symmetric).

Dual of the Space λ_N

The space λ_N is an AK-BK space under the norm N, and so from Proposition 3.9, $\lambda_N^* = (\lambda_N, N)^* = \lambda_N^\beta = (\lambda_N)^\beta$; Ruckle [215] obtains this as Corollary 3.3 of a more general result, namely, Proposition 3.42. Indeed, he first introduces the following

DEFINITION 3.40 For a p.s.n. N, the *dual* p.s.n. is defined as the function $N^*\colon \omega \to \mathbb{R}^*$, given by

$$N^*(y) = \sup\left\{\sup_n \left|\sum_{i=1}^{n} x_i y_i\right| : N(x) \le 1\right\}$$

EXERCISE 3.41 Verify that N^* is a p.s.n.

PROPOSITION 3.42 Corresponding to a p.s.n. N, the dual λ_N^* of λ_N is isometrically isomorphic to S_{N^*}.

Proof. Let $f \in \lambda_N^*$. If x is such that $N(x) \le 1$, then

$$\left|\sum_{i=1}^{n} x_i f(e^i)\right| = |f(x^{(n)})| \le \|f\| N(x^{(n)}) \le \|f\| N(x) \le \|f\|$$

and so $N^*(\{f(e^i)\}) < \infty$. Thus $\{f(e^i)\} \in S_{N^*}$. Hence we have a map $F\colon \lambda_N^* \to S_{N^*}$ with $F(f) = \{f(e^i)\}$. As ϕ is dense in λ_N, F is injective; also $N^*(F(f)) \le \|f\|$.

Let now $y \in S_{N^*}$ so that $N^*(y) < \infty$. Define functionals f_n $(n \ge 1)$ on λ_N by

$$f_n(x) = \sum_{i=1}^{n} x_i y_i$$

Then

$$|f_n(x)| = N(x)\left|\sum_{i=1}^{n} \frac{x_i}{N(x)} y_i\right| \le N(x)N^*(y)$$

and so each $f_n \in \lambda_N^*$ and $\|f_n\| \le N^*(y)$ for $n \ge 1$. Using Theorem 1.3.20, we find the functional f on λ_N, where

$$f(x) = \lim_{n\to\infty} f_n(x) \qquad x \in \lambda_N$$

belongs to λ_N^*. Clearly $f(e^i) = y_i$ and $\|f\| \le N^*(y)$. Hence F is surjective.

We thus find that F is bijective and $N^*(F(f)) = \|f\|$ for $f \in \lambda_N^*$. □

We also have

PROPOSITION 3.43 For a p.s.n. N, $S_{N^*} = (S_N)^\gamma$.

Proof. The inclusion $S_{N*} \subset (S_N)^\gamma$ is clear from the definition of N*. So, let us choose $y \in (S_N)^\gamma$. Then $\sup_n |\Sigma_{i=1}^n x_i y_i| < \infty$ for each $x \in S_N$. Define a sequence $\{p_n\}$ of seminorms on S_N as follows:

$$p_n(x) = \left|\sum_{i=1}^{n} x_i y_i\right| \qquad n \geq 1$$

Obviously, the set $\{p_n(x) : n \geq 1\}$ is bounded for each x in S_N. Hence $\{p_n\}$ is equicontinuous, from Proposition 1.8.4. Therefore

$$N^*(y) = \sup \{\sup_n p_n(x) : N(x) \leq 1\} < \infty \qquad \square$$

EXERCISE 3.44 Let N be a p.s.n. Then for any x in ω, show that $N^{**}(x) = (N^*)^*(x) = N(x)$. Also, if N is balanced, so is N*. [Hint: Prove $N^{**}(x^{(n)}) = N(x^{(n)})$ for each $n \geq 1$ for the first part.]

4. NORMAL TOPOLOGY

There are quite many interesting results which depend upon the notion of the normal topology introduced in the last section. It will be convenient to collect here various equivalent forms of this topology. Let us start with

DEFINITION 4.1 Let λ be a sequence space. Let $x \in \lambda$ and $M \subset \lambda$. Then (i) x is said to be *positive, written* $x > 0$, if $x_i \geq 0$, $i \geq 1$, and $x_i \neq 0$ for at least one $i \geq 1$; (ii) x is called *strictly positive, denoted* by $x >> 0$, if $x_i > 0$ for $i \geq 1$; (iii) the *normal cover* of M, *denoted* by $\{M\}^N$, is the set $\{y : y \in \omega, |y_i| \leq |x_i|, i \geq 1$, for some x in M$\}$; (iv) M is called *normal* or *solid* if $M = \{M\}^N$; and (v) x is said to *dominate* M provided $|y_n| \leq |x_n|$ for each $y \in M$ and $n \geq 1$. Further, we use the *symbol* $\mathcal{N}$ to represent the *family of all normal covers* $\{u\}^N$, for each $u > 0$, $u \in \lambda^\times$, *together with all their subsets*.

DEFINITION 4.2 Let λ be a sequence space and $\mathcal{N}$ correspond to the normal covers in $\lambda^\times$. For each $A \in \mathcal{N}$, let

$$p_A(x) = \sup\left\{\sum_{i\geq1} |x_i y_i| : y \in A\right\} \qquad x \in \lambda$$

Then we *write* $\eta_N \equiv \eta_N(\lambda,\lambda^\times)$ for the topology on λ generated by $\{p_A : A \in N\}$; also, we use the *symbol* $\eta_p \equiv \eta_p(\lambda,\lambda^\times)$ for the topology on λ generated by $\{p_u : u \in \lambda^\times, u > 0\}$, where p_u is defined in (3.22).

PROPOSITION 4.3 For any sequence space λ, we have

$$\eta(\lambda,\lambda^\times) = \eta_p(\lambda,\lambda^\times) = \eta_N(\lambda,\lambda^\times)$$

Proof. Let $\{x^\alpha\}$ be a net in λ with $x^\alpha \to 0$ in $\eta_p(\lambda,\lambda^\times)$. Choose $y \in \lambda^\times$ and $A \in N$ arbitrarily. Then $|y| \in \lambda^\times$ and $A = \{z : |z_i| \le u_i\}$ for some $u \in \lambda^\times$, $u > 0$. Hence $p_y(x^\alpha) = p_{|y|}(x^\alpha) \to 0$, and

$$p_z(x^\alpha) \le p_u(x^\alpha) \qquad \forall z \in A \text{ and each } \alpha$$

The preceding inequality yields $p_A(x^\alpha) \to 0$. Thus

$$\eta(\lambda,\lambda^\times), \eta_N(\lambda,\lambda^\times) \subset \eta_p(\lambda,\lambda^\times)$$

Since

$$\eta_p(\lambda,\lambda^\times) \subset \eta(\lambda,\lambda^\times), \eta_N(\lambda,\lambda^\times)$$

is always true, we are therefore done. □

From the point of view of the theory of locally convex spaces it would be very interesting to know if the locally convex topology $\eta(\lambda,\lambda^\times)$ is compatible with the dual structure $\langle\lambda,\lambda^\times\rangle$, since $\sigma(\lambda,\lambda^\times) \subset \eta(\lambda,\lambda^\times)$; in other words, we would be interested to know if $\eta(\lambda,\lambda^\times) \subset \tau(\lambda,\lambda^\times)$. This question will be settled in a later section (cf. Theorem 8.14); however, it seems more desirable at the moment to ascertain if $\sigma(\lambda,\lambda^\times) = \eta(\lambda,\lambda^\times)$ is true in general. Before we present a formal counterexample in this direction, let us look at the sets giving rise to the topologies $\sigma(\lambda,\lambda^\times)$ and $\eta(\lambda,\lambda^\times)$. While $\sigma(\lambda,\lambda^\times)$ is given by the system of neighborhoods of zero consisting of all polars F° where F is the balanced convex hull of a finite number of elements of $\lambda^\times$ (that is, F is a finite dimensional balanced convex subset of $\lambda^\times$), the topology $\eta(\lambda,\lambda^\times)$ is generated by the system of neighborhoods of zero consisting of all polars M° where $M = \{u\}^N$, $u \in \lambda^\times$. Let us now pass on to the precise

EXAMPLE 4.4 Here $\sigma(\phi,\omega) \neq \eta(\phi,\omega)$. Indeed, let $u \in \lambda^\times$. Further, we choose u such that infinitely many $u_i \neq 0$ ($i \in J \subset \mathbb{N}$). Then

$$u_i e^i \in M = \{u\}^N \qquad i \in J$$

Thus M is not finite dimensional and hence M° cannot be a neighborhood of zero in $\sigma(\lambda,\lambda^\times)$, although M° is a zero neighborhood in $\eta(\lambda,\lambda^\times)$.

We can also give a different constructive proof. In fact, let

$$B = \bigcap_{i=1}^{\infty} \{x : x \in \phi,\ p_{e^i}(x) \leq 1\}$$

Since $\{x : x \in \phi,\ p_e(x) \leq 1\} \subset B$, B is a zero neighborhood in $\eta(\phi,\omega)$. If B were a zero neighborhood in $\sigma(\phi,\omega)$, we would have found a $u \in \omega$ with

$$A = \{x : x \in \phi,\ q_u(x) \leq 1\} \subset B$$

Suppose $J \subset \mathbb{N}$ such that $u_i \neq 0$, $i \in J$. If J is just a singleton $\{i_0\}$, define $x \in \phi$ by

$$x = \{0, \ldots, 0, u_{i_0}^{-1}, \alpha, 0, 0, \ldots\} \qquad |\alpha| > 1$$

Hence $x \in A$, $x \notin B$, and so $A \not\subset B$. If J consists of more than one element, let $i_1, i_2 \in J$ ($i_1 < i_2$) such that $u_{i_1}, u_{i_2} \neq 0$. Choose a scalar α with $|\alpha u_{i_1}^{-1}|, |\alpha u_{i_2}^{-1}| > 1$. Define $x \in \phi$ by

$$x = \{0, \ldots, 0, \alpha u_{i_1}^{-1}, 0, \ldots, 0, -\alpha u_{i_2}^{-1}, 0, 0, \ldots\}$$

Then $x \in A$, $x \notin B$. Hence, again $A \not\subset B$. Therefore, B is not a zero neighborhood in $\sigma(\phi,\omega)$.

EXERCISE 4.5 Show that $\sigma(\ell^2,\ell^2) \neq \eta(\ell^2,\ell^2)$.

EXERCISE 4.6 Prove that $\sigma(\omega,\phi) = \eta(\omega,\phi)$.

As we have seen above, $\sigma(\lambda,\lambda^\times)$ and $\eta(\lambda,\lambda^\times)$ are not equivalent in general; still it is surprising to note that convergence of sequences is the same in both of these topologies (cf. Corollary 4.12). Indeed, this follows from the theorem stated and proved below. Let us remark that this theorem is due to Köthe and Toeplitz [143] and was subsequently sharpened by Allen [6]; for the vector-valued version, we refer to Ref. 83.

THEOREM 4.7 Let λ be a sequence space and μ be a subspace of $\lambda^\times$ such that μ is normal. Then $\sigma(\lambda,\mu)$- and $\eta(\lambda,\mu)$-Cauchy sequences are the same in λ.

Proof. It is sufficient to prove that each $\sigma(\lambda,\mu)$-Cauchy sequence $\{x^p\} \subset \lambda$ is $\eta(\lambda,\mu)$-Cauchy. Suppose this is not so. Then we find an $\varepsilon > 0$, a $y \in \mu$, and increasing sequences $\{p_i\}$ and $\{q_i\}$ such that

$$\sum_{k\geq 1} |(x_k^{p_i} - x_k^{q_i})y_k| > \varepsilon \qquad \forall i \geq 1 \tag{4.8}$$

For each $i \geq 1$, one can find $N_i \in \mathbb{N}$ with

$$\sum_{k\geq N_i+1} |(x_k^{p_i} - x_k^{q_i})y_k| < \frac{\varepsilon}{5} \qquad \forall i \geq 1 \tag{4.9}$$

Choosing an integer i_1 arbitrarily and writing N_1 for N_{i_1}, we find

$$\sum_{k=1}^{N_1} |(x_k^{p_{i_1}} - x_k^{q_{i_1}})y_k| > \frac{4}{5}\varepsilon \tag{4.10}$$

Put $z_k = c_k y_k$ where $|c_k| = 1$, $k \geq 1$, and choose the arguments of the c_k's $(1 \leq k \leq N_1)$ so that

$$(x_k^{p_{i_1}} - x_k^{q_{i_1}})z_k \geq 0$$

Then $\{z_k\} \in \mu$ and from (4.9) and (4.10) we get

$$\left|\sum_{k\geq 1} (x_k^{p_{i_1}} - x_k^{q_{i_1}})z_k\right| > \frac{4}{5}\varepsilon - \frac{1}{5}\varepsilon > \frac{1}{5}\varepsilon$$

Since $\{x^p\}$ is $\sigma(\omega,\phi)|\lambda$-Cauchy (i.e., Cauchy in the topology of coordinatewise convergence), we can determine an $i_2 \in \mathbb{N}$ with $i_2 > i_1$ (and consequently $p_{i_2} > p_{i_1}$, $q_{i_2} > q_{i_1}$) such that

$$\sum_{k=1}^{N_1} |(x_k^{p_{i_2}} - x_k^{q_{i_2}})z_k| \leq \frac{1}{5}\varepsilon$$

One also determines an N_2 in $\mathbb{N}$ with $N_2 > N_1$ for which (4.9) is true, and so is the inequality in (4.10) when i_1 and N_1 are replaced respectively by i_2 and N_2. Further, if the arguments of the c_k's are so chosen that

$$(x_k^{p_{i_2}} - x_k^{q_{i_2}})z_k \geq 0 \qquad \text{for } N_1+1 \leq k \leq N_2$$

then

$$\sum_{k=N_1+1}^{N_2} |(x_k^{p_{i_2}} - x_k^{q_{i_2}})z_k| = \sum_{k=1}^{N_2} - \sum_{k=1}^{N_1} > \frac{3}{5}\varepsilon$$

Hence from these last three inequalities, we obtain

$$\left|\sum_{k\geq 1} (x_k^{p_{i_2}} - x_k^{q_{i_2}})z_k\right| \geq \sum_{k=N_1+1}^{N_2} (x_k^{p_{i_2}} - x_k^{q_{i_2}})z_k - \sum_{k=1}^{N_1} |(x_k^{p_{i_2}} - x_k^{q_{i_2}})z_k|$$
$$- \sum_{k\geq N_2+1} |(x_k^{p_{i_2}} - x_k^{q_{i_2}})y_k| > \frac{1}{5}\varepsilon$$

Since the foregoing inequality is valid for all arguments of z_k with $k > N_2$, we conclude that $\{z_k\} \in \mu$. Proceeding in this way we find an element $\{z_k\} \in \mu$ for which

$$\left|\sum_{k\geq 1} (x_k^{p_{i_m}} - x_k^{q_{i_m}})z_k\right| > \frac{1}{5}\varepsilon \qquad m \geq 1 \tag{*}$$

However, (*) leads to a contradiction. □

Remark: In the preceding theorem, the hypothesis that μ is normal cannot be dropped. In fact, we have

EXAMPLE 4.11 Let $\lambda = \ell^1$ and $\mu = a \subsetneq \lambda^\times = \ell^\infty$. One can check that a is not normal. Consider the sequence $\{x^n\} \subset \lambda$, where for each $n \geq 1$,

$$x_i^n = \left(\frac{n}{n+1}\right)^i \qquad i \geq 1$$

Then for $y \in \mu$, there exists j such that $y_{i+1} = -y_i$, $i \geq j$, and so

$$p_y(x^m - x^n) = \sum_{i=1}^{j} |(x_i^m - x_i^n)y_i| + |y_{j+1}| \sum_{i \geq j+1} |(x_i^m - x_i^n)|$$

$$\geq \sum_{i=1}^{j} |(x_i^m - x_i^n)y_i| + |y_{j+1}| \left| (m + 1)\left(\frac{m}{m + 1}\right)^{j+1} - (n + 1)\left(\frac{n}{n + 1}\right)^{j+1} \right| \not\to 0 \qquad \text{as } m,n \to \infty$$

Thus $\{x^n\}$ is not $\eta(\ell^1,a)$-Cauchy. On the other hand, for any $y \in a$,

$$q_y(x^m - x^n) \leq \left| \sum_{i=1}^{j} (x_i^m - x_i^n)y_i \right| + |y_{j+1}| \left| \left(\frac{m}{m + 1}\right)^{j+1} \frac{m + 1}{2m + 1} - \left(\frac{n}{n + 1}\right)^{j+1} \frac{n + 1}{2n + 1} \right| \to 0 \qquad \text{as } m,n \to \infty$$

thus forcing $\{x^n\}$ to be $\sigma(\ell^1,a)$-Cauchy.

An application of Proposition 1.2.11 immediately yields

COROLLARY 4.12 In a sequence space λ, a sequence $\{x^n\}$ is $\sigma(\lambda,\lambda^\times)$ [resp. $\sigma(\lambda,\mu)$]-convergent if and only if it is $\eta(\lambda,\lambda^\times)$ [resp. $\eta(\lambda,\mu)$]-convergent.

In practice it is comparatively easier to calculate the $\sigma(\omega,\phi)|\lambda$-limit of a sequence $\{x^n\}$ contained in a sequence space λ, and as we know, this limit may not be the $\sigma(\lambda,\mu)$-limit of $\{x^n\}$ for a subspace μ of $\lambda^\times$. Even if we restrict the sequence $\{x^n\}$ further, e.g., if we consider $\{x^n\}$ to be $\sigma(\lambda,\mu)$-Cauchy, then the existence of the $\sigma(\omega,\phi)|\lambda$-limit of $\{x^n\}$ as x does not necessarily guarantee that $x^n \to x$ in $\sigma(\lambda,\mu)$. To illustrate this fact, let us consider the following simple

EXAMPLE 4.13 Let $\lambda = \ell^1$ and $\mu = c \subsetneq \ell^\infty = \lambda^\times$. Clearly $e^n \to 0$ in $\sigma(\omega,\phi)|\lambda$. If $y \in c$, then

$$q_y(e^m - e^n) = |y_m - y_n| \to 0 \qquad \text{as } m,n \to \infty$$

Therefore $\{e^n\}$ is $\sigma(\lambda,\mu)$-Cauchy. However, $e^n \not\to 0$ in $\sigma(\lambda,\mu)$.

To overcome this difficulty, we need restrict μ; indeed, one has

PROPOSITION 4.14 Let λ and μ be sequence spaces with μ being normal and $\mu \subset \lambda^{\times}$. Suppose $\{x^n\}$ is a sequence in λ such that $x^n \to x$ in $\sigma(\omega,\phi)|\lambda$, $x \in \lambda$. Then $x^n \to x$ in $\sigma(\lambda,\mu)$ if and only if $\{x^n\}$ is $\sigma(\lambda,\mu)$-Cauchy.

Proof. Let $\varepsilon > 0$ and $y \in \mu$ be chosen arbitrarily. By Theorem 4.7, there exists $N \equiv N(\varepsilon,y) \in \mathbb{N}$ such that

$$p_y(x^m - x^n) = \sum_{i\geq 1} |(x_i^m - x_i^n)y_i| < \varepsilon \qquad \forall m,n \geq N$$

$$\Longrightarrow \sum_{i=1}^{M} |(x_i^m - x_i^n)y_i| < \varepsilon \qquad \forall m,n \geq N \text{ and } M \geq 1$$

The preceding inequality immediately leads to the required result. □

Strongest Locally Normal Topology

Toward the end of this section, let us pass on to the discussion of a certain kind of locally convex topology on a normal sequence space which we shall need in the final section of Chapter 4.

Throughout this subsection we assume that λ is a normal sequence space equipped with any locally convex locally normal topology (cf. remark after Definition 3.21). For each x in λ, the set $\{x\}^N$ is balanced, convex, and bounded in λ. Let $\lambda_x^\infty = \mathrm{sp}\{\{x\}^N\}$. Then λ_x^∞ is a normed space under the norm $\|\cdot\|_x$, where $\|\cdot\|_x$ is the Minkowski functional corresponding to $\{x\}^N$ (cf. discussion following Proposition 1.10.6). Observe that

$$\lambda = \cup\{\lambda_x^\infty : x \in \lambda\}$$

and let us denote by P_x the inclusion map $\lambda_x^\infty \to \lambda$. Thus we are in a position to define the inductive limit locally convex topology on λ (Definition 1.6.7) with the help of $\{\lambda_x; P_x : x \in \lambda\}$. We denote this *topology* by τ_λ^∞. By the remark following Definition 1.6.7, a base for 0-neighborhoods in τ_λ^∞ consists of sets B where B is the balanced convex hull of a set of the form $\cup\{\alpha_x\{x\}^N : x \in \lambda\}$, where $\alpha_x > 0$. However, the balanced convex hull of a normal subset of λ is normal; thus B is normal. Therefore, τ_λ^∞ is a locally normal topology.

Let us note that if B is an absorbing, balanced, convex, and normal subset of λ, then B is a 0-neighborhood in τ_λ^∞. Indeed, $B = \{y : y \in \lambda, |y_i| \leq |x_i|, i \geq 1$, for some x in $B\}$, and so if $z \in \lambda$, $\alpha_z\{z\}^N \subset B$ for some $\alpha_z > 0$, in other words, $B \cap \lambda_z^\infty$ is a 0-neighborhood in $(\lambda_z^\infty, \|\cdot\|_z)$. Since $z \in \lambda$ is arbitrary, B is a 0-neighborhood for $(\lambda, \tau_\lambda^\infty)$.

The foregoing discussion leads to the following

PROPOSITION 4.15 For a normal sequence space λ, the topology τ_λ^∞ is the strongest locally convex locally normal topology.

EXERCISE 4.16 Show that the balanced convex hull $\Gamma(B)$ of a normal set B in a normal sequence space λ is normal. [Hint: Let $|x| \le |y|$, $y \in \Gamma(B)$; express $x_j = \beta_j(\alpha_1 z_j^1 + \cdots + \alpha_n z_j^n)$ where $|\beta_j| \le 1$, $j \ge 1$, $z^i \in B$, $1 \le i \le n$, and $\Sigma_{i=1}^n |\alpha_i| \le 1$.]

Concerning the AK-character of the sequence space of this subsection we have the following interesting result (Ref. 57, p. 90):

PROPOSITION 4.17 Let λ be a normal sequence space equipped with a locally convex locally normal topology T. Then the T-closure $\bar{\phi}$ of ϕ is $\{x : x \in \lambda,\ x^{(n)} \to x \text{ in } T\}$.

Proof. Let p denote an absolutely monotone seminorm in D_T. Assume that $x \in \bar{\phi}$. Then to each $\varepsilon > 0$, there exists y in ϕ such that $p(x - y) \le \varepsilon$. If n_0 in $\mathbb{N}$ is the length of y [cf. Definition 6.1(i)], it follows that $|x - x^{(m)}| \le |x - y|$ for all $m \ge n_0$. Hence $p(x - x^{(m)}) \le \varepsilon$, for $m \ge n_0$. □

EXERCISE 4.18 Show that the closure of ϕ in $(\ell^\infty, \|\cdot\|_\infty)$ is c_0, while the closure of ϕ in $(\ell^\infty, \eta(\ell^\infty, \ell^1))$ is ℓ^∞.

Next we have (cf. Ref. 57)

PROPOSITION 4.19 Let λ be a normal sequence space equipped with a locally convex locally normal topology T. Suppose $x \in \lambda$ and $I_x = \{i : x_i \ne 0\}$. If for some $y \in \lambda$, $x_i/y_i \to 0$ as $i \to \infty$ in I_x, then $x^{(n)} \to x$ in T.

Proof. Observe that $x^{(n)} \to x$ in $(\lambda_y^\infty, \|\cdot\|_y)$. Hence $x^{(n)} \to x$ in $(\lambda, \tau_\lambda^\infty)$. But $T \subset \tau_\lambda^\infty$, and so $x^{(n)} \to x$ in T. □

Remark: In the above theorem, the condition $x_i/y_i \to 0$ is not in general necessary for the result $x^{(n)} \to x$. For instance, consider

EXAMPLE 4.20 Let $\lambda = \ell^\infty$ and $T = \eta(\ell^\infty,\ell^1)$. Then $e^{(n)} \to e$; however, for no y in ℓ^∞, $1/y_i \to 0$.

Remark: In view of Example 4.20, it is natural to look for the class of normal sequence spaces for which the condition stated in Proposition 4.19 is also necessary for the convergence $x^{(n)} \to x$. The solution to this problem is, however, postponed to Theorem 4.9.18.

To conclude, we provide the following information:

PROPOSITION 4.21 For any normal sequence space λ, the space $(\lambda_x^\infty, \|\cdot\|_x)$ is a BK-space for each x in λ.

Proof. Let $\{y^n\}$ be Cauchy in λ_x^∞. For each $\varepsilon > 0$, there exists n_0 such that $y^n - y^m \in \varepsilon\{x\}^N$ for $m,n \geq n_0$. Hence

$$|y_i^n - y_i^m| \leq \varepsilon|x_i| \qquad m,n \geq n_0;\ i \geq 1$$

Therefore $y_i^n \to y_i$ $(i \geq 1)$ and $|y| \leq \alpha|x|$ for some $\alpha > 0$. Similarly there follows the K-ness of $(\lambda_x^\infty, \|\cdot\|_x)$. □

5. PERFECT, SIMPLE, AND SYMMETRIC SPACES

In this section we present some basic properties of perfect, simple, and symmetric sequence spaces. These spaces, respectively, play important roles in the study of duality theory (Ref. 140), matrix transformations (Refs. 100, 101), and ideals of operators on Hilbert spaces (Ref. 59).

Perfect Spaces

Below we give a characterization of perfect (*vollkommen*) sequence spaces and also mention a few useful applications of this result. Let us begin with

THEOREM 5.1 A sequence space λ is perfect if and only if λ is $\sigma(\lambda,\lambda^\times)$-sequentially complete.

Proof. Let $\lambda = \lambda^{\times\times}$ and suppose $\{x^n\}$ is $\sigma(\lambda,\lambda^\times)$-Cauchy. Thus, to each $\varepsilon > 0$ and $y \in \lambda^\times$, we find with the help of Theorem 4.7 an M in $\mathbb{N}$ such that $p_y(x^m - x^n) < \varepsilon$ for all $m,n \geq M$. Define $x \in \omega$ by

$$x_i = \lim_{n\to\infty} x_i^n \qquad i \geq 1$$

Hence for each p in $\mathbb{N}$ there corresponds an integer $R \geq M$ with

$$|(x_i^n - x_i)y_i| < \varepsilon p^{-2} \qquad \forall n \geq R,\ 1 \leq i \leq p$$

Therefore

$$\sum_{i=1}^{p} |(x_i^M - x_i)y_i| \leq \sum_{i=1}^{p} |(x_i^M - x_i^n)y_i| + \sum_{i=1}^{p} |(x_i^n - x_i)y_i|$$

$$< \varepsilon + \frac{\varepsilon}{p} \qquad \text{for all large } n$$

Thus

$$\sum_{i\geq 1} |(x_i^n - x_i)y_i| \leq \varepsilon \qquad \forall n \geq M \tag{*}$$

From the above inequality it also follows that

$$\sum_{i\geq 1} |x_i y_i| \leq \varepsilon + \sum_{i\geq 1} |x_i^M y_i| < \infty$$

where $y \in \lambda^\times$ is arbitrary. Therefore $x \in \lambda^{\times\times} = \lambda$. Returning to (*) once again, we find that $p_y(x^n - x) \leq \varepsilon$ for all $n \geq M$, giving thus

$$x^n \to x \text{ in } \sigma(\lambda,\lambda^\times) \qquad x \in \lambda$$

Sufficiency: To establish perfectness of λ, suppose $x \in \lambda^{\times\times}$. Observe that $\{x^{(n)}\} \subset \lambda$, and since for any y in $\lambda^\times$,

$$\left|\sum_{i\geq 1} (x_i^{(m)} - x_i^{(n)})y_i\right| \leq \sum_{i=m+1}^{n} |x_i y_i| \to 0 \qquad \text{as } m,n \to \infty$$

we see that $\{x^{(n)}\}$ is $\sigma(\lambda,\lambda^\times)$-Cauchy, and so $x^{(n)} \to z$ with $z \in \lambda$. Clearly $z = x$, and so $\lambda = \lambda^{\times\times}$. □

COROLLARY 5.2 A sequence space λ is perfect if and only if λ is $\eta(\lambda,\lambda^\times)$-sequentially complete. Further, λ is perfect if and only if λ is $\eta(\lambda,\lambda^\times)$-complete.

PROPOSITION 5.3 If λ is a normal sequence space, then $(\lambda^\times, \sigma(\lambda^\times, \lambda))$ and $(\lambda^\times, \eta(\lambda^\times, \lambda))$ are sequentially complete.

Proof. An application of Theorem 4.7 shows immediately that $\sigma(\lambda^\times, \lambda)$- and $\eta(\lambda^\times, \lambda)$-Cauchy sequences in $\lambda^\times$ are the same. Assume now $\{x^n\}$ to be an $\eta(\lambda^\times, \lambda)$-Cauchy sequence in $\lambda^\times$. Then $x_i^n \to x_i$ as $n \to \infty$ for every $i \geq 1$, where $x = \{x_i\}$. To get the result, proceed as in the proof of the necessity part of Theorem 5.1, with the roles of λ and $\lambda^\times$ interchanged. □

Remark: A generalization of Proposition 5.3, especially the part that $(\lambda^\times, \sigma(\lambda^\times, \lambda))$ is sequentially complete, appears in Proposition 4.2.2. Moreover, one may refer to Ref. 83 for a vector-valued analog of Proposition 5.3.

PROPOSITION 5.4 If λ is a perfect sequence space, then $\sigma(\lambda, \lambda^\times)$ and $\beta(\lambda, \lambda^\times)$ define the same bounded sets in λ.

Proof. Let A be $\sigma(\lambda, \lambda^\times)$-bounded. By Proposition 1.7,2, $A^{\circ\circ}$ is balanced, convex, $\sigma(\lambda, \lambda^\times)$-bounded, and $\sigma(\lambda, \lambda^\times)$-closed. Making use of Theorems 5.1 and 1.7.15, we find that $A^{\circ\circ}$ is $\beta(\lambda, \lambda^\times)$-bounded and so is A. □

Still more general is the following result, essentially due to Allen [6]:

THEOREM 5.5 Let λ be a sequence space and μ be a subspace of $\lambda^\times$ such that $(\mu, \sigma(\mu, \lambda))$ is sequentially complete. Then $\sigma(\lambda, \mu)$- and $\beta(\lambda, \mu)$-bounded sets are the same.

The proof of this result makes use of

PROPOSITION 5.6 Let λ be a sequence space and μ be a subspace of $\lambda^\times$. Then for a $\sigma(\lambda, \mu)$-bounded sequence $\{x^n\}$ in λ and $b = \{b_i\} \in \ell^1$, the sequence $\{y^n\}$ defined as

$$y^n = \sum_{i=1}^{n} b_i x^i \qquad n \geq 1$$

is $\sigma(\lambda, \mu)$-Cauchy.

Proof. For z in μ, there exists a constant $M \equiv M(z)$ such that

$$q_z(x^n) \le M \qquad \text{for all } n \ge 1$$

For $\varepsilon > 0$, there exists an integer $n_0 \in \mathbb{N}$ such that

$$\sum_{i>n_0} |b_i| < \frac{\varepsilon}{M}$$

Hence for $p > m > n_0$,

$$q_z(y^p - y^m) = q_z\left(\sum_{n=m+1}^{p} b_n x^n\right) < \varepsilon \quad \square$$

Proof of Theorem 5.5. Let us assume that a $\sigma(\lambda,\mu)$-bounded subset A of λ is not $\beta(\lambda,\mu)$-bounded. Thus for each $\varepsilon > 0$ there correspond $x^1 \in A$ and $y^1 \in B$ such that

$$|\langle x^1, y^1\rangle| \ge 1 + \varepsilon \tag{*}$$

Since A is $\sigma(\lambda,\mu)$-bounded, there exists a constant $k_1 \equiv k_1(y^1) > 0$ with

$$q_{y^1}(x) = |\langle x, y^1\rangle| \le k_1 \qquad \forall x \text{ in } A$$

Also the boundedness of B in $\sigma(\mu,\lambda)$ implies the existence of an $M_1 \equiv M_1(x^1) > 0$ with

$$q_{x^1}(y) = |\langle x^1, y\rangle| \le M_1 \qquad \forall y \text{ in } B$$

Let us observe that if $p_k > p_{k-1}$, $k \ge 1$, with $p_0 = 0$, then $\Sigma_{k\ge1} 2^{-p_{k-1}} < \infty$, and so for any $\{y^k\} \subset B$, the sequence $\{z^n\}$ is $\sigma(\mu,\lambda)$-convergent in μ (say, to z) by Proposition 5.6, where

$$z^n = \sum_{k=1}^{n} 2^{-p_{k-1}} y^k \qquad \text{and} \qquad z = \sum_{k\ge1} 2^{-p_{k-1}} y^k$$

Now choose p_1 so that

$$2^{-p_1+1} \le \varepsilon M_1^{-1}$$

and choose $p_2, p_3, \ldots$ arbitrarily subject to the restriction that $p_{k-1} < p_k$; also let $\{y^k\} \subset B$ with y^1 as above. In view of an observation made earlier we have a corresponding z belonging to μ. Then

$$
\begin{aligned}
|\langle x^1, z\rangle| &\ge |\langle x^1, y^1\rangle| - 2^{-p_1}|\langle x^1, y^2\rangle| - 2^{-p_2}|\langle x^1, y^3\rangle| - \cdots \\
&\ge 1 + \varepsilon - M_1 2^{-p_1}(1 + 2^{-p_2+p_1} + 2^{-p_3+p_1} + \cdots) \ge 1
\end{aligned}
$$

Corresponding to $2^{p_1}(k_1 + 2 + \varepsilon)$ we can find, as we did in obtaining (*), elements x^2 and y^2 with $x^2 \in A$ and $y^2 \in B$ such that

$$|\langle x^2, y^2\rangle| \ge 2^{p_1}(k_1 + 2 + \varepsilon)$$

We can also find M_2 and $k_2 > 0$ such that

$$|\langle x^2, y\rangle| \le M_2 \qquad \forall y \text{ in } B$$

and

$$|\langle x, y^2\rangle| \le k_2 \qquad \forall x \text{ in } A$$

Choose $p_2 > p_1$ such that

$$2^{-p_2+1} \le \varepsilon M_2^{-1}$$

and take p_3, p_4, ... arbitrarily with $p_{k-1} < p_k$; also let $\{y^k\} \subset B$ with y^1 and y^2 being the same as above. Let z be the element of μ corresponding to $\{p_k\}$ and $\{y^k\}$. Then

$$
\begin{aligned}
|\langle x^2, z\rangle| &\ge 2^{-p_1}|\langle x^2, y^2\rangle| - |\langle x^2, y^1\rangle| - 2^{-p_2}|\langle x^2, y^3\rangle| - \cdots \\
&\ge 2 + \varepsilon - 2^{-p_2}M_2(1 + 2^{p_2-p_3} + 2^{p_2-p_4} + \cdots) \\
&\ge 2 + \varepsilon - \varepsilon = 2
\end{aligned}
$$

The foregoing process implies the existence of a z in μ and a sequence $\{x^n\} \subset A$, z being dependent on $\{x^n\}$ such that

$$q_z(x^n) \ge n \qquad \forall n \ge 1$$

thereby contradicting the $\sigma(\lambda,\mu)$-boundedness of A. □

COROLLARY 5.7 For a normal sequence space λ, $\sigma(\lambda,\lambda^\times)$- and $\beta(\lambda,\lambda^\times)$-bounded subsets of λ are the same.

Indeed, this follows from Proposition 5.3.

EXERCISE 5.8 For a normal sequence space λ, show that $(\lambda, \tau(\lambda, \lambda^{\times}))$ is a W-space. [Hint: Use Proposition 1.10.5.]

Note: For deeper results on perfect sequence spaces, cf. Propositions 2.3, 2.4, 2.8, 2.13, 2.14, and 2.15 of Chapter 4.

Simple Sequence Spaces

In the past few years considerable interest has emerged in the spaces of analytic or entire sequences; see for instance Ref. 77 for several historical and stimulating ideas, and also Refs. 163 and 116 for general review (for spaces of entire functions represented by Dirichlet series and spaces of entire functions of several complex variables, one may refer to Refs. 94, 113, 117, 121, and 122). A number of theorems have been proved about matrix transformations involving these sequence spaces, using a variety of techniques (cf. Refs. 99, 198, and 255, and numerous references given therein). One property of these spaces is that each bounded subset is contained in the normal hull of a point belonging to the space; see Refs. 78, 120, and 146. In this subsection we study those sequence spaces which have this property and obtain their elementary structure theorems; applications are reserved for a later section.

DEFINITION 5.9 Let $\langle\lambda, \mu\rangle$ form a dual system and let T be any locally convex topology compatible with the dual structure. Then λ is called *simple relative* to $\langle\lambda, \mu\rangle$ if each T-bounded set in λ is dominated by a point of λ.

Remarks: For the definition of "domination by a point," see Definition 4.1. If $\mu = \lambda^{\times}$ in the above definition, we say merely that λ is *simple* (cf. Ref. 100).

The following result sharpens an earlier result of a similar nature due to Jacob [101], when $\mu = \lambda^{\times}$.

THEOREM 5.10 Suppose λ is simple relative to $\langle\lambda, \mu\rangle$, where μ is a normal sequence subspace of $\lambda^{\times}$. Then a sequence $\{x^n\}$ converges in $(\lambda, \sigma(\lambda, \mu))$ if and only if $\{x^n\}$ converges in $(\lambda,\sigma(\omega,\phi)|\lambda)$ and is T-bounded in λ.

Proof. Assume first that $x^n \to x$ in $(\lambda,\sigma(\omega,\phi)|T)$ and $\{x^n\}$ is T-bounded. There exists $y \in \lambda$ with

$$|x_i^n| \le |y_i| \qquad \forall n,i \ge 1$$

Choose $\varepsilon > 0$ and $u \in \mu$ arbitrarily. Then for some $N \equiv N(\varepsilon,x,y,u)$ in $\mathbb{N}$ we have

$$\sum_{i>N} |y_i u_i| < \frac{\varepsilon}{4} \qquad \sum_{i>N} |x_i u_i| < \frac{\varepsilon}{4}$$

We can then find an M in $\mathbb{N}$ with $M \equiv M(N,u)$ such that

$$\sum_{i=1}^{N} |(x_i^n - x_i)u_i| < \frac{\varepsilon}{2} \qquad \forall n \ge M$$

Thus for $n \ge M$,

$$q_u(x^n - x) \le \sum_{i=1}^{N} |(x_i^n - x_i)u_i| + \sum_{i>N} |y_i u_i| + \sum_{i>N} |x_i u_i| < \varepsilon$$

The other part is straightforward. □

Next, we have (Refs. 100 and 101)

PROPOSITION 5.11 Every normal simple sequence space λ is $\sigma(\lambda,\lambda^\times)$-sequentially complete.

Proof. Let $\{x^n\}$ be a $\sigma(\lambda,\lambda^\times)$-Cauchy sequence in λ. One can define an $x \in \omega$ with

$$x_i = \lim_{n\to\infty} x_i^n \qquad \forall i \ge 1$$

Proceeding as in the proof of Theorem 5.1, we find that $x \in \lambda^{\times\times}$ and [cf. (*) in the proof of the theorem referred to]

$$\sum_{i\ge 1} |(x_i^n - x_i)y_i| \le \varepsilon \qquad \forall n \ge M \equiv M(y) \tag{**}$$

where $y \in \lambda^\times$. Now for some u in λ,

$$|x_i^n| \le |u_i| \qquad \forall n,i \ge 1$$

$$\Longrightarrow \quad |x_i| \le |u_i| \qquad \forall i \ge 1$$

and so $x \in \lambda$. The required result follows from (**). □

EXERCISE 5.12 Prove that each simple normal sequence space is perfect.

For a dual system $\langle\lambda,\lambda^\times\rangle$ a weakly convergent sequence in λ is not necessarily strongly convergent; for instance, consider

EXAMPLE 5.13 Let $\lambda = \ell^\infty$. Then $\lambda^\times = \ell^1$. Here $e^n \to 0$ in $(\ell^\infty,\sigma(\ell^\infty,\ell^1))$. By Proposition 6.12, $e^n \not\to 0$ in $\beta(\ell^\infty,\ell^1)$.

Remark: Using the characterization of bounded subsets of $(\ell^1,\sigma(\ell^1,\ell^\infty))$ (cf. Proposition 6.10), we conclude that $\lambda^\times$ in Example 5.13 is not simple. If $\lambda^\times$ is simple we have the following proposition (Ref. 100) which generalizes a number of results including that of Lascarides [147].

PROPOSITION 5.14 Consider the dual system $\langle\lambda,\lambda^\times\rangle$, where $\lambda^\times$ is simple [i.e., each $\sigma(\lambda^\times,\lambda)$-bounded subset of $\lambda^\times$ is dominated by a point in $\lambda^\times$]. Then each $\sigma(\lambda,\lambda^\times)$-convergent sequence in λ is $\beta(\lambda,\lambda^\times)$-convergent.

Proof. Let $\{x^n\} \subset \lambda$ with $x^n \to 0$ in $\sigma(\lambda,\lambda^\times)$. Suppose B is an arbitrary $\sigma(\lambda^\times,\lambda)$-bounded subset of $\lambda^\times$. There exists a $y \in \lambda^\times$ such that y dominates B. Choose $\varepsilon > 0$ arbitrarily. There exists $N \equiv N(\varepsilon,y)$ in $\mathbb{N}$ such that (cf. Corollary 4.12) $p_y(x^n) \le \varepsilon$, for all $n \ge N$. Thus for $n \ge N$,

$$q_B(x^n) = \sup\left\{\left|\sum_{i\ge1} u_i x_i^n\right| : u \in B\right\} \le p_y(x^n) \le \varepsilon$$

and so $x^n \to 0$ in $\beta(\lambda,\lambda^\times)$. □

PROPOSITION 5.15 If λ is a simple sequence space, then so is $\lambda^{\times\times}$.

Proof. Note that $\lambda^{\times\times\times} = \lambda^\times$. By Theorem 8.14, $\sigma(\lambda^{\times\times},\lambda^\times)$- and $\eta(\lambda^{\times\times},\lambda^\times)$-bounded subsets of $\lambda^{\times\times}$ are the same. Suppose A is a $\sigma(\lambda^{\times\times},\lambda^\times)$-bounded subset of $\lambda^{\times\times}$; hence to each y in $\lambda^\times$ there corresponds a $k_y > 0$ such that

$$\sum_{i\ge1} |x_i y_i| \le k_y \qquad \text{uniformly in } x \in A$$

If $B = \{x^{(n)} : n \ge 1,\ x \in A\}$, then $B \subset \lambda$ and B is $\sigma(\lambda,\lambda^\times)$-bounded. Thus for u in λ,

$$|x_i| \le |u_i| \qquad \forall i \ge 1$$

That is, A is dominated by u. □

Symmetric Sequence Spaces

Let us recall the definition of a symmetric sequence space and that of Π. Suppose P denotes the semigroup of all one-to-one mappings of $\mathbb{N}$ into itself. We have the following result, which is a slight improvement of Garling [57].

PROPOSITION 5.16 If λ is a monotone symmetric sequence space then for any x in λ and σ in P, $x_\sigma \in \lambda$.

Proof. We can find a ρ in Π such that $\rho(i) = \sigma(i)$ when i is odd. So

$$x_\rho = \{x_{\sigma(1)}, x_{\rho(2)}, x_{\sigma(3)}, x_{\rho(4)}, \ldots\} \in \lambda$$

Since λ is monotone (i.e., $m_0\lambda \subset \lambda$), then

$$\{x_{\sigma(1)}, 0, x_{\sigma(3)}, 0, \ldots\} \in \lambda$$

Similarly

$$\{0, x_{\sigma(2)}, 0, x_{\sigma(4)}, \ldots\} \in \lambda$$

Hence, by addition, $x_\sigma \in \lambda$. □

Note: From above we find that if $x \in \omega$ and $\sigma \in P$, the sequence x_σ is obtained by deleting a finite or an infinite number of terms and rearranging the whole lot.

For $x \in \omega$ and $\sigma \in P$, define $x^\sigma = \{x_i^\sigma\}$ as follows:

$$x_i^\sigma = \begin{cases} x_i & i = \sigma(j) \text{ for some } j \\ 0 & \text{otherwise} \end{cases}$$

DEFINITION 5.17 For x in ω and σ in P, x^σ is called the σ *close-up* of x.

Note: Let us observe that the σ close-up of x is the same as the canonical preimage of x_σ for $\sigma \in P$.

PROPOSITION 5.18 If λ is a monotone symmetric sequence space, then $x \in \lambda$ if and only if $x^\sigma \in \lambda$ for every σ in P.

Proof. For σ in P define $e^\sigma = \{e_i^\sigma\}$ by

$$e_i^\sigma = \begin{cases} 1 & \text{if } i = \sigma(j) \text{ for some } j \\ 0 & \text{otherwise} \end{cases}$$

Clearly $e^\sigma \in m_0$ for each σ in P. Let now $x \in \lambda$. Then $x^\sigma = x \cdot e^\sigma \in m_0\lambda$ and so $x^\sigma \in \lambda$. The other part is obvious. □

EXERCISE 5.19 If λ is symmetric, so is then $\lambda^\times$; but the converse is not true. [Hint: Take $\lambda = a$.]

After Garling [57] we have

PROPOSITION 5.20 If λ is a normal symmetric sequence space, then either $\lambda \subset c_0$, or $\lambda = \ell^\infty$, or $\lambda = \omega$.

Proof. c_0 is normal and symmetric. If $\lambda \subset c_0$, there is nothing to prove. So, let $\lambda \not\subset c_0$, which implies the existence of an $x \in \lambda$ with $x \notin c_0$. Hence, for some $\varepsilon > 0$, there exists an increasing sequence $\{n_i\}$ such that $|x_{n_i}| \geq \varepsilon$, $i \geq 1$. Define $\sigma \in P$ by $\sigma(i) = n_i$, $i \geq 1$. By Proposition 5.16, $x_\sigma \in \lambda$. Here $x_\sigma = \{x_{n_i}\} = \{x_{\sigma(i)}\}$, and as λ is normal, the constant sequence $\{\varepsilon\} \in \lambda$. Thus $\ell^\infty \subset \lambda$. Consequently if $\lambda \subset \ell^\infty$ we find that $\lambda = \ell^\infty$.

Finally, let $\lambda \not\subset \ell^\infty$. There exists an x in λ with $x \notin \ell^\infty$. Suppose $y \in \omega$. For some increasing sequence $\{n_i\}$, we find that $|x_{n_i}| > |y_i|$, $i \geq 1$. As before, define $\sigma \in P$ by $\sigma(i) = n_i$. Arguing as in the preceding paragraph (we once again make use of the normality of λ) we obtain $y \in \lambda$. Therefore $\lambda = \omega$. □

If the space λ in the foregoing proposition is further restricted, one has the following (Ref. 34):

PROPOSITION 5.21 If λ is a perfect symmetric sequence space other than ϕ or ω, then $\ell^1 \subset \lambda \subset \ell^\infty$.

Proof. Since $\lambda \neq \omega$ it follows from Proposition 5.20 that $\lambda \subset \ell^\infty$. Also, $\lambda^\times$ is perfect and symmetric (cf. Exercise 3.16); therefore $\lambda^\times \subset \ell^\infty$ (since $\lambda^\times \neq \omega$), which in turn implies that $\ell^1 \subset \lambda$. □

After Garling [57] we have

DEFINITION 5.22 For $x \in \omega$, let

$$x'_i = \begin{cases} \text{the ith nonzero term of } x & \text{if such exists} \\ 0 & \text{otherwise} \end{cases}$$

The sequence $x' = \{x'_i\}$ is called the *closing up* of x.

For instance, if $x = \{1, 0, 0, 2, 0, 0, 3, \ldots\}$, $x' = \{1, 2, \ldots\}$; if $x = e^i$, $x' = \{1, 0, 0, 0, \ldots\}$ for every $i \geq 1$.

If infinitely many terms in an $x \in \omega$ are nonzero, there exists a $\sigma \in P$ such that $x' = x_\sigma$. As an illustration, let $x = \{1, 2, 0, 3, 4, 0, 5, 6, 0, \ldots\}$. Then $x' = x_\sigma$ where $\sigma(1) = 1$, $\sigma(2) = 2$, $\sigma(3) = 4$, $\sigma(4) = 5$, $\sigma(5) = 7$, $\sigma(6) = 8$, etc.

PROPOSITION 5.23 If λ is a monotone symmetric sequence space, then $x \in \lambda$ if and only if $x' \in \lambda$.

Proof. Let $x' = \{z_i\} = x_\sigma$, where $\sigma \in P$, $\sigma(i) = n_i$, $i \geq 1$. If x' is in λ, it follows that

$$u = \{z_1, 0, z_3, 0, z_5, 0, \ldots\} \in \lambda$$

$$v = \{0, z_2, 0, z_4, 0, z_6, \ldots\} \in \lambda$$

since λ is monotone. We can now find ρ and δ in Π such that $\rho(n_i) = i$ if i is odd, and $\delta(n_i) = i$ if i is even. Then u_ρ and v_δ are in λ and therefore $x = u_\rho + v_\delta$ is in λ. Necessity follows by Proposition 5.16. □

DEFINITION 5.24 The *symmetric dual* of an x in ω is the space x^δ with

$$x^\delta = \left\{ y : y \in \omega;\ \sum_{i \geq 1} |y_i x_{\rho(i)}| < \infty \quad \forall \rho \in \Pi \right\}$$

Note: Observe that x^δ is perfect and symmetric.

We have the following result (Ref. 216):

PROPOSITION 5.25 Let x and y be in ω. Then

(i) $x \in y^\delta$ if and only if $y \in x^\delta$.

(ii) $x^\delta = \phi$ if and only if $x \notin \ell^\infty$.

(iii) $x^\delta = \omega$ if and only if $x \in \phi$.

(iv) $x^\delta = \ell^\infty$ if and only if $x \in \ell^1$, $x \notin \phi$.

(v) $x^\delta = \ell^1$, if $x \in \ell^\infty$, $x \notin c_0$.

Proof. (i) Let $y \in x^\delta$. Then for any ρ in Π,

$$\sum_{i\geq 1} |y_i x_{\rho^{-1}(i)}| < \infty$$

Let $\rho^{-1}(i) = j$; then $i = \rho(j)$. Thus

$$\sum_{j\geq 1} |x_j y_{\rho(j)}| < \infty \qquad \forall \rho \in \Pi$$

or $x \in y^\delta$. The other part of (i) follows similarly.

(ii) Let $x^\delta = \phi$. If possible, let $x \in \ell^\infty$. By Exercise 2.5, $\ell^1 = (\ell^\infty)^\delta \subset x^\delta = \phi$, which is not true by hypothesis. Assume now $x \notin \ell^\infty = (\ell^1)^\times$. Therefore, there exists a y in ℓ^1 such that $\Sigma_{i\geq 1} |x_i y_i| = \infty$. Clearly $y \notin x^\delta$. Hence $\ell^1 \not\subset x^\delta$. Using Proposition 5.18 and the fact that x^δ is perfect and symmetric, we conclude that $x^\delta = \phi$.

(iii) If $x^\delta = \omega$, then

$$y \in x^\delta \qquad \forall y \in \omega$$

or

$$x \in y^\delta \qquad \forall y \in \omega$$

Choosing $y \notin \ell^\infty$ we find $y^\delta = \phi$ by (ii). Thus $x \in \phi$. The other part is obviously true.

(iv) Assume that $x^\delta = \ell^\infty$. Then $e \in x^\delta$ and so $x \in \ell^1$. Clearly $x \notin \phi$, otherwise $\ell^\infty = \omega$ by (iii). On the other hand, let $x \in \ell^1$, $x \notin \phi$. By (iii) $x^\delta \subsetneq \omega$. Again, $x \in \ell^1 \Rightarrow (\ell^1)^\delta \subset x^\delta$, or $\ell^\infty \subset x^\delta$. As $x^\delta \supsetneq \phi$ by (iii), Proposition 5.18 yields $x^\delta = \ell^\infty$.

(v) Let us suppose that $x \in \ell^\infty$, $x \notin c_0$. There exists an $\varepsilon > 0$ and an increasing sequence $\{n_i\}$ such that

$$|x_{n_i}| > \varepsilon \qquad i \geq 1 \tag{*}$$

Define $\sigma \in P$ by $\sigma(i) = n_i$, $i \geq 1$. Write $x' = x^\sigma$. Then clearly $x^\delta \subset (x')^\delta \equiv x'^\delta$ (say). Further, $x'^\delta \subset \ell^1$. Indeed, let $y \in x'^\delta$. Then

$$\sum_{i\geq 1} |y_i x'_{\rho(i)}| < \infty \qquad \forall \rho \in \Pi$$

In particular, setting $\rho(i) = i$, $i \geq 1$, and using (*) above we have

$$\sum_{i\geq 1} |y_{n_i}| < \infty$$

If $\{m_i\} \subset \mathbb{N}$ and is complementary to $\{n_i\}$, define a $\rho \in \Pi$ by $\rho(n_i) = m_i$ and $\rho(m_i) = n_i$, $i \geq 1$. Thus from (*) again,

$$\sum_{i\geq 1} |y_{m_i}| < \infty$$

Therefore $y \in \ell^1$, i.e., $x^\delta \subset \ell^1$. As $x \in \ell^\infty$, it follows that $\ell^1 \subset x^\delta$. Hence $x^\delta = \ell^1$. □

In view of Proposition 5.25, it would be worthwhile to restrict attention to the δ-duals of those sequences in c_0 which are not in ℓ^1. Indeed, the results which we shall discuss will lead to the converse of statement (v) of the preceding proposition. Let us first consider (Ref. 57, p. 92 and Ref. 216, p. 831)

DEFINITION 5.26 The *reduced form* of a sequence $x \in c_0$ is the decreasing sequence $\hat{x} = \{\hat{x}_i\}$ where $\hat{x}_1, \hat{x}_2, \hat{x}_3, \ldots$ exhaust the nonzero values assumed by $|x_1|, |x_2|, |x_3|, \ldots$, allowing repeated values. A sequence x is *in reduced form* if $x = \hat{x}$.

Note: Clearly, the reduced form $\hat{x}$ of $x \in c_0$ is obtained by permuting the nonnegative modulii of the coordinates of x'. Though this permutation is not necessarily unique, $\hat{x}$ is always determined uniquely. Analytically we may express $\hat{x} = \{\hat{x}_n\}$ by

$$\hat{x}_n = \inf\{\sup\{|x_i| : i \notin J\} : J \subset \mathbb{N}, |J| < n\}$$

where $|J|$ represents the number of elements of the set J (cf. Ref. 60).

EXERCISE 5.27 Let λ be a normal symmetric subspace of c_0. Then (i) show that $x \in \lambda$ if and only if $\hat{x} \in \lambda$; and (ii) for $x \in c_0$, prove that $x^\delta = \hat{x}^\delta$. [Hint: Make use of Proposition 5.23 for (i).]

After Ruckle [216], we have

THEOREM 5.28 Let $x \in c_0$ and $x \notin \ell^1$. For $y \in \omega$, define

$$Q_x(y) = \sup_{\pi\in\Pi} \sum_{i\geq 1} |x_{\pi(i)} y_i|$$

Then Q_x is a proper, balanced, symmetric sequential norm and

$$Q_x(y) = \begin{cases} \Sigma_{i\geq 1} \hat{x}_i\hat{y}_i & y \in c_0 \\ \infty & y \notin c_0 \end{cases} \tag{*}$$

Further, S_{Q_x} and λ_{Q_x} are normal symmetric spaces and $S_{Q_x} = \lambda_{Q_x} = x^\delta$.

Proof. If we write $N_\pi(y) = \Sigma_{i\geq 1} |x_{\pi(i)}y_i|$ for $\pi \in \Pi$, then N_π is an extended seminorm satisfying the property

$$N_\pi(y) = \sup_n N_\pi(y^{(n)})$$

Consequently, $Q_x(y) = \sup_\pi N_\pi(y)$ is also an extended seminorm possessing the property

$$Q_x(y) = \sup_n Q_x(y^{(n)})$$

Obviously, Q_x is a norm and $Q_x(e^i) = \sup_n |x_n|$, for each $i \geq 1$. Hence Q_x is a proper sequential norm.

To prove (*), assume first that $y \notin c_0$. Then from Proposition 5.25, $y^\delta \subset \ell^1$ and therefore $x \notin y^\delta$. Hence $Q_x(y) = \infty$. For $y \in c_0$ let us choose any member π of Π. For $n \in \mathbb{N}$, we can find a $\sigma \in \Pi$ such that $\hat{y}_{\sigma(1)}$, $\hat{y}_{\sigma(2)}, \ldots, \hat{y}_{\sigma(n)}$ is a rearrangement of $\hat{y}_1, \hat{y}_2, \ldots, \hat{y}_n$ satisfying

$$\hat{y}_{\sigma(i)} \geq |y_{\pi(i)}| \qquad \text{for } 1 \leq i \leq n$$

Hence

$$\sum_{i=1}^{n} |x_i y_{\pi(i)}| \leq \sum_{i=1}^{n} |x_i \hat{y}_{\sigma(i)}| \leq \sum_{i=1}^{n} \hat{x}_i\hat{y}_i$$

as $\hat{x}_1 \geq \hat{x}_2 \geq \cdots \geq \hat{x}_n$ and $\hat{y}_1 \geq \hat{y}_2 \geq \cdots \geq \hat{y}_n$. Therefore

$$Q_x(y) \leq \sum_{i\geq 1} \hat{x}_i\hat{y}_i$$

For the other inequality, let us choose $\varepsilon > 0$. Then we can find $n \in \mathbb{N}$ such that

$$\sum_{i=1}^{n} \hat{x}_i\hat{y}_i + \varepsilon > \sum_{i\geq 1} \hat{x}_i\hat{y}_i$$

Choose π, $\eta \in \Pi$ such that $|y_{\pi(i)}| = \hat{y}_i$ and $|x_{\eta(i)}| = \hat{x}_i$ for $i \le n$. Then

$$Q_x(y) \ge \sum_{i\ge 1} |x_i y_{\eta^{-1}\circ\pi(i)}| \ge \sum_{i=1}^{n} |x_{\eta(i)} y_{\pi(i)}| > \sum_{i\ge 1} \hat{x}_i \hat{y}_i - \varepsilon$$

Hence $Q_x(y) \ge \Sigma_{i\ge 1} \hat{x}_i \hat{y}_i$ and (*) follows. This in turn implies that Q_x is balanced and symmetric.

It also follows from (*) that S_{Q_x} is normal and symmetric, and $S_{Q_x} = \hat{x}^\delta$. Therefore $S_{Q_x} = x^\delta$ by Exercise 5.27. To show the symmetric property of λ_{Q_x}, consider $z \in \lambda_{Q_x}$ and $\pi \in \Pi$. As Q_x is symmetric, we have

$$Q_x\left(\sum_{i=1}^{n} z_i e^i\right) = Q_x\left(\sum_{i=1}^{n} z_i e^{\pi^{-1}(i)}\right)$$

for each $n \ge 1$. Thus the convergence of $\Sigma_{i\ge 1} z_i e^i$ implies the convergence of $\Sigma_{i\ge 1} z_i e^{\pi^{-1}(i)}$ and vice versa. Since

$$\sum_{i\ge 1} z_i e^{\pi^{-1}(i)} = \sum_{i\ge 1} z_{\pi(i)} e^i$$

it follows that $z_\pi \in \lambda_{Q_x}$. Hence λ_{Q_x} is symmetric. λ_{Q_x} is normal as Q_x is balanced.

To prove $S_{Q_x} \subset \lambda_{Q_x}$, it suffices to show that $\hat{y} \in \lambda_{Q_x}$ whenever $y \in S_{Q_x}$, in view of Proposition 5.23. Now $\hat{y} \in \lambda_{Q_x}$ if and only if

$$\lim_{n\to\infty} Q_x(\hat{y} - \hat{y}^{(n)}) = \lim_{n\to\infty} \sum_{i\ge 1} \hat{x}_i \hat{y}_{n+i} = 0$$

So for $y \in S_{Q_x}$, we show that

$$\lim_{n\to\infty} \sum_{i\ge 1} \hat{x}_i \hat{y}_{n+i} = 0$$

Let $\varepsilon > 0$ be given. There exists an integer $N_1 \in \mathbb{N}$ such that

$$\sum_{i\ge N_1+1} \hat{x}_i \hat{y}_i < \frac{\varepsilon}{2}$$

Then for any $n \in \mathbb{N}$,

$$\sum_{i\ge N_1+1} \hat{x}_i \hat{y}_{n+i} \le \sum_{i\ge N_1+1} \hat{x}_i \hat{y}_i < \frac{\varepsilon}{2}$$

Since $\hat{y} \in S_{Q_x} \subset c_0$ by Proposition 5.23 and (*), there exists $N_2 \in \mathbb{N}$ such that

$$\hat{y}_n < \frac{\varepsilon}{2\sum_{i=1}^{N_1} \hat{x}_i} \qquad \forall n \geq N_2$$

Hence for $n \geq N_2$,

$$\sum_{i\geq 1} \hat{x}_i \hat{y}_{n+i} = \sum_{i=1}^{N_1} \hat{x}_i \hat{y}_{n+i} + \sum_{i\geq N_1+1} \hat{x}_i \hat{y}_{n+i}$$

$$\leq \frac{\varepsilon}{2\sum_{i=1}^{N_1} \hat{x}_i} \sum_{i=1}^{N_1} \hat{x}_i + \frac{\varepsilon}{2} < \varepsilon \qquad \square$$

Note: Let us observe that each x such that $x \in c_0$ and $x \notin \ell^1$ defines a proper sequential norm Q_x. If there is no confusion, we shall simply write Q for Q_x.

THEOREM 5.29 For $x \in c_0$ and $x \notin \ell^1$,

$$Q^*(y) = \sup_n \left\{ \frac{\sum_{i=1}^n \hat{y}_i}{\sum_{i=1}^n \hat{x}_i} \right\}$$

Proof. By definition of dual norm,

$$Q^*(y) = \sup\left\{\sup_n \left| \sum_{i=1}^n a_i y_i \right| : Q(a) \leq 1\right\}$$

$$= \sup\left\{\sup_n \left| \sum_{i=1}^n a_i y_i \right| : \sum_{i\geq 1} \hat{a}_i \hat{x}_i \leq 1\right\}$$

We now show that

$$Q^*(y) = \sup\left\{\sum_{i\geq 1} \hat{a}_i \hat{y}_i : \sum_{i\geq 1} \hat{a}_i \hat{x}_i \leq 1\right\}$$

Indeed, the inequality

$$\left| \sum_{i=1}^n a_i y_i \right| \leq \sum_{i=1}^n \hat{a}_i \hat{y}_i \leq \sum_{i\geq 1} \hat{a}_i \hat{y}_i$$

for any $n \in \mathbb{N}$ implies that

$$Q^*(y) \le \sup\left\{\sum_{i\ge 1} \hat{a}_i\hat{y}_i : \sum_{i\ge 1} \hat{a}_i\hat{x}_i \le 1\right\}$$

To show the reverse inequality, for a given $n \in \mathbb{N}$ we choose $m \in \mathbb{N}$ so large that $\hat{y}_1, \hat{y}_2, \ldots, \hat{y}_n$ are included in $\{|y_1|, |y_2|, \ldots, |y_m|\}$. Let $\pi \in \Pi$ be such that $\hat{y}_i = |y_{\pi(i)}|$, $i \le n$. Write $b_i = (y_i/|y_i|)\hat{a}_{\pi^{-1}(i)}$. As $|b_i| = \hat{a}_{\pi^{-1}(i)}$, it follows that $\hat{b} = \hat{a}$ and therefore

$$\sum_{i=1}^{m} b_i y_i = \sum_{i=1}^{m} \hat{a}_{\pi^{-1}(i)} |y_i| = \sum_{i=1}^{m} \hat{a}_i |y_{\pi(i)}| \ge \sum_{i=1}^{n} \hat{a}_i |y_{\pi(i)}| = \sum_{i=1}^{n} \hat{a}_i\hat{y}_i$$

implies

$$Q^*(y) \ge \sup\left\{\sum_{i\ge 1} \hat{a}_i\hat{y}_i : \sum_{i\ge 1} \hat{a}_i\hat{x}_i \le 1\right\}$$

Now

$$\begin{aligned}
\sum_{i=1}^{n} \hat{a}_i\hat{y}_i &= \sum_{i=1}^{n-1} (\hat{a}_i - \hat{a}_{i+1})\left(\sum_{j=1}^{i} \hat{y}_j\right) + \hat{a}_n \sum_{j=1}^{n} \hat{y}_j \\
&= \sum_{i=1}^{n-1} (\hat{a}_i - \hat{a}_{i+1}) \frac{\sum_{j=1}^{i} \hat{y}_j}{\sum_{j=1}^{i} \hat{x}_j} \sum_{j=1}^{i} \hat{x}_j + \hat{a}_n \frac{\sum_{j=1}^{n} \hat{y}_j}{\sum_{j=1}^{n} \hat{x}_j} \sum_{j=1}^{n} \hat{x}_j \\
&\le \sup_n \frac{\sum_{j=1}^{n} \hat{y}_j}{\sum_{j=1}^{n} \hat{x}_j}\left[\sum_{i=1}^{n-1} (\hat{a}_i - \hat{a}_{i+1}) \sum_{j=1}^{i} \hat{x}_j + \hat{a}_n \sum_{j=1}^{n} \hat{x}_j\right] \\
&= \sup_n \frac{\sum_{j=1}^{n} \hat{y}_j}{\sum_{j=1}^{n} \hat{x}_j} \sum_{i=1}^{n} \hat{a}_i\hat{x}_i
\end{aligned}$$

Therefore, for $Q(a) = \Sigma_{i\ge 1} \hat{a}_i\hat{x}_i \le 1$,

$$\sum_{i=1}^{n} \hat{a}_i\hat{y}_i \le \sup_n \frac{\sum_{j=1}^{n} \hat{y}_j}{\sum_{j=1}^{n} \hat{x}_j} \qquad \forall n \ge 1$$

Hence

$$Q^*(y) \ge \sup_n \frac{\sum_{j=1}^{n} \hat{y}_j}{\sum_{j=1}^{n} \hat{x}_j}$$

For the other inequality let us choose $\varepsilon > 0$. Then there exists an $n_0 \in \mathbb{N}$ such that

$$\frac{\sum_{i=1}^{n_0} \hat{y}_i}{\sum_{i=1}^{n_0} \hat{x}_i} > \sup_n \frac{\sum_{i=1}^{n} \hat{y}_i}{\sum_{i=1}^{n} \hat{x}_i} - \varepsilon$$

Define a sequence $\{b_i\}$ as follows:

$$b_i = \begin{cases} \dfrac{1}{\sum_{i=1}^{n_0} \hat{x}_i} & i \le n_0 \\ 0 & i > n_0 \end{cases}$$

Obviously $\sum_{i=1}^{n_0} \hat{x}_i \hat{b}_i = 1$. But

$$\sum_{i=1}^{n_0} \hat{b}_i \hat{y}_i = \frac{\sum_{i=1}^{n_0} \hat{y}_i}{\sum_{i=1}^{n_0} \hat{x}_i} > \sup_n \frac{\sum_{i=1}^{n} \hat{y}_i}{\sum_{i=1}^{n} \hat{x}_i} < \infty$$

$$\Longrightarrow Q^*(y) \ge \sup_n \frac{\sum_{i=1}^{n} \hat{y}_i}{\sum_{i=1}^{n} \hat{x}_i} \qquad \square$$

PROPOSITION 5.30 Let $x \in c_0 \sim \ell^1$ and $y \in \omega$. Then $y^\delta \supset x^\delta$ if and only if

$$\sup_n \frac{\sum_{i=1}^{n} \hat{y}_i}{\sum_{i=1}^{n} \hat{x}_i} < \infty \qquad (*)$$

Proof. If (*) holds, then $y \in S_{Q^*}$ from Theorem 5.29. But $S_{Q^*} = \lambda_N^* = \lambda_N^\beta = (x^\delta)^\beta = x^{\delta\delta}$ in view of Propositions 3.42, 3.9, and 2.7. Hence $y^\delta \supset x^{\delta\delta\delta} = x^\delta$.

If $y^\delta \supset x^\delta$, then $y \in y^{\delta\delta} \subset x^{\delta\delta} = S_{Q^*}$ and hence (*) follows from Theorem 5.29. $\square$

We now come to the desired

PROPOSITION 5.31 If $x^\delta = \ell^1$, then $x \in \ell^\infty \sim c_0$.

Proof. Let $x^\delta = \ell^1$. Then $x \in x^{\delta\delta} = \ell^\infty$. Assume that $x \in c_0$. If $y = e$, then $y^\delta = \ell^1$ by Proposition 5,25(v). Hence from Proposition 5.30,

$$\sup_n \frac{\sum_{i=1}^n \hat{y}_i}{\sum_{i=1}^n \hat{x}_i} < \infty$$

Here $\Sigma_{i=1}^n \hat{y}_i = n$, and therefore

$$\sup_n \frac{n}{\sum_{i=1}^n \hat{x}_i} < \infty$$

This is not possible, as

$$\inf_n \frac{\sum_{i=1}^n \hat{x}_i}{n} = \lim_{n\to\infty} \frac{1}{n} \sum_{i=1}^n \hat{x}_i = 0$$

Therefore $x \in \ell^\infty \sim c_0$. □

Next, let us consider only the duals of $x^\delta = \lambda_Q = S_Q$ ($Q \equiv Q_x$, $x \in c_0 \sim \ell^1$). By Propositions 2.7 and 3.9, the α-, β-, γ-, δ-, and the topological duals of x^δ are the same and they can further be identified with S_{Q*} (cf. Proposition 3.42). By Proposition 5.20, $S_{Q*} \subset c_0$, or $S_{Q*} = \ell^\infty$, or $S_{Q*} = \omega$. However, in view of Propositions 5.25 and 5.31 and the restriction on x, the possibilities that $S_{Q*} = \ell^\infty$ or ω are ruled out. Hence $S_{Q*} \subset c_0$. As far as the AK-character of S_{Q*} is concerned, we have the following result, essentially due to Garling [57, p. 98].

PROPOSITION 5.32 An element y in S_{Q*} has the AK-property if and only if

$$\frac{\sum_{i=1}^n \hat{y}_i}{\sum_{i=1}^n \hat{x}_i} \to 0 \qquad \text{as } n \to \infty \tag{*}$$

and *a fortiori* an element y in $(x^\delta)^*$ possesses the AK-property if and only if y satisfies (*).

Proof. As the convergence of the nth sections of an element y in S_{Q*} to y is equivalent to the convergence of $\{\hat{y}^{(n)}\}$ to $\hat{y}$ (cf. Exercise 5.36 given below), we need prove this result only for those y in S_{Q*} that are in the reduced form. So, let $y = \hat{y}$ be an arbitrary element in S_{Q*} and write

$$s_n = \sum_{i=1}^{n} \hat{x}_i \qquad \text{and} \qquad t_n = \sum_{i=1}^{n} \hat{y}_i$$

First, suppose (*) is not true. Then there exist $\varepsilon > 0$ and a sequence $\{n_i\} \subset \mathbb{N}$ such that $t_{n_i}/s_{n_i} > \varepsilon$ for all $i \geq 1$. Since $s_n \to \infty$, $t_n \to \infty$ with n (note that $\{t_n\}$ is increasing), for given $n > 0$ we can find i_0 in $\mathbb{N}$ such that $n_{i_0} > n$, $2t_n \leq t_{n_{i_0}}$, and $t_{n_{i_0}}/s_{n_{i_0}} > \varepsilon$. Then

$$Q^*(y - y^{(n)}) = \sup_p \frac{\sum_{i=1}^{p} \hat{y}_{n+i}}{\sum_{i=1}^{p} \hat{x}_i} = \sup_p \frac{t_{n+p} - t_n}{s_p}$$

$$\geq \frac{t_{n_{i_0}} - t_n}{s_{n_{i_0}-n}} \geq \frac{t_{n_{i_0}} - (1/2)t_{n_{i_0}}}{s_{n_{i_0}}} > \frac{1}{2}\varepsilon$$

The above inequality is true for any n in $\mathbb{N}$ and so $y^{(n)} \not\to y$. Therefore

$$y^{(n)} \to y \implies \frac{t_n}{s_n} \to 0$$

Conversely, let (*) be true and suppose $y^{(n)} \not\to y$. Since $\{Q^*(y^{(n)} - y)\}$ is monotonically decreasing and bounded, we may assume that

$$\mu = \lim_{n\to\infty} Q^*(y^{(n)} - y)$$

where $\mu > 0$. Then $Q^*(y) \geq Q^*(y^{(n)} - y) \geq \mu$ for every $n \geq 1$. As

$$Q^*(y) = \sup_n \frac{t_n}{s_n} \geq \mu$$

we find n_1 with $t_{n_1}/s_{n_1} \geq \mu/2$. But

$$Q^*(y - y^{(n_1)}) = \sup_p \frac{t_{n_1+p} - t_{n_1}}{s_p} \geq \mu$$

Therefore one finds $p > 0$ such that

$$\frac{t_{n_1+p} - t_{n_1}}{s_p} \geq \frac{1}{2}\mu$$

Now $s_p \geq s_{n_1+p} - s_n$; thus

$$\frac{1}{2}\mu \le \frac{t_{n_1+p} - t_{n_1}}{s_{n_1+p} - s_{n_1}}$$

If we write $n_2 = n_1 + p$, then $n_2 > n_1$ and

$$\frac{1}{2}\mu \le \frac{t_{n_2} - t_{n_1}}{s_{n_2} - s_{n_1}}$$

The preceding inequality along with $t_{n_1}/s_{n_1} \ge \mu/2$ implies that $t_{n_2}/s_{n_2} \ge \mu/2$. Proceeding in this manner, we obtain an increasing sequence $\{n_i\}$ such that $t_{n_i}/s_{n_i} \ge \mu/2$ for $i \ge 1$. However, this leads to a contradiction. □

Immediate consequences of the preceding result are the following corollaries.

COROLLARY 5.33 $x^{(n)} \not\to x$ in S_{Q^*} and so S_{Q^*} is not an AK-space.

COROLLARY 5.34 S_{Q^*} is not even an AD-space.

Proof. Otherwise, to each $\varepsilon > 0$, we find y in ϕ having length ℓ (say) such that $Q^*(x - y) < \varepsilon$. If $m \ge \ell$, then $Q^*(x - x^{(m)}) \le Q^*(x - y) < \varepsilon$, a contradiction. □

COROLLARY 5.35 S_Q and S_{Q^*} are not reflexive spaces and hence ℓ^p $(1 < p < \infty)$ cannot be expressed as S_{Q_x} for any x in $c_0 \sim \ell^1$.

Proof. The norm topology on S_{Q^*} is $\beta(S_{Q^*}, S_Q)$ (cf. Ref. 92, p. 202), and therefore S_Q is not reflexive, by Corollary 5.33 and Proposition 2.27; the nonreflexivity of S_{Q^*} is now a consequence of Proposition 1.9.5(ii). □

EXERCISE 5.36 For y in S_{Q^*}, show that $y^{(n)} \to y$ if and only if $\hat{y}^{(n)} \to \hat{y}$ in the norm Q^*. [Hint: For necessity (sufficiency), to $\varepsilon > 0$ choose n_0 and then m_0 in $\mathbb{N}$ such that $Q^*(y - y^{(n_0)}) < \varepsilon$ $[Q^*(\hat{y} - \hat{y}^{(n_0)}) < \varepsilon]$ and $|y_1|, \ldots, |y_{n_0}|$ $(\hat{y}_1, \ldots, \hat{y}_{n_0})$ are included in $\hat{y}_1, \ldots, \hat{y}_{m_0}$ $(|y_1|, \ldots, |y_{m_0}|)$; then for $m \ge m_0$, $Q^*(\hat{y} - \hat{y}^{(m)}) < \varepsilon$ $[Q^*(y - y^{(m)}) < \varepsilon]$.]

Remark: For $x \in c_0 \sim \ell^1$, the spaces S_Q and S_{Q^*} are not expressible as ℓ^p $(1 \le p \le \infty)$. Indeed, this fact is clear from Propositions 5.25, 5.31, and Corollary 5.35.

The final result of this subsection makes use of the following simple

EXERCISE 5.37 Let λ be a perfect symmetric space. Then show that $\lambda = \bigcup\{x^{\delta\delta} : x \in \lambda\} = \bigcup\{x^\delta : x^\delta \supset \lambda^\delta\} = \bigcap\{x^\delta : x \in \lambda^\delta\}$.

THEOREM 5.38 Let λ be a perfect symmetric BK-space relative to the norm $\|\cdot\|$. Then there exists a balanced symmetric, sequential norm N such that $\lambda = S_N$.

Proof. As λ is not ϕ or ω, it follows from Proposition 5.21 that $\ell^1 \subset \lambda \subset \ell^\infty$. If $\lambda = \ell^\infty$, then its usual sup norm is a balanced symmetric sequential norm N for which $S_N = \ell^\infty$. Therefore in view of Propositions 5.20 and 5.21, it is sufficient to prove the result for those λ that satisfy $\ell^1 \subset \lambda \subset c_0$.

From Exercise 5.37, $\lambda = \bigcap\{y^\delta : y \in \lambda^\delta\}$. Therefore $\lambda \subset y^\delta$ for each $y \in \lambda^\delta$. Applying Proposition 4.3.1, there exists a constant m_y such that

$$m_y Q_y(x) \le \|x\| \qquad x \in \lambda$$

Clearly

$$m_y Q_y(x) = \sum_{i\ge1} \widehat{m_y y_i} \hat{x}_i$$

Write

$$N = \sup\{m_y Q_y : y \in \lambda^\delta\}$$

As $m_y Q_y(e^i) = m_y Q_y(e^1) \le \|e^1\| < \infty$ for each $i \ge 1$ and each $y \in \lambda^\delta$, it follows from Exercise 3.39 that N is a balanced symmetric p.s.n. Also, $N(x) \le \|x\|$ for $x \in \lambda \Rightarrow \lambda \subset S_N$. On the other hand, $N(x) < \infty \Rightarrow x \in y^\delta$ for each $y \in \lambda^\delta$. Therefore $S_N \subset \lambda$. □

6. DUALITY BETWEEN PERFECT SPACES

As remarked in the beginning of Section 3, one of the easiest ways in which we can endow a sequence space λ with a natural locally convex topology is to consider the duality of λ with $\lambda^\times$ and λ^β. In this section we confine our attention to the duality of λ and $\lambda^\times$. It is advantageous to restrict λ to be a perfect space. Indeed, our attention will be directed toward specific perfect sequence spaces and their Köthe duals. As a consequence of the duality structure amongst these spaces and their Köthe duals, we get several polar topologies whose construction reveals a number of interesting features from the point of view of examples and counterexamples in the structural study of locally convex spaces and the theory of AK-spaces, the latter being of great use in the Schauder basis theory.

Since the weakly bounded subsets are the basic tools in the construction of polar topologies, we have therefore included in each subsection that follows, a characterization of such subsets for the perfect sequence space in question.

Duality between ϕ and ω

We require

DEFINITION 6.1 (i) The subscript of the last nonzero coordinate of an x in ϕ is said to be *length* of x, and (ii) a set $A \subset \phi$ is called of *bounded length* ℓ, if for each x in A, $x_i = 0$ for $i = \ell + 1, \ell + 2, \ldots$.

We have (cf. Refs. 34 and 84 for a generalization)

THEOREM 6.2 A subset B of ϕ is $\sigma(\phi,\omega)$-bounded if and only if

(i) There exist constants $r_i > 0$, $i \geq 1$, with $|x_i| \leq r_i$, for each x in B.

(ii) B is of bounded length.

Proof. (i) and (ii) readily imply the $\sigma(\phi,\omega)$-boundedness of B.

Assume therefore the $\sigma(\phi,\omega)$-boundedness of B. Thus for each $i \geq 1$ there corresponds an $r_i > 0$ with

$$q_{e^i}(x) \leq r_i \qquad \forall x \text{ in } B$$

and this gives (i).

If (ii) were not true, we would have gotten a subsequence $\{\ell_n\}$ from $\mathbb{N}$, $\ell_{n-1} < \ell_n \to \infty$ as $n \to \infty$, and a sequence $\{x^n\}$ from B, with

$$x_i^n = \begin{cases} 0 & \text{if } i > \ell_n,\ n \geq 1 \\ \text{nonzero} & \text{if } i = \ell_n \end{cases}$$

Let

$$u_i = \begin{cases} \dfrac{1}{x^1_{\ell_1}} & i = \ell_1 \\ 0 & 1 \leq i \leq \ell_1 - 1 \end{cases}$$

Then whatever be u_i for $i > \ell_1$, one has

$$\left| \sum_{i\geq 1} u_i x_i^1 \right| = |u_{\ell_1} x_{\ell_1}| = 1$$

Further,

$$\left| \sum_{i\geq 1} u_i x_i^2 \right| = \left| u_{\ell_1} x^2_{\ell_1} + \sum_{i=\ell_1+1}^{\ell_2} u_i x_i^2 \right|$$

Now choose u_i for $\ell_1 + 1 \leq i \leq \ell_2$ as follows

$$u_i = \begin{cases} \dfrac{2 + (r_{\ell_1}/|x^1_{\ell_1}|)}{x^2_{\ell_2}} & \text{if } i = \ell_2 \\ 0 & \text{if } \ell_1 + 1 \leq i \leq \ell_2 - 1 \end{cases}$$

Then

$$\left| \sum_{i\geq 1} u_i x_i^2 \right| \geq 2 + \frac{r_{\ell_1}}{|x^1_{\ell_1}|} - \frac{|x^2_{\ell_1}|}{|x^1_{\ell_1}|} \geq 2$$

since $|x^2_{\ell_1}| \leq r_{\ell_1}$ by (i). Note that the preceding inequality is valid for any value of u_i when $i > \ell_2$. Proceeding in this way we get a $u \in \omega$ for which

$$\left| \sum_{i\geq 1} u_i x_i^n \right| \geq n \qquad n \geq 1$$

However, this inequality contradicts the assumption that B is $\sigma(\phi,\omega)$-bounded, and so (ii) follows. □

PROPOSITION 6.3 We have

$$\sigma(\omega,\phi) = \eta(\omega,\phi) = \beta(\omega,\phi)$$

and each of the above topologies is the same as the topology of coordinatewise convergence on ω.

Proof. In view of the remarks following Definition 3.1 and Proposition 3.9, and Exercise 4.6, it is sufficient to establish that $\eta(\omega,\phi) \supset \beta(\omega,\phi)$. If A is any $\sigma(\phi,\omega)$-bounded subset of ϕ, then A is of bounded length ℓ and $|x_i| \leq r_i$, $i \geq 1$ (cf. Theorem 6.2 for notation). Let

$$R_\ell = \{r_1,\ldots,r_\ell,0,0,\ldots\}$$

Then

$$A \subset \{R_\ell\}^N$$

Therefore each 0-neighborhood in $\beta(\omega,\phi)$ contains a 0-neighborhood in $\eta(\omega,\phi)$. □

EXERCISE 6.4 (i) Prove that $(\omega,\sigma(\omega,\phi))$ is a Fréchet as well as a Montel space; (ii) show that ϕ is dense in $(\omega,\beta(\omega,\phi))$ and that $(\omega,\beta(\omega,\phi))^* = \phi$; (iii) if ϕ^* is the topological dual of $(\phi,\sigma(\phi,\phi))$, prove that $(\phi^*,\beta(\phi^*,\phi))^* = \phi$; (iv) prove that a set $B \subset \omega$ is $\sigma(\omega,\phi)$-bounded if and only if there exists a sequence $\{r_i\} \subset \mathbb{R}_+$ such that $|x_i| \leq r_i$, $i \geq 1$, for all $x \in B$; and (v) establish the nonbarreledness of $(\phi,\sigma(\phi,\omega))$. [Hints: For (i), observe that $\sigma(\omega,\phi)$ is generated by $\{q_{e^i}\}$ and use Theorem 5.1; the other part is a consequence of Tychnov's theorem. Part (ii) follows from the Hahn Banach theorem and Proposition 6.3; (v) follows from (iv) and Proposition 1.10.11.]

EXERCISE 6.5 Prove that $(\omega,\sigma(\omega,\phi))$ cannot have a continuous norm. [Hint: Use the fact that the coordinatewise convergence topology is the same as $\sigma(\omega,\phi)$.]

Remark: An alternative proof of Exercise 6.4(v) is to be found in Ref. 125.

PROPOSITION 6.6 One has

$$\sigma(\phi,\omega) \subsetneq \eta(\phi,\omega) = \beta(\phi,\omega)$$

and sequential convergence is the same in $(\phi,\sigma(\phi,\omega))$ and $(\phi,\beta(\phi,\omega))$.

Proof. If A is a $\sigma(\omega,\phi)$-bounded subset of ω, there exists $\{r_i\}$ [cf. Exercise 6.4(iv)] such that

$$A \subset \{r_i\}^N$$

This inclusion together with Proposition 4.3 yields the first part of the result, namely, $\eta(\phi,\omega) = \beta(\phi,\omega)$; for the other part, see Example 4.4. The last part follows by applying Corollary 4.12 and the first part proved above. □

After Woods [269, p. 20] we have

PROPOSITION 6.7 The space (ϕ,T), $T = \sigma(\omega,\phi)|\phi$, is a dense subspace of $(\omega,\beta(\omega,\phi))$ and it is not a W-space.

Proof. Because of Exercise 6.4(ii), we need prove that (ϕ,T) is not a W-space. It is clear that $\phi^* = \phi$. Let

$$A = \{x : x \in \phi,\ |x_n| \le \frac{1}{n},\ n \ge 1\}$$

and

$$B = \left\{\frac{n+1}{n} e^n : n \ge 1\right\}$$

Then A is absorbing, balanced, convex, and T-closed, and so it is a barrel in (ϕ,T). By Exercise 6.4(iv), B is T-bounded. If for some $\alpha > 0$, $B \subset \alpha A$, then $\alpha \ge n + 1$ for $n \ge 1$. Thus $\alpha = \infty$ and so B is not absorbed by A. Using Theorem 1.10.4(i), we conclude that (ϕ,T) is not a W-space. □

Duality between ℓ^1 and ℓ^∞

Let us begin with

PROPOSITION 6.8 A set $B \subset \ell^\infty$ is $\sigma(\ell^\infty,\ell^1)$-bounded if and only if there exists an $M > 0$ such that

$$|x_i| \le M \qquad \text{for all } x \text{ in } B \text{ and } i \ge 1$$

Proof. Suppose B is $\sigma(\ell^\infty,\ell^1)$-bounded. By Proposition 5.4, B is $\beta(\ell^\infty,\ell^1)$-bounded. Let $A = \{e^i\}$. Then A is $\sigma(\ell^1,\ell^\infty)$-bounded and so $B \subset MA°$ for some $M > 0$. This proves the "only if" part. For the converse, let $y \in \ell^1$. Then

$$q_y(x) \le M\|y\|_1 \qquad \forall x \text{ in } B$$

thereby forcing B to be $\sigma(\ell^\infty,\ell^1)$-bounded. □

PROPOSITION 6.9 A sequence $\{x^p\}$ in ℓ^1 is $\sigma(\ell^1,\ell^\infty)$-convergent if and only if it is $\beta(\ell^1,\ell^\infty)$-convergent; in particular, $\sigma(\ell^1,\ell^\infty)$- and $\beta(\ell^1,\ell^\infty)$-Cauchy sequences in ℓ^1 are the same.

Proof. Suppose $x^p \to x$ in $\sigma(\ell^1,\ell^\infty)$. By Corollary 4.12, $x^p \to x$ in $\eta(\ell^1,\ell^\infty)$. Therefore, to $\varepsilon > 0$ there corresponds an $N \equiv N(\varepsilon,e)$ in $\mathbb{N}$ such that

$$p_e(x^p - x) \le \varepsilon \qquad \forall p \ge N$$

Thus for any $\sigma(\ell^\infty,\ell^1)$-bounded subset B of ℓ^∞ we have (cf. Proposition 6.8)

$$x^p - x \in \varepsilon M B^\circ \qquad \forall p \ge N$$

and this gives the $\beta(\ell^1,\ell^\infty)$-convergence of $\{x^p\}$ to x. The converse is obvious. For the other part, one may refer back to Proposition 1.2.11. □

Let us now characterize $\sigma(\ell^1,\ell^\infty)$-bounded subsets of ℓ^1 by

PROPOSITION 6.10 A subset B of ℓ^1 is $\sigma(\ell^1,\ell^\infty)$-bounded if and only if there exists an $M > 0$ with

$$\sum_{i\ge1} |x_i| \le M \qquad \forall x \in B$$

In other words, a subset B of ℓ^1 is $\sigma(\ell^1,\ell^\infty)$-bounded if and only if it is $\beta(\ell^1,\ell^\infty)$-bounded.

Proof. By Proposition 1.2.9 and Corollary 4.12, $\sigma(\ell^1,\ell^\infty)$- and $\eta(\ell^1,\ell^\infty)$-boundedness are the same. Thus, given B to be $\sigma(\ell^1,\ell^\infty)$-bounded, there corresponds an $M > 0$ such that

$$p_e(x) \le M \qquad \forall x \text{ in } B$$

and the required inequality follows. The converse is straightforward. □

PROPOSITION 6.11 A subset B of ℓ^1 is $\sigma(\ell^1,\ell^\infty)$-compact if and only if it is $\beta(\ell^1,\ell^\infty)$-compact. Also, a $\sigma(\ell^1,\ell^\infty)$- or $\beta(\ell^1,\ell^\infty)$bounded subset B of ℓ^1

is $\sigma(\ell^1,\ell^\infty)$- or $\beta(\ell^1,\ell^\infty)$-relatively compact if and only if

$$\lim_{n\to\infty} \sup_{x\in B} \sum_{i\geq n} |x_i| = 0 \tag{*}$$

Proof. The first part of the proposition follows by combining Theorem 3.10 and Proposition 6.9. For the other part we may assume B to be either $\sigma(\ell^1,\ell^\infty)$-bounded or $\beta(\ell^1,\ell^\infty)$-bounded (cf. Proposition 6.10). Now assume in addition that B is $\sigma(\ell^1,\ell^\infty)$- or $\beta(\ell^1,\ell^\infty)$-relatively compact. If (*) is not true, then there corresponds an increasing sequence $\{n_k\}$ such that for some $\varepsilon > 0$,

$$A_{n_k} \geq \varepsilon > 0 \qquad k \geq 1, \text{ with } A_n = \sup_{x\in B} \sum_{i\geq n} |x_i|$$

Hence B contains a sequence $\{x^{n_k}\}$ such that

$$\sum_{i\geq n_k} |x_i^{n_k}| \geq \varepsilon \qquad \forall k \geq 1$$

Let $p_1 = n_1$. We can find $p_2 = n_{k_0}$ for some k_0 such that

$$\sum_{i\geq p_2} |x_i^{p_2}| \geq \varepsilon \qquad \text{and} \qquad \sum_{i\geq p_2} |x_i^{p_1}| < \frac{\varepsilon}{2}$$

Proceeding in this way we can find an increasing subsequence $\{p_k\}$ of $\{n_k\}$ such that

$$\sum_{i\geq p_k} |x_i^{p_k}| \geq \varepsilon \qquad \text{and} \qquad \sum_{i\geq p_{k+1}} |x_i^{p_k}| < \frac{\varepsilon}{2} \qquad k \geq 1$$

Hence

$$\sum_{i\geq 1} |x_i^{p_k} - x_i^{p_\ell}| > \frac{\varepsilon}{2} \qquad \forall k,\ell \geq 1$$

For otherwise, say for $k > \ell$ (similarly one can argue for $\ell > k$),

$$\sum_{i\geq p_k} |x_i^{p_k}| \leq \frac{\varepsilon}{2} + \sum_{i\geq p_k} |x_i^{p_\ell}| \leq \frac{\varepsilon}{2} + \sum_{i\geq p_{\ell+1}} |x_i^{p_\ell}| < \varepsilon$$

which gives a contradiction. Therefore $\{x^{p_k}\}$, which belongs to B, cannot converge in $(\ell^1,\beta(\ell^1,\ell^\infty))$, and this contradicts the fact that B is $\beta(\ell^1,\ell^\infty)$-relatively compact.

On the other hand, let (*) be satisfied for a subset B of ℓ^1 which is given to be $\sigma(\ell^1,\ell^\infty)$-bounded. It is clear that B is coordinatewise bounded. Suppose $\{x^n\} \subset B$ such that $\{x^n\}$ is coordinatewise convergent to x, i.e., $x^n \to x$ in $\sigma(\omega,\phi)|\ell^1$. Now, for $k \geq 1$,

$$\sum_{i\geq n} |x_i^k| \leq A_n \Longrightarrow \sum_{i\geq n} |x_i| \leq A_n$$

$$\Longrightarrow \sum_{i\geq n} |x_i^k - x_i| \leq 2A_n \qquad k,n \geq 1$$

Thus $x^n \to x$ in $\sigma(\ell^1,\ell^\infty)$. An application of Theorem 3.11 now yields the $\sigma(\ell^1,\ell^\infty)$-relative compactness of B. □

PROPOSITION 6.12 A net $\{x^\alpha\}$ in ℓ^∞ converges to x relative to $\beta(\ell^\infty,\ell^1)$ if and only if to each $\varepsilon > 0$ there corresponds an $\alpha_0 \equiv \alpha_0(\varepsilon)$ such that

$$|x_i^\alpha - x_i| \leq \varepsilon \qquad \forall i \geq 1,\ \alpha \geq \alpha_0 \tag{*}$$

Proof. Let the given condition (*) be true. Choose an arbitrary $\sigma(\ell^1,\ell^\infty)$-bounded subset A of ℓ^1. Invoking both the notation and the result of Proposition 6.10, one obtains

$$\left|\sum_{i\geq 1} (x_i^\alpha - x_i)y_i\right| \leq \varepsilon M$$

valid for all $\alpha \geq \alpha_0$ and $y \in A$, giving thus $x^\alpha - x \in \varepsilon M°$ for all $\alpha \geq \alpha_0$. □

EXERCISE 6.13 Prove that $\sigma(\ell^\infty,\ell^1) \neq \beta(\ell^\infty,\ell^1)$. [Hint: Apply Proposition 6.12 to conclude that $e^{(n)} \not\to e$ in $\beta(\ell^\infty,\ell^1)$; however, $e^{(n)} \to e$ in $\sigma(\ell^\infty,\ell^1)$.]

The following result, due to Levin and Saxon [149], distinguishes between C- and S-spaces in Definition 1.10.1.

PROPOSITION 6.14 The set $B = \{e^n : n \geq 1\}$ is $\sigma(\ell^1,\ell^\infty)$-bounded but is not $\sigma(\ell^1,\ell^\infty)$-relatively compact; consequently $(\ell^\infty,\tau(\ell^\infty,\ell^1))$ in an S-space but not a C-space.

Proof. In view of Theorem 5.1 and Proposition 6.10, we need show that B is not $\sigma(\ell^1,\ell^\infty)$-relatively compact. One readily finds that (*)

in Proposition 6.10 is not satisfied and thus B is not $\sigma(\ell^1,\ell^\infty)$-relatively compact. For the same proof we can also proceed directly as follows. Let $y \in \ell^1$. There exists an $N \equiv N(y,1/2)$ in $\mathbb{N}$ such that

$$\sum_{i\geq N+1} |y_i| < \frac{1}{2}$$

Define $z \in \ell^\infty$ by

$$z_i = \begin{cases} 0 & i \leq N \\ 2 & i \geq N+1 \end{cases}$$

Then $|\langle y,z\rangle| < 1$. Further, $|\langle e^n - y, z\rangle| \geq 2 - |\langle y,z\rangle| > 1$ for all $n \geq N+1$. Hence $e^n - y \in \{z\}^\circ$ for at most finitely many n in $\mathbb{N}$, and so y cannot be a $\sigma(\ell^1,\ell^\infty)$-limit point of B. □

COROLLARY 6.15 $(\ell^\infty,\tau(\ell^\infty,\ell^1))$ is not barreled and hence $(\ell^\infty,\beta(\ell^\infty,\ell^1))$ is not separable.

Proof. This follows from Propositions 1.10.2 and 1.10.14. □

COROLLARY 6.16 $(\ell^\infty,\tau(\ell^\infty,\ell^1))$ is a W-space without being infrabarreled.

Proof. Indeed, make use of Proposition 6.14 and Definition 1.10.1 to conclude the W-ness of the space; then combine Proposition 1.10.5 and Corollary 6.15. □

EXERCISE 6.17 Show that $(\ell^1,\eta(\ell^1,\ell^\infty))^* = \ell^\infty$ and hence prove that $\{e\}^N$ is $\sigma(\ell^\infty,\ell^1)$-compact. Also show that $e^{(n)} \to e$ in $\tau(\ell^\infty,\ell^1)$. [Hint: We have $\sigma \subset \eta \subset \beta$; $(\ell^1,\sigma(\ell^1,\ell^\infty))^* = \ell^\infty = (\ell^1,\beta(\ell^1,\ell^\infty))^*$. If $f \in \{e\}^N$ then $|f(x)| \leq p_e(x)$ for each x in ℓ^1, giving the $\eta(\ell^1,\ell^\infty)$-equicontinuity of $\{e\}^N$. Now apply the Alaoglu-Bourbaki theorem. For the last part, use Proposition 6.11.]

The last part of the previous exercise is contained in a more general result given below.

PROPOSITION 6.18 The space $(\ell^\infty,\tau(\ell^\infty,\ell^1))$ is semi-Montel.

Proof. We need show that each $\sigma(\ell^\infty,\ell^1)$-bounded subset B of ℓ^∞ is $\tau(\ell^\infty,\ell^1)$-relatively compact. This is accomplished by using Theorem 3.11.

Thus, let $\{x^n\} \subset B$ with $x_i^n \to x_i$, where $x \in \omega$. By Proposition 6.8, $|u_i| \le M$ for all $u \in B$ and $i \ge 1$, where $M > 0$. Hence $\sup\{|x_i| : i \ge 1\} \le M$ and so $x \in \ell^\infty$. Let A be an arbitrary balanced, convex, and $\sigma(\ell^1, \ell^\infty)$-compact subset of ℓ^1, and $\varepsilon > 0$. On account of Proposition 6.11 we can find an N in $\mathbb{N}$ such that

$$\sum_{i \ge N+1} |y_i| \le \frac{\varepsilon}{3M} \qquad \forall y \in A$$

Therefore for $y \in A$,

$$\begin{aligned} |\langle x^n - x, y\rangle| &\le \left|\sum_{i=1}^{N} (x_i^n - x_i)y_i\right| + \sum_{i \ge N+1} |x_i^n||y_i| + \sum_{i \ge N+1} |x_i||y_i| \\ &\le \sum_{i=1}^{N} |(x_i^n - x_i)||y_i| + \frac{2\varepsilon}{3} \end{aligned}$$

Since A is $\sigma(\ell^1, \ell^\infty)$-bounded,

$$\sum_{i=1}^{N} |y_i| \le K \qquad \forall y \in A$$

where $K > 0$. We can choose an n_0 in $\mathbb{N}$ such that

$$|x_i^n - x_i| \le \frac{\varepsilon}{3K} \qquad \forall n \ge n_0 \text{ and } 1 \le i \le N$$

Therefore

$$|\langle x^n - x, y\rangle| \le \varepsilon \qquad \forall n \ge n_0$$

uniformly in $y \in A$. Thus $x^n \to x$ in $\tau(\ell^\infty, \ell^1)$. Hence from Theorem 3.11, B is $\tau(\ell^\infty, \ell^1)$-relatively compact. □

Duality between ℓ^p and ℓ^q $(1 < p,q < \infty)$

We now consider ℓ^p and ℓ^q spaces with $p^{-1} + q^{-1} = 1$. The spirit in which the discussion of this section was initiated first requires us to prove

THEOREM 6.19 A subset B of ℓ^p is $\sigma(\ell^p, \ell^q)$-bounded if and only if there exists an M with

$$\sum_{i \ge 1} |x_i|^p \le M \qquad \forall x \text{ in } B \tag{6.20}$$

Proof. Necessity. We are given that B is $\sigma(\ell^p,\ell^q)$-bounded, and so by Proposition 5.4, B is $\beta(\ell^p,\ell^q)$-bounded. Assume that (6.20) does not hold. Let $\varepsilon > 0$ be chosen arbitrarily and fixed. We can find an x^1 in B such that

$$\sum_{i\geq 1} |x_i^1|^p > 1 + \varepsilon$$

and an n_1 in $\mathbb{N}$ with

$$\sum_{i\geq n_1+1} |x_i^1|^p \leq \varepsilon$$

Then

$$s_1 \equiv \sum_{i=1}^{n_1} |x_i^1|^p > 1$$

Similarly we can find an x^2 in B and an integer $n_2 > n_1$ such that

$$s_2 \equiv \sum_{i=1}^{n_2} |x_i^2|^p > 2^p$$

Proceeding in this way, one thus obtains a sequence $\{x^k\} \subset B$ and an increasing sequence $\{n_k\} \subset \mathbb{N}$ such that

$$s_k \equiv \sum_{i=1}^{n_k} |x_i^k|^p > k^p \qquad k \geq 1$$

For every $k \geq 1$, define $y^k \in \omega$ by

$$y_i^k x_i^k = \frac{|x_i^k|^p}{s_k^{1/q}} \qquad 1 \leq i \leq n_k$$

and

$$y_i^k = 0 \qquad i > n_k$$

Then

$$\sum_{i\geq 1} |y_i^k|^q = \sum_{i=1}^{n_k} \frac{|x_i^k|^{(p-1)q}}{s_k} = 1$$

for $k \geq 1$. Therefore $\{y^k\} \subset \ell^q$ and is $\sigma(\ell^q,\ell^p)$-bounded. Now

$$\left|\sum_{i\geq 1} x_i^k y_i^k\right| = \sum_{i=1}^{n_k} \frac{|x_i^k|^p}{s_k^{1/q}} = s_k^{1/p} > k$$

and thus B is not $\beta(\ell^p,\ell^q)$-bounded. Consequently (6.20) must be true.

The other part follows by an application of the well-known Hölder's inequality for infinite sums. □

EXERCISE 6.21 Prove that the unit ball in ℓ^2 is $\sigma(\ell^2,\ell^2)$-bounded but is not totally bounded in the norm of ℓ^2.

EXERCISE 6.22 Show that $\sigma(\ell^p,\ell^q) \neq \beta(\ell^p,\ell^q)$, where $p > 1$, $1/p + 1/q = 1$. [Hint: $\{e^n\}$ is weakly convergent to zero in ℓ^p but it is not even $\beta(\ell^p,\ell^q)$-Cauchy; indeed, $q_A(e^n - e^m) = 1$, where $A = \{e^i\}$ and $n > m$.]

Duality between δ *and* d

By Proposition 5.4, $\sigma(\delta,d)$- and $\beta(\delta,d)$-bounded subsets of δ are the same. From now on, we will call a subset B of δ just bounded if it is T-bounded, where T is any locally convex topology on δ satisfying $\sigma(\delta,d) \subset T \subset \beta(\delta,d)$.

Following Toeplitz [253, p. 226] we have

PROPOSITION 6.23 A subset $B \subset \delta$ is bounded if and only if

(i) B is $\sigma(\delta,\phi)$-bounded.

(ii) To every $\varepsilon > 0$ there exists an $n_0 \equiv n_0(\varepsilon)$ in $\mathbb{N}$ such that

$$|x_n| \leq \varepsilon^n \qquad \forall n \geq n_0 \text{ and } x \text{ in } B$$

Proof. Let the conditions (i) and (ii) be satisfied. Choose an arbitrary element y from d. Then for a suitable $\varepsilon > 0$, there exists an $n_1 \equiv n_1(\varepsilon)$ such that $|y_n| \leq (2\varepsilon)^{-n}$ for $n \geq n_1$. If $n_2 = \max\{n_1,n_0\}$ then

$$\sum_{i\geq n_2} |x_i y_i| \leq \sum_{i\geq 1} \frac{1}{2^i} \qquad \forall x \text{ in } B$$

Because of (i) there exists a constant $M \equiv M(n_2) > 0$ such that

$$\sum_{i=1}^{n_2-1} |x_i y_i| \leq M$$

Thus B is $\sigma(\delta,d)$-bounded.

On the other hand, let B be $\sigma(\delta,d)$-bounded. (i) is then readily verified. To verify (ii), suppose it is not satisfied. Then for some $\varepsilon > 0$, an increasing sequence $\{n_k\}$, and a sequence $\{x^k\} \subset B$, we have

$$|x^k_{n_k}| > \varepsilon^{n_k} \qquad k \geq 1$$

Define $y \in \omega$ by

$$y_n = \begin{cases} \dfrac{n_k}{|x^k_{n_k}|} & n = n_k \\ 0 & n \neq n_k \end{cases}$$

Then $y \in d$ and

$$p_y(x^k) \geq |x^k_{n_k}|\,|y_k| = n_k$$

Therefore B is not $\eta(\delta,d)$-bounded and so it is not $\sigma(\delta,d)$-bounded. This contradiction proves (ii). □

Following the proof of Proposition 6.23, replacing ε by $1/r$ ($r < \infty$), one can prove the following result of Toeplitz [253].

EXERCISE 6.24 Prove that a subset $B \subset \Pi_r$ is $\sigma(\Pi_r, d_{1/r})$-bounded if and only if

(i) B is $\sigma(\Pi_r, \phi)$-bounded.

(ii) To each $\varepsilon > 0$ there exists an $n_0 \equiv n_0(\varepsilon)$ in $\mathbb{N}$ such that

$$|x_n| \leq \left(\frac{1}{r} + \varepsilon\right)^n \qquad \forall n \geq n_0 \text{ and } x \text{ in } B$$

Remark: The sequence space $(\delta, \sigma(\delta,d))$ is simple, as can be seen from the following result of Toeplitz [253, p. 228].

PROPOSITION 6.25 A set $B \subset \delta$ is $\sigma(\delta,d)$-bounded if and only if there exists a $y \in \delta$ with $y \geq 0$ such that

$$|x_n| \leq y_n \qquad \forall x \in B \text{ and } n \geq 1 \tag{*}$$

Proof. If (*) holds then the singleton $\{y\}$ is $\sigma(\delta,d)$-bounded by the previous result and therefore so is the set B.

Let us now assume that B is $\sigma(\delta,d)$-bounded. Put

$$y_n = \sup\{|x_n| : x \in B\}$$

By (ii) of Proposition 6.23, for each $\varepsilon > 0$,

$$y_n \le \varepsilon^n \qquad \forall n \ge n_0 \equiv n_0(\varepsilon)$$

$$\Longrightarrow \quad \lim_{n\to\infty} y_n^{1/n} = 0$$

Therefore $y \in \delta$ and (*) follows. □

EXERCISE 6.26 Show that a subset B of Π_r is $\sigma(\Pi_r,d_{1/r})$-bounded if and only if there exists a y in Π_r with $y \ge 0$ such that

$$|x_n| \le y_n \qquad \forall x \text{ in B and } n \ge 1$$

Note: For results on boundedness of subsets in certain spaces of entire functions, which we may regard as subspaces of certain sequence spaces or matrix spaces, we refer the reader to Refs. 78, 80, 119, 120, and 146.

Let us pass on to the characterization of bounded subsets of d_r $(r \ge 0)$. Accordingly, we have (cf. Ref. 253)

PROPOSITION 6.27 A subset B of d_r $(r \ge 0)$ is $\sigma(d_r,\Pi_{1/r})$-bounded if and only if

(i) B is $\sigma(d_r,\phi)$-bounded.

(ii) There exist an $\varepsilon > 0$ and an $n_0 \equiv n_0(\varepsilon)$ such that

$$|x_n| \le (r + \varepsilon)^{-n} \qquad \forall x \text{ in B and } n \ge n_0$$

Proof. First assume that B is $\sigma(d_r,\Pi_{1/r})$-bounded. Then (i) clearly follows. Suppose (ii) is not satisfied. Consequently there exist a sequence $\{x^k\} \subset B$ corresponding to $\{1/k\}$ and an increasing sequence $\{n_k\}$ such that

$$|x^k_{n_k}| > \left(r + \frac{1}{k}\right)^{-n_k} \qquad k \ge 1$$

Define $y \in \omega$ by

$$y_n = \begin{cases} \dfrac{n_k}{|x^k_{n_k}|} & n = n_k \\ 0 & n \neq n_k \end{cases}$$

One easily verifies that $y \in \Pi_{1/r}$. Now

$$p_y(x^k) \geq n_k \to \infty \qquad \text{as } k \to \infty$$

Therefore B is not $\eta(d_r,\Pi_{1/r})$-bounded. By Corollary 4.12, B is not $\sigma(d_r,\Pi_{1/r})$-bounded. This contradiction proves (ii).

On the other hand, let (i) and (ii) be satisfied. Choose an arbitrary member y of $\Pi_{1/r}$. Let $0 < \varepsilon_1 < \varepsilon$. There exists an $n_1 \equiv n_1(\varepsilon_1)$ in $\mathbb{N}$ such that

$$|y_n| < (r + \varepsilon_1)^n \qquad n \geq n_1$$

If $n_2 = \max\{n_0,n_1\}$, then

$$\sum_{n\geq n_2} |x_n y_n| \leq \sum_{i\geq 1} \left(\frac{r + \varepsilon_1}{r + \varepsilon}\right)^i \qquad \forall x \in B$$

It remains only to use (i) to conclude the $\eta(d_r,\Pi_{1/r})$-boundedness of B. □

Finally, we have

EXERCISE 6.28 Prove that a set $B \subset d_r$ $(r \geq 0)$ is $\sigma(d_r,\Pi_{1/r})$-bounded if and only if there exists a $y \in d_r$ with $y \geq 0$ such that

$$|x_n| \leq y_n \qquad \forall x \in B \text{ and } n \geq 1$$

Sometimes more useful is

EXERCISE 6.29 Prove that a set $B \subset d_r$ is $\sigma(d_r,\Pi_{1/r})$-bounded if and only if there exist $\alpha > 0$ and R with $0 < R < 1/r$ such that $|x_n| \leq \alpha R^n$ for all $x \in B$ and $n \geq 1$.

7. DUALITY BETWEEN NONPERFECT SPACES

The motivation for this section is the same as outlined in the beginning of the last section. This time we confine our attention to the duality structure of λ with $\lambda^{\times}$ and λ^{β} when λ is not perfect. In the process of investigation we obtain several concrete examples which turn out to be very useful for many purposes in functional analysis, especially to provide a stock of counterexamples for numerous problems related to the structural study of locally convex spaces and the Schauder basis theory therein.

Duality between c_0 *and* ℓ^1

The $\mathcal{S}$-topologies derived from the duality between c_0 and ℓ^1 possess strikingly interesting properties. Let us begin with one of the most commonly used results, namely

PROPOSITION 7.1 The space $(c_0, \sigma(c_0, \ell^1))$ is not sequentially complete.

Proof. One may use Theorem 5.1 to obtain this result, or give a direct proof as follows. Consider the sequence $\{e^{(n)}\}$ in c_0. Then for any y in ℓ^1,

$$q_y(e^{(n)} - e^{(m)}) \le \sum_{i=m+1}^{n} |y_i| \qquad n > m$$

Hence $\{e^{(n)}\}$ is $\sigma(c_0, \ell^1)$-Cauchy in c_0. If $e^{(n)} \to x$ in $(c_0, \sigma(c_0, \ell^1))$ for some $x \in c_0$, it follows that

$$q_{e^i}(e^{(n)} - x) \to 0 \qquad \text{as } n \to \infty, \text{ for each } i \ge 1$$

$$\Longrightarrow \quad |1 - x_i| = 0 \qquad \forall i \ge 1$$

Therefore $x = e \notin c_0$. Thus the Cauchy sequence $\{e^{(n)}\}$ does not converge in $(c_0, \sigma(c_0, \ell^1))$. □

EXERCISE 7.2 If T denotes the usual sup norm topology on c_0, show that $\tau(c_0, \ell^1) = T$. [Hint: T is compatible with $\langle c_0, \ell^1 \rangle$ and so $\sigma(c_0, \ell^1) \subset T \subset \tau(c_0, \ell^1)$; however, $\beta(c_0, \ell^1) = T$.]

The next result is due to Garling [56].

PROPOSITION 7.3 The norm topology T on ℓ^1 defines the same convergent sequences as the Mackey topology $\tau(\ell^1,c_0)$. Consequently, the norm bounded sets in ℓ^1 are the same as $\sigma(\ell^1,c_0)$-bounded sets.

Proof. Here we are confining our attention to the dual system $<\ell^1,c_0>$. Clearly $\tau(\ell^1,c_0) \subset T$. To prove the reverse inclusion, let $\{x^n\}$ be a sequence in ℓ^1 such that $x^n \to 0$ in $\tau(\ell^1,c_0)$ and $\inf\|x^n\| = \alpha > 0$, where $\|\cdot\|$ is the usual norm on ℓ^1. We can find a subsequence $\{y^k\}$ of $\{x^n\}$ and an increasing sequence $\{n_k\}$ of nonnegative integers with $n_1 = 0$ such that

$$\sum_{i=n_k+1}^{n_{k+1}} |y_i^k| \geq \frac{1}{2}\alpha \qquad \forall k \geq 1$$

Define $\{f^k\} \subset c_0$ by the relation

$$f_i^k = \begin{cases} \dfrac{\overline{y^k}}{|y_i^k|} & n_k < i \leq n_{k+1} \\ 0 & \text{otherwise} \end{cases}$$

Obviously $f^k \to 0$ in $\sigma(c_0,\ell^1)$ and so $B = \{f^k : k \geq 1\} \cup \{0\}$ is $\sigma(c_0,\ell^1)$-compact. Let A be the S-closed balanced convex hull of B in c_0, S being the sup norm topology on c_0. Using Exercise 7.2 we find that $(c_0,\tau(c_0,\ell^1))$ is complete [as $S = \tau(c_0,\ell^1)$] and therefore A is $\tau(c_0,\ell^1)$-complete. By Theorem 1.11.9, A is $\sigma(c_0,\ell^1)$-compact [in the theorem referred to, replace (X,T) by (c_0,S)]. Now

$$q_{f^k}(y^k) = \left|\sum_{i=n_k+1}^{n_{k+1}} y_i^k \frac{\overline{y_i^k}}{|y_i^k|}\right| \geq \frac{1}{2}\alpha > \frac{1}{4}\alpha$$

for all $k \geq 1$; therefore $(4/\alpha)y^k \notin A^\circ$, $k \geq 1$, and so $y^k \not\to 0$ in $\tau(\ell^1,c_0)$. Since $\{y^k\}$ is a subsequence of $\{x^n\}$, this leads to a contradiction. For the last part, use Theorem 1.7.16. □

COROLLARY 7.4 Sequential convergence in $(\ell^1,\tau(\ell^1,\ell^\infty))$ is the same as in $(\ell^1,\beta(\ell^1,c_0))$.

Remark: A result of Grothendieck and Kalton [108, p. 74] implies a result which includes Proposition 7.3 as a special case.

A frequently used result is

PROPOSITION 7.5 $(c_0,\sigma(c_0,\ell^1))$ is a W-space which is not infrabarreled and a fortiori not barreled.

Proof. If B is a $\sigma(c_0,\ell^1)$-bounded subset of c_0 then it is also $\tau(c_0,\ell^1)$-bounded. By Exercise 7.2, B is $\beta(c_0,\ell^1)$-bounded. Thus the first part is proved. Since ℓ^1 is of uncountable dimension, $\sigma(c_0,\ell^1)$ cannot be metrizable. Therefore $\sigma(c_0,\ell^1) \subsetneq \tau(c_0,\ell^1)$ and consequently $(c_0,\sigma(c_0,\ell^1))$ is not infrabarreled [cf. Proposition 1.10.7(i)]. The last part follows from Proposition 1.10.5. □

A widely used result in Schauder basis theory is (cf. Ref. 124)

PROPOSITION 7.6 $(\ell^1,\tau(\ell^1,c_0))$ is sequentially barreled and hence a W-space but is not an S-space; also, this space is not σ-infrabarreled and hence not σ-barreled.

Proof. The space $(c_0,\tau(c_0,\ell^1))$ is sequentially complete (cf. Exercise 7.2), and therefore from Proposition 1.10.12, the space $\ell^1 = (c_0,\tau(c_0,\ell^1))^*$ is $\tau(\ell^1,c_0)$-sequentially barreled; the W-ness of the space also follows from the same proposition. The third part of the result follows by applying Proposition 7.1. To disprove the σ-infrabarreledness of the given space, consider the sequence $\{e^{(n)}\} \subset c_0$. Then $\{e^{(n)}\}$ is $\beta(c_0,\ell^1)$-bounded (i.e., norm bounded in c_0). The sequence $\{e^{(n)}\}$ is not $\tau(\ell^1,c_0)$-equicontinuous on ℓ^1. For, if $\{e^{(n)}\}$ were $\tau(\ell^1,c_0)$-equicontinuous, the sequence $\{e^{(n)}\}$ would be $\sigma(c_0,\ell^1)$-relatively compact by the Alaoglu-Bourbaki theorem 1.7.12. In particular, $\{e^{(n)}\}$ would contain a subsequence which would converge to an element of $(c_0,\sigma(c_0,\ell^1))$. Since $\{e^{(n)}\}$ is $\sigma(c_0,\ell^1)$-Cauchy (cf. proof of Proposition 7.1), there follows the convergence of $\{e^{(n)}\}$ in $(c_0,\sigma(c_0,\ell^1))$. However, this is not true. □

Remark: The last part of the preceding result is explained in Ref. 95; indeed, see Ref. 149, p. 102.

EXERCISE 7.7 Show that $(\ell^1, \tau(\ell^1, c_0))$ is a W-space by using Proposition 1.10.6. Also, prove that this space is semireflexive without being reflexive.

PROPOSITION 7.8 The space $(\ell^1, \sigma(\ell^1, c_0))$ is quasicomplete, and hence sequentially complete, but not complete.

Proof. For the first part use Theorem 1.8.6. From Grothendieck's completion theorem 1.11.6 (where we take $X = c_0$ and T the usual sup norm topology on c_0) the completion of $(\ell^1, \sigma(\ell^1, c_0))$ is the space c_0'. Now $\phi \subsetneq c_0$; hence there exists an $f \in c_0'$ (see p. 19 of Ref. 264) such that ($\{1/n\} \in c_0$ but $\notin \phi$)

$$f\left(\left\{\frac{1}{n}\right\}\right) = 1 \qquad \text{and} \qquad f(x) = 0 \qquad \forall x \in \phi$$

Thus f cannot be continuous on $c_0 = \bar{\phi}$, the T-closure of ϕ in c_0. Consequently $\ell^1 = c_0^* \subsetneq c_0'$. □

Duality between k *and* ℓ^1

Let us recall that the balanced convex hull ΓA of a compact subset A of a TVS X is not necessarily compact. For instance, consider the space $(\phi, \sigma(\phi, \ell^\infty))$ and its subset $A = \{(1/n)e^n : n \geq 1\}$. The set $\{A, 0\}$ is clearly $\sigma(\phi, \ell^\infty)$-compact. The sequence $\{y^n\}$, where

$$y^n = \sum_{i=1}^{n} \frac{\lambda_i}{i} e^i \qquad \text{with } \lambda_i > 0, \ \sum_{i \geq 1} \lambda_i \leq 1$$

is contained in $\Gamma\{A, 0\}$. It is easily verified that $\{y^n\}$ is $\sigma(\phi, \ell^\infty)$-Cauchy but does not converge in $(\phi, \sigma(\phi, \ell^\infty))$. Hence $\Gamma\{A, 0\}$ is not compact in $(\phi, \sigma(\phi, \ell^\infty))$.

In contrast to the above situation we have

PROPOSITION 7.9 The set

$$A = \{y^n : n \geq 1\} \cup \{0\} \qquad y^n = e^n - e^{n+1}, \ n \geq 1$$

is compact in $(\ell^1, \sigma(\ell^1, k))$ and so is the set $\overline{\Gamma A}$.

Proof. The first part is obvious. For the remaining part, first let us observe that

$$\overline{A} = \left\{\{\beta_1, \beta_2 - \beta_1, \ldots, \beta_n - \beta_{n-1}, -\beta_n, 0, 0, \ldots\} : \sum_{i=1}^{n} |\beta_i| \leq 1, 1 \leq n < \infty\right\}$$

where $\beta_0 = 0$. By Theorem 3.11, the set $\overline{A}$ is $\sigma(\omega,\phi)$-relatively compact in ω and so this set is $\sigma(\omega,\phi)$-relatively sequentially compact. Let now $\{a^p\}$ be an arbitrary sequence in $\overline{A}$. Then there exists a subsequence of $\{a^p\}$ which we denote by $\{a^p\}$ again, such that $a^p \to a$ in $\sigma(\omega,\phi)$. To prove the $\sigma(\ell^1,k)$-relative sequential compactness of $\overline{A}$, it is sufficient to establish that $a \in \ell^1$ and $a^p \to a$ in $\sigma(\ell^1,k)$. It is clear that $\Sigma_{i\geq 1}|a_i| \leq 2$ and so $a \in \ell^1$. Let $\alpha e + x$ be an arbitrary element of k where $\alpha \in \mathbb{K}$ and $x \in \phi$. Then under the usual bilinear functional $\langle\cdot,\cdot\rangle$ for the system $\langle\ell^1,k\rangle$,

$$\langle a^p - a, \alpha e + x\rangle = \langle a^p, x\rangle - \langle a, \alpha e + x\rangle = \langle a^p - a, x\rangle - \alpha \sum_{i\geq 1} a_i$$

since for each $p \geq 1$, $\Sigma_{i\geq 1} a_i^p = 0$. Next we show that $\Sigma_{i\geq 1} a_i = 0$. Suppose $\beta_n = \Sigma_{i=1}^n a_i$. Then $\beta_n = \lim_{p\to\infty} \Sigma_{i=1}^n a_i^p = \lim_{p\to\infty} \beta_n^p$, since

$$a^p = \{\beta_1^p, \beta_2^p - \beta_1^p, \ldots, \beta_n^p - \beta_{n-1}^p, -\beta_n^p, 0, 0, \ldots\}$$

Therefore, for each $M \geq 1$,

$$\sum_{n=1}^{M} |\beta_n^p| \xrightarrow{p} \sum_{n=1}^{M} |\beta_n|$$

But for all $M \geq 1$ and $p \geq 1$, $\Sigma_{n=1}^M |\beta_n^p| \leq 1$, and thus $\{\beta_n\} \in \ell^1$, and so $\beta_n \to 0$ as $n \to \infty$. Consequently,

$$\langle a^p - a, \alpha e + x\rangle = \langle a^p - a, x\rangle$$

where the right-hand side clearly tends to zero as $p \to \infty$, and so $a^p \to a$ in $(\ell^1,\sigma(\ell^1,k))$. This finishes the proof of $\sigma(\ell^1,k)$-relative sequential compactness of $\overline{A}$. We are done if we apply Theorem 3.11 once again. □

Remark: The preceding result is essentially due to Dubinsky and Retherford [46] who used this result for a different purpose in Schauder basis theory.

EXERCISE 7.10 Prove the compactness of $\overline{\Gamma A'}$ in Proposition 7.9 without using Theorem 3.11. [Hint: Use Exercise 6.4, part (iv), to conclude $\sigma(\omega,\phi)$-boundedness of $\Gamma A'$, and use part (i) of the same exercise for its relative compactness; now take a net $\{a^{\nu}\}$ in $\Gamma A'$ and proceed as above.]

EXERCISE 7.11 Prove that (i) $e^{(n)} \to e$ in $(k,\sigma(k,\ell^1))$ but $e^{(n)} \not\to e$ in $(k,\tau(k,\ell^1))$, and thus $\sigma(k,\ell^1) \subsetneq \tau(k,\ell^1)$; (ii) $(k,\tau(k,\ell^1))$ is not sequentially complete; (iii) $(\ell^1,\sigma(\ell^1,k))$ is not sequentially complete; and (iv) $(\ell^1,\sigma(\ell^1,k))$ is not barreled. [Hint: For (i) observe that $\langle e^{(n)} - e, e^n - e^{n+1}\rangle = 1$, $n \geq 1$, and use Proposition 7.9; for (iii) take $\alpha_n = (-1)^{n+1}/n$ and show that $\{\Sigma_{i=1}^n \alpha_i e^i\}$ is $\sigma(\ell^1,k)$-Cauchy but does not converge in $(\ell^1,\sigma(\ell^1,k))$; and for (iv), consider the set $A = \{e^n\}$, which is $\sigma(k,\ell^1)$-bounded but not finite dimensional, and use Proposition 1.10.11.]

Duality between ℓ^p $(0 < p < 1)$ *and* ℓ^∞

The structure of an ℓ^p $(p \geq 1)$ is well known. On the other hand, not so much is known about the space ℓ^p when $0 < p < 1$. Recent investigations by Shapiro [234] and Stiles [241] have revealed a number of interesting properties of ℓ^p $(0 < p < 1)$. In this subsection we single out only those that are relevant to our further work, especially properties that are useful for investigating the failure of the famous weak basis theorem in Schauder basis theory (cf. Ref. 125). Let us remind the reader that ℓ^p $(0 < p < 1)$ can be endowed with its natural paranorm $|\cdot|_p$, where

$$|x|_p = \sum_{i\geq 1} |x_i|^p \qquad x \text{ in } \ell^p \ (0 < p < 1)$$

Throughout this subsection we assume that ℓ^p $(0 < p < 1)$ is equipped with this paranorm, and we shall write T_p for the topology on ℓ^p generated by $|\cdot|_p$.

PROPOSITION 7.12 $(\ell^p,|\cdot|_p)$ is a complete p-normed (and therefore locally bounded) space, and $(\ell^p)^\times = (\ell^p)^* = \ell^\infty$, where $0 < p \leq 1$.

Proof. The proof of this result runs precisely as in the case of ℓ^1. □

Note: One may look into into Ref. 140 or Ref. 205 for the above proof.

Shapiro [233, p. 45] and Stiles [241, p. 412] independently proved the following result whose analog for ℓ^1 is well known (for instance, see Ref. 140, p. 280). This result also appears partially in Ref. 234, p. 371.

PROPOSITION 7.13 Every separable locally bounded F-space X is isomorphic to a quotient of ℓ^p, $0 < p < 1$.

Proof. By Proposition 1.4.9, there exists a p-norm on X, which we denote by $|\cdot|_p$ once again, for some p with $0 < p < 1$, such that $|\cdot|_p$ generates the topology of X. The separability property of X permits us to choose a sequence $\{x_n\}$ in $S = \{x : x \in X, |x|_p \le 1\}$ such that $\{x_n\}$ is dense in S. If $\alpha \in \ell^p$, then for $m \le n$ in $\mathbb{N}$,

$$\left|\sum_{i=m}^{n} \alpha_i x_i\right|_p \le \sum_{i=m}^{n} |\alpha_i x_i|_p \le \sum_{i=m}^{n} |\alpha_i|^p \to 0 \qquad \text{as } m,n \to \infty$$

Hence there exists a uniquely defined element x in X with

$$x = \sum_{i\ge1} \alpha_i x_i \quad .$$

Consequently there exists a linear map $T: \ell^p \to X$,

$$T(\alpha) = \sum_{i\ge1} \alpha_i x_i$$

which is continuous also, since $|T(\alpha)|_p \le |\alpha|_p$. The map T is also onto. Indeed, if $x \in X$ is chosen arbitrarily with $|x|_p \le 1$ then one may find a subsequence $\{x_{n_k}\}$ inductively with the property that

$$|x - (x_{n_1} + 2^{-1}x_{n_2} + \cdots + 2^{-(k-1)}x_{n_k})|_p < 2^{-kp}$$

Define $\beta \in \ell^p$ by

$$\beta_i = \begin{cases} 2^{-(k-1)} & i = n_k,\ k \ge 1 \\ 0 & i \ne n_k,\ k \ge 1 \end{cases}$$

Then

$$T(\beta) = \lim_{N\to\infty} \sum_{k=1}^{N} 2^{-(k-1)} x_{n_k} = x$$

and so T is onto. If M denotes the kernel of T, we easily find that the map ψ: $\ell^p/M \to X$, $\psi(\hat{\alpha}) = T(\alpha)$, is a topological isomorphism between ℓ^p/M and X. □

The next two results are due to Shapiro [234, p. 372] and Stiles [241, p. 413]; however, Shapiro's version of Proposition 7.14, which follows next, is more general than that of Stiles.

PROPOSITION 7.14 For each p, $0 < p < 1$, the space ℓ^p contains a proper closed subspace M such that if $f \in (\ell^p)^*$ vanishes on M then $f \equiv 0$.

Proof. It is well known (cf. Ref. 140) that $L^p \equiv L^p[0,1]$, $0 < p < 1$, is a separable locally bounded non-locally-convex F-space. Invoking both the notation and the result in Proposition 7.13, replacing therein X by L^p, we find that the functional $\hat{f}$ defined on ℓ^p/M by $\hat{f}(\hat{\alpha}) = f(\alpha)$ is continuous on ℓ^p/M. Hence $\hat{f} \circ \psi^{-1} \in (L^p)^*$, which in turn implies that $f \equiv 0$, since $(L^p)^* = \{0\}$. □

Using Proposition 1.6.2, there follows

COROLLARY 7.15 The space ℓ^p $(0 < p < 1)$ is not locally convex.

COROLLARY 7.16 For each p, $0 < p < 1$, ℓ^p contains a proper closed subspace M such that M is $\sigma(\ell^p,\ell^\infty)$-dense in ℓ^p.

PROPOSITION 7.17 Let $0 < p < 1$. The topology $\tau(\ell^p,\ell^\infty)$ is metrizable and $(\ell^p,\tau(\ell^p,\ell^\infty))$ is not sequentially complete; moreover, $\tau(\ell^p,\ell^\infty)) \subsetneq T_p$ and $\tau(\ell^p,\ell^\infty)$ is the norm topology T_1 of ℓ^1.

Proof. But for the last part, the result follows from Propositions 1.8.8 and 1.8.9, since ℓ^p is not locally convex (Corollary 7.15). In view of Propositions 7.12, 1.8.8, and Theorem 1.4.10, the space $(\ell^p,\tau(\ell^p,\ell^\infty))$ is normable. □

Duality between ℓ^1 and m_0

Hereafter in this subsection we consider only the dual system $\langle\ell^1,m_0\rangle$. The most useful result is the following (compare this with Proposition 6.9).

PROPOSITION 7.18 Convergence of sequences in ℓ^1 relative to $\sigma(\ell^1,m_0)$ and the usual norm $\|\cdot\|_1$ of ℓ^1 is the same. Therefore, $(\ell^1,\sigma(\ell^1,m_0))$ is sequentially complete.

Proof. Suppose there is a sequence $\{x^n\} \subset \ell^1$ such that $x^n \to 0$ in $\sigma(\ell^1,m_0)$ but $\|x^n\|_1 \not\to 0$. Hence for some $\varepsilon > 0$ there exists an increasing sequence $\{n_k\} \subset \mathbb{N}$ such that

$$\sum_{i\geq 1} |x_i^{n_k}| > \varepsilon \qquad k \geq 1$$

Let $m_1 = n_1$ and choose $N_1 \equiv N_1(m_1,\varepsilon)$ in $\mathbb{N}$ with

$$\sum_{i\geq N_1+1} |x_i^{m_1}| < \frac{\varepsilon}{15}$$

Thus

$$\sum_{i=1}^{N_1} |x_i^{m_1}| > \varepsilon - \frac{\varepsilon}{15} = \frac{14\varepsilon}{15}$$

Using Corollary 3.3.4 we find a subset $\sigma_1 \subset [1,N_1]$ of positive integers such that

$$\left|\sum_{i\in\sigma_1} x_i^{m_1}\right| > \frac{14\varepsilon}{60} > \frac{13\varepsilon}{60}$$

Next choose $m_2 > m_1$ $(m_2 \in \{n_k\})$ with

$$\sum_{i=1}^{N_1} |x_i^{m_2}| < \frac{\varepsilon}{15}$$

We can determine $N_2 > N_1$, $N_2 \in \mathbb{N}$, $N_2 \equiv N_2(m_2,\varepsilon)$ so that

$$\sum_{i\geq N_2+1} |x_i^{m_2}| < \frac{\varepsilon}{15}$$

Therefore

$$\sum_{i=1}^{N_2} |x_i^{m_2}| > \varepsilon - \frac{\varepsilon}{15} = \frac{14\varepsilon}{15}$$

$$\sum_{i=N_1+1}^{N_2} |x_i^{m_2}| > \frac{14\varepsilon}{15} - \frac{\varepsilon}{15} = \frac{13\varepsilon}{15}$$

Using Corollary 3.3.4, we can now determine a $\sigma_2 \subset [N_1 + 1, N_2]$ with

$$\left|\sum_{i\in\sigma_2} x_i^{m_2}\right| > \frac{13\varepsilon}{60}$$

Proceeding in this way we find sequences $\{m_\ell\} \subset \{n_k\}$, $\{N_\ell\} \subset \mathbb{N}$, and $\{\sigma_\ell\}$ with $\sigma_\ell \subset [N_{\ell-1}, N_\ell]$ such that

$$\sum_{i\geq N_\ell+1} |x_i^{m_\ell}| < \frac{\varepsilon}{15} \qquad \sum_{i=1}^{N_{\ell-1}} |x_i^{m_\ell}| < \frac{\varepsilon}{15}$$

$$\sum_{i=N_{\ell-1}+1}^{N_\ell} |x_i^{m_\ell}| > \frac{13\varepsilon}{15} \qquad \text{and} \qquad \left|\sum_{i\in\sigma_\ell} x_i^{m_\ell}\right| > \frac{13\varepsilon}{60} \qquad \ell \geq 1$$

where $N_0 = 0$. Define $y = \{y_i\}$ by

$$y_i = \begin{cases} 1 & N_{\ell-1} + 1 \leq i \leq N_\ell,\ i \in \sigma_\ell,\ \ell \geq 1 \\ 0 & \text{otherwise} \end{cases}$$

Then $y \in m_0$ and

$$\left|\sum_{i\geq 1} x_i^{m_\ell} y_i\right| \geq \left|\sum_{i\in\sigma_\ell} x_i^{m_\ell}\right| - \sum_{i=1}^{N_{\ell-1}} |x_i^{m_\ell}| - \sum_{i\geq N_\ell+1} |x_i^{m_\ell}|$$

$$> \frac{13\varepsilon}{60} - \frac{\varepsilon}{15} - \frac{\varepsilon}{15} = \frac{\varepsilon}{12}$$

$$\Longrightarrow \quad q_y(x^{m_\ell}) > \frac{\varepsilon}{12}$$

The last inequality shows that $x^n \not\to 0$ in $\sigma(\ell^1, m_0)$, which contradicts our earlier assumption. Since $(\ell^1, \|\cdot\|_1)$ is a Banach space, the last part follows by an application of Proposition 1.2.11. □

Remark: The last part of the above result also follows as a special case of Proposition 4.2.2 by putting $\lambda = m_0$ and noting that $\lambda^\times = \ell^1$.

PROPOSITION 7.19 The space m_0 is dense in $(\ell^\infty, \tau(\ell^\infty, \ell^1))$, and the completion of $(m_0, \tau(m_0, \ell^1))$ is $(\ell^\infty, \tau(\ell^\infty, \ell^1))$.

Proof. By Theorem 8.3, $(\ell^\infty, \tau(\ell^\infty, \ell^1))$ is an AK-space and so it is an AD-space; also, $\phi \subset m_0 \subset \ell^\infty$. Thus $\bar{m}_0 = \ell^\infty$, where the closure is taken with respect to $\tau(\ell^\infty,\ell^1)$. Finally, observe that $(\ell^\infty,\tau(\ell^\infty,\ell^1))$ is complete (cf. Proposition 4.2.3). □

EXERCISE 7.20 Show that m_0 is dense in ℓ^∞ relative to its norm topology.

We need some preparation for the next result. For a compact Hausdorff topological space X, let us denote by C(X) and M(X), respectively, the spaces of scalar-valued continuous functions on X and of regular complex-valued Borel measures on X (cf. Refs. 86 and 246). Then $M(X) = C(X)^*$, where C(X) is equipped with the sup norm and M(X) is given the total variation norm (cf. Ref. 48, p. 265; Ref. 245, p. 397; Ref. 225, p. 43). A subset S of C(X) is called C-*normal* if for any pair A,B of disjoint closed subsets of X, there exists an $f \in S$ such that $f|_A = 0$ and $f|_B = 1$; and a compact Hausdorff space X is an N-*space* if for $K \subset M(X)$, the C-normality of $\{f \in C(X) : \sup_{\mu\in K} |\mu(f)| < \infty\}$ implies the boundedness of K (cf. Ref. 228). We now quote a result of Seever [228], namely

> A compact Hausdorff space X is an N-space if and only if for a Banach space Y and a bounded linear operator $u : Y \to C(X)$ with normal range, u is onto.

which yields the barreledness of m_0 in ℓ^∞, as shown in the following (Ref. 18, p. 513):

PROPOSITION 7.21 Consider ℓ^∞ equipped with its usual sup norm. Then m_0 is a barreled subspace of ℓ^∞ and it is of first category.

Proof. Let $\beta(\mathbb{N})$ be the Stone-Čech compactification of the discrete space $\mathbb{N}$ (cf. Ref. 47, p. 243 and Ref. 135, p. 152). Then ℓ^∞ can be regarded as $C(\beta(\mathbb{N}))$ (Ref. 134, p. 209). Moreover, $\beta(\mathbb{N})$ is an N-space and m_0 is a C-normal subspace of ℓ^∞. Hence it follows from Seever's result above, Exercise 7.20, and Proposition 1.10.20, (ii) $\Longrightarrow$ (i), that m_0 is barreled.

To prove the other part, let m_n, $n \ge 1$, denote the collection of all sequences x such that the cardinality of the set consisting of the coordinates of x is at most n. Clearly, each m_n is closed in ℓ^∞ and $m_0 = \bigcup_{n\ge1} m_n$. Also, in every neighborhood of $x \in m_n$, we can find a point which is not in m_n. Thus the interior of m_n, $n \ge 1$, is empty. Hence m_0 is of first category. □

Note: Most of the barreled spaces occurring in the theory of locally convex spaces are of second category. But here we observe that m_0 behaves in a different manner.

Remark: From the preceding result and Theorem 1.5.6, we can prove that $m_0^\gamma = \ell^1$ (cf. Proposition 2.12). Indeed, let $y \in m_0^\gamma$ and define the continuous operators $F_n^y : m_0 \to \mathbb{K}$ by

$$F_n^y(x) = \sum_{i=1}^{n} x_i y_i \qquad n \geq 1$$

Then for each $x \in m_0$, $\{F_n^y(x) : n \geq 1\}$ is bounded in $\mathbb{K}$ and so

$$|F_n^y(x)| \leq M\|x\|_\infty \qquad \forall x \in m_0$$

Hence

$$\sup_n \left|\sum_{i=1}^{n} \alpha_i y_i\right| \leq M \qquad \text{uniformly in } \alpha \in \bar{a}$$

where $\bar{a}$ is the set of all sequences whose coordinates are either 0 or 1. Finally, make use of Theorem 3.6.6 and Proposition 3.6.7.

Dual of ℓ^∞

For the sake of completeness, we reproduce below the procedure for obtaining the topological dual $\ell^{\infty*}$ of $(\ell^\infty, \|\cdot\|_\infty)$. We need some preparatory notes and follow Ref. 48, p. 296; Ref. 90, p. 357; and Ref. 245, p. 401. For a nonempty set X, let R denote a ring of subsets of X. The symbol σ_E $(E \in R)$ denotes a *partition* $E_1, \ldots, E_n$ of E : $E_i \in R$, $E_i \cap E_j = \phi$, $\cup_{i=1}^n E_i = E$. By a *charge* μ on R we mean a $\mathbb{K}$-valued finitely additive set function such that $|\mu(E)| < \infty$ for each $E \in R$, and the triplet (X,R,μ) is called a *charged space*; further, if $X \in R$ and $|\mu(X)| < \infty$, then (X,R,μ) is called a *completely charged space*. Let us use the symbol ba(X,R) to mean the *space of all charges on a ring* R, equipped with the norm $\|\mu\|$ with

$$\|\mu\| = \sup_{E \in R} \sup_{\sigma_E} \sum_{i=1}^{n} |\mu(E_i)|$$

In case $X \in R$, then

$$\|\mu\| = \sup_{\sigma_X} \sum_{i=1}^{n} |\mu(E_i)|$$

It is known (Ref. 48, p. 160) that ba(X,R) is a Banach space under the norm $\|\mu\|$; in particular, if Φ_∞ stands for the family of all subsets of $\mathbb{N}$, then ba$(\mathbb{N},\Phi_\infty)$ is a Banach space under the norm $\|\mu\|$,

$$\|\mu\| = \sup_{\sigma_{\mathbb{N}}} \sum_{i=1}^{n} |\mu(E_i)|$$

Corresponding to a completely charged space (X,R,μ), one can talk about the integral of a function $f\colon X \to \mathbb{K}$ as follows. For a partition $\sigma_X = \{E_i : 1 \le i \le N\}$, choose arbitrary points $n_i \in E_i$ $(1 \le i \le N)$ and let

$$f_\sigma \equiv f(\sigma; n_1, \ldots, n_N) = \sum_{i=1}^{N} f(n_i)\mu(E_i)$$

If the net $\{f_\sigma\}$ converges in $\mathbb{K}$, say to I, then f is said to be μ-*integrable* over X. This is expressed as

$$I = \int_X f\, d\mu \qquad \text{or} \qquad \int f\, d\mu$$

For the f defined above, if $f^{-1}[M] \in R$ for each semi-open rectangle $M \subset \mathbb{K}$, then f is called μ-*measurable* (here $X \in R$). If (X,R,μ) is a completely charged space and $f\colon X \to \mathbb{K}$ is μ-measurable and bounded, then $\int f\, d\mu$ exists (Ref. 245, p. 402). Finally, let us note that

$$\left|\int f\, d\mu\right| \le \sup\{|f(x)| : x \in X\} \sup_{\sigma_X} \sum_{i=1}^{n} |\mu(E_i)|$$

$$\le \|\mu\| \sup\{|f(x)| : x \in X\}$$

and if X is a normed space and $f \in X^*$, then

$$\left|\int f\, d\mu\right| \le \|f\|\|\mu\|$$

The foregoing discussion leads us to conclude that each $x \in \ell^\infty$ is μ-integrable corresponding to any charge μ on Φ_∞.

We are now prepared to state and prove the basic result of this subsection, namely,

THEOREM 7.22 There exists an isometric isomorphism F from $\ell^{\infty *}$ onto the space ba$(\mathbb{N},\Phi_\infty)$, where

$$F(f) = \mu_f \qquad \mu_f(E) = f(\chi_E) \qquad E \in \Phi_\infty \tag{*}$$

$$F^{-1}(\mu) = f_\mu \qquad f_\mu(x) = \int_{\mathbb{N}} x \, d\mu \qquad x \in \ell^\infty \tag{**}$$

and

$$\|F(f)\| = \|f\| \qquad f \in \ell^{\infty*}$$

Proof. Consider an $f \in \ell^{\infty*}$ and define μ_f as in (*). Then μ_f is a (complete) charge on Φ_∞ and so we have a map $F: \ell^{\infty*} \to ba(\mathbb{N}, \Phi_\infty)$. If $F(f) = 0$, then from (*), f vanishes on m_0. In view of Exercise 7.20, $f = 0$. Thus F is one-to-one. Let now $\mu \in ba(\mathbb{N}, \Phi_\infty)$. Then for each $x \in \ell^\infty$, the integral

$$\int_{\mathbb{N}} x \, d\mu$$

exists and consequently defines an $f_\mu \in \ell^{\infty\prime}$. Now

$$|f_\mu(x)| = \left|\int_{\mathbb{N}} x \, d\mu\right| \le \|\mu\| \sup_{i\ge1}|x(i)| = \|\mu\|\|x\|$$

$$\Longrightarrow \quad \|f_\mu\| \le \|\mu\| \quad \Longrightarrow \quad f_\mu \in \ell^{\infty*} \tag{***}$$

Hence F is onto.

Let $\varepsilon > 0$ and choose a $\sigma_{\mathbb{N}} = \{E_1, \ldots, E_N\}$ such that

$$\sum_{i=1}^{N} |\mu_f(E_i)| > \|\mu_f\| - \varepsilon$$

where $\mu_f = F(f)$, $f \in \ell^{\infty*}$. Define $x \in \ell^\infty$ by

$$x_n = \begin{cases} \dfrac{\overline{\mu_f(E_i)}}{|\mu_f(E_i)|} & \text{if } n \in E_i \text{ and } \mu_f(E_i) \ne 0 \\[2ex] 0 & \text{if } n \in E_i \text{ and } \mu_f(E_i) = 0 \end{cases}$$

Then $\|x\|_\infty \le 1$ and

$$f(x) = \int x \, d\mu_f = \sum_{i=1}^{N} \int_{E_i} x \, d\mu_f = \sum_{i=1}^{N} |\mu_f(E_i)|$$

$$\Longrightarrow \quad \|f\| \ge |f(x)| \ge \sum_{i=1}^{N} |\mu_f(E_i)| > \|\mu_f\| - \varepsilon$$

Hence $\|F(f)\| \le \|f\|$. Now each f corresponds to some $\mu = F(f)$, and so from (***), $\|f\| \le \|F(f)\|$. Therefore $\|F(f)\| = \|f\|$. □

Note: There seems to be another way of looking at the dual $\ell^{\infty *}$ of ℓ^∞. Indeed, ℓ^∞ is the space $C(\beta(\mathbb{N}))$ as outlined in Proposition 7.21. Hence $\ell^{\infty *}$ can also be regarded as the space of all $\mathbb{K}$-valued finite regular Borel measures μ on $\beta(\mathbb{N})$ normed by the total variation of μ (cf. Refs. 86 and 246). However, this sort of dual does not seem to be of much interest, as the structure of $\beta(\mathbb{N})$ is quite complicated.

8. MACKEY CONVERGENCE OF NTH SECTIONS

Let (λ,T) be a locally convex K-space. Earlier (cf. Section 3) we stressed the importance of proving the AK character of (λ,T) and we have shown that when T is $\sigma(\lambda,\lambda^\times)$ or $\eta(\lambda,\lambda^\times)$ then (λ,T) is always an AK-space. In other words, if we confine our attention to the dual system $\langle\lambda,\lambda^\times\rangle$ then λ equipped with either of the polar topologies $\sigma(\lambda,\lambda^\times)$ or $\eta(\lambda,\lambda^\times)$ is always an AK-space. There are other polar topologies on λ as well, e.g., $\tau(\lambda,\lambda^\times)$ and $\beta(\lambda,\lambda^\times)$. A natural question is: Is (λ,T) also an AK-space when T is $\tau(\lambda,\lambda^\times)$ or $\beta(\lambda,\lambda^\times)$? Apparently, an answer to this problem would depend upon the inner structure of the sequence space λ, for instance, its monotonocity, normality, or perfectness. The following example suggests that we need not bother in general to verify the AK-property of $(\lambda,\beta(\lambda,\lambda^\times))$, since λ is perfect in this case.

EXAMPLE 8.1 Consider the space $(\ell^\infty,\beta(\ell^\infty,\ell^1))$. Here $e \in \ell^\infty$ and $e^{(n)} \not\to e$ in $\beta(\ell^\infty,\ell^1)$; cf. Exercise 6.13.

Let us therefore turn our attention to determining when $(\lambda,\tau(\lambda,\lambda^\times))$ is an AK-space. At least this result is not true in general; for instance, consider

EXAMPLE 8.2 Consider the space $(k,\tau(k,\ell^1))$. Here $e^{(n)} \not\to e$ in $\tau(k,\ell^1)$. Indeed, $\{e^{(n)}\}$ is not even $\tau(k,\ell^1)$-Cauchy; cf. Exercise 7.11.

Remarks: In the preceding example, the space k is not even monotone. Thus to expect that $(\lambda,\tau(\lambda,\lambda^\times))$ becomes an AK-space, we should at least start from the assumption that λ is monotone, since we have been unable to produce any example of a monotone space λ for which $(\lambda,\tau(\lambda,\lambda^\times))$ is not an AK-space. In fact, this line of thinking has been justified by a recent result of Bennett [15], according to which each monotone space λ is an AK-space relative to the topology $\tau(\lambda,\lambda^\times)$. However, much earlier Köthe [139] was able to prove the same result for an arbitrary normal sequence space λ. Bennett's result, whose proof makes use of certain deep results on subseries convergence of an infinite series, is postponed to a later chapter. In practice quite many sequence spaces which we consider are normal spaces, and therefore we prefer here to give a detailed discussion leading to the proof of Köthe's theorem mentioned just above. Formally this result is stated as follows.

THEOREM 8.3 If λ is a normal sequence space, then for each x in λ,

$$x^{(n)} \to x \qquad \text{in } \tau(\lambda,\lambda^\times)$$

Diagonal Transformations and Compatibility of $\eta(\lambda,\lambda^\times)$

To prove Theorem 8.3 we require several new concepts and results which we proceed to consider. First we have

DEFINITION 8.4 If $v = \{v_i\}$ is a sequence and λ is a sequence space, then the sequence space $\mu = \{vx : x \in \lambda\}$ is called the *diagonal transform* of λ relative to v. The map $T_v\colon \lambda \to \mu$, $T_v(x) = vx$, is called the *diagonal transformation* of λ onto μ.

If $v = \{v_i\}$ is such that $|v| >> 0$ then the map T_v is *one-to-one* (injective) and in this case $\mu^\times$ is given by

$$\mu^\times = \left\{\frac{y}{v} : y \in \lambda^\times\right\} = T^\times_{v^{-1}}[\lambda^\times]$$

where $T^\times_{v^{-1}}$ is the *diagonal transformation of* $\lambda^\times$ *onto* $\mu^\times$, $v^{-1} = \{1/v_i\}$, and $y/v = yv^{-1}$.

Now we have the following simple

PROPOSITION 8.5 Let λ be a sequence space and $v \in \omega$ with $|v| >> 0$. Then (i) $T_v\colon \lambda \to \mu$ is a topological isomorphism from $(\lambda,\sigma(\lambda,\lambda^\times))$ [resp. $(\lambda,\eta(\lambda,\lambda^\times))$] onto $(\mu,\sigma(\mu,\mu^\times))$ [resp. $(\mu,\eta(\mu,\mu^\times))$]; and (ii) $T^\times_{v^{-1}}\colon \lambda^\times \to \mu^\times$

is a topological isomorphism from $(\lambda^{\times}, \sigma(\lambda^{\times}, \lambda))$ [resp. $(\lambda^{\times}, \eta(\lambda^{\times}, \lambda))$] onto $(\mu^{\times}, \sigma(\mu^{\times}, \mu))$ [resp. $(\mu^{\times}, \eta(\mu^{\times}, \mu))$].

Proof. For all x in λ and y in $\lambda^{\times}$ we have

$$\left\langle T_v(x), \frac{y}{v}\right\rangle = \langle x, y\rangle = \left\langle x, (T^{\times}_{v^{-1}})^{-1}\left(\frac{y}{v}\right)\right\rangle$$

and

$$\langle T_v^{-1}(vx), y\rangle = \langle x, y\rangle = \langle vx, T_{v^{-1}}(y)\rangle$$

The above relations give the continuity of the maps in the weak topologies. Replacing each term by its modulus (i.e., a sequence x is to be replaced by $|x|$) in the above relations we get the continuity of the maps relative to the normal topologies. In view of the foregoing bilinear relations, let us note that $(T^{\times}_{v^{-1}})^{-1}$ is the adjoint to T_v, and $T^{\times}_{v^{-1}}$ is the adjoint to T_v^{-1}. □

In the discussion that follows, let J and L stand for two infinite subsequences of $\mathbb{N}$ such that $J \cap L = \emptyset$ and $J \cup L = \mathbb{N}$.

EXERCISE 8.6 Prove that if λ is monotone, normal, or perfect, so is the sectional subspace λ_J.

Let us now formally put the following

DEFINITION 8.7 Let λ be a sequence space and J be an infinite subsequence of $\mathbb{N}$. The collection of canonical preimages of all x in λ_J is called the *canonical preimage* of λ_J and is usually denoted by $\bar{\lambda}_J$.

EXERCISE 8.8. If λ is monotone, prove that $\bar{\lambda}_J$ is a subspace of λ and $\lambda = \bar{\lambda}_J \oplus \bar{\lambda}_L$.

The proof of the following result, which also appears in Ref. 43, p. 187, under the additional assumption that λ is normal, is straightforward and so omitted.

PROPOSITION 8.9 Let λ be a sequence space and J be as before; then $(\lambda^{\times})_J = (\lambda_J)^{\times}$, the common value being denoted by $\lambda_J^{\times}$, and

$$\lambda^{\times} = \overline{\lambda_J^{\times}} \oplus \overline{\lambda_L^{\times}}$$

PROPOSITION 8.10 Let λ and μ be two sequence spaces such that μ is monotone and $\mu \subset \lambda^\beta$. Then the map $T_J \equiv T_J^\lambda : (\lambda,\sigma(\lambda,\mu)) \to (\lambda_J,\sigma(\lambda_J,\mu_J))$, $T_J(\{x_i\}) = \{x_{n_i}\}$, where $J = \{n_i\}$, is continuous; this result remains valid if σ is replaced by η and $\mu \subset \lambda^\beta$ is replaced by $\mu \subset \lambda^\times$.

Proof. Consider a net $\{x^\alpha\}$ in λ with $x^\alpha \to 0$ in $\sigma(\lambda,\mu)$. Choose $\varepsilon > 0$ and $\{y_{n_i}\} \in \mu_J$ arbitrarily. If z denotes the canonical preimage of $\{y_{n_i}\}$ then $z \in \mu$, and so there exists an $\alpha_0 \equiv \alpha_0(\varepsilon,z)$ such that

$$\left|\sum_{i\geq 1} x^\alpha_{n_i} y_{n_i}\right| < \infty \qquad \alpha \geq \alpha_0$$

$$\Longrightarrow \quad x^\alpha_{n_i} \to 0 \qquad \text{in } \sigma(\lambda_J,\mu_J)$$

The other part follows similarly. □

Remarks: Let us observe that λ_J and $\bar{\lambda}_J$ are algebraically isomorphic to each other under the natural map $\hat{T}_J$: $\lambda_J \to \bar{\lambda}_J$, with $\hat{T}_J(\{x_{n_i}\}) = \{x_i\}$, $\{x_i\}$ being the canonical preimage of $\{x_{n_i}\}$, $J = \{n_i\}$. We use the *notation* $x_J = \{x_{n_i}\} = \{x_{J,n_i}\}$ for any element of λ_J and $\bar{x}_J = \hat{T}(x_J) = \{\bar{x}_{J,i}\}$. Now the following is readily proved.

PROPOSITION 8.11 Let λ and μ be two sequence spaces with $\mu \subset \lambda^\beta$. The map $\hat{T}_J$: $(\lambda_J,\sigma(\lambda_J,\mu_J)) \to (\bar{\lambda}_J,\sigma(\bar{\lambda}_J,\bar{\mu}_J))$ is a topological isomorphism.

PROPOSITION 8.12 If λ and μ are two sequence spaces such that λ is monotone and $\mu \subset \lambda^\beta$, then a subset $B \subset \lambda_J$ is $\sigma(\lambda_J,\mu_J)$-bounded (resp. compact) if and only if $\hat{T}_J(B)$ is $\sigma(\lambda,\mu)$-bounded (resp. compact).

Proof. By Exercise 8.8, $\bar{\lambda}_J$ is a subspace of λ. The rest of the proof follows from Proposition 8.11. □

PROPOSITION 8.13 Let λ and μ be two monotone sequence spaces with $\mu \subset \lambda^\beta$. Then a subset $B \subset \lambda_J$ is $\beta(\lambda_J,\mu_J)$-bounded if and only if $\hat{T}_J(B)$ is $\beta(\lambda,\mu)$-bounded.

Proof. Let $B \subset \lambda_J$ be $\beta(\lambda_J,\mu_J)$-bounded. As λ is monotone, $\hat{T}_J(B) \subset \lambda$. Suppose now A is an arbitrary $\sigma(\mu,\lambda)$-bounded subset of μ. Then by Proposition 8.10, $T_J^\mu(A)$ is $\sigma(\mu_J,\lambda_J)$-bounded. Hence for some $\alpha > 0$,

$$B \subset \alpha[T_J^\mu(A)]^\circ$$

$$\Longrightarrow \sup_{\substack{x \in B \\ y \in T_J^\mu(A)}} \left| \sum_{i \geq 1} x_i y_i \right| \leq \alpha \qquad \Longrightarrow \sup_{\substack{w \in \hat{T}_J(B) \\ z \in A}} \left| \sum_{i \geq 1} w_{n_i} z_{n_i} \right| \leq \alpha$$

and this gives the $\beta(\lambda,\mu)$-boundedness of $\hat{T}_J(B)$.

On the other hand, let $\hat{T}_J(B)$ be $\beta(\lambda,\mu)$-bounded. Choose an arbitrary $\sigma(\mu_J,\lambda_J)$-bounded subset of μ_J. By Proposition 8.12, $\hat{T}_J(A)$ is $\sigma(\mu,\lambda)$-bounded, and so for some $\alpha > 0$,

$$\hat{T}_J(B) \subset \alpha[\hat{T}_J(A)]^\circ$$

$$\Longrightarrow \sup_{\substack{x \in \hat{T}_J(B) \\ y \in \hat{T}_J(A)}} \left| \sum_{i \geq 1} x_i y_i \right| \leq \alpha \qquad \Longrightarrow \sup_{\substack{w \in B \\ z \in A}} \left| \sum_{i \geq 1} w_{n_i} z_{n_i} \right| \leq \alpha$$

and so B is $\beta(\lambda_J,\mu_J)$-bounded. □

Remark: The preceding result is to be found in a weaker form in Ref. 43, Lemma 2(iv).

The following is a very useful result and is the one promised earlier in the remarks after Proposition 4.3.

THEOREM 8.14 For a sequence space λ, the topology $\eta(\lambda,\lambda^\times)$ is compatible with the dual system $\langle\lambda,\lambda^\times\rangle$; that is, $\sigma(\lambda,\lambda^\times) \subset \eta(\lambda,\lambda^\times) \subset \tau(\lambda,\lambda^\times)$.

Proof. In view of Proposition 4.3, it is sufficient to establish that for each $y \in \lambda^\times$, the set $\{y\}^N$, which is already balanced and convex, is also $\sigma(\lambda^\times,\lambda)$-compact [observe that $\{y\}^N$ is already $\sigma(\lambda^\times,\lambda)$-closed]. If $y \in \phi$, the set $\{y\}^N$ clearly satisfies condition (iv) of Theorem 3.10 and therefore it is $\sigma(\lambda^\times,\lambda)$-compact. Essentially we have to deal with two more cases, namely, when (i) $|y| \gg 0$ and (ii) $y_i \neq 0$ for $i \in J$, where J is some infinite subsequence of $\mathbb{N}$. To dispose of case (i), let us write $\mu = T_y[\lambda]$. Then $\mu \subset \ell^1$ and so $e \in \mu^\times$. From Exercise 6.17, the set $\{e\}^N$ is $\sigma(\mu^\times,\mu)$-compact, and thus by Proposition 8.5(ii), $\{y\}^N$ is $\sigma(\lambda^\times,\lambda)$-compact. Let us now take up the case (ii) and consider λ_J and $\lambda_J^\times$. If $z = \{y_{n_i}\} \in \lambda_J$, then from (i) above, $\{z\}^N$ is $\sigma(\lambda_J^\times \lambda_J)$-compact, and therefore by Proposition 8.12, $\{y\}^N = \hat{T}_J[\{z\}^N]$ is $\sigma(\lambda^\times,\lambda)$-compact. □

The Sequence Spaces λ_x *and* $\lambda_x^\times$

The proof of $x^{(n)} \to x$ in $\tau(\lambda,\lambda^\times)$ is facilitated by introducing the concept of λ_x as given in

DEFINITION 8.15 For an arbitrary $x \in \omega$, let

$$\lambda_x = \left\{y : y \in \omega, \sum_{i\geq 1} |x_i y_i| < \infty\right\}$$

If $x \in \omega$, $|x| >> 0$, then $\lambda_x = T_{x^{-1}}[\ell^1]$ and $\lambda_x^\times = T_x^\times[\ell^\infty]$. In general we have

PROPOSITION 8.16 Let J and L be as before (cf. remarks preceding Exercise 8.6). Let $x = \{x_i\}$ be such that $x_i \neq 0$ for $i \in J$ and $x_i = 0$ for $i \in L$. Then

$$\lambda_x = \bar{\mu}_J \oplus \bar{\omega}_L \qquad \text{and} \qquad \lambda_x^\times = \bar{\nu}_J \oplus \bar{\phi}_L$$

where

$$\bar{\mu}_J = \hat{T}_J[T_{x_J^{-1}}[\ell_J^1]] \qquad \bar{\omega}_L = \hat{T}_L[\omega_L]$$

$$\bar{\nu}_J = \hat{T}_J[T_{x_J}^\times[\ell_J^\infty]] \qquad \bar{\phi}_L = \hat{T}_L[\phi_L]$$

Proof. Straightforward computations. □

PROPOSITION 8.17 Let $x \in \omega$ with $x_i \neq 0$, $i \in J$. For any sequence space λ_J, suppose μ_J is the diagonal transform of λ_J by x_J. Then T_{x_J}: $(\lambda_J,\sigma(\lambda_J,\lambda_J^\times)) \to (\mu_J,\sigma(\mu_J,\mu_J^\times))$ is a topological isomorphism. This result remains valid if σ is replaced by η.

Proof. As for Proposition 8.5. □

PROPOSITION 8.18 For $J \subset \mathbb{N}$, let $A \subset \ell_J^1$ be $\sigma(\ell_J^1,\ell_J^\infty)$-compact; then

$$\lim_{m\to\infty} \sup_{\{y_{n_i}\}\in A} \left\{\sum_{i\geq m} |y_{n_i}|\right\} = 0$$

and consequently for x in ℓ_J^∞

$$x^{(n_m)} - x \xrightarrow{m} 0 \qquad \text{in } \tau(\ell_J^\infty,\ell_J^1)$$

Proof. By Proposition 8.12, $\hat{T}_J[A]$ is $\sigma(\ell^1,\ell^\infty)$-compact; now follow the proof of the necessity part of Proposition 6.11 (second part). □

THEOREM 8.19 For any $x \in \omega$,

$$x^{(n)} - x \to 0 \qquad \text{in } \tau(\lambda_x^\times, \lambda_x)$$

Proof. Observe that $x \in \lambda_x^\times$ and so $x^{(n)} - x \in \lambda_x^\times$. If $x \in \phi$, $\lambda_x = \omega$ and $\lambda_x^\times = \phi$, and so the result follows from Proposition 6.6. If $|x| >> 0$, then $\lambda_x = T_{x^{-1}}[\ell^1]$ and $\lambda_x^\times = T_x^\times[\ell^\infty]$, and the result follows from Propositions 8.5 and 8.18 where we replace J by $\mathbb{N}$. Let us consider the case when $x_i \neq 0$ for $i \in J$, and as usual let $L = \mathbb{N} \sim J$. By Proposition 8.16,

$$x = \bar{y}_J + \bar{z}_L \qquad \bar{y}_J \in \bar{\nu}_J \qquad \bar{z}_L \in \bar{\phi}_L$$

There exist a $b \in \ell^\infty$, uniquely defined on J, and an ℓ in $\mathbb{N}$, such that

$$\bar{y}_{J,i} = \begin{cases} b_i x_i & i \in J \\ 0 & i \in L \end{cases}$$

and $\bar{z}_{L,i} = 0$ for $i > \ell$. If $m \geq \ell$, then

$$x - x^{(m)} = \bar{y}_J - \bar{y}_J^{(m)} = \{0,\ldots,0,\bar{y}_{J,m+1},\bar{y}_{J,m+2},\ldots\}$$

Let A be any balanced, convex, and $\sigma(\lambda_x,\lambda_x^\times)$-compact subset of λ_x. If $u \in A$, then from Proposition 8.16 there exist sequences $\{\alpha_i\} \in \ell^1$ and $\{z_i\} \in \omega$, uniquely defined on J and L, respectively, such that

$$u_i = \begin{cases} \dfrac{\alpha_i}{x_i} & i \in J \\ z_i & i \in L \end{cases}$$

Thus for $m \geq \ell$,

$$|\langle x - x^{(m)}, u\rangle| \leq M \sum_{i \geq k} |\alpha_{n_i}| \tag{*}$$

where $n_k \geq m + 1$ and $M > 0$ with $|b_i| \leq M$, $i \geq 1$. It is clear that $T_J[A]$ is $\sigma((\lambda_x)_J,(\lambda_x^\times)_J)$-compact (Proposition 8.10) and so $T^{-1}_{x_J^{-1}}[T_J[A]]$ is $\sigma(\ell_J^1,\ell_J^\infty)$-compact (cf. Proposition 8.17). Thus from Proposition 8.18,

$$\lim_{k\to\infty} \sup_{\{\alpha_{n_i}\}\in T^{-1}_{x_J^{-1}}[T_J[A]]} \sum_{i\geq k} |\alpha_{n_i}| = 0 \qquad (**)$$

From (*) and (**) we get the required result. □

PROPOSITION 8.20 If λ is a normal sequence space, then

$$\lambda = \cup\{\lambda_x^\times : x \in \lambda\}$$

Proof. The inclusion

$$\lambda \subset \cup\{\lambda_x^\times : x \in \lambda\}$$

is immediate. If $x \in \phi$, then $\lambda_x^\times = \phi \subset \lambda$. If $x_i \neq 0$, $i \geq 1$, where $x \in \lambda$, then $\lambda_x^\times = T_x^\times[\ell^\infty]$. Thus $y \in \lambda_x^\times$ means $y = bx$ with $b \in \ell^\infty$, $x \in \lambda$. Since λ is normal, by Exercise 2.2, $y \in \lambda$. Hence $\lambda_x^\times \subset \lambda$. Finally, let $x = \{x_i\} \in \lambda$ be such that $x_i \neq 0$ for $i \in J$ and $x_i = 0$ for $i \in L$, where $J \cap L = \emptyset$, $J \cup L = \mathbb{N}$. Using Proposition 8.16 and the fact that λ is normal, we once again find that $\lambda_x^\times \subset \lambda$. □

Proof of Theorem 8.3. Let $x \in \lambda$. Then $\lambda_x^\times \subset \lambda$, or $\lambda^\times \subset \lambda_x = \lambda_x^{\times\times}$ (λ_x is perfect). By Theorem 8.19, $x^{(n)} - x \to 0$ in $\tau(\lambda_x^\times,\lambda_x)$ and therefore $x^{(n)} - x \to 0$ in $\tau(\lambda_x^\times,\lambda^\times)$. Hence $x^{(n)} - x \to 0$ in $\tau(\lambda,\lambda^\times)$. □

EXERCISE 8.21 Let λ be normal. If either (i) every $\sigma(\lambda^\times,\lambda)$-bounded subset of $\lambda^\times$ is $\sigma(\lambda^\times,\lambda)$-relatively compact, or (ii) the space $(\lambda,\tau(\lambda,\lambda^\times))$ is barreled, show that $x^{(n)} - x \to 0$ in $\beta(\lambda,\lambda^\times)$ for each x in λ.

EXERCISE 8.22 Let λ be perfect. If either (i) every $\sigma(\lambda,\lambda^\times)$-bounded subset of λ is $\sigma(\lambda,\lambda^\times)$-relatively compact, or (ii) (λ,T) is semireflexive, where T is any locally convex topology on λ compatible with $\langle\lambda,\lambda^\times\rangle$, prove that $y^{(n)} - y \to 0$ in $\beta(\lambda^\times,\lambda)$ for each y in $\lambda^\times$.

EXERCISE 8.23 If λ is a normal sequence space, show that $(\lambda,\tau(\lambda,\lambda^\times))$ is separable. [Hint: See the remark after Definition 3.4.]

EXERCISE 8.24 Show that in an arbitrary sequence space λ, if $A \subset \lambda$ is $\sigma(\lambda,\lambda^\times)$-bounded, then $\{A\}^N$ is $\eta(\lambda,\lambda^\times)$-bounded. [Hint: For any u in $\{A\}^N$ there exists an x in A with $\Sigma_{i\geq 1} |u_i y_i| \leq p_y(x)$, where $y \in \lambda^\times$ is arbitrarily chosen; now apply Theorem 8.14 to conclude the $\eta(\lambda,\lambda^\times)$-boundedness of A.]

Chapter 3

CONVERGENCE OF SERIES

1. INTRODUCTION

Various notions of convergence of an infinite series play a very significant role in several branches of functional analysis. For instance, in the theory of Schauder bases, a type of base is associated according to the mode of convergence of the underlying infinite series, which is useful in determining the structure of the space in question; and in the theory of nuclear spaces, the nuclearity of a Fréchet space can be characterized in terms of its absolute convergence base. Indeed, these different modes of convergence find numerous applications in the Schauder basis theory, which we take up in a forthcoming work (Ref. 125). In the theory of inclusion maps of sequence spaces (Chapter 4), the notion of subseries convergence has given rise to several interesting and useful results which have led to further development of summability theory. One can find several such examples where the theory of modes of convergence is used directly or indirectly.

We present in this chapter a detailed and self-contained study of the several notions of convergence of an infinite series in the most general setting of topological vector spaces, and establish various relationships among them. At the end we also give some applications to linear transformations.

In what follows, we consider (X,T) as before to be a Hausdorff TVS or l.c. TVS and $D \equiv D_T$ to be the corresponding family of pseudonorms or seminorms unless otherwise specified. For other notation not explained here, the reader is referred back to the paragraphs before Definitions 1.2.4 and 1.2.8.

The modes of convergence which we will discuss in this chapter are contained in

DEFINITION 1.1 A formal infinite series $\Sigma_{i\geq 1} x_i$, where $\{x_i\}$ is contained in a TVS (X,T), is said to be (i) *convergent* in (X,T) if $\{\Sigma_{i=1}^n x_i\}$ converges in (X,T); (ii) *weakly convergent* in (X,T) if there exists an $x \in X$ such that $\Sigma_{i\geq 1} f(x_i)$ converges to $f(x)$ for each $f \in X^*$; (iii) *absolutely convergent* provided $\Sigma_{i\geq 1} p(x_i) < \infty$ for each p in D; (iv) *bounded multiplier convergent* if for each $b \in \ell^\infty$ the series $\Sigma_{i\geq 1} b_i x_i$ converges in (X,T); (v) *subseries convergent* if for any increasing sequence J in $\mathbb{N}$, the series $\Sigma_{i\in J} x_i$ converges in (X,T); (vi) *unconditionally* or *reordered convergent* if for any permutation σ of $\mathbb{N}$, the series $\Sigma_{i\geq 1} x_{\sigma(i)}$ converges to the same element x in (X,T); and (vii) *unordered* or *Moore-Smith convergent* to x in (X,T) provided

$$T - \lim_{\sigma\in\Phi} S_\sigma = x$$

where the net $\{S_\sigma : \sigma \in \Phi\}$ is given by $S_\sigma = \Sigma_{i\in\sigma} x_i$ and $\Phi = \{\sigma : \sigma$ is finite and is contained in $\mathbb{N}\}$, Φ being partially ordered by the usual set-theoretic inclusion.

Note: Some authors say merely that a series $\Sigma_{i\geq 1} x_i$ converges unconditionally in a TVS (X,T) if $\Sigma_{i\geq 1} x_{\sigma(i)}$ converges in (X,T) for each permutation σ rather than to stress that the convergence point of $\Sigma_{i\geq 1} x_{\sigma(i)}$ is the same for all σ. It can be verified that the former statement is equivalent to the latter; see the remark following Theorem 4.1.

In the sequel we also require

DEFINITION 1.2 A series $\Sigma_{i\geq 1} x_i$ in a TVS (X,T) is said to be (i) T-*Cauchy* if to each $u \in \mathcal{B}$ there corresponds an $N \in \mathbb{N}$ such that $\Sigma_{i=m+1}^n x_i \in u$ for all $m,n \geq N$; (ii) *weakly Cauchy* if for each f in X^*, the series of scalars $\Sigma_{i\geq 1} f(x_i)$ is Cauchy, or equivalently, $\Sigma_{i\geq 1} f(x_i)$ is convergent; (iii) *absolute Cauchy* if for each $p \in D$, the series of reals $\Sigma_{i\geq 1} p(x_i)$ is Cauchy in $\mathbb{R}$, or equivalently, the series $\Sigma_{i\geq 1} p(x_i)$ converges in $\mathbb{R}$; (iv) *unconditionally Cauchy* if for each permutation σ of $\mathbb{N}$, the series $\Sigma_{i\geq 1} x_{\sigma(i)}$ is Cauchy in (X,T); and (v) *unordered Cauchy* if to each $u \in \mathcal{B}$ there exists $\sigma \in \Phi$ such that $S_\lambda - S_\mu \in u$ for all $\lambda,\mu \in \Phi$ with $\sigma \subset \lambda,\mu$.

Note: The weakly convergent (resp. Cauchy) series $\Sigma_{i\geq 1} x_i$ in a TVS (X,T) will also be called $\sigma(X,X^*)$-convergent (resp. -Cauchy).

2. ABSOLUTE CONVERGENCE

When $\sigma = \{1, 2, \ldots, n\} \in \Phi$ we write S_σ as S_n, that is, $S_n = \Sigma_{i=1}^n x_i$, and call S_n the nth partial sum of an infinite series $\Sigma_{i\geq 1} x_i$ in a TVS (X,T). We begin with the frequently used

PROPOSITION 2.1 Every absolutely convergent series in a sequentially complete l.c. TVS is convergent.

Proof. As in classical analysis; for instance, see Naimark [175, p. 72]. □

The converse of the preceding result is not necessarily true even in the strongest case; for instance, consider the series $1 - 1/2 + 1/3 - \cdots + \cdots$ in $\mathbb{R}$. Considering a wider class of spaces, we have the following nontrivial example.

EXAMPLE 2.2 Consider ℓ^p, $p > 1$, with its usual norm $\|\alpha\|_p = (\Sigma_{i\geq 1}|\alpha_i|^p)^{1/p}$, $\alpha \in \ell^p$. Choose p_1 with $1 < p_1 < p$. Let $\alpha_n = n^{-p_1/p}$, $n \geq 1$. The series $\Sigma_{n\geq 1} \alpha_n e^n$ converges in ℓ^p, for we have

$$\left(\left\|\sum_{i=m}^{n} \alpha_i e^i\right\|_p\right)^p = \sum_{i=m}^{n} i^{-p_1} \to 0 \qquad \text{as } m,n \to \infty$$

But

$$\sum_{n\geq 1} \|\alpha_n e^n\|_p = \sum_{n\geq 1} n^{-p_1/p}$$

Hence the series $\Sigma_{i\geq 1} \alpha_i e^i$ does not converge absolutely.

A sort of converse of the foregoing result is contained in Ref. 227, p. 72, Exercise 6^0.

PROPOSITION 2.3 If every absolutely convergent series converges in a metrizable l.c. TVS (X,T), then (X,T) is a Fréchet space.

Proof. It suffices to prove the sequential completeness of (X,T). Let $\{x_n\}$ be a T-Cauchy sequence in X. If d denotes the invariant metric generating the topology T, it follows that there exists a subsequence $\{y_n\}$ of $\{x_n\}$ such that $\Sigma_{n\geq 1} d(y_{n+1},y_n) < \infty$. Hence $\Sigma_{n\geq 1}(y_{n+1} - y_n)$

converges in (X,T), and so $\{y_n\}$ converges in (X,T). Since $\{x_n\}$ is T-Cauchy, $\{x_n\}$ converges in (X,T). □

PROPOSITION 2.4 In an l.c. TVS (X,T), every absolutely convergent series $\Sigma_{i\geq 1} x_i$ is weakly Cauchy.

Proof. Let $f \in X^*$. Then $|f(x)| \leq p(x)$ for all x in X and some $p \in D$. Hence

$$\left|\sum_{i=m}^{n} f(x_i)\right| = \left|f\left(\sum_{i=m}^{n} x_i\right)\right| \leq \sum_{i=m}^{n} p(x_i)$$

from which one easily deduces the result. □

As one might expect, the converse of Proposition 2.4 is not necessarily true. For instance, one has (Ref. 128)

EXAMPLE 2.5 Consider the space $(\ell^1, \tau(\ell^1, k))$. Let $a_i = (-1)^{i+1}/i$, $i \geq 1$. Then the series $\Sigma_{i\geq 1} a_i e^i$ is $\sigma(\ell^1, k)$-Cauchy. For let $y \in k$. We have

$$\left|\sum_{i=m} \langle a_i e^i, y\rangle\right| = \left|\sum_{i=m}^{n} (-1)^{i+1} \frac{y_i}{i}\right| \to 0$$

as $m,n \to \infty$. On the other hand,

$$\sum_{i\geq 1} |a_i| q_e(e^i) = \sum_{i\geq 1} \frac{1}{i} = \infty$$

Therefore, for some seminorm q_A which is continuous in $\tau(\ell^1, k)$, we have

$$\sum_{i\geq 1} q_A(a_i e^i) = \infty$$

Another stronger mode of convergence in metrizable TVS is contained in

DEFINITION 2.6 A series $\Sigma_{i\geq 1} x_i$ in an F*-space (X,δ), δ being the F-norm on X, is *strongly absolutely convergent* if $\Sigma_{i\geq 1} \delta(x_i) < \infty$.

From the above definition it is evident that strong absolute convergence can be talked about only in metrizable TVS and that the notion coincides with absolute convergence in normed spaces. Clearly every strongly absolutely convergent series in any F*-space is absolutely convergent;

the converse of this statement is not necessarily true. For further discussion of this notion one may consult Ref. 49.

3. BOUNDED MULTIPLIER AND SUBSERIES CONVERGENCE

Under special circumstances the notions of bounded multiplier convergence and of subseries convergence can be expressed in terms of unconditional convergence. To accomplish our aim, it will be convenient at this stage to introduce the following notation:

$$\begin{aligned} \bar{a} &= \{\alpha \in \omega : \alpha_n = 1 \text{ or } -1, \forall n \geq 1\} \\ \bar{b} &= \{\beta \in \omega : \beta_n = 0 \text{ or } 1, \forall n \geq 1\} \\ \bar{e} &= \{\varepsilon \in \omega : |\varepsilon_n| \leq 1, \forall n \geq 1\} \\ \bar{d} &= \{\gamma \in \omega : \gamma_n = 1, -1, \text{ or } 0, \forall n \geq 1\} \end{aligned} \tag{3.1}$$

Remark: It is clear that a series $\Sigma_{i\geq 1} x_i$ in a TVS X is (i) bounded multiplier convergent if and only if $\Sigma_{i\geq 1} \varepsilon_i x_i$ converges in X for every $\varepsilon \in \bar{e}$; and (ii) subseries convergent if and only if $\Sigma_{i\geq 1} \beta_i x_i$ converges in X for every β in $\bar{b}$.

EXERCISE 3.2 For any σ in Φ, consider a set $\{x_i : i \in \sigma\}$ in an F*-space $(X, \|\cdot\|)$. Denote by $\bar{a}_\sigma$, $\bar{b}_\sigma$, and $\bar{d}_\sigma$ the finite families of finite sets obtained by restricting the members of $\bar{a}$, $\bar{b}$, and $\bar{d}$ on σ, respectively. Then show that the following inequalities

$$\left\|\sum_{i\in\sigma} \alpha_i x_i\right\| \leq 3 \sup\left\{\left\|\sum_{i\in\sigma_1} x_i\right\| : \sigma_1 \subset \sigma\right\}$$

$$\left\|\sum_{i\in\sigma} \beta_i x_i\right\| \leq \sup\left\{\left\|\sum_{i\in\sigma_1} x_i\right\| : \sigma_1 \subset \sigma\right\}$$

$$\left\|\sum_{i\in\sigma} \gamma_i x_i\right\| \leq 3 \sup\left\{\left\|\sum_{i\in\sigma_1} x_i\right\| : \sigma_1 \subset \sigma\right\}$$

are valid uniformly in $\alpha^\sigma = \{\alpha_i : i \in \sigma\} \in \bar{a}_\sigma$, $\beta^\sigma = \{\beta_i : i \in \sigma\} \in \bar{b}_\sigma$ and $\gamma^\sigma = \{\gamma_i : i \in \sigma\} \in \bar{d}_\sigma$. [Hint: Use the method of proof of Proposition 3.3.]

For a seminormed space we have the following result, due to McArthur and Retherford [170, p. 115], which along with its corollary play a fundamental role in our work.

PROPOSITION 3.3 Let (X,ρ) be a seminormed space. For any σ in Φ, consider a set $\{x_i : i \in \sigma\}$ in X and a set $\{\alpha_i : i \in \sigma\}$ in $\mathbb{K}$. If $k = \sup\{|\alpha_i| : i \in \sigma\}$, then

$$\rho\left(\sum_{i\in\sigma} \alpha_i x_i\right) \le 4k \sup\left\{\rho\left(\sum_{i\in\sigma_1} x_i\right) : \sigma_1 \subset \sigma\right\}$$

Proof. If n is the number of elements in σ, we may write $\{x_i : i \in \sigma\}$ as $\{y_1, \ldots, y_n\}$ and $\{\alpha_i : i \in \sigma\}$ as $\{\beta_i : 1 \le i \le n\}$. Then

$$\rho\left(\sum_{i\in\sigma} \alpha_i x_i\right) = \rho\left(\sum_{i=1}^{n-1} (\beta_i - \beta_{i+1})(y_1 + \cdots + y_i) + \beta_n(y_1 + \cdots + y_n)\right)$$

Assuming first that $\beta_1 \ge \beta_2 \ge \cdots \ge \beta_n > 0$, we get

$$\begin{aligned}\rho\left(\sum_{i\in\sigma} \alpha_i x_i\right) &\le \left[\sum_{i=1}^{n-1} (\beta_i - \beta_{i+1}) + \beta_n\right] \sup\left\{\rho\left(\sum_{i=1}^{m} y_i\right) : 1 \le m \le n\right\}\\ &\le k \sup\left\{\rho\left(\sum_{i\in\sigma_1} x_i\right) : \sigma_1 \subset \sigma\right\}\end{aligned}$$

If $\{\alpha_i : i \in \sigma\}$ is an arbitrary set of real numbers, we write $\sigma = \sigma' \cup \sigma''$ with $\alpha_i \ge 0$ for $i \in \sigma'$ and $\alpha_i < 0$ for $i \in \sigma''$, and following the procedure adopted in proving the preceding inequality, we get

$$\rho\left(\sum_{i\in\sigma} \alpha_i x_i\right) \le 2k \sup\left\{\rho\left(\sum_{i\in\sigma_1} x_i\right) : \sigma_1 \subset \sigma\right\}$$

Finally, if the α_i's are complex numbers, we write $\alpha_j = \lambda_j + i\eta_j$, $i = \sqrt{-1}$. Then

$$\rho\left(\sum_{j\in\sigma} \alpha_j x_j\right) \le \rho\left(\sum_{j\in\sigma} \lambda_j x_j\right) + \rho\left(\sum_{j\in\sigma} \eta_j x_j\right) \le 4 \sup\left\{\rho\left(\sum_{j\in\sigma_1} x_j\right) : \sigma_1 \subset \sigma\right\}$$

from the previous case. □

The following corollary is a well-known result in complex analysis:

COROLLARY 3.4 If $\Sigma_{i\ge1} z_i$ is a series in $\mathbb{C}$ such that

$$\sup\left\{\left|\sum_{i\in\sigma} z_i\right| : \sigma \in \Phi\right\} = M < \infty$$

then

$$\sum_{i\in\sigma} |z_i| \le 4M \qquad \text{for all } \sigma \in \Phi$$

In particular $\Sigma_{i\ge 1} |z_i| \le 4M$.

Proof. Indeed, by Proposition 3.3, replacing $\rho(\cdot)$ by $|\cdot|$ and x_i by z_i, we get

$$\left|\sum_{i\in\sigma} \alpha_i z_i\right| \le 4 \sup_{i\in\sigma} |\alpha_i| \sup_{\sigma_1\subset\sigma} \left|\sum_{i\in\sigma_1} z_i\right|$$

Choose α_i $(i \in \sigma)$ such that $\alpha_i z_i = |z_i|$. Then

$$\sum_{i\in\sigma} |z_i| \le 4M$$

and as $\sigma \in \Phi$ is arbitrary, we get the required result. □

EXERCISE 3.5 Show that Corollary 3.4 remains valid when the set $\mathbb{N}$ is replaced by an arbitrary index set I. See Pietsch [190, p. 21].

The following result characterizes subseries convergence in F-spaces.

THEOREM 3.6 If $\Sigma_{i\ge 1} x_i$ is a series in an F-space, then the following statements are equivalent.

(i) $\Sigma_{i\ge 1} x_i$ is unconditionally convergent.

(ii) $\Sigma_{i\ge 1} x_i$ is subseries convergent.

Proof. (i) $\Rightarrow$ (ii) Suppose (ii) is not true. Then from Remark (ii) following (3.1), there exists β^1 in $\bar{b}$ such that $\Sigma_{i\ge 1} \beta_i^1 x_i$ is not convergent. Hence we can find $\varepsilon > 0$ and increasing sequences $\{p_i\}$ and $\{r_i\}$ with $p_i < r_i < p_{i+1}$ $(i \ge 1)$ such that

$$\left\|\sum_{n=p_i+1}^{r_i} \beta_n^1 x_n\right\| > \varepsilon \qquad \forall i \ge 1$$

Define β in $\bar{b}$ by letting $\beta_n = 0$ for $1 \le n \le p_1$ and for $r_i < n \le p_{i+1}$ $(i \ge 1)$, and $\beta_n = \beta_n^1$ for $p_i < n \le r_i$ $(i \ge 1)$. Then

$$\left\|\sum_{n=p_i+1}^{p_{i+1}} \beta_n x_n\right\| > \varepsilon \qquad \forall i \ge 1$$

We now construct a permutation π of $\mathbb{N}$ as follows. Let M_i denote the number of nonzero β_n's in $(p_i, p_{i+1}]$; then $1 \le M_i \le p_{i+1} - p_i$. For each integer λ, $1 \le \lambda \le M_i$, let $n(\lambda)$ be the λth index for which $\beta_{n(\lambda)} \neq 0$ and $p_i + 1 \le n(\lambda) \le p_{i+1}$. Let us define a permutation π of $\mathbb{N}$ such that $\pi(p_i + \lambda) = n(\lambda)$ and choose $\pi(n)$ arbitrarily for $p_i < n \le p_{i+1}$. Then

$$\left\| \sum_{n=p_i+1}^{p_i+M_i} x_{\pi(n)} \right\| > \varepsilon \qquad \forall i \ge 1$$

Hence $\Sigma_{i\ge 1} x_i$ is not unconditionally convergent and so (ii) is proved.

(ii) $\Longrightarrow$ (i) We first claim the uniform convergence of $\Sigma_{i\ge 1} \beta_i x_i$ relative to β in $\bar{b}$. In other words, to every $\varepsilon > 0$ we claim the existence of k_0 in $\mathbb{N}$ (k_0 being independent of β in $\bar{b}$) such that

$$\left\| \sum_{n=k}^{k+m} \beta_n x_n \right\| < \varepsilon \qquad \forall k \ge k_0,\ m \ge 0, \text{ and } \beta \in \bar{b} \tag{*}$$

Indeed, if (*) were not true, there would exist $\varepsilon > 0$, increasing sequences $\{r_k\}$ and $\{s_k\}$ with $s_k < r_{k+1}$ $(k \ge 1)$, and a sequence $\{\beta^k\} \subset \bar{b}$ such that

$$\left\| \sum_{i=r_k}^{s_k} \beta_i^k x_i \right\| \ge \varepsilon \qquad \forall k \ge 1$$

However, this leads to a contradiction if β in $\bar{b}$ is defined as follows: $\beta_i = 0$ for $1 \le i < r_1$, $s_k < i < r_{k+1}$ $(k \ge 1)$; and $\beta_i = \beta_i^k$ for $r_k \le i \le s_k$ $(k \ge 1)$.

Now, for any permutation π of $\mathbb{N}$, there exists N in $\mathbb{N}$ such that $\pi(n) \ge k_0$ for $n \ge N$. Thus, for $r \ge N$ and $s \ge 0$,

$$\left\| \sum_{k=r}^{r+s} x_{\pi(k)} \right\| = \left\| \sum_{n=i}^{j} \beta_n x_n \right\| < \varepsilon \tag{**}$$

where $i = \inf\{\pi(k) : r \le k \le r + s\}$; $j = \sup\{\pi(k) : r \le k \le r + s\}$; and

$$\beta_n = \begin{cases} 1 & \text{if } n = \pi(k),\ r \le k \le r + s \\ 0 & \text{otherwise} \end{cases}$$

From (*) and (**), there follows the convergence of the series $\Sigma_{k\ge 1} x_{\pi(k)}$ and we get (i). □

The following gives still more information (Ref. 208, p. 327):

PROPOSITION 3.7 For a series $\Sigma_{i\geq 1} x_i$ in an F-space X, the following statements are equivalent:

(i) $\Sigma_{i\geq 1} x_i$ is unconditionally convergent.

(ii) $\Sigma_{i\geq 1} \beta_i x_i$ converges in X uniformly in $\beta \in \bar{b}$.

(iii) $\Sigma_{i\geq 1} \alpha_i x_i$ converges in X uniformly in $\alpha \in \bar{a}$.

(iv) $\Sigma_{i\geq 1} \gamma_i x_i$ converges in X uniformly in $\gamma \in \bar{d}$.

Proof. From the proof of Theorem 3.6, it is clear that (i) $\Leftrightarrow$ (ii).

(ii) $\Rightarrow$ (iii) Let (iii) be not true. There exist $\varepsilon > 0$, increasing sequences $\{p_i\}$ and $\{q_i\}$ with $q_i < p_{i+1}$ $(i \geq 1)$, and a sequence $\{\alpha^i\}$ in $\bar{a}$ such that

$$\left\| \sum_{n=p_i}^{q_i} \alpha_n^i x_n \right\| > \varepsilon \qquad \forall i \geq 1$$

Define β^+ and β^- in $\bar{b}$ by $\beta_n^{\pm} = 1$ or 0 according as $\alpha_n^i = \pm 1$ or $\alpha_n^i = \mp 1$ for $p_i \leq n \leq q_i$ $(i \geq 1)$, and $\beta_n^{\pm} = 0$ for the rest of the integers n. Then

$$\left\| \sum_{n=p_i}^{q_i} \beta_n^+ x_n \right\| + \left\| \sum_{n=p_i}^{q_i} \beta_n^- x_n \right\| > \varepsilon \qquad \forall i \geq 1$$

By (ii), we find an M in $\mathbb{N}$ such that

$$\left\| \sum_{j=m}^{m+r} \beta_j x_j \right\| \leq \frac{\varepsilon}{2} \qquad \forall m \geq M,\ r \geq 0, \text{ and } \beta \in \bar{b}$$

Choose i in $\mathbb{N}$ with $p_i \geq M$; then

$$\left\| \sum_{n=p_i}^{q_i} \beta_n^+ x_n \right\| + \left\| \sum_{n=p_i}^{q_i} \beta_n^- x_n \right\| \leq \frac{\varepsilon}{2} + \frac{\varepsilon}{2} = \varepsilon$$

which obviously leads to a contradiction. Hence (iii) is proved.

(iii) $\Rightarrow$ (ii) Assume now the truth of (iii). Then to every $\varepsilon > 0$, there exists N in $\mathbb{N}$ such that

$$\left\| \sum_{i=m+1}^{n} \alpha_i x_i \right\| < \frac{\varepsilon}{2} \qquad \forall m,n \geq N,\ N \leq m \leq n$$

uniformly in $\alpha \in \bar{a}$. If $\beta \in \bar{b}$, then $\beta = (1/2)(\alpha + e)$ for some $\alpha \in \bar{a}$, where $e = \{1, 1, \ldots\} \in \bar{a}$. Thus

$$\left\| \sum_{i=m+1}^{n} \beta_i x_i \right\| < \varepsilon \qquad m,n \geq N,\ 1 \leq m \leq n$$

uniformly in $\beta \in \bar{b}$, and we get (ii). So (ii) $\Longleftrightarrow$ (iii).

Finally, observe that (iv) clearly implies (iii). To show (iii) $\Longrightarrow$ (iv), assume $\gamma \in \bar{d}$. We have subsequences J_1 and J_2 of $\mathbb{N}$ such that

$$\gamma_i = \begin{cases} 0 & i \in J_1 \\ 1 & i \in J_2 \\ -1 & i \in \mathbb{N} \sim (J_1 \cup J_2) \end{cases}$$

Define α^1 and $\alpha^2 \in \bar{a}$ by

$$\alpha_i^1 = \begin{cases} 1 & i \in J_1 \cup J_2 \\ -1 & i \in \mathbb{N} \sim (J_1 \cup J_2) \end{cases}$$

$$\alpha_i^2 = \begin{cases} -1 & i \in [\mathbb{N} \sim (J_1 \cup J_2)] \cup J_1 = \mathbb{N} \sim J_2 \\ 1 & i \in J_2 \end{cases}$$

Then $\gamma_i = (\alpha_i^1 + \alpha_i^2)/2$. Following the proof of (iii) $\Longrightarrow$ (ii), we find that (iv) is now easily obtained from (iii). Thus (iii) $\Longleftrightarrow$ (iv). □

An additional structure of local boundedness or local convexity in an F-space makes it possible to characterize bounded multiplier convergence in a fashion similar to Proposition 3.7. In this direction, let us begin with the following result (Ref. 208, p. 327).

THEOREM 3.8 Let $\Sigma_{i\geq 1} x_i$ be a series in a complete l.b. TVS (X,T). Then the following statements are equivalent:

(i) $\Sigma_{i\geq 1} x_i$ is unconditionally convergent.
(ii) $\Sigma_{i\geq 1} \alpha_i x_i$ converges in X uniformly in $\alpha \in \bar{a}$.
(iii) $\Sigma_{i\geq 1} \beta_i x_i$ converges in X uniformly in $\beta \in \bar{b}$.
(iv) $\Sigma_{i\geq 1} \gamma_i x_i$ converges in X uniformly in $\gamma \in \bar{d}$.
(v) $\Sigma_{i\geq 1} \varepsilon_i x_i$ converges in X uniformly in $\varepsilon \in \bar{e}$.
(vi) $\Sigma_{i\geq 1} x_i$ is bounded multiplier convergent.

Proof. By Proposition 1.4.9 there exists a p-homogeneous F-norm on X generating the topology T. Hence from Proposition 3.7, (i) $\Longleftrightarrow$ (ii) $\Longleftrightarrow$ (iii) $\Longleftrightarrow$ (iv). Also, (v) and (vi) are obviously equivalent. The implication (v) $\Longrightarrow$ (iv) is rather straightforward. Thus, to complete the proof, assume the truth of (iv). To show that (v) holds, it suffices to establish the inequality

$$\sup_{0\le\lambda_1\le 1} \|\lambda_1 x_1 + \cdots + \lambda_n x_n\| \le C \sup_{\varepsilon_i = 0 \text{ or } 1} \|\varepsilon_1 x_1 + \cdots + \varepsilon_n x_n\|$$

where C is a constant independent of the integer n. Indeed, we may expand each λ_i in the dyadic form

$$\lambda_i = \sum_{j\ge 1} \frac{\varepsilon_{ij}}{2^j} \qquad \varepsilon_{ij} = 0 \text{ or } 1$$

Therefore,

$$\begin{aligned}\left\|\sum_{i=1}^{n}\left(\sum_{j\ge 1}\frac{\varepsilon_{ij}}{2^j}\right)x_i\right\| &= \left\|\frac{1}{2}\left(\sum_{i=1}^{n}\varepsilon_{i1}x_i\right) + \frac{1}{2^2}\left(\sum_{i=1}^{n}\varepsilon_{i2}x_i\right) + \cdots\right\| \\ &\le \frac{1}{2^p}\sup_{\varepsilon_i=0,1}\left\|\sum_{i=1}^{n}\varepsilon_i x_i\right\| + \frac{1}{2^{2p}}\sup_{\varepsilon_i=0,1}\left\|\sum_{i=1}^{n}\varepsilon_1 x_i\right\| + \cdots \\ &= \left(\sum_{j\ge 1}\frac{1}{2^{jp}}\right)\sup_{\varepsilon_i=0,1}\left\|\sum_{i=1}^{n}\varepsilon_i x_i\right\|\end{aligned}$$

and this gives the required inequality with $C = 1/(2^p - 1) = \Sigma_{j\ge 1} 2^{-jp}$. □

In the preceding result, we can replace local boundedness by local convexity; more specifically, one has

THEOREM 3.9 For a series $\Sigma_{i\ge 1} x_i$ in a sequentially complete l.c. TVX (X,T), the statements (i) through (vi) of Theorem 3.8 are equivalent.

Proof. The implications (i) ⟺ (ii) ⟺ (iii) ⟺ (iv) virtually follow on the lines of the proof of Proposition 3.7. The results (v) ⟺ (vi) and (v) ⟹ (iv) are again straightforward. Finally, it remains to prove that (iv), or equivalently (ii), implies (v). Either we may proceed as in the preceding theorem or we may prove (v) directly from (ii) as follows. To each $\delta > 0$ and equicontinuous set $A \subset X^*$, there exists $N \in \mathbb{N}$ such that

$$\left|f\left(\sum_{i=m+1}^{n}\alpha_i x_i\right)\right| \le \frac{\delta}{2} \qquad \forall m,n \ge N$$

and uniformly in $f \in A$ and $\alpha \in \bar{a}$. For each $f \in A$, let $f_1 = R\ell(f)$ and $f_2 = \mathrm{Im}(f)$. Define $\alpha^1, \alpha^2 \in \bar{a}$ by

$$\alpha_i^1 f_1(x_i) = |f_1(x_i)| \qquad \alpha_i^2 f_2(x_i) = |f_2(x_i)| \qquad i \geq 1$$

Then for arbitrary $\varepsilon \in \bar{e}$,

$$\left|f\left(\sum_{i=m+1}^{n} \varepsilon_i x_i\right)\right| \leq \left|f_1\left(\sum_{i=m+1}^{n} \alpha_i^1 x_i\right)\right| + \left|f_2\left(\sum_{i=m+1}^{n} \alpha_i^2 x_i\right)\right| \leq \delta$$
$$\forall m,n \geq N,\ f \in A$$

Since X is sequentially complete, we get (v). □

Remark: It seems that the hypothesis of local boundedness and local convexity, respectively, in Theorems 3.7 and 3.8 is essential for the validity of (iv) ⟹ (v); in other words, merely the F-character of a TVS is not sufficient to guarantee the truth of (iv) ⟹ (v). This is indeed justified by the following example of Rolewicz and Ryll-Nardzewski [208] which we present here in the form of two lemmas and one proposition.

LEMMA 3.10 In the n-dimensional euclidean plane there is a symmetric open star set A containing all points $p_1, \ldots, p_{3^n}$ of the type $(\varepsilon_1, \ldots, \varepsilon_n)$, where $\varepsilon_i = 1$ or -1 or 0, such that the set

$$A^{n-1} = A + \cdots + A \qquad n - 1 \text{ times}$$

does not contain the unit cube $C = \{(\alpha_1, \ldots, \alpha_n) : |\alpha_i| \leq 1,\ 1 \leq i \leq n\}$.

Proof. First join the points $p_1, \ldots, p_{3^n}$ with the origin of the space and consider the set A_0 formed by such line segments. Clearly the set A_0^{n-1} is $(n - 1)$-dimensional (this situation can be visualized easily when $n = 2$ or 3, in which case we get A_0^{n-1} as a certain collection of finite lines and planes, respectively). Hence we can find sufficiently small ε such that the set $A_0^{n-1} + S_\varepsilon^{n-1}$, where S_ε is the ball of radius ε in the euclidean sense, does not contain the cube C. Let now $A = A_0 + S_\varepsilon$. Then A is obviously symmetric, open, and starlike. □

LEMMA 3.11 Let X be an n-dimensional euclidean space. Then there exists an F-norm $\|\cdot\|$ on X [i.e., $\|x - y\| = \rho(x,y)$, $x,y \in X$, ρ being an invariant metric on X] such that $\|p_i\| \leq 1$, $1 \leq i \leq 3^n$, where the p_i's are the points determined in Lemma 3.10 and there is a point $p \in C$, the unit cube in X, for which $\|p\| \geq n - 1$.

Proof. Let $U_1 = A$ of the preceding lemma. Observe that A is a symmetric neighborhood of $0 \in X$ containing the open ball S_ε for $\varepsilon > 0$. One can find a ball $U_{1/2}$ centered at the origin such that $U_{1/2} + U_{1/2} \subset U_1$. Proceeding in this manner, we get a sequence $\{U_{1/2^n}\}$ of balls at origin such that

$$U_{1/2^{n+1}} + U_{1/2^{n+1}} \subset U_{1/2^n} \qquad n = 0, 1, 2, \ldots$$

Let r be a dyadic number, that is,

$$r = n + \sum_{i=1}^{m} \frac{\varepsilon_i}{2^i}$$

where $\varepsilon_i = 1$ or 0, and define

$$U_r = U_n + \varepsilon_1 U_{1/2} + \cdots + \varepsilon_m U_{1/2^m}$$

where $U_n = A + \cdots + A$ (n times). Then U_r is a symmetric neighborhood of the origin. If $x \neq 0$, it is possible to find $U_{1/2^n}$ for some n large enough so that $x \notin U_{1/2^n}$; also, for any two dyadic numbers r and s, $U_r + U_s \subset U_{r+s}$. Now define

$$\|x\| = \inf\{r : x \in U_r\}$$

Then the above observations immediately lead to the fact that $\|\cdot\|$ is an F-norm on X. As $p_i \in U_1$, $1 \le i \le 3^n$, $\|p_i\| \le 1$. By Lemma 3.10, there exists a point $p = (\alpha_1, \ldots, \alpha_n) \notin A^{n-1} = U_{n-1}$ and so $\|p\| \ge n - 1$. □

PROPOSITION 3.12 There exists an F-space X and an infinite series $\Sigma_{i\ge1} x_i$ in X for which statement (iv) of Theorem 3.8 holds, but (v) does not.

Proof. Let X_k be a 2^k-dimensional euclidean space equipped with the F-norm $\|\cdot\|_k = 2^{-k}\|\cdot\|$, where $\|\cdot\|$ is the F-norm on X_k as constructed in Lemma 3.11.

Define X to be the space of all sequences $x = \{x_n\}$ such that

$$\delta(x) \equiv \sum_{k\ge1} \|(x_{2^{k-1}+1}, x_{2^{k-1}+2}, \ldots, x_{2^k})\|_{k-1} + |x_1| < \infty$$

Clearly (X,δ) is an F-space, the corresponding invariant metric ρ on X being given by $\rho(x,y) = \delta(x - y)$.

Let $\{\gamma_n\}$ be an arbitrary sequence of numbers 1 or -1 or 0. It is easily verified that $\Sigma_{n\ge1} \gamma_n e^n$ is convergent; indeed, one has

$$\delta\left(\sum_{i=m}^{n} \gamma_i e^i\right) \le \delta(A_0) + \delta(A_{k+1}) + \cdots + \delta(A_{k_1}) + \delta(A_0')$$

where k is the smallest integer with $m < 2^k$, k_1 is the largest integer with $n > 2^{k_1}$, and

$$A_0 = \sum_{i=m}^{2^k} \gamma_i e^i \qquad A_j = \sum_{i=2^{j-1}+1}^{2^j} \gamma_i e^i \qquad A_0' = \sum_{i=2^{k_1}+1}^{n} \gamma_i e^i$$

Now, making use of Lemma 3.11, one has

$$\delta(A_0) = \|(0,\ldots,0,\gamma_m,\gamma_{m+1},\ldots,\gamma_{2^k})\|_{k-1} \le \frac{1}{2^{k-1}}$$

$$\delta(A_j) = \|(\gamma_{2^{j-1}+1},\ldots,\gamma_{2^j})\|_{j-1} \le \frac{1}{2^{j-1}}$$

$$\delta(A_0') = \|(\gamma_{2^{k_1}+1},\ldots,\gamma_n,0,\ldots,0)\|_{k_1} \le \frac{1}{2^{k_1}}$$

where $j = k + 1, \ldots, k_1$. Therefore

$$\delta\left(\sum_{i=m}^{n} \gamma_i e^i\right) \le \frac{1}{2^{k-1}} + \frac{1}{2^k} + \cdots + \frac{1}{2^{k_1}} < \frac{1}{2^{k-2}} < \frac{4}{m}$$

which in turn establishes the required convergence. Thus the series $\Sigma_{i\ge 1} e^i$ in X satisfies (iv) of Theorem 3.8.

To prove the other part of the proposition, we once again make use of Lemma 3.11 to get for each $k \in \mathbb{N}$ a point $p^k \in X_k$, $p^k = (\lambda_1^k, \lambda_2^k, \ldots, \lambda_{2^k}^k)$, such that

$$|\lambda_i^k| \le 1 \qquad 1 \le i \le 2^k$$

$$\|p^k\|_k > \frac{1}{2^k}(2^k - 1) \ge \frac{1}{2}$$

where $k = 1, 2, 3, \ldots$

Define a sequence $\{\mu_m : m \ge 1\}$ as follows: $\mu_1 = \mu_2 = 0$; $\mu_m = \lambda_i^k$, where k is the smallest positive integer such that $m > 2^k$ and $i = m - 2^k$. That is,

$$\mu_3 = \lambda_1^1, \quad \mu_4 = \lambda_2^1, \quad \mu_5 = \lambda_1^2, \quad \mu_6 = \lambda_2^2, \quad \mu_7 = \lambda_3^2, \quad \mu_8 = \lambda_4^2,$$

$$\ldots, \quad \mu_{2^k+1} = \lambda_1^k, \quad \mu_{2^k+2} = \lambda_2^k, \quad \ldots, \quad \mu_{2^{k+1}} = \lambda_{2^k}^k, \quad \ldots$$

Clearly the sequence $\{\mu_m\}$ is bounded by 1, i.e., $\{\mu_m\} \in \bar{e}$; but for $k \geq 1$,

$$\delta\left(\sum_{i=2^k+1}^{2^{k+1}} \mu_i e^i\right) = \|(\lambda_1^k, \ldots, \lambda_{2^k}^k)\|_k \geq \frac{1}{2}$$

Thus the series $\Sigma_{i\geq 1} \mu_i e^i$ does not converge in X. Thus (v) of Theorem 3.8 is not satisfied. □

4. UNCONDITIONAL AND UNORDERED CONVERGENCE

One of the most important concepts in the theory of bases is that of an unconditional Schauder base, which decidedly requires the idea of unconditional convergence of a series and its variations, including unordered convergence. Accordingly, we begin with the following theorem, whose analog for normed spaces was first obtained by Hilderbrandt [91].

THEOREM 4.1 A series $\Sigma_{i\geq 1} x_i$ in a TVS (X,T) is unconditionally convergent if and only if it is unordered convergent.

Proof. First, suppose that the given series is unordered convergent to x. Then for each $u \in \mathcal{B}$ there corresponds $\sigma_0 \in \Phi$ such that

$$\sum_{i\in\sigma} x_i \in x + u \qquad \text{for all } \sigma \in \Phi \text{ with } \sigma \supset \sigma_0$$

For any given permutation π of $\mathbb{N}$ there exists $\mu_0 \in \Phi$ such that $\pi(\mu_0) = \sigma_0$. Let $n_0 = \max\{i : \pi(i) \in \sigma_0\} = \max\{i : i \in \mu_0\}$. Then $\mu_0 \subset \{1,2,\ldots,N\}$ and so $\sigma_0 \subset \pi(\{1,2,\ldots,N\})$ for $N > n_0$. Thus

$$\sum_{i=1}^{N} x_{\pi(i)} \in x + u \qquad \forall N > n_0,\ N \in \mathbb{N}$$

and this gives rise to unconditional convergence of the series to x.

Suppose now that the given series is unconditionally convergent to x. To prove the result, assume that the given series is not unordered convergent to x. Hence there exists some neighborhood u of $0 \in X$ such that to each $\sigma_0 \in \Phi$ there corresponds $\sigma \in \Phi$, $\sigma_0 \subset \sigma$, with

$$\sum_{i\in\sigma} x_i - x \notin u$$

Choose $v \in \mathcal{B}$ with $v + v \subset u$. From our assumption we find an $m_1 \in \mathbb{N}$ such that

$$-\sum_{i\in\sigma_1} x_i + x \in v \qquad \sigma_1 = \{1,2,\ldots,m_1\}$$

Choose $\sigma_2 \in \Phi$, $\sigma_1 \subset \sigma_2$, and

$$\sum_{i\in\sigma_2} x_i - x \notin u$$

Let $m_3 \in \mathbb{N}$ with $m_3 > \max\{i : i \in \sigma_2\}$ and $\sigma_3 = \{1,2,\ldots,m_3\}$. Then

$$-\sum_{i\in\sigma_3} x_i + x \in v$$

Again, choose $\sigma_4 \in \Phi$ with $\sigma_3 \subset \sigma_4$, $\sigma_3 \neq \sigma_4$, and

$$\sum_{i\in\sigma_4} x_i - x \notin u$$

Proceeding in this way, we find sequences $\{\sigma_n\} \subset \Phi$ and $\{m_1, m_3, m_5, \ldots\} \subset \mathbb{N}$ with $\sigma_{n-1} \subset \sigma_n$, $\sigma_{n-1} \neq \sigma_n$, $\sigma_{2n-1} = \{1, 2, \ldots, m_{2n-1}\}$, $m_{2n-1} > \max\{i : i \in \sigma_{2n-2}\}$, where $n \geq 2$, such that

$$-\sum_{i\in\sigma_{2n-1}} x_i + x \in v \qquad \sum_{i\in\sigma_{2n}} x_i - x \notin u \qquad n \geq 1$$

Writing elements of the sets $\sigma_1, \sigma_2 - \sigma_1, \ldots, \sigma_n - \sigma_{n-1}, \ldots, n \geq 1$, $\sigma_0 = \emptyset$, one after another, one gets a permutation π of $\mathbb{N}$ such that $\{\Sigma_{i=1}^n x_{\pi(i)}\}$ is not Cauchy; indeed,

$$\sum_{i\in\sigma_{2n}-\sigma_{2n-1}} x_i = \left(\sum_{i\in\sigma_{2n}} x_i - x\right) + \left(x - \sum_{i\in\sigma_{2n-1}} x_i\right) \notin v \qquad n \geq 1$$

Hence $\Sigma_{i\geq 1} x_{\pi(i)}$ is not convergent, a contradiction. □

Remark: The proof of Theorem 4.1 suggests the following: If $\Sigma_{i\geq 1} x_{\pi(i)}$ converges in a TVS (X,T) for each permutation π, then all these permuted series converge to the same point. Indeed, the convergence of all these permuted series implies the unordered convergence of $\Sigma_{i\geq 1} x_i$. If this were not the case, then $\Sigma_{i\in\sigma} x_i \not\to x$ for any $x \in X$; in particular,

$$\sum_{i \in \sigma} x_i \not\to x \qquad \text{where } x = \sum_{i \geq 1} x_i$$

Let us now proceed as in the proof of the second part of Theorem 4.1. Then we find a permutation π such that $\Sigma_{i \geq 1} x_{\pi(i)}$ is not T-Cauchy, thus contradicting the fact that $\Sigma_{i \geq 1} x_{\pi(i)}$ converges for each permutation π. So, there exists $y \in X$ such that

$$\sum_{i \in \sigma} x_i \to y$$

Following the proof of the first part of Theorem 4.1, we now deduce that

$$\sum_{i=1}^{n} x_{\pi(i)} \to y$$

for each permutation π.

Note: Following is an alternative proof of the second part of the preceding result. We follow Weill [262, p. 13].

As before, assume that the given series is not unordered convergent. This, coupled with the assumption of unconditional convergence of the same series, yields that $\{S_\sigma : \sigma \in \Phi\}$ is not a T-Cauchy net in X. Hence for some $u \in \mathcal{B}$ and each $\sigma_n^* \in \Phi$ $(n \geq 1)$, where $\inf \sigma_n^* > n$, we have

$$\sum_{i \in \sigma_n^*} x_i \notin u$$

Choose σ_1 with $\Sigma_{i \in \sigma_1} x_i \notin u$. We can find $\sigma_2 \in \Phi$ with $\inf \sigma_2 > \sup \sigma_1$ and $\Sigma_{i \in \sigma_2} x_i \notin u$. Next, choose $\sigma_3 \in \Phi$ with $\inf \sigma_3 > \sup \sigma_2$ and $\Sigma_{i \in \sigma_3} x_i \notin u$, and so on. Thus we get a sequence $\{\sigma_n\} \subset \Phi$ with $\inf \sigma_n > \sup \sigma_{n-1}$, $n \geq 1$, $\sigma_0 = \{1\}$, and $\Sigma_{i \in \sigma_n} x_i \notin u$. For each $\sigma \in \Phi$ write $\hat{\sigma} = \{i : 1 \leq i \leq \sup \sigma\}$. We may adjoin the following sets:

$$\hat{\sigma}_1 - \sigma_1, \quad \sigma_1, \quad \hat{\sigma}_2 - (\sigma_2 \cup \hat{\sigma}_1), \quad \sigma_2, \quad \sigma_3 - (\sigma_3 \cup \hat{\sigma}_2), \quad \sigma_3, \quad \ldots$$
$$\hat{\sigma}_n - (\sigma_n \cup \hat{\sigma}_{n-1}), \quad \sigma_n, \quad \ldots$$

to define a permutation π on $\mathbb{N}$. One can easily check that to each $n \in \mathbb{N}$ there correspond integers $n_1, n_2 \in \mathbb{N}$ with $n_2 \geq n_1 \geq n$ and $\sigma_n = \{p(n_1), p(n_1 + 1), \ldots, p(n_2)\}$. Hence

$$\sum_{i=n_1}^{n_2} x_{\pi(i)} = \sum_{i\in\sigma_n} x_i \notin u$$

This contradiction once again establishes the required result.

The preceding proof as well as the proof of the first part of Theorem 4.1 immediately lead to the following result:

PROPOSITION 4.2 A series $\Sigma_{i\geq 1} x_i$ in a TVS X is unconditionally Cauchy if and only if it is unordered Cauchy.

From Theorem 4.1 and Corollary 3.4 we derive

PROPOSITION 4.3 A series $\Sigma_{i\geq 1} z_i$ in $\mathbb{C}$ is unconditionally convergent if and only if there is $M > 0$ for which

$$\sum_{i\in\sigma} |z_i| \leq M \qquad \forall\sigma \in \Phi$$

Proof. Let $\sigma_0 \in \Phi$ and $z \in \mathbb{C}$. Then for any $\sigma \in \Phi$, we have

$$\left|\sum_{i\in\sigma} z_i\right| \leq \left|\sum_{i\in\sigma\cup\sigma_0} z_i - z\right| + |z| + \sum_{i\in\sigma_0} |z_i|$$

Assuming now the given series is unconditionally convergent to z, we deduce a $\sigma_0 \in \Phi$ for which the right-hand estimate is bounded by M/4 (say). Now apply Corollary 3.4 to get the first part of the proposition.

To prove the converse, let $M_0 = \sup\{\Sigma_{i\in\sigma}|z_i| : \sigma \in \Phi\}$. There exists a sequence $\{\sigma_n\} \subset \Phi$, $\sigma_n \subset \sigma_{n+1}$, $n \geq 1$, such that

$$M_0 \leq \sum_{i\in\sigma_n} |z_i| + \frac{1}{n} \qquad \forall n \geq 1$$

Hence for all σ with $\sigma \in \Phi$ and $\sigma \cap \sigma_n = \emptyset$, $n \geq 1$, one has

$$\sum_{i\in\sigma} |z_i| \leq \frac{1}{n}$$

If we set $S_n = \Sigma_{i\in\sigma_n} z_i$, it follows that $\{S_n\}$ is a Cauchy sequence in $\mathbb{C}$ which converges to an element S in $\mathbb{C}$. Thus to each $\varepsilon > 0$ there corresponds $N \in \mathbb{N}$, $N \geq 2/\varepsilon$ such that $|S_N - S| \leq \varepsilon/2$. Hence, for each $\sigma \in \Phi$ with $\sigma \supset \sigma_N$, we have

$$|S_\sigma - S| = \left| \sum_{i \in \sigma - \sigma_N} z_i + S_N - S \right| \le \frac{1}{N} + \frac{\varepsilon}{2} \le \varepsilon$$

which in turn implies the unconditional convergence of the required series. □

A frequently useful criterion for unconditional convergence in locally convex spaces (see Ref. 167, p. 194; Ref. 262, p. 18) is contained in

THEOREM 4.4 A series $\Sigma_{i\ge1} x_i$ in a sequentially complete l.c. TVS (X,T) is unconditionally convergent if and only if $\Sigma_{i\ge1} |f(x_i)|$ converges uniformly in $f \in A$ for any given equicontinuous subset $A \subset X^*$.

Proof. Suppose the series is unconditionally convergent and let A be an arbitrary equicontinuous subset of X^*. From Proposition 1.7.6, there exists a $u \in \mathcal{B}$ with $A \subset u°$. Using Theorem 4.1, one gets an $N \in \mathbb{N}$ such that

$$\sum_{i\in\sigma} x_i \in u \qquad \forall \sigma \in \Phi \text{ with } \inf \sigma \ge N$$

Thus

$$\left| f\left(\sum_{i\in\sigma} x_i \right) \right| \le 1 \qquad \forall f \in A \text{ and } \sigma \in \Phi \text{ with } \inf \sigma \ge N$$

and this inequality along with an application of Corollary 3.4 yields

$$\sum_{i\ge N} |f(x_i)| < 4 \qquad \text{uniformly in } f \in A$$

Hence the first part is proved.

To establish the sufficiency, let us assume that for each equicontinuous subset A of X^*, the series $\Sigma_{i\ge1} |f(x_i)|$ converges uniformly in $f \in A$. Let $c \in \ell^\infty$ and $u \in \mathcal{B}$. From Proposition 1.7.6, one finds an equicontinuous subset A of X^* with $A° \subset u$, and so by hypothesis there exists an N in $\mathbb{N}$ such that

$$\left| f\left(\sum_{i=m}^{n} c_i x_i \right) \right| \le k \qquad \forall n,m \ge N \text{ and } f \in A$$

where $k = \sup\{|c_i| : i \ge 1\}$. If $\lambda_i = c_i/k$, one finds, since X is sequentially complete, that $\Sigma_{i\ge1} \lambda_i x_i$ converges in X. Hence by Theorem 3.9, (vi) $\Longrightarrow$ (i), the series $\Sigma_{i\ge1} x_i$ is unconditionally convergent. □

Note: In addition to the characterizations of unconditional convergence mentioned in this section, the reader is referred to Theorems 3.6, 3.8, 3.9, and Proposition 3.7 in the last section for further criteria for this mode of convergence in terms of subseries convergence and bounded multiplier convergence.

EXERCISE 4.5 If a series $\Sigma_{i\geq 1} x_i$ in an l.c. TVS (X,T) is subseries convergent, show that it is unconditionally convergent. [Hint: Use the techniques of proof of Theorem 3.6 and Proposition 4.2 to conclude the unordered Cauchy character of the series and make use of Proposition 1.7.4; see also Ref. 202, p. 153.]

EXERCISE 4.6 Show that a series $\Sigma_{i\geq 1} x_i$ in a TVS (X,T) is unordered Cauchy if and only if to each $u \in \mathcal{B}$ there corresponds a $\sigma_0 \in \Phi$ such that $S_\sigma \in u$ for all σ in Φ with $\sigma \cap \sigma_0 = \emptyset$.

5. INTERRELATIONSHIPS OF TYPES OF CONVERGENCE

To emphasize the distinctions among the notions of convergence treated in the preceding paragraphs, we take up in this section a study of the relationships among them. Some of these notions are only restatements of one another. For instance, in any TVS, unconditional convergence and unordered convergence are the same, and so are subseries convergence and its equivalent form mentioned in the remark after (3.1). Some results are not so trivial; for example, see Theorems 3.6, 3.8, 3.9, and Proposition 3.7.

In any finite dimensional space, all these notions are equivalent, and therefore we consider only infinite dimensional TVS. However, the richer the structure of a TVS, the better are the chances of these notions coming close to one another. Indeed, in any nuclear Fréchet space, all these notions are equivalent; consequently, to embark upon this analysis, we confine our attention to the following three types of problems:

(i) When unconditional convergence implies bounded multiplier convergence.

(ii) When absolute convergence implies unconditional convergence.

(iii) When unconditional convergence implies absolute convergence.

To deal with (i), let us recall Proposition 3.12. We state and prove the following result of Turpin [258], the proof of which is closely related to that of Theorem 3.8, (iv) $\Rightarrow$ (v) (cf. also Ref. 208, Theorem 1).

PROPOSITION 5.1 Let X be an F-space which is also a $P(1/2^n)$ space. Then each unconditionally convergent series $\Sigma_{i\geq 1} x_i$ in X is bounded multiplier convergent.

Proof. Let $\Sigma_{i\geq 1} x_i$ be unconditionally convergent. Our result would follow if we could show that $\Sigma_{i\geq 1} \alpha_i x_i$ converges in X for any given sequence $\{\alpha_n\}$ with $0 \leq \alpha_n \leq 1$, $n \geq 1$.

Let $u \in \mathcal{B}$ be chosen arbitrarily. From Definition 1.10.1 (viii), we get a $v \in \mathcal{B}$ such that

$$v + \frac{1}{2} v + \cdots + \frac{1}{2^n} v + \cdots \subset u$$

By Proposition 3.7, (i) $\Rightarrow$ (ii), we deduce the existence of an N in $\mathbb{N}$ such that

$$\sum_{i=m}^{n} \beta_i x_i \in v \qquad \forall m,n \geq N$$

uniformly in $\beta = \{\beta_i\} \in \bar{b}$. Now take $\{\alpha_n\}$ as suggested above and expand each α_n in the dyadic system:

$$\alpha_n = \sum_{r\geq 0} \frac{\alpha_{n,r}}{2^r} \qquad \alpha_{n,r} = 0 \text{ or } 1$$

Then for $m,n \geq N$,

$$\sum_{i=m}^{n} \alpha_i x_i = \sum_{i=m}^{n} \left(\sum_{r\geq 0} \frac{\alpha_{i,r}}{2^r} \right) x_i = \sum_{r\geq 0} \frac{1}{2^r} \sum_{i=m}^{n} \alpha_{i,r} x_i$$

$$\in v + \frac{1}{2} v + \cdots + \frac{1}{2^r} v + \cdots \subset u$$

Since $u \in \mathcal{B}$ is arbitrary, we get the result. □

With regard to problem (ii) above, let us recall that the notions of absolute convergence and unconditional convergence are equivalent in any finite dimensional TVS: indeed, this is the classical result of Riemann (cf. Ref. 164, p. 22). Let us further observe that in a sequentially complete locally convex space, each absolutely convergent series is unconditionally convergent, and it seems that the local convexity of a TVS plays a central role in forcing an absolutely convergent series to be unconditionally convergent. In fact, one has

PROPOSITION 5.2 An F-space (X,T) is a Fréchet space if and only if every absolutely convergent series in X is unconditionally convergent.

Proof. Assume first that (X,T) is a Fréchet space and suppose that $\Sigma_{i\geq 1} x_i$ is absolutely convergent. For any $p \in D$, $\gamma = \{\gamma_i\} \in \bar{d}$, and positive integers m and n with $m \leq n$, we have

$$p\left(\sum_{i=m}^{n} \gamma_i x_i\right) \leq \sum_{i=m}^{n} p(x_i)$$

which tends to zero as $m,n \to \infty$. Hence the unconditional convergence of $\Sigma_{i\geq 1} x_i$ follows from Theorem 3.9.

To establish the sufficiency, assume that (X,T) is not locally convex. We may choose the system $\mathcal{B}$ as $\{u_m : m \geq 1\}$, with $u_{m+1} \subset (1/2)u_m$, $m \geq 1$. Following Propositions 1.8.8 and 1.8.9, we deduce the existence of a balanced and convex neighborhood v of 0 in (X,T) such that $u_m \not\subset v$, $m \geq 1$; that is, $\mathrm{con}(u_m) \not\subset v$, $m \geq 1$. Thus for each $m \geq 1$ there are elements $x_1^{(m)}$, ..., $x_{n_m}^{(m)}$ of u_m and reals $\alpha_1^{(m)}$, ..., $\alpha_{n_m}^{(m)}$ in $\mathbb{R}^+$ such that

$$\sum_{i=m}^{n_m} \alpha_i^{(m)} x_i^{(m)} \notin v \qquad \sum_{i=1}^{n_m} \alpha_i^{(m)} = 1 \tag{*}$$

We can arrange the elements $\alpha_i^{(m)} x_i^{(m)}$ in a sequence $\{y_n\}$. It is seen that the series $\Sigma_{n\geq 1} y_n$ is absolutely convergent in (X,T). In fact, let us denote by p_k the pseudonorm generated by u_k. Then for $M,N > k$, we have

$$\sum_{m=M}^{N} \sum_{i=1}^{n_m} p_k(\alpha_i^{(m)} x_i^{(m)}) \leq \sum_{m=M}^{N} \frac{1}{2^{m-k}} < \frac{1}{2^{M-1-k}}$$

since $u_m \subset (1/2^{m-k})u_k$ and consequently $p_k \leq (1/2^{m-k})p_m$. However, it follows from (*) that the series $\Sigma_{n\geq 1} y_n$ is not unconditionally convergent. This contradiction completes the proof. □

We take up problem (iii), and to begin we recall the following *theorem of Dvoretzky and Rogers* [50]:

THEOREM 5.3 Let X be a Banach space. Then each unconditionally convergent series is absolutely convergent if and only if X is finite dimensional.

In view of this theorem, in every infinite dimensional Banach space there exists an unconditionally convergent series which is not absolutely convergent. This fact has been further strengthened by Dvoretzky [49, Theorem 3]:

THEOREM 5.4 In each infinite dimensional locally bounded (l.b. TVS) complete space there exists an unconditionally convergent series which is not absolutely convergent.

Rolewicz [206] has claimed a further generalization of the preceding result; however, in accordance with the present terminology, the word "absolutely" in his theorem needs replacement by "strongly absolutely;" if we go that way, we may state the theorem as follows:

THEOREM 5.5 In every infinite dimensional F*-space there exists an unconditionally convergent series which is not strongly absolutely convergent.

Note: Proofs of the two theorems above involve the idea of short straight lines (see for instance Ref. 19, Theorem 9) and are rather lengthy; the scope of the present book prevents us from including them.

Remarks: Theorem 5.4 gives only a partial answer to problem (iii) mentioned in the beginning of this section. In general, the solution is not known. In case of locally convex spaces, the problem has been solved by Grothendieck (see Refs. 70, 72, 73, and 74) in the form of

THEOREM 5.6 Let (X,T) be a Fréchet space. Then each unconditionally convergent series in X is absolutely convergent if and only if (X,T) is nuclear.

Once again, the proof of the theorem does not find its scope within the framework of this book and one may either consult Pietsch [190] or Rolewicz [207, p. 180]. [Note: The reader may, however, easily verify the truth of the sufficiency part of this theorem by using the definition of absolutely summing operators and Theorem 3.8, (i) $\Longleftrightarrow$ (ii).]

Remark: In Theorem 5.5, one cannot replace strongly absolutely convergent series by absolutely convergent series, for otherwise the space of all entire functions equipped with the usual compact-open topology (Refs. 114 and 116), which is already known to be a non-locally-bounded Fréchet and nuclear space (Ref. 121 and 173), would be finite dimensional--a contradiction to the fact that this space is infinite dimensional.

Comments on the Dvoretzky-Rogers Theorem

For any l.c. TVS (X,T) and any perfect sequence space λ, let

$$\lambda[X] = \{\{x_i\} : x_i \in X,\ i \geq 1, \text{ and } \{f(x_i)\} \in \lambda,\ \forall f \in X^*\}$$

and

$$\lambda(X) = \{\{x_i\} : x_i \in X,\ i \geq 1, \text{ and } \{p(x_i)\} \in \lambda,\ \forall p \in D\}$$

In view of Theorem 4.4, Theorem 5.3 can be rephrased as

THEOREM 5.7 Let X be a Banach space. Then $\ell^1[X] = \ell^1(X)$ if and only if X is finite dimensional.

Theorem 5.7 still holds if ℓ^1 is replaced by ℓ^p $(1 < p < \infty)$. This is shown in Ref. 75.

Rosier [214] has shown that Theorem 5.7 remains true when ℓ^1 is replaced by any perfect sequence space λ such that $(\lambda, \eta(\lambda, \lambda^\times))$ is non-nuclear (cf. Theorem 4.7.9).

The question whether Theorem 5.7 is still valid when ℓ^1 is replaced by any perfect Banach sequence space has been partially answered by De Grande-De Kimpe [38, p. 142]. Kalton and Ruckle [111] have also strengthened the Dvoretzky-Rogers theorem in another direction, in terms of the space $L_p(\mu)$, using the techniques of the duality of vector-valued sequence spaces. The subject matter of the preceding discussion does not, however, fall within the scope of the present project and therefore a detailed study is postponed to our work in Ref. 131.

6. UNORDERED BOUNDEDNESS

The purpose of this section is to give a useful criterion for weak unconditional convergence like that of Proposition 4.3. In the course of our discussion we need the concept of unordered boundedness of an infinite series defined as follows:

DEFINITION 6.1 A series $\Sigma_{i\geq 1} x_i$ in a TVS X is said to be *unordered bounded* if the net $\{S_\sigma : \sigma \in \Phi\}$ is bounded in X.

In what follows we first take up the characterization of unordered boundedness of an infinite series, and although this result can be proved by the methods and techniques used earlier, it is interesting to prove it by using the following result of McArthur [167, p. 193]:

THEOREM 6.2 Let (X,T) be an l.c. TVS containing a sequence $\{x_i\}$. Then the following statements are equivalent:

(i) $\{x_i\}$ is $\sigma(X,X^*)$-Cauchy $\Longrightarrow$ $\{x_i\}$ is T-Cauchy.

(ii) $\{f_n\}$ is an equicontinuous sequence in X^* with $\lim_{n\to\infty} f_n(x_i) = 0$ for each $i \geq 1 \Longrightarrow \lim_{n\to\infty} f_n(x_i) = 0$ uniformly in $x_i \in \{x_j\}$.

Proof. (i) $\Longrightarrow$ (ii) To prove this implication consider $U_{\varepsilon/2} = \{\lambda : |\lambda| \leq \varepsilon/2\}$ for a given $\varepsilon > 0$. Then by equicontinuity of $\{f_n\}$, there exists a neighborhood $v \in \mathcal{B}$ such that $v \subset f_n^{-1}[U_{\varepsilon/2}]$ for all $n \geq 1$. Also, if $\{x_i\}$ is a $\sigma(X,X^*)$-Cauchy sequence, by (i) there exists $N = N(v) \in \mathbb{N}$ such that $x_i - x_j \in v$ for all $i,j \geq N$. Hence $|f_n(x_i - x_j)| \leq \varepsilon/2$ for all $n \geq 1$ and $i,j \geq N$. Since $\lim_{n\to\infty} f_n(x_i) = 0$ for $i \geq 1$, it follows that $f_n(x_i - x_j) \xrightarrow{n} 0$ for $i,j \in \mathbb{N}$, and hence one can find a positive integer M such that $|f_n(x_i - x_j)| \leq \varepsilon/2$ for all $n \geq M$ and $1 \leq i,j < N$. Therefore $|f_n(x_i - x_j)| \leq \varepsilon/2$ for all $n \geq M$ and uniformly in $i,j \in \mathbb{N}$. One can now easily derive $\lim_{n\to\infty} f_n(x_i) = 0$ uniformly in $x_i \in \{x_j\}$.

(ii) $\Longrightarrow$ (i) Assume (i) is not true. Then there exists a neighborhood $v \in \mathcal{B}$ and an increasing sequence $\{i_n\} \subset \mathbb{N}$ such that $x_{i_{n+1}} - x_{i_n} \notin v$ for all $n \geq 1$. Then by Proposition 1.6.3, we can find a sequence $\{f_n\} \subset X^*$ such that $\sup\{|f_n(x)| : x \in v\} < |f_n(x_{i_{n+1}} - x_{i_n})|$. In particular, we can choose $\{f_n\}$ such that $f_n(x_{i_{n+1}} - x_{i_n}) = 1$, $\sup\{|f_n(x)| : x \in v\} < 1$. Thus the sequence $\{f_n\}$ is equicontinuous and therefore pointwise bounded, by Proposition 1.7.6. Hence there exists a subsequence $\{f_{1,m}(x_1)\}$ of $\{f_n(x_1)\}$ such that $f_{1,m}(x_1) \xrightarrow{m} r_1$, for some $r_1 \in \mathbb{R}$. Considering $\{f_{1,m}(x_2)\}$, we get a subsequence $\{f_{2,m}(x_2)\}$ of $\{f_{1,m}(x_2)\}$ such that $f_{2,m}(x_2) \xrightarrow{m} r_2$, where

$r_2 \in \mathbb{R}$. Observe that $\{f_{2,m}\} \subset \{f_{1,m}\} \subset \{f_m\}$. We proceed in this way indefinitely to get sequences $\{f_{n,m}\}$, $m,n \geq 1$, such that $\{f_m\} \supset \{f_{1,m}\} \supset \{f_{2,m}\} \supset \cdots \supset \{f_{n,m}\} \supset \cdots$ and $\lim_{m\to\infty} f_{n,m}(x_n) = r_n$, $n \geq 1$. Let us consider the diagonal sequence $\{f_{n,n}\}$ which, being equicontinuous, has a $\sigma(X^*,X)$-cluster point g, by Theorem 1.7.12. One can also easily check that $\lim_{n\to\infty} f_{n,n}(x_i) = r_i$, $i \geq 1$. Hence $g(x_i) = r_i$, $i \geq 1$. Thus we conclude that there is a subsequence $\{f_{n_k}\}$ of $\{f_n\}$, having a $\sigma(X^*,X)$-cluster point g such that $\lim_{k\to\infty} f_{n_k}(x_i) = g(x_i)$, $i \geq 1$. Moreover, the sequence $\{f_{n_k} - g\}$ is equicontinuous, $(f_{n_k} - g)(x_i) \to 0$ as $k \to \infty$ for $i \geq 1$, and the sequence $\{g(x_i)\}$ is Cauchy. Consequently, $(f_{n_k} - g)(x_{i_{n_{k+1}}} - x_{i_{n_k}}) = 1 - g(x_{i_{n_{k+1}}} - x_{i_{n_k}})$ and $|g(x_{i_{n_{k+1}}} - x_{i_{n_k}})| \leq 1/2$ for $k \geq k_0$ imply $|(f_{n_k} - g)(x_{i_{n_{k+1}}} - x_{i_{n_k}})| \geq 1/2$, for all $k \geq k_0$. Hence $\{f_{n_k} - g\}$ does not converge to zero uniformly on $\{x_i - x_j : i,j \geq 1\}$. Since the uniform convergence of $\{f_{n_k} - g\}$ on $\{x_i - x_j : i,j \geq 1\}$ to zero is equivalent to its uniform convergence to zero on $\{x_i\}$, we arrive at a contradiction and the result follows. □

The following is also known (Ref. 170):

THEOREM 6.3 Let $\Sigma_{i=1}^{\infty} x_i$ be a series in an l.c. TVS (X,T). Then the following statements are equivalent:

(i) For an equicontinuous subset B of X*, there is a constant M_B such that $\Sigma_{i\geq 1} |f(x_i)| \leq M_B$ for all $f \in B$.

(ii) $\Sigma_{i\geq 1} |f(x_i)| < \infty$ for each $f \in X^*$.

(iii) $\Sigma_{i\geq 1} x_i$ is unordered bounded.

(iv) For an arbitrary continuous seminorm ρ on X,

$$C_\rho = \sup\left\{\rho\left(\sum_{i\in\sigma} x_i\right) : \sigma \in \Phi\right\} < \infty$$

(v) For $p \in D$, $\sup\{p(\Sigma_{i\in\sigma} x_i) : \sigma \in \Phi\} < \infty$.

(vi) For each $c = \{c_i\} \in c_0$, the partial sums of $\Sigma_{i\geq 1} c_i x_i$ form a Cauchy sequence.

Proof. (i) $\Longrightarrow$ (ii) Obvious.

(ii) $\Longrightarrow$ (iii) For any $f \in X^*$ and $\sigma \in \Phi$, $|f(S_\sigma)| \le \Sigma_{i\ge 1} |f(x_i)| < \infty$. Thus $\{S_\sigma : \sigma \in \Phi\}$ is weakly bounded, and hence bounded, by the Mackey theorem.

(iii) $\Longrightarrow$ (iv) C_ρ is clearly finite by continuity of ρ and (iii).

(iv) $\Longrightarrow$ (v) Trivial.

(v) $\Longrightarrow$ (vi) Let $M_p = \sup\{p(\Sigma_{i\in\sigma} x_i) : \sigma \in \Phi\}$, $p \in D$. For $\varepsilon > 0$ and $\{c_i\} \in c_0$, there exists $N \equiv N(\varepsilon,p)$ such that $|c_i| < \varepsilon/4M_p$, whenever $i \ge N$. Hence from Corollary 3.3, $p(\Sigma_{i=r}^{s} c_i x_i) \le 4M_p \sup_{r\le i\le s} |c_i| < \varepsilon$ for $s \ge r \ge N$. Thus (vi) follows.

(vi) $\Longrightarrow$ (ii) For $f \in X^*$ and $\{c_i\} \in c_0$, the series $\Sigma_{i\ge 1} c_i f(x_i)$ obviously converges. (ii) now follows from

LEMMA 6.4 If $\Sigma_{i\ge 1} a_i$ is a series of reals such that $\Sigma_{i\ge 1} c_i a_i$ converges whenever $\{c_i\} \in c_0$, then $\Sigma_{i\ge 1} |a_i| < \infty$.

Proof. For a given $\{c_i\} \in c_0$, define

$$d_i = \begin{cases} \dfrac{|c_i a_i|}{a_i} & \text{if } a_i \ne 0 \\ 0 & \text{if } a_i = 0 \end{cases}$$

Obviously $\{d_i\} \in c_0$, and convergence of $\Sigma\, d_i a_i$ implies $\Sigma_{i\ge 1} |c_i a_i| < \infty$, i.e., $\{c_i a_i\} \in \ell^1$. Thus, there is a natural mapping $T\colon c_0 \to \ell^1$ with $T(\{c_i\}) = \{c_i a_i\}$. For each $\{c_i\} \in c_0$, define $T_n(\{c_i\})$ to be the nth section of $T(\{c_i\})$. Clearly $\{T_n\}$ converges pointwise to T in c_0 and continuity of T_n, $n \ge 1$, follows from

$$\|T_n(\{c_i\})\| = \sum_{i=1}^{n} |c_i a_i| \le A(n) \sup_{i\ge 1} |c_i| = A(n)\|\{c_i\}\|$$

Therefore T is continuous by Theorem 1.3.20. Hence for each $n \ge 1$,

$$\sum_{i=1}^{n} |a_i| = \|T(e^{(n)})\| \le \|T\|\|e^{(n)}\| = \|T\|$$

and the result follows. □

Returning to the proof of Theorem 6.3, we have proved so far (i) $\Longrightarrow$ (ii) $\Longleftrightarrow$ (iii) $\Longleftrightarrow$ (iv) $\Longleftrightarrow$ (v) $\Longleftrightarrow$ (vi), and we need

(ii) $\Longrightarrow$ (i) Let B be an equicontinuous subset of X*. Then $\rho(x) = \sup\{|f(x)| : f \in B\}$ defines a continuous seminorm on X and by equivalent condition (iv), we have $C_\rho = \sup\{\rho(\Sigma_{i\in\sigma} x_i) : \sigma \in \Phi\} < \infty$. Hence $|f(\Sigma_{i\in\sigma} x_i)| \le C_\rho$ for all $f \in B$ and $\sigma \in \Phi$. Therefore by Corollary 3.3, $\Sigma_{i\ge 1} |f(x_i)| \le 4C_\rho$ for all $f \in B$. □

Remark: In Ref. 167, McArthur proves the equivalence of conditions (i), (ii), (iii), and (vi) by a different method. Indeed, he shows (i) $\Longleftrightarrow$ (ii) $\Longleftrightarrow$ (iii) and (i) $\Longrightarrow$ (vi) $\Longrightarrow$ (ii). The reader can easily verify (iii) $\Longrightarrow$ (i) (cf. Exercise 6.5). The implications (i) $\Longrightarrow$ (ii) $\Longrightarrow$ (iii), (vi) $\Longrightarrow$ (ii), are proved as above. The proof of (i) $\Longrightarrow$ (vi) makes use of Theorem 6.3 and runs as follows:

(i) $\Longrightarrow$ (vi) For an arbitrary member $c = \{c_i\} \in c_0$ and $f \in X^*$, one has $\Sigma_{i\ge 1} |f(c_i x_i)| \le \|c\| \Sigma_{i\ge 1}^{\infty} |f(x_i)| < \infty$, and so $\{\Sigma_{i=1}^{p} c_i x_i : p \in \mathbb{N}\}$ is a $\sigma(X,X^*)$-Cauchy sequence. If $\{f_n\}$ is an equicontinuous sequence in X* with $\lim_{n\to\infty} f_n(\Sigma_{i=1}^{p} c_i x_i) = 0$ for each $p \in \mathbb{N}$, there exists a constant $K > 0$ such that $\Sigma_{i\ge 1} |f_n(x_i)| \le K$ for all $n \in \mathbb{N}$, by our hypothesis. Moreover, $\lim_{n\to\infty} f_n(\Sigma_{i=1}^{p} c_i x_i) = 0$ implies that $\lim_{n\to\infty} f_n(x_i) = 0$ if $c_i \ne 0$. Also, for given $\varepsilon > 0$, there corresponds $N \in \mathbb{N}$ such that $|c_i| \le \varepsilon/2K$ for all $i > N$, and so there is an integer M with $\Sigma_{i=1}^{N} |f_n(c_i x_i)| \le \varepsilon/2$ for all $n \ge M$ Hence

$$\sum_{i\ge 1} |f_n(c_i x_i)| = \sum_{i=1}^{N} |f_n(c_i x_i)| + \sum_{i\ge N+1} |f_n(c_i x_i)| \le \frac{\varepsilon}{2} + \frac{\varepsilon}{2K} \cdot K = \varepsilon$$

$$\text{for all } n \ge M$$

Thus $\lim_{n\to\infty} \Sigma_{i\ge 1} |f_n(c_i x_i)| = 0$, from which we conclude that $\lim_{n\to\infty} f_n(\Sigma_{i=1}^{p} c_i x_i) = 0$ uniformly in $p \in \mathbb{N}$. Now (vi) follows from Theorem 6.2. □

EXERCISE 6.5 Prove the implication (iii) $\Longrightarrow$ (i) of Theorem 6.3. [Hint: Use Proposition 1.7.6 and Proposition 3.3.]

Another set of conditions characterizing unordered boundedness (Ref. 262, p. 15; Ref. 263, p. 471) is contained in

THEOREM 6.6 For a series $\Sigma_{i\ge 1} x_i$ in an l.c. TVS X, the following statements are equivalent:

(i) $\Sigma_{i\geq 1} x_i$ is unordered bounded.

(ii) $\Sigma_{i\geq 1} x_i$ is weakly unordered Cauchy.

(iii) The set $\{\Sigma_{i=1}^n \alpha_i x_i : \{\alpha_i\} \in \bar{a}, n \in \mathbb{N}\}$ is bounded.

(iv) The set $\{\Sigma_{i=1}^n \beta_i x_i : \{\beta_i\} \in \bar{b}, n \in \mathbb{N}\}$ is bounded.

(v) The set $\{\Sigma_{i=1}^n \varepsilon_i x_i : \{\varepsilon_i\} \in \bar{e}, n \in \mathbb{N}\}$ is bounded.

Proof. (i) $\Rightarrow$ (ii) For $f \in X^*$, it follows from (iii) $\Rightarrow$ (ii) of Theorem 6.3 that $\Sigma_{i\geq 1} |f(x_i)| < \infty$. Hence $\Sigma_{i\geq 1} f(x_i)$ is unconditionally convergent, by the Riemann theorem (cf. proof of Proposition 5.1). Consequently, $\Sigma_{i\geq 1} x_i$ is weakly unordered convergent and (ii) follows.

(ii) $\Rightarrow$ (i) If u is an arbitrary $\sigma(X,X^*)$-neighborhood of $0 \in X$, there exists a balanced $\sigma(X,X^*)$-neighborhood v of $0 \in X$ such that $v + v \subset u$. By (ii), there exists $N = N(v)$ with $\Sigma_{i\in\sigma} x_i \in v$ for all $\sigma \in \Phi$, $\inf \sigma > N$. Also, for the set $\{\Sigma_{i\in\lambda} x_i : \lambda \in \Phi, \lambda \subset \{1,2,\ldots,N\}\}$, which is finite, there exists $\alpha > 0$ such that $\Sigma_{i\in\lambda} x_i \in \alpha v$ for all $\lambda \subset \{1,2,\ldots,N\}$. Since any $\sigma \in \Phi$ can be written as $\sigma = \mu \cup \lambda$ where $\inf \mu > N$ and $\lambda \subset \{1,2,\ldots,N\}$, one has for $\sigma \in \Phi$,

$$\sum_{i\in\sigma} x_i = \sum_{i\in\mu} x_i + \sum_{i\in\lambda} x_i \in v + \alpha v \subset \max\{1,\alpha\}u$$

This proves (i).

The implications (i) $\Leftrightarrow$ (iv), (v) $\Rightarrow$ (iii), and (v) $\Rightarrow$ (iv) are obvious and their proofs are therefore omitted. Thus we have proved so far the following:

$$\begin{array}{l}(iv) \Leftrightarrow (i) \Leftrightarrow (ii)\\ \Uparrow\\ (v) \Rightarrow (iii)\end{array}$$

and it remains to show (iii) $\Rightarrow$ (v) and (iv) $\Rightarrow$ (iii).

(iii) $\Rightarrow$ (v) Consider an arbitrary neighborhood u of $0 \in X$. Then by Proposition 1.7.6, there corresponds an equicontinuous subset A of X^* such that $A^\circ \subset u$. Using (iii), there exists a constant $\alpha > 0$ such that for $n \geq 1$ and $\{\alpha_i\} \in \bar{a}$, $\Sigma_{i=1}^n \alpha_i x_i \in \alpha A^\circ$, i.e., $|f(\Sigma_{i=1}^n \alpha_i x_i)| \leq \alpha$ for all $n \geq 1$, all $f \in A$, and $\{\alpha_i\} \in \bar{a}$. Now choose any $n \in \mathbb{N}$, $\{\varepsilon_i\} \in \bar{e}$, and $f \in A$. Write $f_1 = \mathrm{R}\ell(f)$, $f_2 = \mathrm{Im}(f)$, and define

$$\alpha_i = \begin{cases} \dfrac{|f_1(x_i)|}{f_1(x_i)} & \text{if } f_1(x_i) \neq 0 \\ 1 \text{ or } -1 & \text{if } f_1(x_i) = 0 \end{cases}$$

$$\lambda_i = \begin{cases} \dfrac{|f_2(x_i)|}{f_2(x_i)} & \text{if } f_2(x_i) \neq 0 \\ 1 \text{ or } -1 & \text{if } f_2(x_i) = 0 \end{cases}$$

Then

$$\begin{aligned} \left|\sum_{i=1}^{n} \varepsilon_i f(x_i)\right| &\leq \sum_{i=1}^{n} |f_1(x_i)| + \sum_{i=1}^{n} |f_2(x_i)| \\ &= \sum_{i=1}^{n} \alpha_i f_i(x_i) + \sum_{i=1}^{n} \alpha_i f_2(x_i) \\ &= \left|f_1\left(\sum_{i=1}^{n} \alpha_i x_i\right)\right| + \left|f_2\left(\sum_{i=1}^{n} \alpha_i x_i\right)\right| \\ &\leq \left|f\left(\sum_{i=1}^{n} \alpha_i x_i\right)\right| + \left|f\left(\sum_{i=1}^{n} \lambda_i x_i\right)\right| \leq 2\alpha \end{aligned}$$

since $\{\alpha_i\}$ and $\{\lambda_i\} \in \bar{a}$. As $n \in \mathbb{N}$, $f \in A$, and $\{\varepsilon_i\} \in \bar{e}$ are arbitrary, we find that $\Sigma_{i=1}^{n} \varepsilon_i x_i \in 2\alpha A^\circ \subset 2\alpha u$ for all $n \in \mathbb{N}$ and all $\{\varepsilon_i\} \in \bar{e}$. Thus (iii) $\Longrightarrow$ (v).

(iv) $\Longrightarrow$ (iii) Let u and v be as above. Then there is an $\alpha > 0$ such that $\Sigma_{i=1}^{n} \beta_i x_i \in \alpha v$ for all $n \in \mathbb{N}$ and all $\{\beta_i\} \in \bar{b}$. Pick $\{\alpha_i\} \in \bar{a}$ and $n \in \mathbb{N}$ arbitrarily. Let $\sigma_+^{(n)} = \{i : 1 \leq i \leq n \text{ with } \alpha_i = +1\}$ and $\sigma_-^{(n)} = \{i : 1 \leq i \leq n \text{ with } \alpha_i = -1\}$. Then

$$\sum_{i=1}^{n} \alpha_i x_i = \sum_{i \in \sigma_+^{(n)}} \alpha_i x_i - \sum_{i \in \sigma_-^{(n)}} (-\alpha_i) x_i \in \alpha v - \alpha v \subset \alpha u$$

Thus (iv) $\Longrightarrow$ (iii). □

Theorem 6.6 leads to (Ref. 263, pp. 471, 472)

PROPOSITION 6.7 Let X be a $\sigma(X,X^*)$-sequentially complete l.c. TVS and $\Sigma_{i\geq 1} x_i$ a series in X. Then the statements below are equivalent:

(i) $\Sigma_{i\geq 1} x_i$ is unordered bounded.

(ii) $\Sigma_{i\geq 1} x_i$ is weakly unordered convergent.

(iii) $\Sigma_{i\geq 1} x_i$ is weakly unconditionally convergent.

Proof. The implications (i) $\Longleftrightarrow$ (ii) follow from (i) $\Longleftrightarrow$ (ii) of Theorem 6.6. The result (ii) $\Longleftrightarrow$ (iii) is a consequence of Theorem 4.1. □

7. WEAK CONVERGENCE THEOREMS

This section is devoted to a generalization of the well-known result of Orlicz and Pettis concerning the equivalence of weak and strong subseries convergence of a series $\Sigma_{i\geq 1} x_i$ in a Banach space, along with certain of its applications. The main result is

THEOREM 7.1 In a locally convex space (X,T), a series $\Sigma_{i\geq 1} x_i$ is a T-subseries convergent if and only if the series is $\sigma(X,X^*)$-subseries convergent.

Remarks: Theorem 7.1 was first proved by Orlicz [178] for weakly sequentially complete Banach spaces. However, Banach [12, p. 240] observed that the hypothesis of weak sequential completeness was superfluous. Later, a proof of Theorem 7.1 was given by Pettis [185] in 1938 for Banach spaces. Grothendieck [71, p. 141] derived Theorem 7.1 as a special case of a theorem on vector-valued integrals. Kalton [106, pp. 409, 410] recently obtained the above theorem for separable topological groups and then derived the result for separable locally convex spaces. The proof of Theorem 7.1 as given here is due to McArthur [166], and for alternative proofs, the reader is referred to the papers of Robertson [202, p. 153; 203, p. 339] and Jameson [103, Theorem 3]. First we require

LEMMA 7.2 Let $\Sigma_{i\geq 1} x_i$ be a series in an l.c. TVX (X,T) and $S = \{S_\sigma : \sigma \in \Phi\}$. If the condition

Whenever $\{f_n\}$ is an equicontinuous sequence such that

$$f_n(x) \to 0 \text{ for each } x \in \overline{sp}\,\{x_i\}, \text{ then } f_n(x) \to 0 \tag{7.3}$$

uniformly on S is satisfied, then $\Sigma_{i\geq 1} x_i$ is subseries Cauchy.

Proof. We first show that a subset B of X is bounded if for an equicontinuous sequence $\{f_n\} \subset X^*$ such that $\lim_{n\to\infty} f_n(x) = 0$ for each $x \in X$, it follows that $\lim_{n\to\infty} f_n(x) = 0$ uniformly on B. So let us assume that B is not bounded. Then there exists a $u \in \mathcal{B}$ such that for each $n \in \mathbb{N}$, $B \not\subset nu$. Therefore there exists a sequence $\{x_n\} \notin B$, $x_n \notin nu$, $n \geq 1$, and consequently there is $\{f_n\} \subset X^*$ such that $|f_n(x)| \leq 1/n$ for all $x \in u$ and $f_n(x_n) \geq 1$. Obviously $\{f_n\}$ is equicontinuous and $\lim_{n\to\infty} f_n(x) = 0$ on X but not uniformly on B. Thus B is bounded, and in particular, the set S is bounded. Hence $\Sigma_{i\geq 1} |f(x_i)| < \infty$ for each $f \in X^*$, by Theorem 6.3.

Now to prove the lemma we suppose that there exists a subseries $\Sigma_{i\geq 1} x_{k_i}$ whose partial sums do not form a Cauchy sequence. Then there exists a $v \in \mathcal{B}$ and an increasing sequence $\{m_n\} \subset \mathbb{N}$ such that for every $n \geq 1$, $s_n = \Sigma_{i=m_n+1}^{m_{n+1}} x_{k_i} \notin v$. As in the proof of Theorem 6.2 we get here an equicontinuous sequence $\{f_n\} \subset X^*$ with $f_n(s_n) = 1$, $\sup\{|f_n(x)| : x \in v\} < 1$, and consequently a subsequence $\{f_{p_n}\}$ of $\{f_n\}$ which has a $\sigma(X^*,X)$-cluster point f_0 with the property that $\lim_{n\to\infty} f_{p_n}(x) = f_0(x)$ for every $x \in \overline{\mathrm{sp}}\{x_i\}$. By (7.3), we have $\lim_{n\to\infty} f_{p_n}(x) = f_0(x)$ uniformly for $x \in S$. Since $\Sigma_{i\geq 1} |f_0(x_i)| < \infty$ for a given $\varepsilon > 0$, there exists $N \in \mathbb{N}$ such that $\Sigma_{i\geq N} |f_0(x_i)| < \varepsilon/2$. Thus for sufficiently large n such that $p_n \geq N$, $|f_0(s_{p_n})| < \varepsilon/2$. Also we can find $N' \in \mathbb{N}$, $N' > N$, such that if $n \geq N'$, $|f_{p_n}(x) - f_0(x)| < \varepsilon/2$ for all $x \in S$. Thus for sufficiently large n, $|f_{p_n}(s_{p_n})| \leq |f_{p_n}(s_{p_n}) - f_0(s_{p_n})| + |f_0(s_{p_n})| < \varepsilon$, which is a contradiction. □

Proof of Theorem 7.1. It is sufficient to show that if $\Sigma_{i\geq 1} x_i$ is $\sigma(X,X^*)$-subseries convergent, then it is T-subseries convergent. So let $\Sigma_{i\geq 1} x_i$ be $\sigma(X,X^*)$-subseries convergent. Hence $\Sigma_{i\geq 1}|f(x_i)| < \infty$ for each $f \in X^*$, by the Riemann theorem. Thus $\{f(x_i)\} \in \ell^1$ for each $f \in X^*$. Now for an equicontinuous sequence $\{f_n\}$ in X^* with $\lim_{n\to\infty} f_n(x) = 0$ for each $x \in \overline{\mathrm{sp}}\{x_i\}$, we show that

$$\lim_{n\to\infty} \sum_{i\geq 1} |f_n(x_i)| = 0$$

i.e., $\{f_n(x_i)\}_{i\geq 1} \xrightarrow{n} 0$ in $\beta(\ell^1,\ell^\infty)$ or in the norm topology of ℓ^1. To prove this it suffices to show, in view of Proposition 2.6.9, that for each $\{m_i\} \in \ell^\infty$,

$$\lim_{n\to\infty} \sum_{i\geq 1} m_i f_n(x_i) = 0$$

which can be further reduced to proving

$$\lim_{n\to\infty} \sum_{i\geq 1} \varepsilon_i f_n(x_i) = 0$$

where $\varepsilon_i = \pm 1$ or 0. For such a sequence $\{\varepsilon_i\}$, write $\sigma_+ = \{i : \varepsilon_i \geq 0\}$ and $\sigma_- = \{i : \varepsilon_i < 0\}$. By hypothesis, there exist x_{σ_+} and x_{σ_-} such that $f(x_{\sigma_+}) = \Sigma_{i\in\sigma_+} f(x_i)$ and $f(x_{\sigma_-}) = \Sigma_{i\in\sigma_-} f(x_i)$ for every $f \in X^*$.

Note that $x_{\sigma_+}, x_{\sigma_-} \in \overline{sp}\{x_i\}$. For if $x_{\sigma_+} \notin \overline{sp}\{x_i\}$, then by the Hahn-Banach theorem there exists $f \in X^*$ with $f(x_{\sigma_+}) \neq 0$ and $f(x) = 0$ for each $x \in \overline{sp}\{x_i\}$. This, however, implies a contradiction, since $f(x_{\sigma_+}) = \Sigma_{i\in\sigma_+} f(x_i) = 0$. Hence

$$\lim_{n\to\infty} \sum_{i\geq 1} \varepsilon_i f_n(x_i) = \lim_{n\to\infty} \left[\sum_{i\in\sigma_+} f_n(x_i) - \sum_{i\in\sigma_-} f_n(x_i)\right]$$

$$= \lim_{n\to\infty} f_n(x_{\sigma_+} - x_{\sigma_-}) = 0$$

Thus $\lim_{n\to\infty} \Sigma_{i\geq 1} |f_n(x_i)| = 0$, from which it is evident that $\lim_{n\to\infty} f_n(x) = 0$ uniformly in $x \in S$. Consequently, from Lemma 7.2, it follows that $\Sigma_{i\geq 1} x_i$ is T-subseries Cauchy. An application of Proposition 1.7.7 shows that $\Sigma_{i\geq 1} x_i$ is T-subseries convergent. □

PROPOSITION 7.3 In a weakly sequentially complete l.c. TVS X, a series $\Sigma_{i\geq 1} x_i$ is weakly unconditionally convergent if and only if it is unconditionally convergent.

Proof. If $\Sigma_{i\geq 1} x_i$ is weakly unconditionally convergent, it follows from Proposition 3.7, (i) ⇒ (ii), that $\Sigma_{i\geq 1} x_i$ is weakly subseries convergent. Consequently, the series $\Sigma_{i\geq 1} x_i$ is subseries convergent, by Theorem 7.1. However, X is sequentially complete (see Proposition 1.7.7). Hence by Proposition 3.7, (ii) ⇒ (i), $\Sigma_{i\geq 1} x_i$ is unconditionally convergent. The other part of the proposition is obvious. □

We derive the following important result (Ref. 263).

THEOREM 7.4 In a $\sigma(X,X^*)$-sequentially complete l.c. TVS X, a series $\Sigma_{i\geq 1} x_i$ is unconditionally convergent if and only if it is unordered bounded.

Proof. The result follows from Proposition 6.8 and 7.3. □

The following result is given in Ref. 33.

PROPOSITION 7.5 Let X be a complete or barreled locally convex space with a $\sigma(X^*,X^{**})$-complete dual X^*. Then a series $\Sigma_{i\geq 1} f_i$ in X^* is unconditionally convergent in $\beta(X^*,X)$ if and only if for every $x \in X$, $\Sigma_{i\geq 1} |f_i(x)| < \infty$.

Proof. If $\Sigma_{i\geq 1} |f_i(x)| < \infty$, the set $\{\Sigma_{i\in\sigma} f_i : \sigma \in \Phi\}$ is obviously $\sigma(X^*,X)$-bounded. Hence it is $\beta(X^*,X)$-bounded, by Theorem 1.7.18 or Theorem 1.8.3. Thus $\Sigma_{i\geq 1} f_i$ is $\beta(X^*,X)$-unconditionally convergent from the preceding theorem. The converse is obvious. □

8. UNORDERED PRECOMPACTNESS

In an earlier section (cf. §6) we examined the situation when the set $\{S_\sigma : \sigma \in \Phi\}$ is bounded and in this article we go a little deeper to determine when this set is precompact, compact, or relatively compact. To accomplish the aim, let us introduce

DEFINITION 8.1 A series $\Sigma_{i\geq 1} x_i$ in a TVS (X,T) is said to be *unordered precompact* or *compact* according as the net $\{S_\sigma : \sigma \in \Phi\}$ is precompact or compact in (X,T).

The first result of this section is due to Robertson [20] and is as follows:

THEOREM 8.1 A series in a TVS (X,T) is unordered precompact if and only if it is unordered (unconditionally) Cauchy.

Proof. Suppose that the given series is unordered Cauchy and let $u \in \mathcal{B}$. By Exercise 4.6 there exists a σ_0 in Φ such that $S_\sigma \in u$ whenever $\sigma \cap \sigma_0 = \emptyset$. Let $F = \{S_\mu : \mu \subset \sigma_0\}$; then F is finite, and for any $\sigma \in \Phi$, one has

$$S_\sigma = S_{\sigma\cap\sigma_0} + S_{\sigma\sim\sigma_0} \in F + u$$

By the definition it follows that $\{S_\sigma : \sigma \in \Phi\}$ is precompact in (X,T).

Conversely, let the series $\Sigma_{i\geq 1} x_i$ be unordered precompact but not unordered Cauchy. Hence there exist $u \in \mathcal{B}$ and a sequence $\{\sigma_n\} \subset \Phi$ with $\sigma_i \cap \sigma_j = \emptyset$ for $i \neq j$ such that $S_{\sigma_n} \notin u$, $n \geq 1$. Set $y_n = S_{\sigma_n}$. Then the set B of finite partial sums of the series $\Sigma_{n\geq 1} y_n$ is contained in $\{S_\sigma : \sigma \in \Phi\}$, and so it is precompact and hence also bounded. We can find a $v \in \mathcal{B}$ with $v + v \subset u$. Then there exists an M in $\mathbb{N}$ such that $B \subset Mv$. Next, choose a $w \in \mathcal{B}$ such that

$$\underbrace{w + w + \cdots + w}_{M \text{ times}} \subset v$$

Since the set $\{y_n : n \in \mathbb{N}\}$ is precompact, there exists an integer N such that

$$y_{n_i} \in y_N + w \qquad \text{for } i \geq 1$$

Hence

$$\sum_{i=1}^{M} y_{n_i} \in My_N + v$$

and consequently

$$-My_N \in -B + v \subset Mv + v \subset Mu$$

Thus $y_N \in u$. But $y_N = S_{\sigma_N} \notin u$. This contradiction proves the result. □

Note: The proof of the first part of the foregoing result also appears in Ref. 166, Lemma 4, (A) implies (C). Robertson [202, pp. 147-148] has also given an alternative proof of the second part of the above theorem when X is an l.c. TVS.

In general, subseries convergence is a stronger condition than unconditional or unordered convergence. We have to therefore restrict ourselves to get a result corresponding to Theorem 8.1 for subseries convergence. Indeed, the following result in this direction is due to Robertson [202] once again (cf. Ref. 203 also for further remarks); however, the proof of the second part of this theorem which we adopt here is due to Jameson [103] and is, in turn, a simple consequence of a known exercise in general topology (see, for example, Ref. 157, p. 176, Problem 12).

PROPOSITION 8.2 A series $\Sigma_{i\geq 1} x_i$ in a TVS (X,T) is subseries convergent if and only if the set $A = \{S_\sigma : \sigma \in \Phi\}$ is relatively compact. The set B of all finite or infinite partial sums is then compact.

Proof. Let A be relatively compact. By Theorem 8.1, the given series is unordered Cauchy and so it is convergent in the complete set A, and a similar argument applies to any subseries (see also the method of proof of Theorem 3.6).

To prove the converse, let us observe that $A \subset B$, and if we can prove that B is compact, the result will follow. Indeed, we proceed to prove that B is the continuous image of $\bar{b} = \Pi_{i\geq 1} Z_i$, where $Z_i = \{0,1\}$, $i \geq 1$, and each Z_i is equipped with its discrete topology; however, let us observe that $\bar{b}$ is compact by Tychonoff's well-known theorem. Define therefore $f\colon \bar{b} \to B$ by $f(\beta) = \Sigma_{i\geq 1} \beta_i x_i$. Let $u \in \mathcal{B}$; there exists $v \in \mathcal{B}$ such that $v + v \subset u$. By hypothesis, the given series is unordered Cauchy, and therefore (cf. Exercises 4.5 and 4.6) there exists $\sigma_0 \in \Phi$ such that $S_\sigma \in v$ for all σ in Φ with $\sigma \cap \sigma_0 = \emptyset$. Hence it follows (since v is closed) that $S_J \in v$ for all subsequences J of $\mathbb{N}$ for which $J \cap \sigma_0 = \emptyset$, $S_J = \Sigma_{i\in J} x_i$. Choose β^1 and β^2 in $\bar{b}$ such that $\beta_i^1 = \beta_i^2$ for $i \in \sigma_0$. (Note that $\{0\} \times \{0\} \times \cdots \times \{0\} \times \Pi_{i\in\mathbb{N}\sim\sigma_0} (Z_i)$ with $\{0\}$ taken σ_0 times, is a zero neighborhood in $\bar{b}$.) Let σ_1 be the set of $i \in \sigma_0$ for which $\beta_i^1 = 1$. Then $f(\beta^1) - S(\sigma_1) \in v$; $f(\beta^2) - S(\sigma_1) \in v$ from above. Hence $f(\beta^1) - f(\beta^2) \in u$, and so f is continuous. As f is onto, the required result follows. □

A close analysis of the proof of the second part of the preceding proposition suggests that we might be in a position to prove the same for bounded multiplier convergence; in view of Exercise 3.13 it should not be taken for granted that it follows from Proposition 8.2. In fact, we have (Ref. 103)

PROPOSITION 8.3 Let (X,T) be an l.c. TVS and consider a formal series $\Sigma_{i\geq 1} x_i$. If this series is bounded multiplier convergent then the set $A = \{\Sigma_{i\geq 1} \varepsilon_i x_i : \varepsilon = \{\varepsilon_i\} \in \bar{e}\}$ is compact in X.

Proof. The proof is like that of the preceding result. Observe that we can regard $\bar{e}$ as the set $I^{\mathbb{N}}$, $I = \{z : z \text{ in } \mathbb{C}, |z| \leq 1\}$ and on $I^{\mathbb{N}}$ we consider the usual product topology under which it is a compact space. Define $f\colon I^{\mathbb{N}} \to X$, $f(\gamma) = \Sigma_{i\geq 1} \gamma_i x_i$, $\gamma \in \bar{e}$. Choose an arbitrary $u \in \mathcal{B}$. There exists $v \in \mathcal{B}$ such that $v + v + v \subset u$. Using the technique involved in the proof of (v) $\Longleftrightarrow$ (vi) of Theorem 3.8, we find an integer $N \geq 1$ such that

$$\sum_{i\geq N+1} \varepsilon_i x_i \in v \qquad \forall \varepsilon \in \bar{e}$$

Let ε^0 be fixed in $\bar{e}$. Let $\varepsilon \in \bar{e}$ be arbitrary such that $|\varepsilon_1^0 - \varepsilon_i|$ is sufficiently small for $1 \leq i \leq N$. Then $\Sigma_{i=1}^N (\varepsilon_i^0 - \varepsilon_i)x_i \in v$, and hence for all such ε in $\bar{e}$ we have $f(\varepsilon^0) - f(\varepsilon) \in u$, confirming the continuity of the function f. □

It is well known that in general the balanced convex hull of a precompact set in a TVS is not necessarily precompact; not even in locally bounded spaces is this true. Robertson has obtained conditions on a formal series in a class of TVS for which the balanced convex hull D of $A = \{S_\sigma : \sigma \in \Phi\}$ is precompact. The partial converse of this result is also obtained. Indeed, we have the following result of Robertson [202] whose proof is still different from his.

PROPOSITION 8.4 Let (X,T) be a locally bounded space. If a series $\Sigma_{i\geq 1} x_i$ in X is unordered Cauchy then the set D above is precompact. If D is precompact in X, then the series $\Sigma_{i\geq 1} x_i$ is bounded multiplier Cauchy.

Proof. From the proof of Theorem 3.6, (i) $\Longrightarrow$ (ii), it follows that the given series is subseries Cauchy and so $\Sigma_{i\geq 1} \beta_i x_i$ is Cauchy uniformly in $\beta \in \bar{b}$. The proof of Theorem 3.8, (iv) $\Longrightarrow$ (v), implies that $\Sigma_{i\geq 1} \varepsilon_i x_i$ is Cauchy uniformly in $\varepsilon \in \bar{e}$ (or equivalently, this series is bounded multiplier Cauchy). Thus to each given $u \in \mathcal{B}$ there corresponds a positive integer N such that

$$\sum_{i=m}^{n} \varepsilon_i x_i \in u \qquad \forall n \geq m > N$$

uniformly in $\{\varepsilon_i\} \in \bar{e}$. If $\sigma_N = \{1,\ldots,N\}$, we thus get

$$\sum_{i\in\sigma} \varepsilon_i x_i \in u \qquad \forall\sigma \text{ in } \Phi \text{ with } \sigma \cap \sigma_N = \emptyset$$

We now recall that (Ref. 202, pp. 148-149)

$$C \subset D \subset 4C$$

where $C = \{\Sigma_{i\in\sigma} \lambda_i x_i : |\lambda_i| \leq 1 \text{ for each } i, \text{ and } \sigma \in \Phi\}$. The required precompactness now follows as in the first part of the proof of Theorem 8.1. The last part of the proposition can also be disposed of along the lines of Theorem 8.1. □

Remark: For slight generalizations of the results of this section to general families in TVS and series in topological groups, see Refs. 106 and 202.

Weak Compactness and Subseries Convergence

Here we investigate conditions to be imposed on the series $\Sigma_{i\geq 1} x_i$ in a TVS X and the structure of X so that the set $\{S_\sigma : \sigma \in \Phi\}$ becomes weakly compact. The main result, due to McArthur [166], is stated and proved as follows (McArthur has also obtained an application of this result in vector-valued measures).

THEOREM 8.5 Let $\Sigma_{i\geq 1} x_i$ be a series in a complete l.c. TVS (X,T). Then the following conditions are equivalent:

(i) $\Sigma_{i\geq 1} x_i$ is subseries convergent in X.

(ii) $\Sigma_{i\geq 1} x_i$ is $\sigma(X,X^*)$-subseries convergent in X.

(iii) The set $A = \{S_\sigma : \sigma \in \Phi\}$ is T-precompact in X.

(iv) Whenever $\{f_n\}$ is an equicontinuous sequence in X^* such that $f_n(x) \to 0$ for x in $[x_i]$, then $f_n(x) \to 0$ uniformly in x in A.

(v) The set A is relatively compact in $(X,\sigma(X,X^*))$.

Proof. (i) $\Longrightarrow$ (iv) Suppose we have (i). From Theorems 3.9 and 4.1, we find that the given series is unordered Cauchy, and so from Theorem 8.1, the set S is precompact in X. Take the sequence $\{f_n\}$ as required in (iv). There exists $p \in D_T$ such that $|f_n(x)| \leq p(x)$ for every x in X and uniformly in $n \geq 1$. Let $\varepsilon > 0$ be chosen arbitrarily and $U_{p,\varepsilon} = \{x : x \in X, p(x) \leq \varepsilon/2\}$. From the precompactness of S, there exists a finite set $F \subset S$ such that $S \subset F + U_{p,\varepsilon}$. From the hypothesis on $\{f_n\}$, there exists an $N \in \mathbb{N}$, $N \equiv N(F,\varepsilon)$ such that $|f_n(z)| \leq \varepsilon/2$ for all $n \geq N$ and $z \in F$. Thus, if y is in S, $y = z + x^*$, where $z \in F$ and $x^* \in U_{p,\varepsilon}$. Hence

$$|f_n(y)| \leq |f_n(z)| + |f_n(x^*)| \leq \frac{\varepsilon}{2} + p(x^*) \qquad \text{for } n \geq N$$

or

$$|f_n(y)| \leq \varepsilon$$

for all $n \geq N$ and uniformly in $y \in S$. Thus (iv) follows.

(iv) $\Longrightarrow$ (i) This is a consequence of Lemma 7.2 and the completeness of X.

(i) $\Longleftrightarrow$ (ii) This follows from Theorem 7.1.

(ii) $\Longleftrightarrow$ (v) Proposition 8.2 yields these implications.

(i) $\Longleftrightarrow$ (iii) We need apply Theorems 3.9 and 8.1.

Summing up, we have established the following:

$$\begin{array}{ccccccc} \text{(iii)} & \Longleftrightarrow & \text{(i)} & \Longleftrightarrow & \text{(ii)} & \Longleftrightarrow & \text{(v)} \\ & & \Updownarrow & & & & \\ & & \text{(iv)} & & & & \end{array}$$

The proof of the result is thus complete. □

9. LINEAR TRANSFORMATIONS AND CONVERGENCE CRITERIA

If we attempt to study various modes of convergence and boundedness by means of transformations, it turns out that in some situations we obtain linear operators from a sequence space to a TVS. Thus a comprehensive study of the notions of convergence requires a good deal of knowledge of these operators from various points of view, and vice versa. Let us begin with (Ref. 167)

THEOREM 9.1 Let (X,S) be an l.c. TVS. Then the following statements hold:

(i) If T is a continuous linear transformation from c_0 into X with $T(e^i) = x_i$, $i \geq 1$, then for each $c = \{c_i\} \in c_0$, $T(c) = \Sigma_{i\geq 1} c_i x_i$, where the series $\Sigma_{i\geq 1} x_i$ satisfies $\Sigma_{i\geq 1} |f(x_i)| < \infty$ for each $f \in X^*$.

(ii) If $\Sigma_{i\geq 1} x_i$ is a series in X such that $\Sigma_{i\geq 1} c_i x_i$ converges for each $c = \{c_i\} \in c_0$, then $T(c) = \Sigma_{i\geq 1} c_i x_i$ defines a continuous linear transformation from c_0 into X with strongly continuous adjoint T^* from X^* into ℓ^1, and $T^*(f) = \{f(x_i)\}$, $f \in X^*$.

(iii) If X is also sequentially complete and the series $\Sigma_{i\geq 1} x_i$ in X satisfies $\Sigma_{i\geq 1} |f(x_i)| < \infty$ for each $f \in X^*$, then $T(c) = \Sigma_{i\geq 1} c_i x_i$ defines a continuous linear transformation from c_0 to X.

Proof. The statement (i) is immediate from the continuity of T and the fact that $c = \Sigma_{i\geq 1} c_i e^i$ for each $c = \{c_i\} \in c_0$. The last part follows from Theorem 6.3, (vi) $\Rightarrow$ (ii).

For the proof of (ii), we observe that the map $T: c_0 \to X$, defined as $T(c) = \Sigma_{i\geq 1} c_i x_i$, is obviously linear. Also, from Theorem 6.3, we can define a linear transformation $L: X^* \to \ell^1$ as $L(f) = \{f(x_i)\}$, $f \in X^*$. For $c \in c_0$ and $f \in X^*$, the equalities

$$\langle T(c),f\rangle = f(T(c)) = \sum_{i\geq 1} c_i f(x_i) = \langle c,L(f)\rangle$$

imply that $L = T^*$, and also T is continuous by Proposition 1.12.3. To prove the strong continuity of L, take a net $\{f_\alpha\} \subset X^*$ that is $\beta(X^*,X)$-convergent to 0, i.e., $f_\alpha(x) \xrightarrow{\alpha} 0$ uniformly on any bounded subset B of X. In particular, take $B = \{\Sigma_{i\in\sigma} x_i : \sigma \in \Phi\}$, which is bounded by (iii) of Theorem 6.3. Thus for $\varepsilon > 0$, there exists α_0 such that $|f_\alpha(\Sigma_{i\in\sigma} x_i)| < \varepsilon/4$ for all $\sigma \in \Phi$ and $\alpha \geq \alpha_0$. In view of Corollary 3.4, it follows that

$$\|L(f_\alpha)\| = \sum_{i\geq 1} |f_\alpha(x_i)| \leq \varepsilon \qquad \text{for } \alpha \geq \alpha_0$$

i.e., $L(f_\alpha) \xrightarrow{\alpha} 0$ in the norm topology of ℓ^1, thereby proving the strong continuity of L or T*.

To prove (iii), we observe that the series $\Sigma_{i\geq 1} c_i x_i$, $c = \{c_i\} \in c_0$, converges, from (ii) $\Longrightarrow$ (vi) of Theorem 3.6 and the sequential completeness of X. It now remains to apply (ii) of this result to get (iii). □

THEOREM 9.2 For a series $\Sigma_{i\geq 1} x_i$ in an l.c. TVS (X,R), let $L: X^* \to \omega$ be a map defined by $L(f) = \{f(x_i)\}$, $f \in X^*$. Then the following statements are true.

(i) L is a strongly continuous mapping from X* into ℓ^1 if and only if

$$\sum_{i\geq 1} |f(x_i)| < \infty \qquad f \in X^*$$

(ii) If L is the adjoint of a linear transformation T from c_0 into X, then for each $c = \{c_i\} \in c_0$, $T(c) = \Sigma_{i\geq 1} c_i x_i$.

(iii) If $L(X^*) \subset \ell^1$, then $L^*: \ell^\infty \to X^{**}$, where X** is the dual of $(X^*, \beta(X^*,X))$, exists, and $(L^*(b))(f) = \Sigma_{i\geq 1} b_i f(x_i)$ for $b = \{b_i\} \in \ell^\infty$ and $f \in X^*$. If X is also sequentially complete, then $L = T^*$, where $T(c) = \Sigma_{i\geq 1} c_i x_i$, $c = \{c_i\} \in c_0$, is a linear transformation from c_0 to X.

Proof. To prove (i), one may consult the proof of (ii) of the preceding theorem to show the strong continuity of L. The other implication is obvious.

To prove (ii), we observe that the map $T: c_0 \to X$ is continuous by Proposition 1.12.3. Hence for arbitrary $c \in c_0$ and $f \in X^*$, one has

$$f(T(c)) = \langle T(c),f\rangle = \langle c,T^*(f)\rangle = \langle c,L(f)\rangle = \sum_{i\geq 1} c_i f(x_i)$$

This, in particular, implies that $f(T(e^i)) = f(x_i)$ for all $f \in X^*$. Therefore $T(e^i) = x_i$ since X* is total over X. Now by continuity of T, we have $T(c) = \Sigma_{i\geq 1} c_i x_i$.

To prove (iii), we have the strong continuity of the map L by (i). Thus L* exists by Propositions 1.12.1 and 1.12.2, i.e., L* takes ℓ^∞ into X**. Moreover, for $b = \{b_i\} \in \ell^\infty$ and $f \in X^*$ one has

$$(L^*(b))(f) = \langle L^*(b),f\rangle = \langle b,L(f)\rangle = \sum_{i\geq 1} b_i f(x_i)$$

If X is also sequentially complete, then the convergence of $\Sigma_{i\geq 1} c_i x_i$ for $c = \{c_i\} \in c_0$, follows from Theorem 6.3, (ii) $\Longrightarrow$ (vi). Write $T(c) = \Sigma_{i\geq 1} c_i x_i$. Then $L = T^*$, in view of (ii) of Theorem 9.1. □

The following theorem (Ref. 167) is a generalization of a result due to Gelfand [61]:

THEOREM 9.3 Let (X,R) be a TVS and $\Sigma_{i\geq 1} f_i$ be a series in X^*. Then the set $S = \{\Sigma_{i\in\sigma} f_i : \sigma \in \Phi\}$ is $\sigma(X^*,X)$-bounded if and only if for each $x \in X$, $\{f_i(x)\} \in \ell^1$. A linear transformation T from X into ℓ^1 is continuous if and only if there exists a sequence $\{f_i\} \subset X^*$ such that $S = \{\Sigma_{i\in\sigma} f_i : \sigma \in \Phi\}$ is equicontinuous and $T(x) = \{f_i(x)\}$.

Proof. For the first statement, make use of Corollary 3.4 to show that $\{f_i(x)\} \in \ell^1$ if S is $\sigma(X^*,X)$-bounded. The converse is obvious.

Concerning the second statement, let us assume first that the linear transformation $T: X \to \ell^1$ is continuous. Denote by $f_i(x)$ the ith coordinate of $T(x)$ for each $x \in X$, i.e., $T(x) = \{f_i(x)\}$. Obviously the f_i's, $i \geq 1$, are linear functionals. Moreover, for $\varepsilon > 0$, there is a neighborhood V of 0 in X such that $\|T(x)\| = \Sigma_{i\geq 1} |f_i(x)| < \varepsilon$ whenever $x \in V$. Thus for arbitrary $\sigma \in \Phi$,

$$\left|\left(\sum_{i\in\sigma} f_i\right)(x)\right| \leq \sum_{i\geq 1} |f_i(x)| < \varepsilon \qquad \text{for } x \in V$$

implies that the set S is equicontinuous on X.

Conversely, if S is equicontinuous, then for arbitrary $\varepsilon > 0$, there exists a neighborhood V of 0 such that $|\Sigma_{i\in\sigma} f_i(x)| < \varepsilon/4$ for $x \in V$ and $\sigma \in \Phi$. Consequently, by Corollary 3.4, $\Sigma_{i\geq 1} |f_i(x)| \leq \varepsilon$ for $x \in V$. Thus the map $T: X \to \ell^1$ defined by $T(x) = \{f_i(x)\}$ is a continuous linear transformation from X to ℓ^1. □

The next theorem (Ref. 61) provides a criterion for subseries Cauchy series in terms of linear operators.

THEOREM 9.4 A series $\Sigma_{i\geq 1} x_i$ in an l.c. TVS (X,T) is subseries Cauchy if and only if the mapping $L(f) = \{f(x_i)\}$, $f \in X^*$, maps equicontinuous subsets of X^* into totally bounded subsets of ℓ^1, i.e., corresponding to each equicontinuous subset B of X^* and each $\varepsilon > 0$, there exists a positive integer m such that $\Sigma_{i\geq m} |f(x_i)| < \varepsilon$ for all $f \in B$.

Proof. Let $\Sigma_{i\geq 1} x_i$ be subseries Cauchy and $B \subset X^*$ be equicontinuous. Then for $\varepsilon > 0$, the set $V = \{x \in X : |f(x)| \leq \varepsilon/4\}$ is a neighborhood of $0 \in X$. Since $\Sigma_{i\geq 1} x_i$ is unordered Cauchy [cf. the proof of Theorem 3.6,

(ii) $\Longrightarrow$ (i), and Proposition 4.2] there exists an $m_\varepsilon \in \mathbb{N}$ such that if $\sigma \in \Phi$ and $\sigma \cap [1,m_\varepsilon] = \emptyset$, then $\Sigma_{i\in\sigma} x_i \in V$. Hence $|f(\Sigma_{i\in\sigma} x_i)| \le \varepsilon/4$ for all $f \in B$ and $\sigma \in \Phi$ with $\sigma \cap [1,m_\varepsilon] = \emptyset$. Therefore by Corollary 3.4, $\Sigma_{i\ge m_\varepsilon+1} |f(x_i)| \le \varepsilon$ for all $f \in B$. Thus $L(B)$ is totally bounded in view of Propositions 2.6.10 and 2.6.11.

For the converse, we make use of Theorem 6.2 to show that the partial sums of the subseries $\Sigma_{i\ge1} x_{m_i}$ of $\Sigma_{i\ge1} x_i$ form a Cauchy sequence. Indeed, $\{\Sigma_{i=1}^p x_{m_i}\}_{p\ge1}$ is a $\sigma(X,X^*)$-Cauchy sequence, since $\Sigma_{i\ge1} |f(x_i)| < \infty$ for each $f \in X^*$. Now choose $\varepsilon > 0$ and take an equicontinuous sequence $\{f_i\}$ such that $\lim_{n\to\infty} f_n(\Sigma_{i=1}^p x_{m_i}) = 0$ for $p \ge 1$. As $L(\{f_n\})$ is a totally bounded subset of ℓ^1 there exists $i_0 \in \mathbb{N}$ such that $\Sigma_{i\ge i_0+1} |f_n(x_{m_i})| < \varepsilon/2$ for all $n \ge 1$. Then we can find $n_0 \in \mathbb{N}$ such that

$$\sum_{i=1}^{i_0} |f_n(x_{m_i})| < \frac{\varepsilon}{2} \qquad \text{for all } n \ge n_0$$

Thus $\Sigma_{i\ge1} |f_n(x_{m_i})| < \varepsilon$ for $n \ge n_0$, implying $\lim_{n\to\infty} \Sigma_{i\ge1} |f_n(x_{m_i})| = 0$. Hence $\lim_{n\to\infty} f_n(\Sigma_{i=1}^p x_{m_i}) = 0$, uniformly with respect to $p \in \mathbb{N}$. □

Using Proposition 1.13.9, we derive

COROLLARY 9.5 A series $\Sigma_{i\ge1} x_i$ in a sequentially complete l.c. TVS (X,R) is subseries convergent if and only if the map $T: c_0 \to X$, defined by $T(c) = \lim_{n\to\infty} \Sigma_{i=1}^n c_i x_i$ for $c = \{c_i\} \in c_0$, is precompact.

Proof. If $\Sigma_{i\ge1} x_i$ is subseries convergent, then $\Sigma_{i\ge1} |f(x_i)| < \infty$ for each $f \in X^*$, and therefore the map $T: c_0 \to X$ is well defined. Moreover, its adjoint map L, $L(f) = \{f(x_i)\}$ for $f \in X^*$, maps equicontinuous sets into totally bounded sets by Theorem 9.4. Thus T takes bounded sets into totally bounded sets. The converse follows immediately from the above result, Theorem 9.4, and the sequential completeness of X. □

COROLLARY 9.6 Let (X,R) be an infrabarreled space. A series $\Sigma_{i\ge1} x_i$ in X is subseries Cauchy if and only if the mapping $L(f) = \{f(x_i)\}$, $f \in X^*$, is totally bounded from X^* into ℓ^1, which is in turn true if and only if the adjoint L^* from ℓ^∞ to $(X^{**},\beta(X^{**},X^*))$ is totally bounded, where $(L^*(b))(f) = \Sigma_{i\ge1} b_i f(x_i)$ for $b = \{b_i\} \in \ell^\infty$ and $f \in X^*$.

Proof. Since $\beta(X^*,X)$-bounded and equicontinuous subsets of X^* are the same, the required result is immediate from the above. □

Another characterization for Cauchy convergence criterion in terms of linear operators is as follows:

THEOREM 9.7 Let (X,R) be a TVS. Then a series $\Sigma_{i\geq 1} f_i$ in $(X^*,\beta(X^*,X))$ is subseries Cauchy if and only if the mapping $U(x) = \{f_i(x)\}$, $x \in X$, is a totally bounded transformation from X into ℓ^1.

Proof. Let $\Sigma_{i\geq 1} f_i$ be subseries Cauchy in $(X^*,\beta(X^*,X))$. Then it is $\beta(X^*,X)$-unordered Cauchy. Take a bounded subset B of X and choose $\varepsilon > 0$ arbitrarily. Then there exists $N_\varepsilon \in \mathbb{N}$ such that for $\sigma \in \Phi$ with $\sigma \cap [1,N_\varepsilon] = \emptyset$, we have $|\Sigma_{i\in\sigma} f_i(x)| < \varepsilon/4$ for all $x \in B$. Thus by Corollary 3.4, $\Sigma_{i\geq N_\varepsilon} |f_i(x)| \leq \varepsilon$ for all $x \in B$. Consequently, U maps bounded sets into totally bounded sets.

Conversely, we have that the image $U(A)$ of a bounded set A in X is totally bounded. Therefore for $\varepsilon > 0$, there exists $N_\varepsilon \in \mathbb{N}$ such that $\Sigma_{i\geq N_\varepsilon} |f_i(x)| < \varepsilon$ for all $x \in A$. Thus, for $\sigma \in \Phi$ with $\sigma \cap [1,N_\varepsilon] = \emptyset$, one has

$$\left|\sum_{i\in\sigma} f_i(x)\right| \leq \sum_{i\geq N} |f_i(x)| < \varepsilon$$

i.e., $\Sigma_{i\geq 1} f_i$ is $\beta(X^*,X)$-unordered Cauchy. Hence $\Sigma_{i\geq 1} f_i$ is subseries Cauchy [cf. Proposition 4.2 and the proof of Theorem 3.6, (i) $\Longrightarrow$ (ii)]. □

THEOREM 9.8 Let (X,R) and (Y,S) be locally convex spaces with (Y,S) weakly complete. Assume further that $\{f_i\}$ is a sequence in X^*, $\{y_i\}$ a sequence in Y, and $\{\lambda_i\}$ a sequence of scalars. Then for each $x \in X$, the map

$$T(x) = \sum_{i\geq 1} \lambda_i f_i(x) y_i$$

defines a compact linear transformation from X into Y (i.e., maps some neighborhood of 0 in X into a relatively compact set in Y) if any of the following conditions holds:

(i) $\Sigma_{i\geq 1} y_i$ is unconditionally convergent and $\{\lambda_i\} \in \ell^\infty$.

(ii) $\Sigma_{i\geq 1} y_i$ is unordered bounded and $\{\lambda_i\} \in c_0$.

(iii) $\{y_i\}$ is bounded and $\Sigma_{i\geq 1} |\lambda_i| < \infty$.

Proof. Write $V = \{x \in X : |f_i(x)| \leq 1 \text{ for } i \in \mathbb{N}\}$ and $T_n(x) = \Sigma_{i=1}^{n} \lambda_i f_i(x) y_i$ for each $n \geq 1$, where $\{\lambda_i\}$ and $\{y_i\}$ satisfy any of the conditions (i), (ii), or (iii). Clearly V is a neighborhood of 0 in X and $T_n(V)$ is totally bounded for each $n \geq 1$. In case (i), since

$\{\{\lambda_i f_i(x)\} : x \in V\}$ is a bounded subset of ℓ^∞, it follows by Theorem 3.9 that T is well defined and $T_n(x) \xrightarrow{n} T(x)$ uniformly for $x \in V$. Thus T is compact by Lemma 1.3.13. In case (ii), for $\{\lambda_i\} \in c_0$, we have the convergence of the series $\Sigma_{i\geq 1} \lambda_i y_i$ by Theorem 6.3, (iii) $\Rightarrow$ (vi); moreover, $\Sigma_{i\geq 1} y_i$ is unconditionally convergent in view of Theorem 7.4. Thus the result follows from (i). For (iii), one can easily prove that $\Sigma_{i\geq 1} \lambda_i y_i$ is absolutely convergent and hence unconditionally convergent in Y. We now apply (i) with $\{\lambda_i\}$ replaced by $e \in \ell^\infty$ to get the required result. □

Remark: One observes that the compact operators as determined in case (iii) above are nothing but nuclear operators.

10. FURTHER ADVANCES

In this final section of this chapter we take up a few more general results on the convergence of infinite series which have far-reaching consequences and have indeed yielded a number of interesting and useful results in the modern theory of sequence spaces to be discussed in Chapter 4.

From the Orlicz-Pettis theorem we can conclude the convergence of an infinite series in an l.c. TVS (X,T) provided we know that the series is weakly subseries convergent. A stronger version of this statement, due to Bennett and Kalton [16], is contained in

THEOREM 10.1 If the series $\Sigma_{i\geq 1} x_i$ in an l.c. TVS (X,T) is $\sigma(X,X^*)$-subseries convergent, then $\Sigma_{i\geq 1} x_i$ is $\delta(X,X^*)$-convergent in X.

Proof. Since in a finite dimensional space subseries convergence is equivalent to absolute convergence, we have

$$\sum_{i\geq 1} |f(x_i)| < \infty \qquad \forall f \in X^*$$

Hence we can define a linear operator $F: X^* \to \ell^1$ by $F(f) = \{f(x_n)\}$. If $\{\alpha_n\} \in \bar{b}$, then

$$\sum_{n\geq 1} \alpha_n (F(f))_n = \sum_{n\geq 1} \alpha_n f(x_n) = \left\langle \sum_{n\geq 1} \alpha_n x_n, f \right\rangle$$

$$\Rightarrow \quad \langle F(f), \alpha \rangle = \left\langle f, \sum_{n\geq 1} \alpha_n x_n \right\rangle$$

where $\Sigma_{n\geq 1} \alpha_n x_n$ is $\sigma(X,X^*)$-convergent in X. It follows that F is $\sigma(X^*,X)$-$\sigma(\ell^1,m_0)$ continuous. Therefore, for any $\sigma(X^*,X)$-compact subset K of X*, F[K] is $\sigma(\ell^1,m_0)$-compact, and so from Theorem 2.3.10 and Proposition 2.7.18, F[K] is compact in ℓ^1 relative to its norm topology. By Proposition 2.6.11,

$$\lim_{n\to\infty} \sup_{f\in K} \sum_{i\geq n} |f(x_i)| = 0$$

$$\Longrightarrow \quad \lim_{n\to\infty} \sup_{f\in K} \sup_{m\geq n} \left| \sum_{i=n}^{m} f(x_i) \right| = 0$$

Thus $\{\Sigma_{i=1}^{n} x_i\}$ is $\delta(X,X^*)$-Cauchy. By hypothesis, there exists x in X such that

$$\sigma(X,X^*)\text{-}\lim_{n\to\infty} \sum_{i=1}^{n} x_i = x$$

Applying Proposition 1.7.8, we conclude the $\delta(X,X^*)$-convergence of $\Sigma_{i\geq 1} x_i$ to x. □

EXERCISE 10.2 Prove the validity of Theorem 10.1 when $\delta(X,X^*)$ is replaced by the topology of uniform convergence on $\tau(X^*,X)$-precompact subsets of X*. [Hint: Use Proposition 1.12.3.]

Remark: In Theorem 10.1 and Exercise 10.2, one may replace X* by Y such that $\langle X,Y\rangle$ forms a dual system.

Following is a generalization of the notions of bounded multiplier and subseries convergence of an infinite series (Ref. 129).

DEFINITION 10.3 Corresponding to a given sequence space λ, a series $\Sigma_{i\geq 1} x_i$ in an l.c. TVS (X,T) is said to be *weakly λ-unconditionally Cauchy* (w. λ-u.C.) provided $\Sigma_{i\geq 1} \alpha_i x_i$ converges in X for each $\alpha \in \lambda$.

Remarks: If $\lambda = \ell^\infty$ (resp. m_0) the preceding definition reduces to bounded multiplier (resp. subseries) convergence. In case $\lambda = c_0$ and (X,T) is sequentially complete, the notion of w. c_0-u.C. series coincides with that of weakly unconditionally Cauchy (cf. Definition 1.2). If $\lambda = \ell^p$ $(1 < p < \infty)$ the corresponding notion w. ℓ^p-u.C. series is due to Bennett [14, p. 21] although it goes back essentially to Singer [237].

The following theorem (Ref. 129) includes earlier results given in Refs. 14, 170, 237, and 263; see remarks below.

THEOREM 10.4 Let λ be a monotone AK-FK space and (X,T) a sequentially complete l.c. TVS. Then a series $\Sigma_{i\geq 1} x_i$ in X is w. λ-u.C. if and only if $\{f(x_i)\} \in \lambda^\beta$ for $f \in X^*$.

Proof. Let $\Sigma_{i\geq 1} x_i$ be w. λ-u.C. Then $\Sigma_{i\geq 1} \alpha_i x_i$ converges in (X,T) for every $\alpha \in \lambda$, and so $\Sigma_{i\geq 1} \alpha_i f(x_i)$ converges for each $f \in X^*$ and $\alpha \in \lambda$. Hence $\{f(x_i)\} \in \lambda^\beta$ for each $f \in X^*$.

To prove the converse, define the operator $F: \phi \to X$ by

$$F(\alpha) = \sum_{i\geq 1} \alpha_i x_i \qquad \alpha \in \phi$$

If $f \in X^*$, we have

$$\langle F(\alpha), f\rangle = \langle \alpha, \{f(x_i)\}\rangle$$

and consequently F is $\sigma(\phi,\lambda^\beta)$-$\sigma(X,X^*)$ continuous. By Proposition 1.12.2, F is $\tau(\phi,\lambda^\beta)$-$\tau(X,X^*)$ continuous and so from Proposition 2.3.9, F is $\tau(\phi,\lambda^*)$-$\tau(X,X^*)$ continuous. In view of Theorem 4.2.1, the sequence $\{\alpha^{(n)}\}$ is $\tau(\lambda,\lambda^*)$-Cauchy in λ for each $\alpha \in \lambda$. It is clear that $\tau(\lambda,\lambda^*)$ induces on ϕ a metrizable locally convex topology S and so $S = \tau(\phi,\phi^*)$ (cf. Proposition 1.8.7), where $\phi^* = (\phi,S)^*$. But $\phi^* = \lambda^*$, thus giving

$$\tau(\phi,\lambda^*) = \tau(\lambda,\lambda^*)|\phi = S$$

This observation leads us to conclude that $\{\alpha^{(n)}\}$ is $\tau(\phi,\lambda^*)$-Cauchy in ϕ and hence $\{\Sigma_{i=1}^n \alpha_i x_i\}$ is $\tau(X,X^*)$-Cauchy in X. As $T \subset \tau(X,X^*)$, we find that $\Sigma_{i\geq 1} \alpha_i x_i$ converges in (X,T). □

Note: We may considerably relax conditions on λ in Theorem 10.4, but then we need pay a penalty by way of restricting the space X further. Indeed, one has

THEOREM 10.5 Let λ be a monotone sequence space and (X,T) a $\sigma(X,X^*)$-sequentially complete l.c. TVS. A series $\Sigma_{i\geq 1} x_i$ in X is w. λ-u.C. if and only if $\{f(x_i)\} \in \lambda^\beta$ for every $f \in X^*$.

Proof. Necessity follows as in Theorem 10.4. To prove the converse, assume that $\alpha \in \lambda$. By Proposition 2.2.7, $\{f(x_i)\} \in \lambda^\times$, and so

$\Sigma_{i\geq 1} |f(\alpha_i x_i)| < \infty$ for each $f \in X^*$. Thus $\Sigma_{i\geq 1} \alpha_i x_i$ is weakly subseries Cauchy and so $\Sigma_{i\geq 1} \alpha_i x_i$ is weakly subseries convergent. Using either of Theorem 7.1 or Theorem 10.1, we conclude the convergence of $\Sigma_{i\geq 1} \alpha_i x_i$. □

Remarks: If $\lambda = c_0$ in Theorem 10.4, we get Theorem 6.3 (cf. Ref. 170, p. 117 and Ref. 263, Proposition 1.12). If $\lambda = \ell^p$ $(1 < p < \infty)$ in Theorem 10.4, we get a result of Ref. 14, p. 21, and hence that of Singer [237, p. 131]. (Singer's result also follows from Theorem 10.5, since from Lemma 2.10, Ref. 263, the space X is not c_0.) Let us mention that if $\lambda = \ell^1$, the sufficiency part of Theorem 10.4 (and hence, that of Theorem 10.5) involves a rather straightforward argument. Indeed, if $\{f(x_i)\} \in \ell^\infty$ for each $f \in X^*$, then $\{x_i\}$ is T-bounded in X and so [for instance, see Lemma 3.2(i) of Ref. 115] $\Sigma_{i\geq 1} \alpha_i x_i$ converges in (X,T) for $\alpha \in \ell^1$.

Chapter 4

FURTHER DEVELOPMENTS IN SEQUENCE SPACES

1. INTRODUCTION

The basic purpose of this chapter is to present some more sophisticated results from the theory of sequence spaces, which reflect further applications in the Schauder basis, summability, and function theories. Some of these are generalizations of previous results.

Basically we deal with two aspects of the theory in this chapter. First, we explore the AK-ness of a sequence space equipped with polar topologies finer than the Mackey topology, and secondly, we give rudiments of the theory of FK-spaces and matrix transformations thereon, the latter being touched upon somewhat rigorously although certainly not exhaustively.

The terminology followed for sequence spaces and series is that of Chapters 2 and 3, respectively.

Let us once again remind the reader that all sequence spaces λ that we consider contain the space ϕ, and all topological vector spaces are Hausdorff. Also, we recall that the space ω is always assumed to be endowed with its natural locally convex topology, which is either the topology of coordinatewise convergence, or $\sigma(\omega,\phi)$, or $\beta(\omega,\phi)$, which are all equivalent to one another.

2. CONVERGENCE OF NTH SECTIONS

Let $\langle\lambda,\lambda^{\times}\rangle$ be a dual system. In Chapter 2 we investigated conditions imposed on λ which yield the convergence of $\{x^{(n)}\}$ to x relative to T for each x in λ, where T is either $\sigma(\lambda,\lambda^{\times})$, or $\eta(\lambda,\lambda^{\times})$, or $\tau(\lambda,\lambda^{\times})$. This section is primarily devoted to finding restrictions to be laid down on λ so that $x^{(n)} \to x$ in $\delta(\lambda,\lambda^{\times})$ or $\beta(\lambda,\lambda^{\times})$ for each x in λ. Some related results are also included.

Convergence in $\delta(\lambda,\lambda^\times)$

The main result is (Ref. 15)

THEOREM 2.1 If λ is a monotone sequence space, then for each $x \in \lambda$,

$$x^{(n)} \to x \qquad \text{in } \delta(\lambda,\lambda^\times)$$

Proof. Recall that $(\lambda,\sigma(\lambda,\lambda^\times))$ is an AK-space (cf. Proposition 3.19), that is, for each x in λ,

$$\sigma(\lambda,\lambda^\times)\text{-}\lim_{n\to\infty} \sum_{i=1}^{n} x_i e^i = x \tag{*}$$

Suppose J is any subsequence of $\mathbb{N}$ (we need consider only infinite subsequences for our purpose); then for x in λ, $\bar{x}_J \in \lambda$, where $\bar{x}_J$ is the canonical preimage of $x_J = \{x_{n_1}, x_{n_2}, \ldots\}$, J being equal to $\{n_i\}$. Hence

$$\sigma(\lambda,\lambda^\times)\text{-}\lim_{N\to\infty} \sum_{i=1}^{N} x_{n_i} e^{n_i} = \bar{x}_J$$

Consequently the series in (*) is weakly subseries convergent in λ, and so we get the result on applying Theorem 3.10.1. □

Remark: Theorem 2.1 includes Theorem 2.8.3.

The following result (Ref. 15) partially contains Proposition 2.5.3.

PROPOSITION 2.2 If λ is a monotone sequence space, then $(\lambda^\times,\sigma(\lambda^\times,\lambda))$ is sequentially complete.

Proof. Let T denote the $\mathcal{S}$-topology on $\lambda^\times$ where $\mathcal{S}$ is the collection of all $\delta(\lambda,\lambda^\times)$-precompact subsets of λ. It is clear that $\sigma(\lambda^\times,\lambda) \subset T$, and by Theorem 1.11.7, every $\sigma(\lambda^\times,\lambda)$-compact subset B of $\lambda^\times$ is T precompact. We will show that B is in fact T-compact.

To prove the last assertion of the preceding paragraph, it is sufficient to show that $(\lambda^\times,T)$ is complete (cf. Proposition 1.2.13). To accomplish this let $f \in \lambda'$ be such that f_A, the restriction of f to each $A \in \mathcal{S}$, is $\sigma(\lambda,\lambda^\times)$-continuous. It follows that an f of this type is $\delta(\lambda,\lambda^\times)$-sequentially continuous [indeed, if $x^n \to 0$ in $\delta(\lambda,\lambda^\times)$, then $A = \{x^n : n \geq 1\} \cup \{0\}$ is $\delta(\lambda,\lambda^\times)$-precompact, and as $x^n \to 0$ in A relative to $\sigma(\lambda,\lambda^\times)$, therefore $f(x^n) \to 0$]. Thus from Exercise 2.3.8, f can be identified with $\{f(e^i)\}$

since $(\lambda,\delta(\lambda,\lambda^\times))$ is an AK-space from Theorem 2.1. By the exercise referred to, $\{f(e^i)\} \in \lambda^\beta = \lambda^\times$ since λ is monotone (cf. Proposition 2.2.7). Hence $f \in \lambda^\times = (\lambda,\sigma(\lambda,\lambda^\times))^*$. By Grothendieck's completion theorem 1.11.6, $(\lambda^\times,T)$ is therefore complete.

Consequently, T and $\sigma(\lambda^\times,\lambda)$-compact subsets of $\lambda^\times$ are the same, and therefore these two topologies have the same convergent sequences. The main result now follows by an application of Proposition 1.2.11. □

A very useful application of Theorem 2.1 is the following result from Köthe-Toeplitz theory. The proof below is taken from Ref. 15; this result also appears as a simple corollary of a theorem on Schauder bases proved in Ref. 127.

PROPOSITION 2.3 If λ is a perfect sequence space, then $(\lambda,\tau(\lambda,\lambda^\times))$ is complete.

Proof. Let S denote the family of all $\sigma(\lambda^\times,\lambda)$-compact subsets of $\lambda^\times$. Then $\delta(\lambda,\lambda^\times)$ is the S-topology on λ. Suppose $f \in (\lambda^\times)'$ be such that restrictions of f to each $A \in S$ are $\sigma(\lambda^\times,\lambda)$-continuous. As in the proof of the preceding result it turns out that f is $\sigma(\lambda^\times,\lambda)$-sequentially continuous and since $(\lambda^\times,\sigma(\lambda^\times,\lambda))$ is an AK-space (cf. Proposition 2.3.19), we find that f can be identified with $\{f(e^i)\} \in (\lambda^\times)^\beta = \lambda^{\times\times} = \lambda$. Using Theorem 1.11.6, we conclude that $(\lambda,\delta(\lambda,\lambda^\times))$ is complete.

Let $g \in (\lambda^\times)'$ be such that g restricted to each balanced, convex, and $\sigma(\lambda^\times,\lambda)$-compact subset A of $\lambda^\times$ is $\delta(\lambda^\times,\lambda)$-continuous. Suppose $x^n \to 0$ in $(\lambda^\times,\delta(\lambda^\times,\lambda))$ and so $B = \{x^n\} \cup \{0\}$ is $\delta(\lambda^\times,\lambda)$-compact. Observe that $(\lambda^\times,\delta(\lambda^\times,\lambda))$ is complete (replace λ by $\lambda^\times$ in the first part of the proof) and from Proposition 1.2.13, the balanced convex $\delta(\lambda^\times,\lambda)$-closed hull $\hat{B}$ of B is $\delta(\lambda^\times,\lambda)$-compact, i.e., $\hat{B} \in S_1$, the family of all balanced convex $\sigma(\lambda^\times,\lambda)$-compact subsets of $\lambda^\times$. Thus $g(x^n) \to 0$, that is, g is $\delta(\lambda^\times,\lambda)$-sequentially continuous, and since $(\lambda^\times,\delta(\lambda^\times,\lambda))$ is an AK-space (in Theorem 2.1, replace λ by $\lambda^\times$), arguments similar to those in the preceding paragraph yield that g, which is identified as $\{g(e^i)\}$, belongs to λ. Once again, by Grothendieck's completion theorem, $(\lambda,\tau(\lambda,\lambda^\times))$ is complete, since the S_1-topology on λ is $\tau(\lambda,\lambda^\times)$. □

Remark: For a locally convex space (X,T) the topologies $\tau(X,X^*)$ and $\delta(X,X^*)$ are not always the same. In fact, the balanced convex and $\sigma(X^*,X)$-closed hull of a $\sigma(X^*,X)$-compact subset of X^* may not be always $\sigma(X^*,X)$-compact (cf. remarks after the proof of Proposition 2.7.8). For perfect sequence spaces this is not the case; indeed one has

PROPOSITION 2.4 If λ is a perfect sequence space, then $\tau(\lambda,\lambda^\times) = \delta(\lambda,\lambda^\times)$.

Proof. Clearly $\tau(\lambda,\lambda^\times) \subset \delta(\lambda,\lambda^\times)$. On the other hand, let A be an arbitrary $\sigma(\lambda^\times,\lambda)$-compact subset of $\lambda^\times$. Suppose B denotes the balanced, convex, and $\sigma(\lambda^\times,\lambda)$-closed hull of A. By the foregoing result, $(\lambda^\times,\tau(\lambda^\times,\lambda))$ is complete; therefore from Theorem 1.11.9, B is $\sigma(\lambda^\times,\lambda)$-compact. As $B^\circ \subset A^\circ$, we are done. □

Sequential and Bounded Duals

A feature that distinguishes the topological, sequential, and bounded duals of a locally convex space can be found once again by considering distinct sequence spaces. First, we prove the following proposition which sharpens an earlier result in Ref. 124, Proposition 2.3 and Ref. 261, Proposition 1.11.

PROPOSITION 2.5 Let (λ, T) be a locally convex sequence space.

(i) If $\sigma(\lambda,\lambda^\times) \subset T \subset \delta(\lambda,\lambda^\times)$, then

$$(\lambda,T)^* \subset (\lambda,T)^+ \subset \lambda^\beta$$

(ii) If λ is monotone and $\sigma(\lambda,\lambda^\times) \subset T \subset \tau(\lambda,\lambda^\times)$, then

$$(\lambda,T)^+ = (\lambda,T)^* = \lambda^\times$$

Proof. Part (i) follows from Exercise 2.3.8, since $(\lambda,\delta(\lambda,\lambda^\times))$ is an AK-space by Theorem 2.1. From part (i), $(\lambda,T)^* \subset (\lambda,T)^+ \subset \lambda^\beta$ where $\sigma(\lambda,\lambda^\times) \subset T \subset \tau(\lambda,\lambda^\times)$. By compatibility of T, $(\lambda,T)^* = \lambda^\times$; also, $\lambda^\beta = \lambda^\times$, since λ is monotone (cf. Proposition 2.2.7). Hence (ii) follows. □

EXERCISE 2.6 For a monotone sequence space λ, show that

$$[\sigma(\lambda,\lambda^\times)]^+ \subset \tau(\lambda,\lambda^\times) = [\tau(\lambda,\lambda^\times)]^+$$

[Hint: Observe that T is compatible with $\langle\lambda,\lambda^\times\rangle$ when T is $[\sigma(\lambda,\lambda^\times)]^+$ or $[\tau(\lambda,\lambda^\times)]^+$, from Proposition 2.5.]

Remark: Let us note that the condition of monotonocity on λ in Proposition 2.5 cannot be dropped. Indeed, we have the following counterexample (Ref. 124).

EXAMPLE 2.7 Consider the space $(k,\sigma(k,\ell^1))$. Clearly $k^* = k^\times = \ell^1 \subsetneq k^+$. In fact, $\{(-1)^n/n\} \in k^+$ (cf. Ref. 136, p. 165), since

$$\sum_{n\geq 1} \frac{(-1)^n}{n} x_n$$

converges for any $x = \{x_n\}$ in k. Obviously $\{(-1)^n/n\} \notin k^\times$.

We can deduce another characterization of perfect sequence spaces as follows (Ref. 261, p. 354).

PROPOSITION 2.8 A sequence space λ is perfect if and only if $(\lambda^\times,\tau(\lambda^\times,\lambda))$ is sequentially barreled and $[\lambda^\times,\tau(\lambda^\times,\lambda)]^+ = \lambda$.

Proof. Let λ be perfect. By Theorem 2.5.1, $(\lambda,\sigma(\lambda,\lambda^\times))$ is sequentially complete, and so from Proposition 1.10.12, $(\lambda^\times,\tau(\lambda^\times,\lambda))$ is sequentially barreled. The rest of the implication is a consequence of Proposition 2.5(ii), since $\lambda^{\times\times} = \lambda$.

To prove the reverse implication, observe that $(\lambda^\times,\tau(\lambda^\times,\lambda))$ is sequentially barreled and $[\lambda^\times,\tau(\lambda^\times,\lambda)]^* = \lambda = [\lambda^\times,\tau(\lambda^\times,\lambda)]^+$, and hence Proposition 1.10.13 forces $(\lambda^\times)^*$ to be $\sigma((\lambda^\times)^*,\lambda^\times)$-sequentially complete; that is, $(\lambda,\sigma(\lambda,\lambda^\times))$ is sequentially complete. Now apply Theorem 2.5.1. □

The following result (Ref. 261) represents an interesting application of Proposition 2.3 and improves an earlier result in Ref. 64, namely, "If λ is a perfect sequence space and T is any norm topology on λ with the same convergent sequences as $\sigma(\lambda,\lambda^\times)$, then $T = \tau(\lambda,\lambda^\times) = \beta(\lambda,\lambda^\times)$."

PROPOSITION 2.9 Suppose (λ, T) is a perfect bornological space such that T has the same convergent sequences as $\sigma(\lambda,\lambda^\times)$; then $T = \tau(\lambda,\lambda^\times) = \beta(\lambda,\lambda^\times)$.

Proof. By the definition of T, $[\sigma(\lambda,\lambda^\times)]^+ = T^+$. From the remarks following Definition 1.10.21, $T = T^+$; hence using Exercise 2.6, $\sigma(\lambda,\lambda^\times) \subset T \subset \tau(\lambda,\lambda^\times)$. Taking into consideration Proposition 1.8.7, we conclude that $T = \tau(\lambda,\lambda^\times)$ since $(\lambda,T)^* = \lambda^\times$. Now make use of Proposition 2.3 and Proposition 1.8.7 to get the barreledness of (λ,T), where $T = \tau(\lambda,\lambda^\times)$. Finally we use Theorem 1.8.3 to conclude $T = \beta(\lambda,\lambda^\times)$. □

Proposition 1.7.6(ii) may be regarded as a result on the external construction of a locally convex topology T; however, no such result is known concerning the external construction of T^+. In the case of perfect sequence spaces, the situation is comparatively pleasant, and before we state the result, let us make the following definition, after Webb [261], which obviously can be generalized to an arbitrary l.c. TVS.

DEFINITION 2.10 Let T be a locally convex topology on a sequence space λ such that $\sigma(\lambda,\lambda^{\times}) \subset T \subset \tau(\lambda,\lambda^{\times})$. Then T^c is defined to be the *topology on* $\lambda^{\times}$ *of uniform convergence on the* T-*compact subsets of* λ. In this definition we may replace $\lambda^{\times}$ by λ^{β}.

Note: Observe that $[\sigma(\lambda,\lambda^{\times})]^c = \delta(\lambda^{\times},\lambda)$.

We are now ready to state the desired

THEOREM 2.11 Let (λ,T) be a monotone locally convex sequence space where T is compatible with $\langle\lambda,\lambda^{\times}\rangle$. Then T^+ is the topology of uniform convergence on the T^c-compact subsets of $\lambda^{\times}$.

The proof requires

PROPOSITION 2.12 Let (λ,T) satisfy the hypothesis of the preceding theorem. Then a subset K of $\lambda^{\times}$ is T^c-compact if and only if it is T-limited and T^c-closed.

Proof. Suppose first that K is T-limited and T^c-closed, but not T^c-compact. By Theorem 2.3.10, we can select a sequence $\{y^n\} \subset K$ such that $\{y^n\}$ is convergent in K relative to the topology of coordinatewise convergence but does not converge relative to T^c. The latter assertion implies the existence of an $\varepsilon > 0$, a T-compact subset A of λ, and increasing sequences $\{m_k\}$ and $\{n_k\}$ such that

$$\sup_{x \in A} |\langle x, y^{m_k} - y^{n_k}\rangle| > \varepsilon$$

Thus, for each $k \geq 1$ we can find x^k with $|\langle x^k, y^{m_k} - y^{n_k}\rangle| > \varepsilon$. Since A is T-compact, by Theorem 2.3.10 again we can select a subsequence of $\{x^k\}$, say $\{u^k\}$, such that $u^k \to u$ in T, where $u \in A$. By Theorem 2.1, $u^{(i)} \to u$ in T. Now

$$\langle u^k, y^{m_k} - y^{n_k}\rangle = \langle u^k - u, y^{m_k} - y^{n_k}\rangle + \langle u - u^{(i)}, y^{m_k} - y^{n_k}\rangle$$
$$+ \langle u^{(i)}, y^{m_k} - y^{n_k}\rangle$$

So

$$|\langle u^k, y^{m_k} - y^{n_k}\rangle| \le 2 \sup_{y \in K} |\langle u^k - u, y\rangle| + 2 \sup_{y \in K} |\langle u - u^{(i)}, y\rangle|$$
$$+ |\langle u^{(i)}, y^{m_k} - y^{n_k}\rangle|$$

Now K is T-limited, so there exists an M in $\mathbb{N}$ with

$$\sup_{y \in K} |\langle u - u^{(M)}, y\rangle| < \frac{1}{5}\varepsilon$$

Similarly there exists an N in $\mathbb{N}$ such that

$$\sup_{y \in K} |\langle u^k - u, y\rangle| < \frac{1}{5}\varepsilon \qquad \forall k \ge N$$

Since $\{y^n\}$ is coordinatewise Cauchy, we can determine a $P \equiv P(M)$ in $\mathbb{N}$ satisfying

$$|\langle u^{(M)}, y^{m_k} - y^{n_k}\rangle| < \frac{1}{5}\varepsilon \qquad \forall k \ge P$$

Therefore, for all $k \ge \max\{N,P\}$,

$$|\langle u^k, y^{m_k} - y^{n_k}\rangle| < \varepsilon$$

However, the above inequality leads to a contradiction and we are done with the sufficiency part.

For the remaining part it is sufficient to show that each T^c-compact subset of $\lambda^\times$ is T-limited. Assume that this assertion is not true. This means the existence of a T^c-compact subset of $\lambda^\times$ and a sequence $\{x^n\}$ in λ with $x^n \to 0$ in T such that $\sup\{|\langle x^n, y\rangle| : y \in K\} \not\to 0$ as $n \to \infty$. Hence there exist an $\varepsilon > 0$, a subsequence $\{x^k\}$ of $\{x^n\}$, and a sequence $\{y^{n_k}\} \subset K$ such that

$$|\langle x^k, y^{n_k}\rangle| > \varepsilon \qquad \forall k \ge 1$$

Using Theorem 2.3.10, we can select a subsequence of $\{y^{n_k}\}$, which we denote by $\{y^{n_k}\}$ again, such that $y^{n_k} \to y$ in T^c with $y \in K$. Now

$$|\langle x^k, y\rangle| \ge |\langle x^k, y^{n_k}\rangle| - |\langle x^k, y^{n_k} - y\rangle|$$

Observe that $A = \{x^n : n \geq 1\} \cup \{0\}$ is T-compact, and so for some k_0 in $\mathbb{N}$,

$$\sup_{x \in A} |\langle x, y^{n_k} - y\rangle| < \frac{1}{2}\varepsilon \qquad \forall k \geq k_0$$

Therefore $|\langle x^k, y\rangle| > \varepsilon/2$ for all $k \geq k_0$, and this contradicts the nature of $\{x^n\}$. □

Proof of Theorem 2.11. To prove the theorem, let us write

$$S = \{A : A \subset \lambda^\times,\ A \text{ is T-limited}\}$$

and

$$S_1 = \{\bar{A} : A \in S\}$$

where $\bar{A}$ represents the T^c-closure of A. By Proposition 2.5, $\lambda^+ = \lambda^\times$, and hence from Proposition 1.10.23, T^+ is the topology of uniform convergence on T-limited subsets of $\lambda^\times$; that is, T^+ is the S-topology. Observe that each member of S_1 is T^c-compact (cf. Proposition 2.12) and moreover, the S- and S_1-topologies on λ are equivalent. Thus T^+ is equivalent to the S_1-topology. □

PROPOSITION 2.13 For a perfect sequence space λ, $[\tau(\lambda,\lambda^\times)]^c = [\sigma(\lambda^\times,\lambda)]^+$.

Proof. By Proposition 2.4, $[\sigma(\lambda^\times,\lambda)]^c = \delta(\lambda,\lambda^\times) = \tau(\lambda,\lambda^\times)$. Hence from Theorem 2.11, $[\sigma(\lambda^\times,\lambda)]^+$ is the topology of uniform convergence of $\tau(\lambda,\lambda^\times)$-compact subsets of λ, and so from the definition of $[\tau(\lambda,\lambda^\times)]^c$, $[\sigma(\lambda^\times,\lambda)]^+ = [\tau(\lambda,\lambda^\times)]^c$. □

PROPOSITION 2.14 If λ is a perfect sequence space, then

(i) $[\tau(\lambda,\lambda^\times)]^c = \tau(\lambda^\times,\lambda)$

is equivalent to

(ii) $[\tau(\lambda^\times,\lambda)]^c = \tau(\lambda,\lambda^\times)$

Proof. (i) ⟹ (ii) We have (using Proposition 2.13)

$$[\sigma(\lambda^\times,\lambda)]^+ = \tau(\lambda^\times,\lambda)$$

Making use of Theorem 2.3.10, we conclude the equivalence of $\sigma(\lambda^\times,\lambda)$- and $\tau(\lambda^\times,\lambda)$-compact subsets of $\lambda^\times$. Thus

$$[\tau(\lambda^\times,\lambda)]^c = \delta(\lambda,\lambda^\times) = \tau(\tau,\lambda^\times)$$

The implication (ii) ⟹ (i) follows similarly. □

At the end of this subsection we have

PROPOSITION 2.15 Let λ be a sequence space. Then (a) the following two conditions are equivalent:

(i) $[\sigma(\lambda,\lambda^\times)]^+ = [\tau(\lambda,\lambda)^\times]^+$.

(ii) $\sigma(\lambda,\lambda^\times)$- and $\tau(\lambda,\lambda^\times)$-compact subsets of λ are the same.

If λ is also perfect, then (b) the conditions (i) and (ii) are equivalent to

(iii) $\tau(\lambda^\times,\lambda) = [\tau(\lambda,\lambda^\times)]^c$.

Further, a perfect sequence space λ has any one of these three properties (i) through (iii) if and only if the dual $\lambda^\times$ has.

Proof. Observe that (i) is equivalent to saying that $\sigma(\lambda,\lambda^\times)$- and $\tau(\lambda,\lambda^\times)$-convergent sequences in λ are the same. Hence (a) immediately follows from Theorem 2.3.10.

Let λ be perfect. Assume that (iii) is true. From Proposition 2.14,

$$\tau(\lambda,\lambda^\times) = [\tau(\lambda^\times,\lambda)]^c = [\sigma(\lambda,\lambda^\times)]^+$$

by Proposition 2.13 (replace λ by $\lambda^\times$ here). Hence (ii) follows. Condition (ii) obviously implies (iii). The last part is easily disposed of with the help of Proposition 2.14. □

Note: Köthe [140, p. 418] gives a different approach to the proof of Proposition 2.15.

Topologies T^b *and* T^p

Let us recall the dual X^b for a locally convex space (X,T) and the topologies T^b and T^p. We know that $T \subset T^+ \subset T^b$ and $T \subset T^p \subset T^b$ (cf. Proposition 1.10.24). A natural question is that of the relationship or the comparability between T^+ and T^p. In general there does not exist any such relationship between these two latter topologies, as revealed by the following two examples (Ref. 261).

EXAMPLE 2.16 Let $\lambda = \ell^1$ and $T = \sigma(\ell^1,\ell^\infty)$. Since $\sigma(\ell^1,\ell^\infty)$- and $\beta(\ell^1,\ell^\infty)$-bounded subsets of ℓ^1 are the same (Proposition 2.5.4), $T^b = \beta(\ell^1,\ell^\infty)$. Also, from Proposition 2.6.9, $T^+ = \beta(\ell^1,\ell^\infty)$. By Proposition 1.10.24, $T^p \subset T^+$. Our claim is that $T^p \neq T^+$. For otherwise, each $\sigma(\ell^1,\ell^\infty)$-bounded subset of ℓ^1 [being already $\sigma(\ell^1,\ell^\infty)$-precompact by Proposition 1.7.10] is

T^p-precompact, and so it is $\beta(\ell^1,\ell^\infty)$-precompact. However, this is absurd [for example, consider $\{e^n\}$, which is $\sigma(\ell^1,\ell^\infty)$-bounded but not $\beta(\ell^1,\ell^\infty)$- or norm precompact]. Thus $T^p \subsetneq T^+$.

EXAMPLE 2.17 Let $\lambda = \ell^\infty$, $T = \tau(\ell^\infty,\ell^1)$. It is clear that T^b is the usual sup norm topology of ℓ^∞ (see Proposition 2.6.8). By Exercise 2.5, $T^+ = \tau(\ell^\infty,\ell^1)$. Thus $T^+ = T \subset T^p$ and so $T^+ \subset T^p$. We assert that $T^+ \neq T^p$, for otherwise $(\ell^\infty,T^p)^* = (\ell^\infty,T^+)^* = \ell^1$. But $(\ell^\infty,T^p)^* = (\ell^\infty)^b$ by Proposition 1.10.24, where $(\ell^\infty)^b$ is the usual norm dual of ℓ^∞. This contradiction proves $T^+ \subsetneq T^p$.

From Proposition 1.10.24, $T^p \subset T^b$. If $T = \sigma(\omega,\phi)$ then $T^p = T^b$. The following example gives $T^p \subsetneq T^b$.

EXAMPLE 2.18 Consider the space of Example 2.17. Assume here $T^p = T^b$. Now consider any norm bounded subset of ℓ^∞. Then B is $\sigma(\ell^\infty,\ell^1)$-relatively compact. Now, as noted in Proposition 2.6.9, the $\sigma(\ell^1,\ell^\infty)$- and $\tau(\ell^1,\ell^\infty)$-convergent sequences in ℓ^1 are the same. Thus, in view of Proposition 2.15, B is $\tau(\ell^\infty,\ell^1)$-precompact and so it is T^p-compact. By our assumption, B is T^b-precompact. However, this is not true in general and so $T^p \subsetneq T^b$.

The Space λ_0

Let us now give a general method of constructing counterexamples from sequence spaces. The idea behind this method stems from a remark made by Köthe in Ref. 140, p. 269, and the description given below is due to Webb [261].

For an arbitrary monotone sequence space λ, let us recall the subspace λ_0 constructed in Chapter 2, Section 2. Consider the dual system $\langle\lambda,\lambda^\times\rangle$ and $\langle\lambda_0,\lambda^\times\rangle$. Then we have the following four results (Ref. 261).

PROPOSITION 2.19 For a normal sequence space λ, the topologies $\beta(\lambda^\times,\lambda)$ and $\beta(\lambda^\times,\lambda_0)$ on $\lambda^\times$ are the same.

Proof. Obviously $\beta(\lambda^\times,\lambda_0) \subset \beta(\lambda^\times,\lambda)$, since $\lambda_0 \subset \lambda$. To prove the reverse inclusion, consider an arbitrary $\sigma(\lambda,\lambda^\times)$-bounded subset A of λ and let $B = \{A\}^N$. By Exercise 2.8.23, B is $\sigma(\lambda,\lambda^\times)$-bounded. Hence $D = B \cap \phi$ is a normal subset of λ_0 that is $\sigma(\lambda_0,\lambda^\times)$-bounded. Moreover,

$D° = B°$. Indeed, $B° \subset D°$ is readily verified. Further, if $x \in B$ then $x^{(n)} \in D$ for all $n \geq 1$, and so for an arbitrary y in $D°$ and any x in B,

$$|\langle x^{(n)}, y\rangle| \leq 1 \qquad \forall n \geq 1$$

But $x^{(n)} \to x$ in $\sigma(\lambda,\lambda^{\times})$ and therefore $|\langle x, y\rangle| \leq 1$ for all x in B; that is, $D° \subset B°$. As $A \subset B$, we have $D° \subset A°$. □

PROPOSITION 2.20 If λ is normal, then the topology $\eta(\lambda^{\times},\lambda_0)$ on $\lambda^{\times}$ is compatible with the dual system $\langle\lambda^{\times},\lambda_0\rangle$.

Proof. Since $\sigma(\lambda^{\times},\lambda_0) \subset \eta(\lambda^{\times},\lambda_0)$ is obviously true, we need show that $\eta(\lambda^{\times},\lambda_0) \subset \tau(\lambda^{\times},\lambda_0)$. To accomplish this, consider an arbitrary point $x \in \lambda_0$. Let $M = \{x\}^N$. Following the proof of Theorem 2.8.14, one can show that M is $\sigma(\lambda,\lambda^{\times})$-compact. Since $M \subset \lambda_0$, we find that M is a balanced, convex, and $\sigma(\lambda_0,\lambda^{\times})$-compact subset of λ_0. Finally observe that $\{x\}°$ is a zero-neighborhood in $\eta(\lambda^{\times},\lambda_0)$ and $M° \subset \{x\}°$. □

PROPOSITION 2.21 For a monotone sequence space λ, $\eta(\lambda^{\times},\lambda_0)$- and $\eta(\lambda^{\times},\lambda)$-bounded subsets of $\lambda^{\times}$ are the same.

Proof. Suppose there exists an $\eta(\lambda^{\times},\lambda_0)$-bounded subset B of $\lambda^{\times}$ which is not $\eta(\lambda^{\times},\lambda)$-bounded. Hence for some y in λ,

$$\sup_{x\in B} \sum_{i\geq 1} |x_i||y_i| = \infty$$

It is clear that for each k in $\mathbb{N}$ there exists an x^k in B with

$$\sum_{i\geq 1} |x_i^k||y_i| > k$$

But we proceed to construct a sequence $\{x^k\} \subset B$ with the sum of the corresponding infinite series being greater than $k \cdot 2^k$ for each $k \geq 1$, so that we may select a finite number of terms having sum exceeding k. This is achieved by dividing the infinite series into 2^k parts using the following means of dividing the set $\mathbb{N}$ into 2^k equivalence classes (Ref. 89, p. 21): "If $N > 0$ is an integer then two elements m and n of $\mathbb{N}$ are equivalent provided $m - n$ is divisible by N, and we write this as $m \equiv n \pmod N$."

We can find an $x^1 \in B$ such that

$$\sum_{i\geq 1} |x_i^1||y_i| > 1 \cdot 2 = 1(1 + 1)$$

Using the preceding argument we can choose an integer j_1 (= 0 or 1) such that

$$\sum_{\substack{i \geq 1 \\ i \equiv j_1 (\mathrm{mod}\ 2)}} |x_i^1||y_i| > 1$$

Hence we can find an n_1 in $\mathbb{N}$, n_1 being a multiple of 2, with

$$\sum_{\substack{i=1 \\ i \equiv j_1 (\mathrm{mod}\ 2)}}^{n_1} |x_i^1||y_i| > 1 \tag{*}$$

Since $y^{(n_1)} \in \phi \subset \lambda_0$ and B is $\eta(\lambda^\times, \lambda_0)$-bounded, there exists M > 0 such that

$$\sup_{x \in B} \sum_{i=1}^{n_1} |x_i||y_i| \leq M$$

$$\Longrightarrow \quad \sup_{x \in B} \sum_{i \geq n_1+1} |x_i||y_i| = \infty$$

As before choose an x^2 in B with

$$\sum_{i \geq n_1+1} |x_i^2||y_i| > 2 \cdot 2^2 = 2 + 2 + 2 + 2$$

By the above argument we divide the preceding sum into four parts such that each sum corresponds to indices i ($\geq n_1 + 1$) which are integers modulo j for j = 0, 1, 2, and 3. We have for some j_2 (= 0, or 1, or 2, or 3) that

$$\sum_{\substack{i \geq n_1+1 \\ i \equiv j_2 (\mathrm{mod}\ 2^2)}} |x_i^2||y_i| > 2$$

One can choose $n_2 \in \mathbb{N}$ with n_2 a multiple of 4 and $n_2 > 2n_1$ such that

$$\sum_{\substack{i=n_1+1 \\ i \equiv j_2 (\mathrm{mod}\ 2^2)}}^{n_2} |x_i^2||y_i| > 2 \tag{**}$$

Proceeding in this way, we get a sequence $\{x^k\}$ in B and sequences $\{n_k\}$ and $\{j_k\}$ of integers satisfying the conditions

(1) n_k is a multiple of 2^k and $n_k > 2n_{k-1}$.

(2) $j_k = 0, 1, \ldots,$ or $2^k - 1$.

$$(3) \quad \sum_{\substack{i=n_{k-1}+1 \\ i\equiv j_k (\mathrm{mod}\ 2^k)}}^{n_k} |x_i^k||y_i| > k,$$

where $k = 1, 2, \ldots,$ and $n_0 = 0$.

Define $a \in m_0$ as follows:

$$a_i = \begin{cases} 1 & \text{if } i \equiv j_k \ (\mathrm{mod}\ 2^k) \text{ and } n_{k-1} < i \le n_k,\ k = 1, 2, \ldots \\ 0 & \text{otherwise} \end{cases}$$

Then

$$\sum_{i=1}^{n_k} a_i = \sum_{\substack{i=1 \\ i\equiv j_1 (\mathrm{mod}\ 2)}}^{n_1} a_i + \sum_{\substack{i=n_1+1 \\ i\equiv j_2 (\mathrm{mod}\ 2^2)}}^{n_2} a_i + \cdots + \sum_{\substack{i=n_{k-1}+1 \\ i\equiv j_k (\mathrm{mod}\ 2^k)}}^{n_k} a_i$$

$$\le \frac{n_1}{2} + \frac{n_2}{2^2} + \cdots + \frac{n_k}{2^k}$$

$$\le \frac{n_k}{2 \cdot 2^{k-1}} + \frac{n_k}{2^2 \cdot 2^{k-2}} + \cdots + \frac{n_k}{2^k} \qquad \text{by (1)}$$

$$= \frac{kn_k}{2^k}$$

Now if $n > n_k$, we have

$$\frac{1}{n}\sum_{i=1}^{n} a_i < \frac{1}{n_k}\sum_{i=1}^{n_k} a_i + \frac{1}{n}\sum_{\substack{i=n_k+1 \\ i\equiv j_{k+1} (\mathrm{mod}\ 2^{k+1})}}^{n} a_i$$

$$\le \frac{k}{2^k} + \frac{n - n_k}{n \cdot 2^{k+1}} < \frac{k}{2^k} + \frac{1}{2^{k+1}} \to 0 \qquad \text{as } k \to \infty$$

Hence $a \in \mathcal{O}$ and therefore $ay \in \lambda_0$. By (3) we then find that

$$\sup_{x\in B} \sum_{i\ge 1} |x_i||a_iy_i| = \infty$$

Thus B is $\eta(\lambda^\times, \lambda_0)$-unbounded, a contradiction. Consequently B is $\eta(\lambda^\times, \lambda)$-bounded. □

Finally we have

PROPOSITION 2.22 Let (λ, T) be a locally convex normal sequence space with $\sigma(\lambda, \lambda^\times) \subset T \subset \tau(\lambda, \lambda^\times)$. (i) If (λ, T) is barreled, then $(\lambda_0, \tau(\lambda_0, \lambda^\times))$ is also barreled. (ii) If (λ,T) is semireflexive, then $\sigma(\lambda^\times,\lambda_0)$- and $\sigma(\lambda^\times,\lambda)$-convergent sequences in $\lambda^\times$ are the same.

Proof. (i) Assume that K is a $\sigma(\lambda^\times,\lambda_0)$-bounded subset of $\lambda^\times$. By Proposition 2.20, K is $\eta(\lambda^\times,\lambda_0)$-bounded, and so from Proposition 2.21, K is $\eta(\lambda^\times,\lambda_0)$-bounded. Thus from the hypothesis, K is $\sigma(\lambda^\times,\lambda)$-relatively compact and so it is $\sigma(\lambda^\times,\lambda_0)$-relatively compact. Consequently (i) is proved [cf. Theorem 1.8.3(ii)].

(ii) Let $y^n \to 0$ in $\sigma(\lambda^\times,\lambda_0)$. If $A = \{y^n : n \geq 1\} \cup \{0\}$, then A is $\sigma(\lambda^\times,\lambda_0)$-bounded. Using Propositions 2.20 and 2.21, we conclude that A is $\sigma(\lambda^\times,\lambda)$-bounded. Observe that A is also $\sigma(\lambda^\times,\lambda)$-closed (indeed, if $x \in \bar{A}$ then only a subsequence of $\{y^n\}$, say $\{y^{n_k}\}$, can converge to x and it turns out that $x = \{0\}$). By Proposition 1.9.2(i), A is $\sigma(\lambda^\times,\lambda)$-compact. It remains only to apply Theorem 2.3.10(iv). □

Remark: We know that an l.c. TVS (X,T) is semireflexive if and only if $\sigma(X^*,X) = \sigma(X^*,X^{**})$. Thus, if (X,T) is semireflexive, then $[\sigma(X^*,X)]^+ = [\sigma(X^*,X^{**})]^+$. The preceding proposition says that the last condition on X* does not necessarily imply the semireflexivity of (X,T). In fact, consider

EXAMPLE 2.23 Let $\lambda = \ell^2$ and take the space $(\lambda_0,\tau(\lambda_0,\lambda^\times))$. If T is the usual norm topology on ℓ^2, then (λ,T) is semireflexive and so $[\sigma(\lambda^\times,\lambda_0)]^+ = [\sigma(\lambda^\times,\lambda)]^+$. But $(\lambda_0,\tau(\lambda_0,\lambda^\times))$ is not semireflexive, for

$$\lambda_0^{**} = (\lambda_0^*,\beta(\lambda_0^*,\lambda_0))^* = (\lambda^\times,\beta(\lambda^\times,\lambda_0))^* = (\lambda^\times,\beta(\lambda^\times,\lambda))^* = \lambda \supsetneq \lambda_0$$

Let us recall a sufficient condition for sequential barreledness stated in the first part of Proposition 1.10.13. The condition therein that $(X,\tau(X,X^+))$ is sequentially complete cannot be replaced by the sequential completeness of $(X,\tau(X,X^*))$ or even by the quasi-completeness of $(X,\tau(X,X^*))$, for we have

EXAMPLE 2.24 Here we consider the space $(\phi,\tau(\phi,\omega_0))$. To begin with let us consider $(\omega_0,\sigma(\omega_0,\phi))$. If A is any $\sigma(\phi,\omega_0)$-bounded subset of ϕ, it follows from Propositions 2.20 and 2.21 that A is $\sigma(\phi,\omega)$-bounded. Thus, by Theorem 2.6.2, A is finite dimensional. From Proposition 1.10.11, we therefore conclude that $(\omega_0,\sigma(\omega_0,\phi))$ is barreled, and consequently $(\phi,\tau(\phi,\omega_0))$ is quasicomplete, by Theorem 1.8.6. It is clear that

$(\omega_0, \sigma(\omega_0, \phi))$ is metrizable and has the completion $(\omega, \sigma(\omega, \phi))$, and thus by the second part of Proposition 1.10.12, $(\phi, \tau(\phi, \omega_0))$ cannot be sequentially barreled.

Note: By Theorem 1.7.18, the space $(\phi, \tau(\phi, \omega_0))$ is a W-space (that is, $\langle\phi, \omega_0\rangle$ forms an M-dual system). As this space is not sequentially barreled, we find that the reverse implication of the first statement of Proposition 1.10.12 is not necessarily valid.

Convergence in $\beta(\lambda, \lambda^\times)$

We now return to the second objective of this section, namely, to find conditions on a sequence space λ so that $x^{(n)} \to x$ relative to $\beta(\lambda, \lambda^\times)$ for each x in λ. At this stage let us remind the reader that for a given sequence space λ it is not necessarily true that $x^{(n)} \to x$ in $\beta(\lambda, \lambda^\times)$ for each x in λ; for instance, see Exercise 2.6.13. On the other hand, $x^{(n)} \to x$ in $\beta(c_0, \ell^1)$ for each x in c_0.

The following result sharpens a theorem in Ref. 140, p. 417.

PROPOSITION 2.25 Let λ be a monotone sequence space. Then the following conditions are equivalent:

(i) $(\lambda, \tau(\lambda, \lambda^\times))$ is barreled.
(ii) $x^{(n)} \to x$ in $\beta(\lambda, \lambda^\times)$ for each x in λ.
(iii) $(\lambda, \beta(\lambda, \lambda^\times))$ is separable.

Proof. (i) $\Rightarrow$ (ii) Suppose A is a $\sigma(\lambda^\times, \lambda)$-bounded subset of $\lambda^\times$. Since λ is $\tau(\lambda, \lambda^\times)$-barreled, A is $\sigma(\lambda^\times, \lambda)$-relatively compact. By Theorem 2.1, $x^{(n)} \to x$ in $\delta(\lambda, \lambda^\times)$, and so for each $\varepsilon > 0$, there corresponds an $N \equiv N(\varepsilon, A)$ in $\mathbb{N}$ such that

$$\sup_{y \in A} |\langle x^{(n)} - x, y\rangle| < \varepsilon \qquad \forall n \geq N$$

$$\Longrightarrow \quad x^{(n)} \to x \qquad \text{in } \beta(\lambda, \lambda^\times)$$

(ii) $\Rightarrow$ (iii) This follows easily from the last sentence of the remark following Definition 2.3.4.

(iii) $\Rightarrow$ (i) Let A be a $\sigma(\lambda^\times, \lambda)$-bounded and closed subset. We show that A is $\sigma(\lambda^\times, \lambda)$-sequentially compact, and it will follow from Theorem 2.3.10 that A is $\sigma(\lambda^\times, \lambda)$-compact. So, let $\{a^n\} \subset A$. By (iii) we may choose a sequence $\{u^n\} \subset \lambda$ that is $\beta(\lambda,\lambda^\times)$-dense in λ. Since $\{a^n\}$ is $\sigma(\lambda^\times,\lambda)$-bounded, by using a diagonal procedure (see, for instance, Ref. 177, p. 220) we can find a subsequence of $\{a^n\}$, also denoted by $\{a^n\}$, such that

$$\lim_{n\to\infty} \langle u^i, a^n\rangle \text{ exists} \qquad \text{for each } i \geq 1$$

Thus for each $i \geq 1$ and $\varepsilon > 0$ there exists a positive integer $n_0 \equiv n_0(\varepsilon,i)$ such that

$$|\langle u^i, a^n - a^m\rangle| \leq \frac{\varepsilon}{2} \qquad \forall m,n \geq n_0$$

Choose x in λ. From the hypothesis, there corresponds u^{i_0} such that

$$\sup_{y\in A} |\langle x - u^{i_0}, y\rangle| \leq \frac{\varepsilon}{4}$$

$$\Longrightarrow \quad |\langle x - u^{i_0}, a^n - a^m\rangle| \leq \frac{\varepsilon}{2} \qquad \forall m,n \geq 1$$

Hence

$$|\langle x, a^n - a^m\rangle| \leq |\langle x - u^{i_0}, a^n - a^m\rangle| + |\langle u^{i_0}, a^n - a^m\rangle| \leq \varepsilon$$

$$\forall m,n \geq n_0 \equiv n_0(\varepsilon,i_0)$$

Therefore $\{a^n\}$ is $\sigma(\lambda^\times,\lambda)$-Cauchy. In view of Proposition 2.2, we conclude that $\{a^n\}$ converges in A relative to $\sigma(\lambda^\times,\lambda)$. We need apply now Theorem 1.8.3 to conclude (i). □

PROPOSITION 2.26 If λ is a monotone sequence space, then the following statements are equivalent:

(i) $x^{(n)} \to x$ in $\beta(\lambda,\lambda^\times)$ for each $x \in \lambda$.

(ii) $\tau(\lambda,\lambda^\times)$- and $\beta(\lambda,\lambda^\times)$-convergent sequences in λ are the same.

(iii) $\tau(\lambda,\lambda^\times)$- and $\beta(\lambda,\lambda^\times)$-compact subsets of λ are the same.

Proof. (i) $\Longrightarrow$ (ii) From the preceding result, the space $(\lambda,\tau(\lambda,\lambda^\times))$ is barreled. Thus $\tau(\lambda,\lambda^\times) = \beta(\lambda,\lambda^\times)$ (cf. Theorem 1.8.3). Hence we get (ii).

(ii) $\Longrightarrow$ (iii) This is a consequence of Theorem 2.3.10.

(iii) $\Longrightarrow$ (i) Choose x in λ arbitrarily. By Theorem 2.1, $x^{(n)} \to x$ in $\tau(\lambda,\lambda^\times)$. Hence $A = \{x^{(n)} : n \geq 1\} \cup \{x\}$ is $\tau(\lambda,\lambda^\times)$-compact and so A is $\beta(\lambda,\lambda^\times)$-compact. By Theorem 2.3.10 again, $x^{(n)} \to x$ in $\beta(\lambda,\lambda^\times)$. □

Concerning the AK-property of $(\lambda^{\times},\beta(\lambda^{\times},\lambda))$ we have

PROPOSITION 2.27 Let λ be a perfect space and T any locally convex topology on λ compatible with $\langle\lambda,\lambda^{\times}\rangle$. Then (λ,T) is semireflexive if and only if $y^{(n)} \to y$ in $\beta(\lambda^{\times},\lambda)$ for each y in $\lambda^{\times}$.

Proof. If (λ,T) is semireflexive then $\beta(\lambda^{\times},\lambda) = \tau(\lambda^{\times},\lambda)$, by Proposition 1.9.2(i). But $y^{(n)} \to y$ in $\tau(\lambda^{\times},\lambda)$ for each y in $\lambda^{\times}$; therefore the necessity of the condition is obtained.

Let now $y^{(n)} \to y$ in $\beta(\lambda^{\times},\lambda)$ for each y in $\lambda^{\times}$. By Proposition 2.25, $(\lambda^{\times},\tau(\lambda^{\times},\lambda))$ is barreled, and so $\tau(\lambda^{\times},\lambda) = \beta(\lambda^{\times},\lambda)$ (cf. Theorem 1.8.3). Hence $(\lambda^{\times},\beta(\lambda^{\times},\lambda))^* = \lambda$, that is, (λ,T) is semireflexive. □

Remark: Let us note that in the proof of the first part of the preceding result we do not use the perfectness of λ.

PROPOSITION 2.28 For a perfect space λ, $\sigma(\lambda,\lambda^{\times})$- and $\beta(\lambda,\lambda^{\times})$-convergent sequences in λ are the same if and only if every $\sigma(\lambda^{\times},\lambda)$-bounded subset of $\lambda^{\times}$ is $\tau(\lambda^{\times},\lambda)$-relatively compact.

Proof. Assume first that $\sigma(\lambda,\lambda^{\times})$- and $\beta(\lambda,\lambda^{\times})$-convergent sequences in λ are the same. Thus

$$[\sigma(\lambda,\lambda^{\times})]^{+} = [\tau(\lambda,\lambda^{\times})]^{+} = [\beta(\lambda,\lambda^{\times})]^{+}$$

Hence by Propositions 2.25 and 2.26, the space $(\lambda,\tau(\lambda,\lambda^{\times}))$ is barreled, and so each $\sigma(\lambda^{\times},\lambda)$-bounded subset A of $\lambda^{\times}$ is $\sigma(\lambda^{\times},\lambda)$-relatively compact. Consequently, by Proposition 2.15, A is $\tau(\lambda^{\times},\lambda)$-relatively compact. Conversely, if $\sigma(\lambda^{\times},\lambda)$-bounded subsets of $\lambda^{\times}$ are $\tau(\lambda^{\times},\lambda)$-relatively compact, then $\beta(\lambda,\lambda^{\times}) = [\tau(\lambda^{\times},\lambda)]^{c}$, and so from Proposition 2.13, $\beta(\lambda,\lambda^{\times}) = [\sigma(\lambda,\lambda^{\times})]^{+}$. □

In conclusion we have

PROPOSITION 2.29 For a monotone sequence space λ such that $(\lambda,\tau(\lambda,\lambda^{\times}))$ is a Montel space, one has $x^{(n)} \to x$ in $\beta(\lambda,\lambda^{\times})$ for each $x \in \lambda$, and $\sigma(\lambda^{\times},\lambda)$- and $\beta(\lambda^{\times},\lambda)$-convergent sequences in $\lambda^{\times}$ are the same. Conversely, if λ is perfect, $x^{(n)} \to x$ in $\beta(\lambda,\lambda^{\times})$ for each x in λ, and $\sigma(\lambda^{\times},\lambda)$- and $\beta(\lambda^{\times},\lambda)$-convergent sequences in $\lambda^{\times}$ are the same, then $(\lambda,\tau(\lambda,\lambda^{\times}))$ is a Montel space.

Proof. The first part follows by applying Propositions 1.9.4, 1.9.5, 2.25, and 2.26. For the second part, let us observe, in view of Proposition 2.25, that $(\lambda,\tau(\lambda,\lambda^\times))$ is barreled. From Proposition 2.28, every $\sigma(\lambda,\lambda^\times)$-bounded subset of λ is $\tau(\lambda,\lambda^\times)$-relatively compact. Thus $(\lambda,\tau(\lambda,\lambda^\times))$ is Montel. □

3. INCLUSION THEOREMS FOR FK-SPACES

The study of inclusion maps from a sequence space into another is inevitable if one is to make a thorough analysis of the theory of matrix transformations, which we shall take up in a subsequent section. Also, some of the inclusion map theorems are helpful in producing concrete examples in the Schauder basis theory and the theory of functions. Above all, these theorems are interesting in themselves.

Indeed, a careful study of infinite matrix transformations reveals that there are certain types of inclusion maps from a sequence space λ into another sequence space μ with $\lambda \subset \mu$ (cf. Ref. 79). It has been further observed that the underlying sequence spaces always enjoy a particular property which is usually referred to as the K-property (K possibly stands for the German word *koordinateweise*) whose importance and motivation have already been seen in Chapter 2. Most of the sequence spaces that we have encountered earlier and shall be dealing with further possess this property. Accordingly, in addition to our earlier assumption that each sequence space contains ϕ, we restrict ourselves in this as well as in the later sections to those spaces which are K-spaces when equipped with linear topologies.

This chapter deals essentially with different types of inclusion maps between distinct FK-spaces. The basic properties of FK-spaces are to be found in Refs. 264 and 272. We will recall only relevant statements together with their possible generalizations. In particular, the following proposition (Ref. 14) is a slight extension of an earlier result due to Zeller [270, Theorem 4.5(a)].

PROPOSITION 3.1 Let (λ,T) and (μ,S) be two Fréchet K-spaces such that $\lambda \subset \mu$. Then the identity map $I\colon (\lambda,T) \to (\mu,S)$ is continuous.

Proof. Let $x^n \to x$ in (λ,T) and $I(x^n) \to y$ in (μ,S). Hence $x_i^n \to x_i$ and $x_i^n \to y_i$ for each $i \geq 1$. Thus $x = y$ and so the graph of I is closed. Consequently, from the closed graph theorem, I is continuous. □

Preliminaries on Matrix Transformations

In the sequel we shall be concerned with a class of linear transformations from sequence spaces to sequence spaces. Each such transformation results from a suitable infinite matrix $A = [a_{ij}]$ whose components a_{ij} belong to $\mathbb{K}$, where a_{ij} is the element of A that is obtained at the meet of ith row and jth column. When fully expressed, we can write A as follows:

$$A = \begin{bmatrix} a_{11} & a_{12} & a_{13} & \cdots & a_{1j} & \cdots \\ a_{21} & a_{22} & a_{23} & \cdots & a_{2j} & \cdots \\ \vdots & & & & & \\ a_{i1} & a_{i2} & a_{i3} & \cdots & a_{ij} & \cdots \\ \vdots & & & & & \end{bmatrix}$$

Suppose further that λ and μ are two sequence spaces such that whenever $x \in \lambda$ then $y \in \mu$, where $y = \{y_i\}$ is given by

$$y_i = \sum_{j\geq 1} a_{ij}x_j$$

it being understood that the series on the right-hand side converges for each $x = \{x_j\}$ and each row in A. In other words, if we treat each x in λ as a column vector with an infinite number of rows, then the product (matrix) $A \cdot x$ exists for each x in λ and $A \cdot x$ belongs to μ. Thus the matrix A defines a linear transformation, known as a *matrix transformation*, from λ into μ, and we designate it by A itself, i.e., $A(x) = y$, $x \in \lambda$, where $A(x) \equiv A \cdot x$.

The following characterization of matrix transformations is essentially due to Köthe and Toeplitz [143, p. 208, Satz 1].

PROPOSITION 3.2 Let λ and μ be two sequence spaces such that λ is monotone. Then a linear transformation A from λ to μ is a matrix transformation if and only if it is $\sigma(\lambda,\lambda^\times)$-$\sigma(\mu,\mu^\times)$ continuous.

Proof. Suppose A is a matrix transformation. Fix a $u \in \mu^\times$. If $x \in \lambda$, let us write $y = A(x)$, where for $i \geq 1$,

$$y_i = \sum_{j\geq 1} a_{ij}x_j \qquad A = [a_{ij}] \tag{*}$$

Thus

$$q_u(A(x)) = \left|\sum_{n\geq 1}\sum_{k\geq 1} u_n a_{nk} x_k\right|$$

Since (*) is satisfied for all $x = \{x_j\}$ in λ, we see that for each $i \geq 1$, $a^i = \{a_{ij} : j \geq 1\} \in \lambda^\beta = \lambda^\times$ (as λ is monotone) and it follows that

$$b^n = \sum_{i=1}^{n} u_i a^i \in \lambda^\times \qquad \forall n \geq 1$$

For $x \in \lambda$,

$$\langle x, b^n \rangle = \sum_{i=1}^{n} \langle x, a^i \rangle u_i = \sum_{i=1}^{n} u_i y_i$$

and so $\{b^n\}$ is $\sigma(\lambda^\times, \lambda)$-Cauchy in $\lambda^\times$. Hence from Proposition 2.2, there exists a unique b in $\lambda^\times$ with

$$\langle x, b \rangle = \lim_{n\to\infty} \langle x, b^n \rangle \qquad \forall x \text{ in } \lambda$$

$$= \sum_{i\geq 1} u_i y_i = \sum_{i\geq 1} \sum_{j\geq 1} u_i a_{ij} x_j$$

Therefore, $q_u(A(x)) = q_b(x)$ for all x in λ, and this yields the required continuity of A.

Conversely, let A be continuous as mentioned. If $x \in \lambda$, then

$$x = \sigma(\lambda, \lambda^\times)\text{-}\lim_{n\to\infty} \sum_{i=1}^{n} x_i e^i$$

Put $A(e^i) = \alpha^i$ and write $a_{ij} = \alpha^i_j$. Thus, letting $y = A(x)$, we find

$$\sum_{i=1}^{n} x_i \alpha^i \to y \qquad \text{in } \sigma(\mu, \mu^\times)$$

and so for each $j \geq 1$,

$$y_j = \langle y, e^j \rangle = \sum_{i\geq 1} x_i \langle \alpha^i, e^j \rangle = \sum_{i\geq 1} a_{ij} x_i$$

Therefore A can be identified with $[a_{ij}]$. □

Another important result in connection with matrix transformations is due to Allen [6] (cf. Ref. 35, Theorem 6.2 II). A slight generalization is contained in

PROPOSITION 3.3 Let λ and μ be two sequence spaces, λ being monotone. Also, let $A = [a_{ij}]$ be an infinite matrix and $A^\perp$ denote the transpose of

A, i.e., $A^\perp = [a_{ji}]$. (i) If A is a matrix transformation from λ to μ, then $A^\perp$ is a matrix transformation from $\mu^\times$ to $\lambda^\times$; conversely, (ii) if μ is perfect and $A^\perp$ is a matrix transformation from $\mu^\times$ to $\lambda^\times$, then A is a matrix transformation from λ to μ.

Proof. (i) We are given that the matrix A represents a matrix transformation from λ to μ and hence A is $\sigma(\lambda,\lambda^\times)$-$\sigma(\mu,\mu^\times)$ continuous. Therefore, the adjoint A* of A takes $\mu^\times$ into $\lambda^\times$ and is $\sigma(\mu^\times,\mu)$-$\sigma(\lambda^\times,\lambda)$ continuous (cf. Proposition 1.12.1). Let $u \in \mu^\times$ and $v = A^*(u)$. Since

$$u = \sigma(\mu^\times,\mu)\text{-}\lim_{n\to\infty} \sum_{j=1}^{n} u_j e^j$$

we have

$$v = A^*(u) = \sigma(\lambda^\times,\lambda)\text{-}\lim_{n\to\infty} \sum_{j=1}^{n} u_j \beta^j$$

where

$$\beta^j = A^*(e^j) \in \lambda^\times \qquad j \geq 1$$

Hence for each $i \geq 1$,

$$v_i = \langle e^i, v\rangle = \sum_{j\geq 1} u_j \langle e^i, \beta^j\rangle = \sum_{j\geq 1} u_j \beta_i^j$$

Thus, we can identify A* with the infinite matrix $[\beta_{ij}]$, where $\beta_{ij} = \beta_i^j$, β^j being the jth column of the matrix. Now for any x in λ and u in $\mu^\times$,

$$\langle A(x), u\rangle = \langle x, A^*(u)\rangle$$

In particular,

$$\langle A(e^i), e^j\rangle = \langle e^i, A^*(e^j)\rangle$$

or

$$\langle\{a_{ki} : k \geq 1\}, e^j\rangle = \langle e^i, \{\beta_{mj} : m \geq 1\}\rangle$$

or

$$a_{ji} = \beta_{ij} \qquad i,j \geq 1$$

Consequently A* is represented by $A^\perp$.

To prove (ii) let us make use of Proposition 3.2 to conclude the $\sigma(\mu^\times,\mu^{\times\times})$-$\sigma(\lambda^\times,\lambda^{\times\times})$ continuity of $A^\perp$. Since $\mu^{\times\times} = \mu$ and $\lambda \subset \lambda^{\times\times}$ we find that $A^\perp$ is $\sigma(\mu^\times,\mu)$-$\sigma(\lambda^\times,\lambda)$ continuous. Hence from Proposition 1.12.1, $(A^\perp)^*$ is a $\sigma(\lambda,\lambda^\times)$-$\sigma(\mu,\mu^\times)$ transformation from λ into μ. But $(A^\perp)^*$ can be identified with $A^{\perp\perp} = A$. Using Proposition 3.2 once again we find that A is a matrix transformation from λ to μ. □

For an infinite matrix A, we introduce

DEFINITION 3.4 The set d_A defined by

$$d_A = \{x : x \in \omega,\ A \cdot x \text{ exists}\}$$

is called the *domain of the matrix* A (from now on we shall abbreviate $A \cdot x$ as Ax). For a subset $\lambda \subset \omega$, we define λ_A by

$$\lambda_A = \{x : x \in \omega,\ Ax \text{ exists and } Ax \in \lambda\}$$

In case λ is a sequence space, we call λ_A a *summability domain* of A; in particular, the spaces c_A, $(c_0)_A$, and ℓ^∞_A are called respectively the *convergence domain*, *null domain*, and *bounded domain* of A. Finally, an $x \in c_A$ is said to be A-*limitable*.

Before we conclude this subsection, we have one more result to state. The usefulness of the following result of Zeller lies in topologizing the space λ_A so that it becomes an FK-space, where λ is already given to be an FK-space. First we state two results of Wilansky and urge the reader to consult Ref. 264 for their proofs (see especially p. 226 and p. 228).

THEOREM 3.5 Let (μ,S) and (λ,T) be two FK-spaces and $I: (\mu,S) \to (\omega,\sigma(\omega,\phi))$ a continuous linear map. Suppose D denotes the collection of seminorms D_S and $\{p \circ I : p \in D_T\}$. If T^* denotes the topology on $I^{-1}[\lambda]$ generated by D, then $(I^{-1}[\lambda],T^*)$ is an FK-space and

$$I: (I^{-1}[\lambda],T^*) \to (\lambda,T)$$

is continuous.

Using Theorem 3.5 we deduce

PROPOSITION 3.6 Let D denote the collection of seminorms $\{p_i : i \geq 1\}$ and $\{q_i : i \geq 1\}$ on d_A, A being an infinite matrix, where

$$p_i(x) = |x_i|$$

and

$$q_i(x) = \sup_n \left| \sum_{j=1}^{n} a_{ij}x_j \right|$$

and S is the topology on d_A generated by D. Then (d_A,S) is an FK-space.

We can now prove the following theorem of Zeller [270, Theorems 4.10(a) and 4.4(c)].

THEOREM 3.7 Let (λ,T) be an FK-space with $D_T = \{r_n\}$ and A an infinite matrix. Suppose S is the topology on λ_A generated by $\{p_i\}$, $\{q_i\}$, and $\{r_i \circ A\}$; then (λ_A,S) is an FK-space and the map A: $(\lambda_A,S) \to (\lambda,T)$ is continuous, where

$$p_i(x) = |x_i| \qquad i \geq 1$$

$$q_i(x) = \sup_n \left| \sum_{j=1}^{n} a_{ij}x_j \right| \qquad i \geq 1$$

and

$$(r_i \circ A)(x) = r_i(A(x)) \qquad i \geq 1$$

Proof. Put $\mu = d_A$ and I = A in Theorem 3.5. First use Proposition 3.6 to conclude the FK-ness of d_A under $\{p_i\} \cup \{q_i\}$ and then use Theorem 3.5. □

Note: If A is row finite (that is, each row $\{a_{ij} : j \geq 1\} \in \phi$) then $d_A = \omega$ and conversely; for instance, see Ref. 264, p. 4. Hence for a sequence space λ and a row finite matrix A, (λ_A,S) is an FK-space, where S is generated by $\{p_i\} \cup \{r_i \circ A\}$ as in Theorem 3.7.

Inclusion Theorems

At the outset let us point out that the study of infinite matrices as linear transformations from a sequence space into another is virtually the same as the study of the inclusion of one sequence space into another. Indeed, let A be an infinite matrix, and λ and μ two sequence spaces. Then A: $\lambda \to \mu$ (A transforms λ into μ) if and only if $\lambda \subset \mu_A$. From this and some other points of view spelled out in the beginning of this section, the rest of this section is devoted to discussing several types of inclusion theorems and their applications. In fact, we explore conditions under which an FK-space λ contains another FK-space μ and then proceed to determine several applications of this theorem when μ is chosen to be a well-behaved FK-space. For all practical purposes the following result (Ref. 129) appears to be sufficiently general.

THEOREM 3.8 Let λ and μ be two AK-FK spaces. Let λ be monotone. Then $\lambda \subset \mu$ if and only if $\mu^* \subset \lambda^*$.

Proof. The necessity part is obvious since $\mu^\beta \subset \lambda^\beta$. Suppose now $\mu^* \subset \lambda^*$ and let $f \in \mu^*$. Then $f = \{f(e^i)\} \in \lambda^\beta$ by Proposition 2.3.9. In Theorem 3.10.4, replace X by μ and x_i by e^i, $i \geq 1$; then we find that to each α in λ, $\Sigma_{i\geq 1} \alpha_i e^i$ converges in μ, say to $\gamma \equiv \gamma(\alpha)$. Since μ is a K-space we find $\alpha = \gamma \in \mu$; that is, $\lambda \subset \mu$. □

Remarks: If we analyze the proof of the sufficiency part of the foregoing result, we can possibly offer a number of alternative weaker conditions. For this purpose one has to look back to Proposition 2.3.6, Corollary 2.3.7, and Exercise 2.3.8. The first attempt in this direction appears to have been made in the course of three years of seminars held at Lehigh University, in which Snyder and Wilansky [239] proved the remaining results of this subsection.

PROPOSITION 3.9 Let (λ,S) and (μ,T) be two FK-spaces such that (μ,T) is also an AD-space and $S|\phi \subset T|\phi$. Then $\mu \subset \lambda$.

Proof. Suppose $x \in \mu$. Then there exists a sequence $\{x^n\}$ in ϕ with $x^n \to x$ in T. Hence $\{x^n\}$ is $T|\phi$-Cauchy and so it is $S|\phi$-Cauchy. Therefore $x^n \to y$ in (λ,S). Since λ and μ are both K-spaces, $x_i^n \to x_i, y_i$ for $i \geq 1$. Thus $x = y \in \lambda$, that is, $\mu \subset \lambda$. □

PROPOSITION 3.10 Let (λ,S) and (μ,T) be two FK-spaces such that (μ,T) is also an AD-space. If each subset of ϕ which is $T|\phi$-bounded is also $S|\phi$-bounded, then $\mu \subset \lambda$.

Proof. The condition on ϕ ensures the continuity of $I: (\phi,T|\phi) \to (\phi,S|\phi)$, $I(x) = x$, by Theorem 1.5.1(iii), and so $T|\phi \supset S|\phi$. Now apply the previous result. □

Proposition 3.10 immediately leads to

PROPOSITION 3.11 Let (λ,S) be an FK-space and (μ,T) an AD-BK space. Suppose $D = \phi \cap \{x : x \in \mu, \|x\| \leq 1\}$ is bounded in (λ,S). Then $\mu \subset \lambda$.

PROPOSITION 3.12 Let (λ,S) and (μ,T) be two FK-spaces such that (μ,T) is an AD-space and $\lambda_s \subset \mu_s$. Then $\mu \subset \lambda$.

Proof. Let $A \subset \phi$ be $T|\phi$-bounded, i.e., A is T-bounded. Choose an arbitrary $f \in \lambda^*$. By hypothesis $f(e^i) = g(e^i)$, $i \geq 1$, where $g \in \mu^*$. It follows that A is $\sigma(\lambda,\lambda^*)$-bounded and so it is S-bounded. In other words, A is $S|\phi$-bounded. Now apply Proposition 3.10. □

Note: One can obtain still further generalizations of Propositions 3.9 through 3.12, the details of which can be found in Ref. 239. For instance, these propositions are valid for Fréchet K-spaces; also, one can easily establish

EXERCISE 3.13 Let (λ,S) and (μ,T) be two K-spaces such that (μ,T) is also an AD-space. Consider the conditions (i) (λ,S) is sequentially complete and (μ,T) is metrizable, and (ii) (λ,S) is complete. Show that if either (a) $S|\phi \subset T|\phi$ and (i) or (ii) is satisfied, or (b) (λ,S) is bornological and (i) or (ii) is satisfied, then $\mu \subset \lambda$.

Remark: The above results of Snyder and Wilansky, excepting possibly Proposition 3.12, remain valid without assuming local convexity of the spaces λ and μ.

The following inclusion theorem, which incidentally gives a characterization of barreled subspaces (indeed, it seems that this result has been motivated by the closed graph theorem of Mahowald--Theorem 1.10.19), is due to Bennett and Kalton [18].

THEOREM 3.14 Let (λ,T) be an FK-space and let μ be a dense subspace of λ. Then the following statements are equivalent:

(i) μ is barreled.
(ii) If (η,S) is an FK-space with $\mu \subset \eta$, then $\lambda \subset \eta$.
(iii) If $\mu \subset \eta \subset \lambda$, where (η,S) is an FK-space, then $\lambda = \eta$.

Proof. (i) $\Rightarrow$ (ii) By Theorem 1.10.17, the identity map I: $\mu \to \eta$ is continuous (μ is equipped with the topology induced by T). Let $x \in \lambda$. Since $\bar{\mu} = \lambda$, there exists a sequence $\{x^n\} \subset \mu$ such that $x^n \to x$ in T. Thus $\{x^n\}$ is S-Cauchy in η and so $x^n \to y$ in (η,S). Because of the K nature of both λ and η, we have $x_i^n \to x_i, y_i$, for $i \geq 1$. Hence $x = y$ and so $\lambda \subset \eta$.

(ii) $\Rightarrow$ (iii) This is obvious.

(iii) $\Rightarrow$ (i) This is accomplished by using Proposition 1.10.20. Let (Y,R) be a Fréchet space and F a continuous linear map from (Y,R) into (λ,T) with $\mu \subset F(Y)$. One observes that $Y/F^{-1}(\{0\})$ can be identified with F(Y) under the mapping $y + F^{-1}(\{0\}) \leftrightarrow F(y)$, $y \in Y$. Thus F(Y) equipped with the topology identified with the quotient topology of $Y/F^{-1}(\{0\})$ (which is in fact a Fréchet topology) is an FK-space. [Indeed, if $x^n \to x$ in F(Y), then $F(y^n) \to F(y)$; $x^n = F(y^n)$, $x = F(y)$, and so $\hat{y}^n \to \hat{y}$. Therefore from Proposition 1.3.17, $F(y^n) \to F(y)$ in $(\lambda,T) \Rightarrow x_i^n \to x_i$ for each $i \geq 1$.] Thus

$$\mu \subset F(Y) \subset \lambda$$

where F(Y) is an FK-space. By (iii), $\lambda = F(Y)$. Now make use of Proposition 1.10.20. □

FK-*spaces Containing* c_0

A class of FK-spaces especially useful for constructing counterexamples in the Schauder basis theory is the one which contains c_0 (the class of Fréchet-K spaces containing c_0 has been termed *0-conservative* by Snyder and Wilansky [239]). This class has equally important applications in summability theory and other related topics.

In the discussion that follows we rely heavily on the following particular case of Proposition 3.12 (cf. Ref. 16, p. 565 and Ref. 239, p. 598).

PROPOSITION 3.15 An FK-space λ contains c_0 if and only if

$$\sum_{i\geq 1} |f(e^i)| < \infty \qquad \forall f \in \lambda^*$$

Proof. The necessity is obvious. [Indeed, let $f \in \lambda^*$; by Proposition 3.1, $f \in c_0^* = \ell^1$. Moreover, we can identify f with $\{f(e^i)\}$.] To prove the converse, observe that $\{f(e^i)\} \in c_0^\beta = \ell^1$ for every $f \in \lambda^*$. Hence from Theorem 3.10.4 (here replace λ by c_0 and X by the FK-space λ) we find that $\Sigma_{i\geq 1} e^i$ is weakly c_0-unconditionally Cauchy. Thus, if $\alpha \in c_0$

then $\Sigma_{i\geq 1} \alpha_i e^i$ converges in λ and we easily conclude that $\alpha \in \lambda$. □

EXERCISE 3.16 Let λ be an FK-space containing c_0. Show that $c_0 \subset S_\lambda \subset W_\lambda$ (cf. Definition 2.3.5). [Hint: Use the fact that c_0 is an AK-space in its sup norm topology, and Proposition 3.1.]

The next subsection deals with the applications of Proposition 3.15.

The Two-Norm Topology on $W_\lambda \cap \ell^\infty$

Throughout this subsection we write λ for an FK-space containing c_0, and let T stand for the FK-topology on λ. In some of the propositions given below, we can drop the assumption that the space c_0 is contained in λ. For the sake of brevity, we write W in place of W_λ. Now $c_0 \subset W$ is always true, and so, to determine the size of W, we consider the space $W \cap \ell^\infty$. Because of the nature of W, the space $W \cap \ell^\infty$ will be seen to be of much use in the Schauder basis theory. The immediate question with which we should be concerned is the topology of $W \cap \ell^\infty$. This space has two topologies inherited from λ and ℓ^∞ and we shall show later that $W \cap \ell^\infty$ equipped with these two topologies can be identified as a two-norm space (see Chapter 1). To be in tune with the two-norm space terminology of $W \cap \ell^\infty$, *we say that* $x^n \to x(\gamma)$ where $x^n, x \in \lambda \cap \ell^\infty$, $n \geq 1$, provided $x^n \to x$ in T and $\sup_n \|x^n\| < \infty$, $\|\cdot\|$ being the usual sup norm on ℓ^∞.

Essentially all results of this subsection are due to Bennett and Kalton [16].

PROPOSITION 3.17 If $x^n \to x(\gamma)$, then $x^n \to x$ in $\sigma(\ell^\infty, \ell^1)$.

Proof. One can quickly verify that

$$B_r = \{y : y \in \ell^\infty, \|y\| \leq r\}$$

is $\sigma(\ell^\infty, \ell^1)$-closed, and thus by the Alaoglu-Bourbaki theorem, B_r is $\sigma(\ell^\infty, \ell^1)$-compact. Since $x^n \to x(\gamma)$, the elements x^n $(n \geq 1)$ and x belong to B_r for some $r > 0$. Using Theorem 2.3.10(iv), we conclude that $x^n \to x$ in $\sigma(\ell^\infty, \ell^1)$. □

The next result is a refinement of an earlier theorem on conull FK-spaces due to Snyder [238, p. 380].

THEOREM 3.18 The following statements are equivalent for each $x \in \lambda$:

(i) $x \in W \cap \ell^\infty$.

(ii) There is a sequence $\{x^n\} \subset \phi$ with $\|x^n\| \le \|x\|$, $n \ge 1$, and $x^n \to x$ in T.

(iii) There is a sequence $\{x^n\} \subset c_0$ with $x^n \to x(\gamma)$.

Proof. (i) $\Rightarrow$ (ii) If $D = \text{con}\,\{x^{(n)} : n \ge 1\}$ then x belongs to the $\sigma(\lambda,\lambda^*)$-closure of D. Hence from Proposition 1.7.4, there exist $x^n \in D$, $n \ge 1$, such that $x^n \to x$ in T. Clearly each $x^n \in \phi$, with

$$x^n = \sum_{i=1}^{M_n} \alpha_i^n x^{(i)} \qquad \alpha_i^n \ge 0 \qquad \text{and} \qquad \sum_{i=1}^{M_n} \alpha_i^n = 1$$

Therefore

$$\|x^n\| \le \|x\| \sup_{1\le j\le M_n} \sum_{i=j}^{M_n} \alpha_i^n \le \|x\|$$

(ii) $\Rightarrow$ (iii). This is obvious from the definition of γ-convergence.

(iii) $\Rightarrow$ (i) We have

$$f(x) = \lim_{n\to\infty} f(x^n) \qquad \forall f \in \lambda^*$$

and

$$f(x^n) = \sum_{i\ge 1} x_i^n f(e^i) \qquad \forall f \in \lambda^*,\ n \ge 1$$

By Proposition 3.15, $\{f(e^i)\} \in \ell^1$ for each $f \in \lambda^*$, and thus, using Proposition 3.17, we obtain

$$\langle x^n - x, \{f(e^i)\}\rangle \to 0 \qquad \forall f \in \lambda^*$$

Therefore

$$f(x) = \sum_{i\ge 1} x_i f(e^i) \qquad \forall f \in \lambda^*$$

Hence $x \in W$. Since x is already in ℓ^∞, $x \in W \cap \ell^\infty$. □

Remark: In the above theorem, the implications (i) $\Rightarrow$ (ii) $\Rightarrow$ (iii) do not make use of the condition that $\lambda \supset c_0$, but this condition is essential for the truth of (iii) $\Rightarrow$ (i). For instance, consider

EXAMPLE 3.19 Let

$$\lambda = \{x : x \in \omega, \sup_i i\,|x_{2i} - x_{2i-1}| < \infty\}$$

Endow λ with the sequence of seminorms $\{p_i\}$ and the norm p where $p_i(x) = |x_i|$ and $p(x) = \sup_i i|x_{2i} - x_{2i-1}|$. Usual elementary methods lead to the completeness of (λ, p), thus forcing $(\lambda, \{p_i\}; p)$ to be an FK-space. It is clear that $c_0 \not\subset \lambda$ (for instance, $\{i^{-1/4}\} \notin \lambda$). Observe that $e \in \lambda$ and $e^{(2n)} \to e(\gamma)$, since $\|e^{(2n)} - e\| = 0$ and $\|e^{(2n)}\| = 0$ for all $n \geq 1$. Thus (iii) is satisfied. On the other hand, $e \notin W \cap \ell^\infty$. For, if $e \in W$, then $\{e^{(n)}\}$ is weakly bounded, and so $\{e^{(n)}\}$ is bounded in λ. But $\|e^{(n)}\| = n$ if n is odd, giving $\sup \|e^{(n)}\| = \infty$. Hence (i) is not satisfied.

PROPOSITION 3.20 The topology induced on $W \cap \ell^\infty$ by T is weaker than the topology induced by $\|\cdot\|$ (norm of ℓ^∞), and B_1 is T-closed in $W \cap \ell^\infty$.

Proof. Let $p \in D_T$. Since $I: c_0 \to \lambda$, $I(x) = x$, is continuous, therefore for some $M > 0$,

$$p(I(x)) \leq M\|x\| \qquad \forall x \text{ in } c_0$$

Suppose $x \in W \cap \ell^\infty$. Invoking both the notation and statement of Theorem 3.18(ii), we find

$$p(x) = \lim_{n\to\infty} p(x^n) \leq M \sup_n \|x^n\| \leq M\|x\|$$

Hence the first part is proved. For the second part, let $x^n \in B_1 \cap W$ with $x^n \to x$ in $(W \cap \ell^\infty, T)$. Then $x_i^n \to x_i$ for each $i \geq 1$ and $\|x\| \leq 1$. Thus $x \in B_1 \cap W$. □

PROPOSITION 3.21 The topologies on $W \cap \ell^\infty$ induced by $\|\cdot\|$ and $\beta(W \cap \ell^\infty, \ell^1)$ are equivalent.

Proof. It is sufficient to prove that $\sigma(\ell^1, W \cap \ell^\infty)$- and $\|\cdot\|_1$-bounded subsets of ℓ^1 are the same, $\|\cdot\|_1$ being the usual norm on ℓ^1. So, let $A \subset \ell^1$ be $\sigma(\ell^1, W \cap \ell^\infty)$-bounded. Thus A is $\sigma(\ell^1, c_0)$-bounded, and this implies that A is $\tau(\ell^1, c_0)$-bounded. Using Proposition 2.7.3, we conclude the $\|\cdot\|_1$-boundedness of A. □

PROPOSITION 3.22 Suppose $x \in \lambda$ and $x^n \in \phi$, $n \geq 1$, such that $x^n \to x(\gamma)$. Then

$$x^n \to x \qquad \text{in } (W \cap \ell^\infty, \delta(W \cap \ell^\infty, \ell^1))$$

Proof. By Theorem 3.18, $x \in W \cap \ell^\infty$. Suppose the required result is false. Without loss of generality we may assume that no subsequence of $\{x^n\}$ converges to x relative to $\delta(W \cap \ell^\infty, \ell^1)$. Hence for some $\delta(W \cap \ell^\infty, \ell^1)$-neighborhood u of zero, $x^n \notin u$ for all $n \geq 1$. Let $K = \sup\{\|x^n\| : n \geq 1\}$.

Now $x_i^n \to x_i$ for each $i \geq 1$. Hence we can find an increasing sequence $\{n_j\} \subset \mathbb{N}$ such that

$$|x_i - x_i^{n_j}| \leq \frac{1}{j} \qquad 1 \leq i \leq j,\ j \geq 1$$

Define $z^j \in \phi$ as follows:

$$z_i^j = \begin{cases} x_i & 1 \leq i \leq j \\ x_i^{n_j} & i > j \end{cases}$$

Then

$$\|z^i - x^{n_j}\| \leq \frac{1}{j} \qquad j \geq 1$$

Therefore, by Proposition 3.21, $z^j - x^{n_j} \to 0$ in $\beta(W \cap \ell^\infty, \ell^1)$. If any subsequence $\{z^{j_k}\}$ of $\{z^j\}$ converges to x relative to $\delta(W \cap \ell^\infty, \ell^1)$, it follows that

$$x^{n_{j_k}} - x = (x^{n_{j_k}} - z^{j_k}) + (z^{j_k} - x) \to 0 \qquad \text{in } \delta(W \cap \ell^\infty, \ell^1)$$

and this is inconsistent with our earlier assumption. Hence no subsequence of $\{z^j\}$ converges to x in $\delta(W \cap \ell^\infty, \ell^1)$.

Using Proposition 3.20, we find that $z^j - x^{n_j} \to 0$ in T and so $z^j - x \to 0$ in T. As $\|z^j\| \leq M$ for all $j \geq 1$, we conclude that $z^j \to x(\gamma)$.

Assume $D_T = \{p_n\}$ where $p_n \leq p_{n+1}$, $n \geq 1$. Let $m_0 = 0$ and suppose $m_1, \ldots, m_j$ have already been determined; choose m_{j+1} such that

$$z^{m_j} = 0 \qquad i \geq m_{j+1}$$

$$p_{j+1}(z^m - z^n) \leq \frac{1}{2^j} \qquad \text{for } n \geq m \geq m_{j+1}$$

This is possible since $z^n \in \phi$, $n \geq 1$, and $\{z^n\}$ is T-Cauchy. If

$$y^j = z^{m_j} - z^{m_{j-1}} \qquad j \geq 1 \qquad \text{and} \qquad z^0 = 0$$

then $\Sigma_{j\geq 1} y^j$ is absolutely convergent relative to T. Hence for any subsequence $\{v^j\}$ of $\{y^j\}$, the series $\Sigma_{j\geq 1} v^j$ converges in (λ, T), by Proposition 3.2.1. Choose now any index i. We can find integers m_j and m_{j+1} such that $m_j \leq i < m_{j+1}$. Therefore

$$\left|\left(\sum_{k=1}^{N} v^k\right)_i\right| \leq \sum_{k\geq 1} |y_i^k| = \sum_{k\geq 1} |z_i^{m_k} - z^{m_{k-1}}|$$

$$= |z_i^{m_j}| + |z_i^{m_{j+1}} - z_i^{m_j}| \leq 3M$$

and so $\Sigma_{k\geq 1} v^k$ converges in γ. Thus from Theorem 3.18,

$$\sum_{k\geq 1} v^k \in W \cap \ell^\infty$$

Moreover, the series $\Sigma_{k\geq 1} v^k$ converges in the topology $\sigma(W \cap \ell^\infty, \ell^1)$. Hence $\Sigma_{j\geq 1} y^j$ is $\sigma(W \cap \ell^\infty, \ell^1)$-subseries convergent. By using Theorem 3.10.1, we find that $\Sigma_{j\geq 1} y^j$ is $\delta(W \cap \ell^\infty, \ell^1)$-convergent to $x \in W \cap \ell^\infty$. Therefore $z^{m_j} \to x$ in $\delta(W \cap \ell^\infty, \ell^1)$, which contradicts our earlier statement.

PROPOSITION 3.23 Let g belonging to $(W \cap \ell^\infty)'$ be such that $g(x^n) \to g(x)$ whenever $x^n \to x(\gamma)$, where $x^n \in \phi$, $n \geq 1$, and $x \in W \cap \ell^\infty$. Then for some α in ℓ^1,

$$g(x) = \sum_{i\geq 1} \alpha_i x_i \qquad \forall x \in W \cap \ell^\infty$$

Proof. Suppose $x \in c_0$. Then $\|x^{(n)} - x\| \to 0$ and $\|x^{(n)}\| \leq \|x\|$ for $n \geq 1$. As $c_0 \subset \lambda$, by Proposition 3.1, $x^{(n)} \to x$ in T. Thus, for each $x \in c_0$,

$$x^{(n)} \to x(\gamma)$$

and so

$$g(x) = \sum_{i\geq 1} x_i g(e^i) \qquad \forall x \in c_0$$

Hence from Lemma 3.6.4, $\{g(e^i)\} \in \ell^1$. Now, for x in $W \cap \ell^\infty$, we find the existence of a sequence $\{x^n\} \subset \phi$ (cf. Theorem 3.18) such that $x^n \to x(\gamma)$. Therefore

$$g(x) = \lim_{n\to\infty} g(x^n) = \lim_{n\to\infty} \sum_{i\geq 1} x_i^n g(e^i) = \lim_{n\to\infty} \langle x^n, \{g(e^i)\}\rangle$$
$$= \langle x, \{g(e^i)\}\rangle = \sum_{i\geq 1} x_i g(e^i)$$

where we have used the fact that $x^n \to x$ in $\sigma(\ell^\infty, \ell^1)$ (cf. Proposition 3.17). □

THEOREM 3.24 The space $(\ell^1, \sigma(\ell^1, W \cap \ell^\infty))$ is sequentially complete.

Proof. Let us confine our attention to the dual system $\langle \ell^1, W \cap \ell^\infty\rangle$. Suppose S denotes the family of all $\delta(W \cap \ell^\infty, \ell^1)$-precompact subsets of $W \cap \ell^\infty$. Clearly S covers the entire space $W \cap \ell^\infty$. We prove the following two facts: (i) the space ℓ^1 is S-complete, S being the S-topology on ℓ^1, and (ii) $\sigma(\ell^1, W \cap \ell^\infty)$-sequential convergence on ℓ^1 is equivalent to S-sequential convergence. Once we show (i) and (ii), the required result follows by an application of Proposition 1.2.11.

(i) Suppose F is the family of all linear functionals on $W \cap \ell^\infty$ such that for each $g \in F$, g_A is $\delta(W \cap \ell^\infty, \ell^1)$-continuous, $A \in S$. If $\{x^n\} \subset \phi$ and $x \in \lambda$ are such that $x^n \to x(\gamma)$, then from Proposition 3.22, $x^n \to x$ in $\delta(W \cap \ell^\infty, \ell^1)$, $x \in W \cap \ell^\infty$. Thus by using Proposition 3.23,

$$g(x) = \sum_{i\geq 1} x_i g(e^i)$$

where $\{g(e^i)\} \in \ell^1$. Consequently, the map $g \to \{g(e^i)\}$ from F to ℓ^1 is a surjection, and it follows from Theorem 1.11.6 that ℓ^1 is S-complete.

(ii) Let now $x^n - x \to 0$ in $(\ell^1, \sigma(\ell^1, W \cap \ell^\infty))$. The set $A = \{x^n - x : n \geq 1\} \cup \{0\}$ is $\sigma(\ell^1, W \cap \ell^\infty)$-compact. Suppose u is an arbitrary $\delta(W \cap \ell^\infty, \ell^1)$-precompact subset of $W \cap \ell^\infty$. For $\varepsilon > 0$, there exists a finite subset $G = \{y^1, \ldots, y^m\}$ of u such that

$$u \subset G + \varepsilon A^\circ$$

Now one can find an integer N such that

$$|\langle x^n - x, y^i\rangle| \leq \varepsilon \qquad \forall n \geq N,\ 1 \leq i \leq m$$

If $z \in u$ then $z - y^i \in \varepsilon A^\circ$ for some i, $1 \leq i \leq m$, thus giving

$$|\langle x^n - x, z - y^i\rangle| \leq \varepsilon \qquad \forall n \geq 1$$

Therefore, for $z \in u$,

$$|\langle x^n - x, z\rangle| \le \varepsilon + |\langle x^n - x, y^i\rangle| \le 2\varepsilon \qquad \forall n \ge N$$

and as $z \in u$ is arbitrary, we find that $x^n - x \in \varepsilon u^\circ$ for all $n \ge N$. Hence $x^n - x \to 0$ in S and (ii) is proved. □

Note: In the proof of the above theorem we have avoided the use of Grothendieck's precompactness theorem referred to in Ref. 16, p. 569.

Concerning the *mixed topology* γ^+ on $W \cap \ell^\infty$, which is defined as the finest locally convex topology for which $x^n \to x(\gamma)$ coincides with its γ^+-convergence, we have

THEOREM 3.25 All three topologies (i) γ^+, (ii) $\tau(W \cap \ell^\infty, \ell^1)$, and (iii) $\delta(W \cap \ell^\infty, \ell^1)$ on $W \cap \ell^\infty$ are equivalent.

Proof. First we show that γ^+ is compatible with the dual system $\langle W \cap \ell^\infty, \ell^1\rangle$. Indeed, let g be a γ^+-continuous linear functional on $W \cap \ell^\infty$. If $\{x^n\} \subset \phi$ is such that $x^n \to x(\gamma)$ where $x \in W \cap \ell^\infty$, then $x^n \to x$ in γ^+, and so $g(x^n) \to g(x)$. Hence from Proposition 3.23, we have

$$g(x) = \sum_{i\ge 1} \alpha_i x_i \qquad \forall x \text{ in } W \cap \ell^\infty$$

where $\alpha \in \ell^1$. Therefore g is $\sigma(W \cap \ell^\infty, \ell^1)$-continuous. Thus

$$\gamma^+ \subset \tau(W \cap \ell^\infty, \ell^1) \subset \delta(W \cap \ell^\infty, \ell^1)$$

Finally we show that whenever $\{x^n\}$, $x \in W \cap \ell^\infty$ with $x^n \to x(\gamma)$, then $x^n \to x$ in $\delta(W \cap \ell^\infty, \ell^1)$, and once we have done so, it will follow that $\delta(W \cap \ell^\infty, \ell^1) \subset \gamma^+$. So, to prove this assertion, assume that it is not true. Then we have a sequence $\{x^n\}$ and an x in $W \cap \ell^\infty$ such that $x^n \to x(\gamma)$ and for some $u \in D_\delta$, $x^n - x \notin u$ for $n \ge 1$, D_δ being the usual family of seminorms associated with $\delta(W \cap \ell^\infty, \ell^1)$. By Theorem 3.18, there is a sequence $\{x^{n,m}\}$ for each $n \ge 1$ with $x^{n,m} \in \phi$, $m \ge 1$, such that

$$x^{n,m} \xrightarrow{m} x^n(\gamma)$$

Taking into account Proposition 3.22, one finds

$$x^{n,m} \xrightarrow{m} x^n \qquad \text{in } \delta(W \cap \ell^\infty, \ell^1)$$

If d denotes the metric generating the topology T, the foregoing arguments allow us to choose an increasing sequence $\{m_n\}$ such that

$$x^{n,m_n} - x^n \in \frac{1}{2} u$$

and

$$d(x^{n,m_n}, x^n) \leq \frac{1}{n}$$

where $n \geq 1$.

It is easily verified that $x^{n,m_n} \to x(\gamma)$. By Proposition 3.22,

$$\delta(W \cap \ell^\infty, \ell^1)\text{-}\lim_{n\to\infty} x^{n,m_n} = x$$

that is to say,

$$x^{n,m_n} - x \in \frac{1}{2} u$$

for all large n. Therefore $x^n - x \in u$ for all large n. This, however, contradicts our earlier assumption. □

THEOREM 3.26 The space $(W \cap \ell^\infty, \tau(W \cap \ell^\infty, \ell^1))$ is complete.

Proof. To begin with, let us observe that the restriction g_R of each $g \in \lambda^* = (\lambda,T)^*$ to $W \cap \ell^\infty$ is γ^+-continuous (by definition), and so it is $\tau(W \cap \ell^\infty, \ell^1)$-continuous by the preceding theorem. Thus g_R is $\sigma(W \cap \ell^\infty, \ell^1)$-continuous for each $g \in \lambda^*$. Consequently if $x^\alpha \to 0$ in $\sigma(W \cap \ell^\infty, \ell^1)$ then $g(x^\alpha) \to 0$ for each g in λ^*, and we conclude that the inclusion map $I: W \cap \ell^\infty \to \lambda$ is $\sigma(W \cap \ell^\infty, \ell^1)$-$\sigma(\lambda,\lambda^*)$ continuous. Hence from Proposition 1.12.3, I is $\tau(W \cap \ell^\infty, \ell^1)$-$\tau(\lambda,\lambda^*) = T$ continuous.

To prove the main result, suppose $\{x^\alpha\}$ is a $\tau(W \cap \ell^\infty, \ell^1)$-Cauchy net in $W \cap \ell^\infty$. From what we have established above it follows that $\{x^\alpha\}$ is T-Cauchy in λ, and so there exists $x \in \lambda$ with $x^\alpha \to x$ in T.

Let now $y \in \ell^1$. Then $y^{(n)} \to y$ in $\sigma(\ell^1, W \cap \ell^\infty)$ [indeed $y^{(n)} \to y$ in $\sigma(\ell^1,\ell^\infty)$] and so the set $A = \{y^{(n)}\} \cup \{y\}$ is $\sigma(\ell^1, W \cap \ell^\infty)$-compact. On using Proposition 1.7.6 we find that $\{y^{(n)}\}$ is $\delta(W \cap \ell^\infty, \ell^1)$-equicontinuous and consequently $\{y^{(n)}\}$ is $\tau(W \cap \ell^\infty, \ell^1)$-equicontinuous by Theorem 3.25. Therefore from the Cauchy character of $\{x^\alpha\}$ relative to $\tau(W \cap \ell^\infty, \ell^1)$, we find that

$$\lim_n \lim_\alpha \langle x^\alpha, y^{(n)}\rangle = \lim_\alpha \lim_n \langle x^\alpha, y^{(n)}\rangle$$

or

$$\lim_\alpha \sum_{i\geq 1} y_i x_i^\alpha = \sum_{i\geq 1} y_i x_i$$

where we have used the fact that $x_i^\alpha \to x_i$ for each $i \geq 1$. Since the above equality is valid for every $y \in \ell^1$, we find $x \in (\ell^1)^\beta = \ell^\infty$. Further, if $g \in \lambda^*$, then from our earlier considerations (see, especially, the beginning of the proof of this as well as Theorem 3.25), $\{g(e^i)\} \in \ell^1$. Therefore,

$$\lim_\alpha \sum_{i\geq 1} g(e^i)x_i^\alpha = \lim_\alpha g(x^\alpha)$$

since $\{x^\alpha\} \subset W \cap \ell^\infty$. Hence from above

$$g(x) = \sum_{i\geq 1} g(e^i)x_i$$

and consequently from the definition of W, $x \in W$. Thus $x \in W \cap \ell^\infty$ and $x^\alpha \to x$ in $\sigma(W \cap \ell^\infty, \ell^1)$. Making use of Proposition 1.7.7, we finally conclude that $x^\alpha \to x$ in the space $(W \cap \ell^\infty, \tau(W \cap \ell^\infty, \ell^1))$. □

From the point of view of basis theory it would be interesting to determine the extent of the AK property for an FK-space λ containing c_0. In general we know that $c_0 \subset S_\lambda \subset W_\lambda$ ($\equiv W$). For such FK-spaces the situation is not pleasant if c_0 is a closed subspace. In fact, this interesting information is furnished in

THEOREM 3.27 The following statements are equivalent:

(i) c_0 is a closed subspace of (λ,T).

(ii) $W = c_0$.

(iii) $W \cap \ell^\infty = c_0$.

(iv) $\tau(W \cap \ell^\infty, \ell^1)$ is metrizable.

Proof. (i) ⟹ (ii) Using Proposition 1.7.4, we find that $W \subset \bar{\phi}$, the T-closure of ϕ in λ. But $\bar{\phi} \subset \bar{c}_0$, and so $W \subset c_0$. Now use Exercise 3.16 to get (ii).

(ii) ⟹ (iii) Immediate.

(iii) ⟹ (iv) We have $\tau(W \cap \ell^\infty, \ell^1) = \tau(c_0, \ell^1)$. Now apply Exercise 2.7.2.

(iv) $\Longrightarrow$ (i) Using (iv) and the previous theorem we conclude that $W \cap \ell^\infty$ is $\tau(W \cap \ell^\infty, \ell^1)$-barreled and hence (cf. Theorem 1.8.3)

$$\tau(W \cap \ell^\infty, \ell^1) = \beta(W \cap \ell^\infty, \ell^1)$$

Hence from Proposition 3.21, $\tau(W \cap \ell^\infty, \ell^1)$ is the topology on $W \cap \ell^\infty$ defined by the norm $\|\cdot\|$ on ℓ^∞. Using Theorem 3.25, we find that $\gamma^+|c_0$ is the same as the sup norm topology S on c_0. If $T_0 \equiv T|c_0 \subsetneq S$, then there exists $\{x^n\} \subset c_0$ with $x^n \to 0$ in T_0, $\sup_n \|x^n\| < \infty$, and $x^n \not\to 0$ in S (note that if $\sup_n \|x^n\| = \infty$ then we find a subsequence $\{x^{n_k}\}$ such that $\|x^{n_k}\| \to \infty$ as $k \to \infty$, and this contradicts the fact that $x^n \to 0$ in T_0). Hence $x^n \to 0$ in $\gamma^+|c_0$ but $x^n \not\to 0$ in S. These two last statements are mutually inconsistent and thus (i) is proved. □

Note: Theorem 3.27 finds applications in establishing "high indices theorems" in summability, due to Meyer-König and Zeller; for related results and references, see §4, p. 571 of Ref. 16.

K-*spaces Containing* ℓ^1, bv, *or* bv_0

After Snyder and Wilansky [239] (cf. also Ref. 14) we have

PROPOSITION 3.28 An FK (resp. a Fréchet K)-space (λ,T) contains ℓ^1 if and only if $\{e^n\}$ (resp. the balanced convex hull B of $\{e^n\}$) is T-bounded in λ.

Proof. The necessity in both cases follows by a direct application of Proposition 3.1, since B is ℓ^1-bounded. For the sufficiency, make use of Proposition 3.12 and the note following that result. □

PROPOSITION 3.29 An FK (resp. a Fréchet K)-space (λ,T) contains bv_0 if and only if $\{e^{(n)}\}$ (resp. the balanced convex hull A of $\{e^{(n)}\}$) is T-bounded in λ.

Proof. The proof is the same as for the preceding result, replacing e^n by $e^{(n)}$. □

EXERCISE 3.30 Show by an example that the local convexity in Proposition 3.28 (first part) cannot be omitted. [Hint: Let $\lambda = \ell^p$, $0 < p < 1$.]

The next result is given in Ref. 14, p. 20.

PROPOSITION 3.31 An FK-space (λ,T) contains bv if and only if $e \in \lambda$ and $\{e^{(n)}\}$ is T-bounded in λ.

Proof. Suppose $bv \subset \lambda$. As $e \in bv$ and $\{e^{(n)}\}$ is bounded in bv, the necessity part follows by an application of Proposition 3.1. For the converse, observe that

$$bv = bv_0 \oplus sp\{e\}$$

As $e \in \lambda$ and $bv_0 \subset \lambda$ (cf. Proposition 3.29) we conclude that $bv_0 \oplus sp\{e\} \subset \lambda$. □

EXERCISE 3.32 Show that a Fréchet K-space (λ,T) contains bv if and only if $e \in \lambda$ and the balanced convex hull of $\{e^{(n)}\}$ is T-bounded in λ.

FK-*spaces Containing* ℓ^p $(1 < p < \infty)$

In this direction we have the following result which is an application of Theorem 3.10.4 (cf. also Ref. 14, p. 22).

PROPOSITION 3.33 An FK-space (λ,T) contains ℓ^p $(1 < p < \infty)$ if and only if

$$\sum_{i\geq 1} |f(e^i)|^q < \infty \qquad \forall f \in \lambda^*$$

where $p^{-1} + q^{-1} = 1$.

Proof. Let $\ell^p \subset \lambda$. Then for $\alpha \in \ell^p$, $\Sigma_{i\geq 1} \alpha_i e^i$ converges in ℓ^p. Hence by Proposition 3.1, $\Sigma_{i\geq 1} \alpha_i e^i$ converges in (λ,T) for every $\alpha \in \ell^p$. Thus $\Sigma_{i\geq 1} e^i$ is weakly ℓ^p-unconditionally Cauchy in (λ,T) and so from Theorem 3.10.4, for every $f \in \lambda^*$, $\{f(e^i)\} \in (\ell^p)^\beta = \ell^q$; in other words,

$$\sum_{i\geq 1} |f(e^i)|^q < \infty \qquad \forall f \in \lambda^*$$

To prove the converse, we have $\{f(e^i)\} \in \ell^q = (\ell^p)^\beta$ for every $f \in \lambda^*$. Hence from Theorem 3.10.4, $\Sigma_{i\geq 1} e^i$ is weakly ℓ^p-unconditionally Cauchy in (λ,T), that is, $\Sigma_{i\geq 1} \alpha_i e^i$ converges in (λ,T) for every $\alpha \in \ell^p$. Therefore $\ell^p \subset \lambda$. □

FK-*spaces Containing* ℓ^∞

The following characterization of such spaces, due to Bennett and Kalton [16] finds applications in biorthogonal systems, to be discussed in our forthcoming work (Ref. 125, Chapter 2).

PROPOSITION 3.34 Let (λ,T) be a separable FK-space. Then $\ell^\infty \subset \lambda$ if and only if $m_0 \subset \lambda$; if $\ell^\infty \subset \lambda$, the inclusion map I: $(\ell^\infty, \|\cdot\|_\infty) \to (\lambda,T)$ is compact (i.e., completely continuous) and $\ell^\infty \subset S_\lambda$.

Proof. Let $m_0 \subset \lambda$. Let I be the inclusion map, I: $(m_0, \tau(m_0,\ell^1)) \to (\lambda,T)$. Suppose $(x,y) \in m_0 \times \lambda$ with $x^\alpha \to x$ in $\tau(m_0,\ell^1)$ and $I(x^\alpha) \to y$ in T. Hence $x_i^\alpha \to x_i$ and $x_i^\alpha \to y_i$, $i \geq 1$, and so the graph of I is closed in the product space of $(m_0,\tau(m_0,\ell^1))$ and (λ,T). Using Kalton's closed graph theorem (cf. Theorem 1.10.18) we conclude that I is continuous, since ℓ^1 is $\sigma(\ell^1,m_0)$-sequentially complete by Proposition 2.7.18 or by Proposition 2.2. The map I can be uniquely extended as $\hat{I}$ (see Theorem 1.3.6) to the completion $(\ell^\infty,\tau(\ell^\infty,\ell^1))$ of $(m_0,\tau(m_0,\ell^1))$ (cf. Proposition 2.7.19). Since $\hat{I}$ is still the identity mapping, $\ell^\infty \subset \lambda$. If $x \in \ell^\infty$ then $x^{(n)} \to x$ in $\tau(\ell^\infty,\ell^1)$ and so $\hat{I}(x^{(n)}) \to \hat{I}(x)$ in T, i.e., $x^{(n)} \to x$ in (λ,T). Hence $\ell^\infty \subset S_\lambda$. The compact character of $\hat{I}$ follows from Proposition 2.6.18.

A related result in this direction is the following (Ref. 16, p. 577).

PROPOSITION 3.35 Let (λ,T) be a separable FK-space. Then $\ell^\infty \subset \lambda$ if and only if $m_0 \subset \lambda + c_0$.

Proof. If $c_0 \subset \lambda$ the result follows from Proposition 3.34. We need prove only the sufficiency part. Since $m_0 \subset \lambda + c_0$, $m_0 \subset \lambda \cap \ell^\infty + c_0$. Hence $\lambda \cap \ell^\infty$ is dense in ℓ^∞. If we could show that ℓ^1 is $\sigma(\ell^1, \lambda \cap \ell^\infty)$-sequentially complete, the result would follow on lines similar to the preceding proposition. Thus to prove the main result it is sufficient to establish the equivalence of the sequential convergence in ℓ^1 relative to the norm $\|\cdot\|$ (of ℓ^1) and $\sigma(\ell^1, \lambda \cap \ell^\infty)$. The backbone of the proof of this assertion is the analysis carried out in the proof of Proposition 2.7.18 with careful modifications--it is not *verbatim*.

Therefore, let $x^n \to 0$ in $\sigma(\ell^1, \lambda \cap \ell^\infty)$ but $\|x^n\| \not\to 0$. Hence there exist an $\varepsilon > 0$ and a strictly increasing sequence $\{n_j\}$ such that

$$\sum_{i>1} |x_i^{n_j}| \geq \varepsilon \qquad j \geq 1$$

Fix $N_1 \in \mathbb{N}$. One can find an $m_1 \in \{n_j\}$ with $m_1 > N_1$ so that

$$\sum_{i=1}^{N_1} |x_i^{m_1}| < \frac{\varepsilon}{2}$$

Now choose $N_2 > m_1$, $N_2 \in \mathbb{N}$, such that

$$\sum_{i \geq N_2+1} |x_i^{m_1}| < \frac{\|x^{m_1}\|}{15}$$

Then

$$\sum_{i=N_1+1}^{N_2} |x_i^{m_1}| = \sum_{i \geq 1} |x_i^{m_1}| - \sum_{i=1}^{N_1} |x_i^{m_1}| - \sum_{i \geq N_2+1} |x_i^{m_1}| > \frac{14}{15} \|x^{m_1}\| - \frac{\varepsilon}{2}$$

Using Corollary 3.3.4, we can determine a $\sigma_1 \subset \mathbb{N}$ with $\sigma_1 \subset [N_1 + 1, N_2]$ such that

$$\left| \sum_{i \in \sigma_1} x_i^{m_1} \right| > \frac{1}{4} \cdot \frac{14}{15} \|x^{m_1}\| - \frac{1}{4} \cdot \frac{\varepsilon}{2}$$

Next, we can find an $m_2 \in \{n_j\}$ with $m_2 > N_2$ and

$$\sum_{i=1}^{N_2} |x_i^{m_2}| < \frac{\varepsilon}{3}$$

Then choose $N_3 > m_2$ such that

$$\sum_{i \geq N_3+1} |x_i^{m_2}| < \frac{\|x^{m_2}\|}{15}$$

Hence

$$\sum_{i=N_2+1}^{N_3} |x_i^{m_2}| > \|x^{m_2}\| - \frac{\varepsilon}{3} - \frac{1}{15} \|x^{m_2}\| = \frac{14}{15} \|x^{m_2}\| - \frac{\varepsilon}{3}$$

Therefore by Corollary 3.3.4 again, we can determine a $\sigma_2 \subset \mathbb{N}$ with $\sigma_2 \subset [N_2 + 1, N_3]$ such that

$$\left| \sum_{i \in \sigma_2} x_i^{m_2} \right| > \frac{1}{4} \cdot \frac{14}{15} \|x^{m_2}\| - \frac{1}{4} \cdot \frac{\varepsilon}{2}$$

Proceeding in this manner, we can determine sequences $\{m_k\}$, $\{N_k\}$, and $\{\sigma_k\}$ with $N_1 < m_1 < N_2 < \cdots < N_k < m_{k+1} < \cdots$, $N_k \in \mathbb{N}$ $(k \geq 1)$, $\{m_k\} \subset \{n_j\}$, and $\sigma_k \subset \mathbb{N}$, $\sigma_k \subset [N_k + 1, N_{k+1}]$ such that for $k \geq 1$, we have

$$\sum_{i=1}^{N_k} |x_i^{m_k}| < \frac{\varepsilon}{k+1} \qquad \sum_{i \geq N_{k+1}+1} |x_i^{m_k}| < \frac{1}{15} \|x^{m_k}\|$$

and

$$\sum_{i=N_k+1}^{N_{k+1}} |x_i^{m_k}| > \frac{14}{15} \|x^{m_k}\| - \frac{\varepsilon}{k+1}$$

$$\left| \sum_{i \in \sigma_k} x_i^{m_k} \right| > \frac{1}{4} \cdot \frac{14}{15} \|x^{m_k}\| - \frac{1}{4} \cdot \frac{\varepsilon}{k+1}$$

Define $y \in m_0$ by $y_i = 1$, $1 \leq i \leq N_1$, and

$$y_i = \begin{cases} 1 & N_k + 1 \leq i \leq N_{k+1},\ i \in \sigma_k,\ k \geq 1 \\ 0 & \text{otherwise} \end{cases}$$

Now $y = u + v$ where $u \in \lambda \cap \ell^\infty$ and $v \in c_0$. We can determine a k_0 so large that $\sup\{|v_i| : i \geq N_k + 1\} < 1/15$ and $k + 1 > 5(5/4 + \|v\|_\infty)$ for $k \geq k_0$. Then for all $k \geq k_0$,

$$\begin{aligned} |\langle x^{m_k}, u\rangle| &\geq \left| \sum_{i\geq 1} x_i^{m_k} y_i \right| - \left| \sum_{i \geq 1} x_i^{m_k} v_i \right| \geq \left| \sum_{i=N_k+1}^{N_{k+1}} x_i^{m_k} y_i \right| \\ &- \sum_{i=1}^{N_k} |x_i^{m_k} y_i| - \sum_{i \geq N_{k+1}+1} |x_i^{m_k} y_i| - \sum_{i=1}^{N_k} |x_i^{m_k} v_i| \\ &- \sum_{i \geq N_k+1} |x_i^{m_k} v_i| > \frac{1}{4}\frac{14}{15} \|x^{m_k}\| - \frac{1}{4}\frac{\varepsilon}{k+1} - \frac{\varepsilon}{k+1} \\ &- \frac{1}{15}\|x^{m_k}\| - \frac{\varepsilon}{k+1}\|v\|_\infty - \|x^{m_k}\| \sup\{|v_i| : i \geq N_k + 1\} \end{aligned}$$

Therefore for $k \geq k_0$,

$$|\langle x^{m_k}, u\rangle| > \frac{2}{5}\|x^{m_k}\| - \left(\frac{5}{4} + \|v\|_\infty\right) \frac{\varepsilon}{k+1} > \frac{2}{5}\varepsilon - \frac{1}{5}\varepsilon = \frac{1}{5}\varepsilon$$

However, the last inequality leads to a contradiction. Thus ℓ^1 is $\sigma(\ell^1, \lambda \cap \ell^\infty)$-sequentially complete (apply Proposition 1.2.11 and the fact that ℓ^1 is sequentially complete relative to $\|\cdot\|$). Arguing as in the previous result we find that the identity map I: $(\lambda \cap \ell^\infty, \tau(\lambda \cap \ell^\infty, \ell^1)) \to (\lambda,T)$ is continuous and thus the unique extension $\hat{I}$: $(\ell^\infty, \tau(\ell^\infty,\ell^1)) \to (\lambda,T)$ is continuous, where $\hat{I}$ is still the identity mapping and $\tau(\ell^\infty,\ell^1)|\lambda \cap \ell^\infty = \tau(\lambda \cap \ell^\infty, \ell^1)$. Therefore $\ell^\infty \subset \lambda$. □

A result more general than Proposition 3.34 is the following (cf. Ref. 17, p. 820):

THEOREM 3.36 Let (λ,T) be a separable FK-space. Let $M_1 = \overline{\lambda \cap \ell^\infty}$ be the closed subspace of ℓ^∞ such that ℓ^∞/M_1 is separable. Then $\ell^\infty \subset \lambda$.

Proof. Let $\mu = c_0 + \lambda$; then μ is also a separable FK-space and ℓ^∞/M is separable, where $M = \overline{\mu \cap \ell^\infty}$, the closure being taken relative to the usual norm of ℓ^∞. By hypothesis we can determine a countable set $\{x^n : n \geq 1\}$ in ℓ^∞ such that $R \equiv sp\{\mu \cap \ell^\infty; x^n, n \geq 1\}$ is dense in ℓ^∞.

Next we show that $\sigma(\ell^1, \mu \cap \ell^\infty)$ and the topology on ℓ^1 obtained by the norm $\|\cdot\|_1$ yield the same convergent sequences. To arrive at this conclusion suppose $a^n \in \ell^1$, $n \geq 1$, with $a^n \to 0$ in $\sigma(\ell^1, \mu \cap \ell^\infty)$ but $\|a^n\|_1 \geq \varepsilon$ for all $n \geq 1$, where ε is some positive number. Then $a^n \to 0$ in $\sigma(\ell^1,c_0)$ and so by Proposition 2.7.3, $\sup_n \|a^n\|_1 < \infty$. Thus $\{a^n\}$ is $\sigma(\ell^1,\ell^\infty)$-bounded. Applying the usual diagonal procedure we can find a subsequence of $\{a^n\}$, which we designate by $\{a^n\}$, such that $\lim_{n\to\infty} \Sigma_{i\geq 1} a_i^m x_i^m$ exists for each $m \geq 1$. Since $\lim_{n\to\infty} \Sigma_{i\geq 1} a_i^n x_i \to 0$ for $x \in \mu \cap \ell^\infty$, we find that $\lim_{n\to\infty} \Sigma_{i\geq 1} a_i^n x_i$ exists for each $x \in R$, and moreover, $\sup\{\|a^n\|_1 : n \geq 1\} < \infty$. If $y \in \ell^\infty$ then to each $\varepsilon_1 > 0$ we have an $x \in R$ with $|x_i - y_i| < \varepsilon_1$ for all $i \geq 1$, and

$$\left|\sum_{i\geq 1} (a_i^m - a_i^n)x_i\right| < \varepsilon_1 \qquad \forall m,n \geq N \equiv N(\varepsilon_1,x)$$

$$\Longrightarrow \quad \left|\sum_{i\geq 1} (a_i^m - a_i^n)y_i\right| < \varepsilon_1 + \sup_i |x_i - y_i| \left(\sum_{i\geq 1} |a_i^m| + \sum_{i\geq 1} |a_i^n|\right)$$

where $m,n \geq N$. Hence $\{a^n\}$ is $\sigma(\ell^1,\ell^\infty)$-Cauchy in ℓ^1 and so $\|a^n - a\|_1 \to 0$, where $a \in \ell^1$. Clearly $a = 0$ and this leads to a contradiction.

In conclusion we find that ℓ^1 is $\sigma(\ell^1, \mu \cap \ell^\infty)$-sequentially complete. Consider the identity map I: $(\mu \cap \ell^\infty, \tau(\mu \cap \ell^\infty, \ell^1)) \to \mu$. Using Theorem 1.10.18, we find that I is continuous (cf. proof of the preceding result).

Let $x \in \ell^\infty$; then $\{x^{(n)}\}$ is $\tau(\ell^\infty,\ell^1)$-Cauchy [since $x^{(n)} \to x$ in $\tau(\ell^\infty,\ell^1)$]. But $x^{(n)} \in \mu$ for all $n \geq 1$ and thus $\{x^{(n)}\}$ is $\tau(\mu \cap \ell^\infty, \ell^1)$-Cauchy. Therefore $\{x^{(n)}\}$ is Cauchy in μ and so $x \in \mu$. Hence $\ell^\infty \subset \mu = c_0 + \lambda$, that is, $m_0 \subset \lambda + c_0$. By Proposition 3.35, $\ell^\infty \subset \lambda$. □

Remark: Note that all the results of this subsection have been proved under the assumption of the separability of the space (λ,T). Bennett and Kalton [18] show that this assumption can be relaxed in the first part of Proposition 3.34; in other words, we have

PROPOSITION 3.37 Let (λ,T) be an FK-space. Then $\ell^\infty \subset \lambda$ if and only if $m_0 \subset \lambda$.

Proof. Let $m_0 \subset \lambda$. Then from Exercise 2.7.20, Proposition 2.7.21, and Theorem 3.14, we conclude $\ell^\infty \subset \lambda$. The converse is obvious. □

FK-*spaces Containing* ℓ^p $(0 < p \leq 1)$

The spaces ℓ^p, $0 < p < 1$, are Fréchet K-spaces when equipped with the usual p-norm $\|\cdot\|_p$ (cf. §2.7) and are dense subspaces of first category of ℓ^1 (cf. Theorem 1.5.2). If we write $\ell = \bigcap_{0<p\geq 1} \ell^p$, then the space ℓ can also be regarded as the countable intersection of the spaces $\ell^{1/n}$, $n \geq 1$, that is, $\ell = \bigcap_{n\geq 1} \ell^{1/n}$. Equipping ℓ with the projective topology defined through the inclusion maps from ℓ to $\ell^{1/n}$, $n \geq 1$, one can easily verify that ℓ is a Fréchet K-space.

Concerning the inclusion of ℓ in an arbitrary FK-space (Ref. 14, p. 22), we have

THEOREM 3.38 An FK-space λ contains ℓ if and only if it contains ℓ^1.

Proof. Let $\ell \subset \lambda$. Since $\|e^j\|_p = 1$ for all $j \geq 1$ and each p, the set $\{e^j : j \geq 1\}$ is bounded in ℓ^p for each p, and consequently it is bounded in ℓ. Moreover, the inclusion map I: $\ell \to \lambda$ is continuous by Theorem 3.1, and hence $\{e^j : j \geq 1\}$ is bounded in λ. Therefore $\ell^1 \subset \lambda$ by Proposition 3.28. The converse is obvious. □

A direct consequence of this result is

COROLLARY 3.39 An FK-space λ contains ℓ^p, $0 < p \leq 1$, if and only if it contains ℓ^1.

Proof. Since $\ell = \bigcap_{0<p\le 1} \ell^p \subset \ell^p \subset \ell^1$ for $0 < p \le 1$, the result is immediate. □

We also derive

PROPOSITION 3.40 ℓ is a barreled subspace of ℓ^1.

Proof. In order to prove the result, we show that $\sigma(\ell^\infty,\ell^1)$ and $\sigma(\ell^\infty,\ell)$ define the same bounded sequences and therefore the same bounded sets in ℓ^∞ (cf. Proposition 1.2.9). Consequently the subspace topology on ℓ induced from ℓ^1 is the same as $\beta(\ell,\ell^\infty)$ and thus ℓ is barreled by Proposition 1.8.3.

Let $\{a^n\}$ be a $\sigma(\ell^\infty,\ell)$-bounded sequence of ℓ^∞. Define a matrix $A = [a_{ij}]$ such that

$$a_{ij} = a_j^i \qquad \text{for } i,j \ge 1$$

Then for $x \in \ell$, we can find a constant $K > 0$ for which one of the following is true

$$|\langle a^i, x\rangle| \le K \qquad \text{for all } i \ge 1$$

$$\Big|\sum_{j\ge 1} a_{ij}x_j\Big| \le K \qquad \text{for all } i \ge 1 \qquad (*)$$

$$|(Ax)_i| \le K \qquad \text{for all } i \ge 1$$

In other words, A maps ℓ into ℓ^∞, or equivalently, $\ell \subset \ell_A^\infty$. Hence ℓ_A^∞ contains ℓ^1 by Theorem 3.38, that is, A transforms ℓ^1 into ℓ^∞. Now repeating the process for $x \in \ell^1$, we conclude that $\{a^n\}$ is $\sigma(\ell^\infty,\ell^1)$-bounded.

Remarks: As ℓ is dense in ℓ^1, the above can also be proved from Theorem 1.10.20. The result in Ref. 265, p. 45, that $\ell^{1/2}$ is a barreled subspace of ℓ^1 follows in particular from Proposition 3.40. Indeed, any subspace of ℓ^1 that contains ℓ is a barreled subspace of ℓ^1.

Scarce Copies of Sequence Spaces

In order to give characterizations of certain sequence spaces useful in the study of summability domains [for example, wedge spaces; (cf. §5)], Bennett introduced the concept of scarce copies of a sequence space in Ref. 15 and continued this study in Ref. 14. He proved several inclusion theorems in terms of scarce copies of a sequence space (Ref. 14) which we give here. We start with

DEFINITION 3.41 Let $r = \{r_n\}$ be a nondecreasing unbounded sequence of positive integers such that $r_1 = 1$ and $r_n = o(n)$. For each $x \in \omega$ and each positive integer n, the *counting function* $c_n(x)$ is defined as the number of nonzero elements in the set $\{x_1, x_2, \ldots, x_n\}$. For a subset λ of ω, we define a set

$$s(\lambda,r) = \{x : x \in \lambda,\ c_n(x) \leq r_n,\ n \geq 1\}$$

Then the linear span of $s(\lambda,r)$ is called a *scarce copy* of λ and is denoted by $S(\lambda,r)$.

Remarks: A scarce copy of a sequence space λ is clearly a subspace of λ, and is normal, monotone, or contains ϕ, according as λ has the same property.

The scarce copies of a normal FK-AK space behave in the following fashion.

PROPOSITION 3.42 Let (λ,T) be a normal FK-AK space and let $S(\lambda)$ be the union of all the scarce copies of λ, i.e., $S(\lambda) = \cup_r S(\lambda,r)$. Then $S(\lambda)$ is a barreled subspace of λ.

Proof. It follows from Propositions 2.2.7 and 2.3.9 that $\lambda^* = \lambda^\times$ and therefore $T = \tau(\lambda,\lambda^\times)$. Further, $S(\lambda) = \lambda_0$ (cf. Definitions 2.2.1). Indeed, if $x \in \lambda_0$ is such that $x = (\alpha_j y_j)$ where $\alpha_j = 0$ or 1, $(1/n)\ \Sigma_{j=1}^n \alpha_j \to 0$ as $n \to \infty$, and $\{y_j\} \in \lambda$, then x is in the scarce copy $S(\lambda,r)$ of λ which corresponds to the sequence $r = \{r_n\}$ defined as $r_n = 1 + \Sigma_{j=1}^n \alpha_j$, $n \geq 1$. Thus $\lambda_0 \subset S(\lambda)$. Conversely, if $x \in S(\lambda)$, then $x \in S(\lambda,r)$ for some $r = \{r_n\}$, where $r_1 = 1$ and $r_n/n \to 0$ as $n \to \infty$. Define a sequence $\alpha = \{\alpha_j\}$ such that $\alpha_j = 1$ for those indices j for which $x_j \neq 0$ and $\alpha_j = 0$ otherwise. Clearly $x = \{\alpha_j x_j\}$, and also $c_n(x) \leq r_n$ implies that $\Sigma_{j=1}^n \alpha_j \leq r_n$, or $(1/n)\ \Sigma_{j=1}^n \alpha_j \leq r_n/n \to 0$ as $n \to \infty$. Hence $\{\alpha_j\} \in \mathcal{O}$ and therefore $x \in \lambda_0$.

Now applying Proposition 2.22, we find that the space $(S(\lambda),\tau(S(\lambda),\lambda^\times))$ is barreled. As $\tau(S(\lambda),\lambda^\times) = \tau(\lambda,\lambda^\times)|S(\lambda)$, the result follows.□

The above result leads to

THEOREM 3.43 Let λ be a given normal FK-AK space. Then an FK-space μ contains every scarce copy of λ if and only if it contains λ.

Proof. Let $S(\lambda)$ be as defined in Proposition 3.41 and assume that $S(\lambda) \subset \mu$. Define the inclusion map $I: S(\lambda) \to \mu$. As $(S(\lambda), \tau(S(\lambda), \lambda^\times))$ is a barreled K-space and μ is an FK-space, the graph of I is closed, and therefore I is continuous, from Theorem 1.10.17. Now extending I to the closure of $S(\lambda)$, i.e., to λ, we immediately get $\lambda \subset \mu$. The converse is immediate. □

Concerning the scarce copies of the space ω, we have

PROPOSITION 3.44 Every scarce copy of ω is barreled.

Proof. Let $S \equiv S(\omega, r)$ be a scarce copy of ω. The result will follow from Proposition 1.8.3 if we show that $\sigma(\phi, S)$- and $\sigma(\phi, \omega)$-bounded sets are the same.

Let us consider a $\sigma(\phi, S)$-bounded subset A of ϕ. Since $\phi \subset S$, we can find a sequence $\{\alpha_i\}$ of positive real numbers such that

$$\sup\{|x_i| : x \in A\} \le \alpha_i \qquad i \ge 1$$

We now show that A is of bounded length. If this is not true, then proceeding as in the proof of Theorem 2.6.2, we can find a subsequence $\{\ell_n\}$ from $\mathbb{N}$, $\ell_{n-1} < \ell_n \to \infty$ as $n \to \infty$, $n < r_{\ell_n}$, a sequence $\{x^n\} \subset A$, and $u \in \omega$ such that

$$\left| \sum_{i \ge 1} u_i x_i^n \right| \ge n \qquad \forall n \ge 1$$

Clearly $u \in S$. Thus A is not $\sigma(\phi, S)$-bounded, which is a contradiction. Hence A is of bounded length and therefore $\sigma(\phi, \omega)$-bounded, by Theorem 2.6.2. □

We derive the following inclusion result:

THEOREM 3.45 Let λ be an FK-space containing a scarce copy of ω. Then $\lambda = \omega$.

Proof. Let $S(\omega, r)$ be a scarce copy of ω such that $S(\omega, r) \subset \lambda$. Since $\phi \subset S(\omega, r)$, it is a barreled dense subspace of ω. Now the result follows from Theorem 1.10.20, (i) $\Longrightarrow$ (ii). □

For the spaces ℓ^p, $0 < p \leq 1$, we have (Ref. 14)

PROPOSITION 3.46 Every scarce copy of $\ell = \bigcap_{0<p\leq 1} \ell^p$ is a barreled subspace of ℓ^1. In particular, every scarce copy of ℓ^1 is barreled.

Proof. Let $S \equiv S(\ell,r)$ be a scarce copy of ℓ. Clearly S is a normal subspace of ℓ^1 and therefore $\sigma(\ell^\infty,S)$- and $\eta(\ell^\infty,S)$-bounded sets are the same in ℓ^∞ (cf. Corollary 2.4.12). Hence, in view of Theorem 1.8.3, it would be sufficient to show that every $\eta(\ell^\infty,S)$-bounded set is $\sigma(\ell^\infty,\ell^1)$-bounded.

Let B be a $\eta(\ell^\infty,S)$-bounded set which is not $\sigma(\ell^\infty,\ell^1)$-bounded. Then by Proposition 2.6.8, we can find an increasing sequence $\{n_k\}$ of integers with $r_{n_k} > k$, $k \geq 1$, and a sequence $\{x^k\} \subset B$, such that

$$|x^k_{n_k}| > 2^{2k} \qquad \forall k \geq 1$$

Define $u \in \omega$ as follows:

$$u_i = \begin{cases} \dfrac{1}{2^k} & i = n_k,\ k \geq 1 \\ 0 & \text{otherwise} \end{cases}$$

Then $u \in S$ and

$$\sup_{x\in B} \sum_{i\geq 1} |x_i u_i| \geq \sup_{k\geq 1} \sum_{i\geq 1} |x^k_i u_i| > 2^k \qquad \forall k \geq 1$$

implies that B is not $\eta(\ell^\infty,S)$-bounded, which contradicts our assumption. Hence the result follows.

Lastly, we derive

THEOREM 3.47 An FK-space λ contains a scarce copy of ℓ if and only if it contains ℓ^1.

Proof. Let λ contain a scarce copy $S(\ell,r) \equiv S$ of ℓ. Since $(S,\beta(S,\ell^\infty))$ is a barreled K-space, the inclusion map $I\colon (S,\beta(S,\ell^\infty)) \to \lambda$ is continuous by Theorem 1.10.17, and hence $\ell \subset \lambda$. Consequently, $\ell^1 \subset \lambda$ from Theorem 3.38. The converse is clear. □

4. DUALITY BETWEEN λ AND λ^β

The basic purpose of this section is to provide certain structure theorems for a sequence space placed in duality with λ^β. In proving all these results, which are due to Bennett and Kalton [18], we make ample use of the elementary properties of inclusion maps and matrix transformations. These results may also be regarded as the inclusion map theorems for the spaces $(\lambda,\tau(\lambda,\lambda^\beta))$.

Barreledness of $(\lambda,\tau(\lambda,\lambda^\beta))$

The main result of this subsection is contained in

THEOREM 4.1 Let λ be an arbitrary sequence space; then the following statements are equivalent:

(i) $(\lambda,\tau(\lambda,\lambda^\beta))$ is barreled.

(ii) If $\mu \equiv (\mu,T)$ is an FK-space and A is a matrix transformation, $A: \lambda \to \mu$, then $A: (\lambda,\tau(\lambda,\lambda^\beta)) \to (\mu,T)$ is continuous.

(iii) If (μ,T) is an FK-space with $\lambda \subset \mu$, then the identity map $I: (\lambda,\tau(\lambda,\lambda^\beta)) \to (\mu,T)$ is continuous.

(iv) If (μ,T) is an FK-space with $\lambda \subset \mu$, then $\lambda \subset W_\mu$.

(v) If (μ,T) is an FK-space with $\lambda \subset \mu$, then $\lambda \subset S_\mu$.

Proof. (i) $\Rightarrow$ (ii) As observed in the proof of Proposition 3.2, $\{a_{ij} : j \geq 1\} \in \lambda^\beta$ for each $i \geq 1$, where $A = [a_{ij}]$. If $(x,y) \in G$, the graph of A, then $x^\alpha \to x$ in $\tau(\lambda,\lambda^\beta)$ and $A(x^\alpha) \to y$ in T. Therefore $x^\alpha \to x$ in $\sigma(\lambda,\lambda^\beta)$ and $(A(x^\alpha))_i \to y_i$, $i \geq 1$. Hence

$$q_{\{a_{ij}:j\geq 1\}}(x^\alpha - x) \to 0 \qquad \sum_{j\geq 1} a_{ij}x_j^\alpha \to y_i, \quad i \geq 1$$

Consequently

$$\sum_{j\geq 1} a_{ij}x_j^\alpha \to \sum_{j\geq 1} a_{ij}x_j, y_i \qquad \text{for } i \geq 1$$

and it follows that $y = A(x)$. Thus we find that the graph of A: $(\lambda,\tau(\lambda,\lambda^\beta)) \to (\mu,T)$ is closed, and so A is continuous by Theorem 1.10.17.

(ii) $\Rightarrow$ (iii) We can identify I with $A = [a_{ij}]$, where $a_{ij} = 1$ if $i = j$ and $a_{ij} = 0$ if $i \neq j$.

(iii) $\Rightarrow$ (iv) In view of Proposition 1.12.3, the map I is $\sigma(\lambda,\lambda^\beta)$-$\sigma(\mu,\mu^*)$ continuous. Since $(\lambda,\sigma(\lambda,\lambda^\beta))$ is an AK-space, for each $x \in \lambda$, $x^{(n)} \to x$ in $\sigma(\mu,\mu^*)$, that is, $x \in W_\mu$. Hence $\lambda \subset W_\mu$.

(iv) $\Rightarrow$ (i) First we show that if $K \subset \lambda^\beta$ is $\sigma(\lambda^\beta,\lambda)$-bounded and closed, then it is $\sigma(\lambda^\beta,\lambda)$-sequentially compact. For this choose an arbitrary sequence $\{a^i\} \subset K$. By the diagonal process we can select a subsequence of $\{a^i\}$, to be denoted by $\{a^i\}$, such that

$$\lim_{i\to\infty} a^i_j = a_j \qquad \forall j \geq 1$$

Set $a^i_j = a_{ij}$ $(i,j \geq 1)$. Since $\{a_{ij} : j \geq 1\} \in K \subset \lambda^\beta$ then for $x \in \lambda$, $\Sigma_{j\geq 1} a_{ij}x_j$ converges, say to y_i for $i \geq 1$, and

$$\left|\sum_{j\geq 1} a_{ij}x_j\right| \leq k_x \qquad \text{for some } k_x > 0$$

Hence $A(x)$ exists and $A(x) = \{(A(x))_i\} \in \ell^\infty$, where $A \equiv [a_{ij}]$. Thus $x \in \ell^\infty_A$, giving $\lambda \subset \ell^\infty_A$. By Theorem 3.7, ℓ^∞_A is an FK-space and so for each x in λ, by (iv), $x^{(n)} \to x$ in $\sigma(\ell^\infty_A,(\ell^\infty_A)^*)$. Now $A: \ell^\infty_A \to \ell^\infty$ is continuous (cf. Theorem 3.7) and therefore from Proposition 1.12.2, A is $\sigma(\ell^\infty_A,(\ell^\infty_A)^*)$-$\sigma(\ell^\infty,(\ell^\infty)^*)$ continuous. Therefore

$$\langle A(x^{(n)}),y\rangle \to \langle A(x),y\rangle \qquad \forall y \text{ in } (\ell^\infty)^*$$

Thus

$$\lim_{n\to\infty}\lim_{i\to\infty} (A(x^{(n)}))_i = \lim_{i\to\infty}\lim_{n\to\infty} (A(x^{(n)}))_i$$

$$\Longrightarrow \quad \lim_{n\to\infty} \sum_{j=1}^{n} a_jx_j = \lim_{i\to\infty} \sum_{j\geq 1} a_{ij}x_j$$

Therefore $\Sigma_{j\geq 1} a_jx_j$ exists, and since $x \in \lambda$ is arbitrary, $\{a_j\} \in \lambda^\beta$; moreover, we have $\langle x,a\rangle = \lim_{i\to\infty} \langle a^i,x\rangle$ for each x in λ^β. As K is $\sigma(\lambda^\beta,\lambda)$-closed, $a = \{a_j\} \in K$, and so K is $\sigma(\lambda^\beta,\lambda)$-sequentially compact. Appealing to Theorem 2.3.10, we conclude that K is $\sigma(\lambda^\beta,\lambda)$-compact and consequently $\beta(\lambda,\lambda^\beta) = \tau(\lambda,\lambda^\beta)$. Hence (i) follows from Theorem 1.8.3.

(v) $\Longrightarrow$ (iv) This is again obvious.

(iv) $\Longrightarrow$ (v) By above we have (i) [(iv) $\Longrightarrow$ (i)]. Now $(\lambda,\sigma(\lambda,\lambda^\beta))$ is an AK-space; therefore from the weak Schauder basis theorem (Ref. 11, p. 109; Ref. 41, p. 9; Ref. 125, Chapter 2, Proposition 7.3), the space $(\lambda,\tau(\lambda,\lambda^\beta))$ is an AK-space. Since (iv) also implies (iii), we immediately get (v). □

Next we have the following result which partially contains a theorem due to Garling [56, p. 976].

PROPOSITION 4.2 Let λ be a B_0-invariant sequence space; then $(\lambda,\tau(\lambda,\lambda^\beta))$ is a barreled AK-space and λ^β is $\sigma(\lambda^\beta,\lambda)$-sequentially complete.

Proof. Essentially the proof of this result makes use of the implication (v) $\Rightarrow$ (i) of Theorem 4.1. So, let (μ,T) be an FK-space with $\lambda \subset \mu$. If $x \in \lambda$, then $x = u \cdot v$ where $u \in B_0$ and $v \in \lambda$. With this choice of x, consider the map T_v: $bv_0 \to \mu$, $T_v(u) = u \cdot v$ [if $\|u\| > 0$, we may consider $(u/\|u\|) \cdot (\|u\|v)$ in place of $u \cdot v$]. Then T_v has a closed graph and hence is continuous. Now

$$x^{(n)} = u^{(n)} \cdot v = T_v(u^{(n)}) \to T_v(u) \qquad \text{in } T$$

Hence $x^{(n)} \to x$ in T. It follows that $\lambda \subset S_\mu$ and so $(\lambda,\tau(\lambda,\lambda^\beta))$ is barreled. The AK-ness of $(\lambda,\tau(\lambda,\lambda^\beta))$ follows as in the proof of (iv) $\Rightarrow$ (v), Theorem 4.1. The last part follows from Proposition 1.10.2.

Note: Theorem 4.1 applies to all AK-FK spaces (λ,T); for instance, the barreledness of $(\lambda,\tau(\lambda,\lambda^\beta))$ in this case follows trivially without recourse to this theorem. Indeed, $(\lambda,\tau(\lambda,\lambda^*))$ is barreled since $T = \tau(\lambda,\lambda^*)$, and by Proposition 2.3.9, $\lambda^\beta = \lambda^*$.

EXERCISE 4.3 By applying Theorem 4.1, (v) $\Rightarrow$ (i), show that for any AK-FK space (λ,T), the space $(\lambda,\tau(\lambda,\lambda^\beta))$ is barreled.

Sequential Completeness of λ^β

Let us recall that if λ is any monotone or normal sequence space then λ^β is $\sigma(\lambda^\beta,\lambda)$-sequentially complete (cf. Propositions 2.2.7, 2.5.3, and 2.2). The next theorem (Ref. 18, p. 517) characterizes the sequential completeness of $(\lambda^\beta,\sigma(\lambda^\beta,\lambda))$ for an arbitrary sequence space λ.

THEOREM 4.4 For an arbitrary sequence space λ, the following statements are equivalent:

(i) λ^β is $\sigma(\lambda^\beta,\lambda)$-sequentially complete.

(ii) If (μ,T) is a separable FK-space and A is an infinite matrix $[a_{ij}]$ with A: $\lambda \to \mu$, then A is $\tau(\lambda,\lambda^\beta)$-T continuous.

(iii) If (μ,T) is a separable FK-space with $\lambda \subset \mu$, then the identity map I: $(\lambda,\tau(\lambda,\lambda^\beta)) \to (\mu,T)$ is continuous.

(iv) If (μ,T) is a separable FK-space with $\lambda \subset \mu$, then $\lambda \subset W_\mu$.

Proof. (i) $\Rightarrow$ (ii) Let us observe that $\{a_{ij} : j \geq 1\} \in \lambda^\beta$ for $i \geq 1$ (see the proof of Proposition 3.2). Let now $x^\alpha \to x$ in $(\lambda,\tau(\lambda,\lambda^\beta))$ and $A(x^\alpha) \to y$ in T. Then $x^\alpha \to x$ in $\sigma(\lambda,\lambda^\beta)$ also, and so

$$\sum_{j\geq 1} a_{ij}x_j^\alpha \to \sum_{j\geq 1} a_{ij}x_j, y_i \qquad \text{for } i \geq 1$$

Hence

$$y_i = \sum_{j\geq 1} a_{ij}x_j \qquad \forall i \geq 1$$

$$\Rightarrow \quad A(x) = y$$

and consequently $A: (\lambda,\tau(\lambda,\lambda^\beta)) \to (\mu,T)$ has a closed graph. Applying Theorem 1.10.18, we obtain (ii).

(ii) $\Rightarrow$ (iii) This is obvious once we identify I with $A = [a_{ij}]$, where $a_{ij} = 1$ for $i = j$, $a_{ij} = 0$ for $i \neq j$.

(iii) $\Rightarrow$ (iv) Same as the proof of Theorem 4.1, (iii) $\Rightarrow$ (iv).

(iv) $\Rightarrow$ (i) To prove this, consider a $\sigma(\lambda^\beta,\lambda)$-Cauchy sequence $\{a^i\}$ in λ^β. Then $\Sigma_{j\geq 1} a_j^i x_j$ converges for each $i \geq 1$ and $x \in \lambda$. So, letting $A = [a_{ij}]$ where $a_{ij} = a_j^i$ $(i,j \geq 1)$ and making use of the Cauchy character of $\{a^i\}$, we find that $\lambda \subset c_A$. Since c_A is a separable FK-space (cf. Theorem 6.27), by (iv),

$$x^{(n)} \to x \qquad \text{in } \sigma(c_A, c_A^*)$$

If $\lim_A$ denotes the linear functional on c_A defined by

$$\lim_A x = \lim_{i\to\infty} \sum_{j\geq 1} a_{ij}x_j \qquad x \in c_A$$

then $\lim_A \in c_A^*$ (cf. Theorem 3.7). Therefore,

$$\lim_A x = \lim_{n\to\infty} \lim_A x^{(n)} = \lim_{n\to\infty} \lim_{i\to\infty} \sum_{j=1}^{n} a_{ij}x_j$$

or

$$\lim_A x = \sum_{j\geq 1} a_j x_j$$

where $a_j = \lim_{i\to\infty} a_{ij}$ (note that $Ax \in c$ for every x in λ, and so $A(e^m) =$

$\{a_{im} : i \geq 1\} \in c$ for every $m \geq 1$). Hence $a = \{a_j\} \in \lambda^\beta$ and

$$\lim_{i\to\infty} \sum_{j\geq 1} a_{ij}x_j = \sum_{j\geq 1} a_jx_j$$

or

$$\langle a^i, x\rangle \xrightarrow{i} \langle a, x\rangle \qquad \forall x \in \lambda$$

where $a \in \lambda^\beta$. □

As pointed out in Ref. 18, p. 548, Theorems 4.1 and 4.4 suggest the natural problem of characterizing those sequence spaces λ having the property that $\lambda \subset S_\mu$ whenever μ is a separable FK-space with $\lambda \subset \mu$. To solve this problem, let us first prove the following structure theorem.

PROPOSITION 4.5 Let λ be a sequence space such that λ^β is $\sigma(\lambda^\beta,\lambda)$-sequentially complete. Then $\tau(\lambda,\lambda^\beta)$ is the projective topology on λ determined by $\{I_\mu;\mu\colon \mu \in A\}$, where A is the family of all separable FK-spaces μ with $\lambda \subset \mu$ and I_μ is the associated identity map $I_\mu\colon \lambda \to \mu$.

Proof. Let T denote the above-mentioned projective limit topology. By Theorem 4.4, (i) $\Rightarrow$ (iii), and Definition 1.3.7, $T \subset \tau(\lambda,\lambda^\beta)$.

For the reverse inclusion, let us consider an arbitrary balanced, convex, and $\sigma(\lambda^\beta,\lambda)$-compact subset B of λ^β. By Theorem 2.3.10, $\sigma(\lambda^\beta,\lambda)$ and $\sigma(\omega,\phi)|\lambda^\beta$ [that is, $\sigma(\lambda^\beta,\phi)$] coincide on B. But $\sigma(\lambda^\beta,\phi)$ is metrizable (the proof of this fact is the same as that of Proposition 1.4.11) and so B is $\sigma(\lambda^\beta,\lambda)$-separable. Let $\{a^i\}$ be a countable set in B such that $\{a^i\}$ is $\sigma(\lambda^\beta,\lambda)$-dense in B. Let us write $A = [a_{ij}]$, where $a_{ij} = a^i_j$ $(i,j \geq 1)$. Since $\{a^i\}$ is $\sigma(\lambda^\beta,\lambda)$-bounded, then for each x in λ,

$$\sup_i |(A(x))_i| = \sup_i \Big|\sum_{j\geq 1} a_{ij}x_j\Big| < \infty$$

$$\Rightarrow A(x) \in \ell^\infty \Rightarrow x \in \ell^\infty_A$$

Hence $\lambda \subset \ell^\infty_A$. We next show that the identity map I: $(\lambda,\tau(\lambda,\lambda^\beta)) \to \ell^\infty_A$ is continuous, where ℓ^∞_A is equipped with the family of seminorms making it an FK-space (cf. Theorem 3.7). By Proposition 1.7.6, K is $\tau(\lambda,\lambda^\beta)$-equicontinuous, and thus we find a $\tau(\lambda,\lambda^\beta)$-continuous seminorm p with $|\langle a^i,x\rangle| \leq p(x)$, valid for all $i \geq 1$ and each x in λ. Hence

$$\|A(x)\|_\infty \le p(x) \Longrightarrow \|I(x)\| \le p(x) \tag{*}$$

Further, if $M_i = \{a^{i,(n)} - a^i : n \ge 1\}$ then $M_i^{\circ\circ}$ is balanced, convex, and $\sigma(\lambda^\beta,\lambda)$-compact (cf. Proposition 1.7.13) and hence, as above, there corresponds a $\tau(\lambda,\lambda^\beta)$-continuous seminorm q_i such that

$$|\langle a^{i,(n)},x\rangle| \le |\langle a^{i,(n)} - a^i, x\rangle| + |\langle a^i,x\rangle| \le q_i(x) + p(x)$$

valid for all $n \ge 1$ and each x in λ. Therefore

$$\sup_n \left|\sum_{j=1}^{n} a_{ij}x_j\right| \le q_i(x) + p(x) \tag{**}$$

From (*) and (**) we conclude the continuity of I as desired.

Now $\bar{\phi}_\sigma = \lambda$, where $\bar{\phi}_\sigma$ is the $\sigma(\lambda,\lambda^\beta)$-closure of ϕ in λ (λ is a $\sigma(\lambda,\lambda^\beta)$-AK-space], and so from Proposition 1.7.4, $\bar{\phi}_\tau = \lambda$, where $\tau = \tau(\lambda,\lambda^\beta)$. Thus λ is ω-separable relative to $\tau(\lambda,\lambda^\beta)$ (cf. remarks just before Proposition 1.2.11), and this gives the $\tau(\lambda,\lambda^\beta)$-separability of λ. The continuity of I forces λ to be separable in ℓ_A^∞ as well. If μ is the closure of λ in ℓ_A^∞, then μ is a separable FK-space containing λ. By the definition of T, $I: (\lambda,T) \to \mu$ is continuous. Hence there exists a T-continuous seminorm p such that

$$\|I(x)\| \le p(x)$$

$$\Longrightarrow \quad \sup_i \left|\sum_{j\ge1} a_{ij}x_j\right| \le p(x) \qquad \forall x \text{ in } \lambda$$

If $a \in K$ then for each given x in λ and $\varepsilon > 0$ there corresponds an i_0 such that

$$\left|\sum_{j\ge1} (a_j - a_j^{i_0})x_j\right| < \varepsilon$$

$$\Longrightarrow \quad \sup_{a\in K} \left|\sum_{j\ge1} a_jx_j\right| < p(x) + \varepsilon$$

$$\Longrightarrow \quad \sup_{a\in K} \left|\sum_{j\ge1} a_jx_j\right| \le p(x)$$

$$\Longrightarrow \quad q_K(x) \le p(x)$$

thereby giving $\tau(\lambda,\lambda^\beta) \subset T$. □

The following is the desired characterization theorem.

THEOREM 4.6 Let λ be an arbitrary sequence space. Then the following two statements are equivalent:

(i) $(\lambda,\tau(\lambda,\lambda^\beta))$ is an AK-space and λ^β is $\sigma(\lambda^\beta,\lambda)$-sequentially complete.

(ii) If μ is a separable FK-space with $\lambda \subset \mu$, then $\lambda \subset S_\mu$.

Proof. (i) $\Rightarrow$ (ii) This follows from Theorem 4.4, (i) $\Rightarrow$ (iii), since $x^{(n)} \to x$ in $\tau(\lambda,\beta^\beta)$ for each x in λ.

(ii) $\Rightarrow$ (i) If (ii) holds then $\lambda \subset W_\mu$ for any separable FK-space μ containing λ. Thus by using Theorem 4.4, (iv) $\Rightarrow$ (i), we find that λ^β is $\sigma(\lambda^\beta,\lambda)$-sequentially complete.

Let $x \in \lambda$ and B be a $\tau(\lambda,\lambda^\beta)$-neighborhood of $0 \in \lambda$. By Proposition 4.5, we have a finite number of zero neighborhoods 0_{α_i}, $1 \le i \le m$, where $0_{\alpha_i} \subset \mu_{\alpha_i}$, μ_{α_i} being a separable FK-space containing λ, such that

$$\bigcap_{i=1}^{m} I_{\alpha_i}^{-1}[0_{\alpha_i}] \subset B$$

Since $\lambda \subset S_{\mu_{\alpha_i}}$ $(1 \le i \le m)$, $x^{(n)} \to x$ in each μ_{α_i}, and consequently there exists an $N \in \mathbb{N}$ such that

$$x^{(n)} - x \in 0_{\alpha_i} \qquad \forall n \ge N,\ 1 \le i \le m$$

$$\Longrightarrow \quad x^{(n)} - x \in I_{\alpha_i}^{-1}[0_{\alpha_i}] \qquad \forall n \ge N,\ 1 \le i \le m$$

$$\Longrightarrow \quad x^{(n)} - x \in B \qquad \forall n \ge N$$

Thus $x^{(n)} \to x$ in $\tau(\lambda,\lambda^\beta)$. □

Remark: If λ is a monotone sequence space then from Theorem 2.1 and Proposition 2.2, the condition (i) of Theorem 4.6 is always satisfied, and thus Theorem 4.6 applies to any monotone sequence space.

Next we have the following characterization of semi-Montel spaces:

THEOREM 4.7 Let λ be a sequence space. Then the following statements are equivalent:

(i) $(\lambda,\tau(\lambda,\lambda^\beta))$ is a semi-Montel space.

(ii) If (μ,T) is a separable FK-space with $\lambda \subset \mu$, then the inclusion map $I: (\lambda,\tau(\lambda,\lambda^\beta)) \to (\mu,T)$ is compact.

Proof. (i) $\Rightarrow$ (ii) If we could show that λ^β is $\sigma(\lambda^\beta,\lambda)$-sequentially complete, the required conclusion would follow immediately from Theorem 4.4, (i) $\Rightarrow$ (iii), and the definition of a compact operator. To do this, let us consider the topology $[\tau(\lambda,\lambda^\beta)]^c$; see Definition 2.10. Let $f \in \lambda'$ such that f_A is $\sigma(\lambda,\lambda^\beta)$-continuous, where A is an arbitrary $\tau(\lambda,\lambda^\beta)$-compact subset of λ. It is easily seen that $f \in \lambda^+ \equiv [\lambda,\sigma(\lambda,\lambda^\beta)]^+$. Hence by Exercise 2.3.8, $f \in \lambda^\beta$. Using Theorem 1.11.6, we find that λ^β is $[\tau(\lambda,\lambda^\beta)]^c$-complete. If A is a $\tau(\lambda,\lambda^\beta)$-compact subset of λ, then A is $\sigma(\lambda,\lambda^\beta)$-compact and so the balanced convex $\sigma(\lambda,\lambda^\beta)$-closed hull of A is $\sigma(\lambda,\lambda^\beta)$-compact (cf. Propositions 1.9.2 and 1.2.13). Therefore $[\tau(\lambda,\lambda^\beta)]^c \supset \tau(\lambda^\beta,\lambda)$ and it follows that $[\tau(\lambda,\lambda^\beta)]^c$ is compatible with $\langle\lambda^\beta,\lambda\rangle$. If $a^n \to 0$ in $\sigma(\lambda^\beta,\lambda)$, then from Proposition 1.7.13, the balanced, convex, and $\sigma(\lambda^\beta,\lambda)$-closed hull D of $\{a^n\}$ is $\sigma(\lambda^\beta,\lambda)$-compact. Let

$$S_1 = \{A : A \subset \lambda,\ A \text{ is } \tau(\lambda,\lambda^\beta)\text{-compact}\}$$

and

$$S_2 = \{B : B \subset \lambda^\beta,\ B \text{ is balanced, convex, and } \sigma(\lambda^\beta,\lambda)\text{-compact}\}$$

Since each $A \in S_1$ is precompact in the S_2-topology, by Theorem 1.11.7, each $B \in S_2$ is precompact in the S_1-topology. Thus D is $[\tau(\lambda,\lambda^\beta)]^c$-precompact. As D is also $[\tau(\lambda,\lambda^\beta)]^c$-closed, it follows from Proposition 1.2.13 that D is $[\tau(\lambda,\lambda^\beta)]^c$-compact, and so $a^n \to 0$ in $[\tau(\lambda,\lambda^\beta)]^c$. Thus $\sigma(\lambda^\beta,\lambda)$ and $[\tau(\lambda,\lambda^\beta)]^c$ have the same convergent sequences and hence λ^β is $\sigma(\lambda^\beta,\lambda)$-sequentially complete.

(ii) $\Rightarrow$ (i) If $x \in \lambda$, then by (ii), $\{x^{(n)}\}$ is T-relatively compact and it follows that $x^{(n)} \to x$ in T. Hence $\lambda \subset S_\mu$, and so by Theorem 4.6, (ii) $\Rightarrow$ (i), λ^β is $\sigma(\lambda^\beta,\lambda)$-sequentially complete. In view of Proposition 4.5, it turns out that $\tau(\lambda,\lambda^\beta)$ is the projective topology, and as the associated maps I_μ are compact, the semi-Montel character of $(\lambda,\tau(\lambda,\lambda^\beta))$ follows from an application of Proposition 1.3.10. □

The following example shows that the natural analog of Theorem 4.7 does not hold.

EXAMPLE 4.8 Let $\lambda = bv$. Then $\lambda^\beta = cs$. Since cs is a normed space with $(cs)^* = bv$, therefore $(cs,\beta(cs,bv))^* = bv$. Hence $(bv,\beta(bv,cs))$ is semireflexive. But cs is not $\sigma(cs,bv)$-sequentially complete. Hence from Theorem 4.4, (i) $\Longrightarrow$ (iii), we can find a separable FK-space μ with $bv \subset \mu$ such that the identity map I: $(bv,\tau(bv,cs)) \to \mu$ is not continuous and so I is not compact.

Finally we have

THEOREM 4.9 For any sequence space λ, the following are equivalent:

(i) $(\lambda,\tau(\lambda,\lambda^\beta))$ is reflexive (resp. Montel).

(ii) If (μ,T) is an FK-space and A is a matrix transformation, A: $\lambda \to \mu$, then A: $(\lambda,\tau(\lambda,\lambda^\beta)) \to (\mu,T)$ is weakly compact (resp. compact).

(iii) If (μ,T) is an FK-space with $\lambda \subset \mu$, the identity map I: $(\lambda,\tau(\lambda,\lambda^\beta)) \to (\mu,T)$ is weakly compact (resp. compact).

Proof. (i) $\Longrightarrow$ (ii) By Proposition 1.9.5, $(\lambda,\tau(\lambda,\lambda^\beta))$ is barreled. Hence A: $(\lambda,\tau(\lambda,\lambda^\beta)) \to (\mu,T)$ is continuous and so A is $\sigma(\lambda,\lambda^\beta)$-$\sigma(\mu,\mu^*)$ continuous (cf. Proposition 1.12.3). Consequently, if K is $\sigma(\lambda,\lambda^\beta)$-bounded and therefore $\sigma(\lambda,\lambda^\beta)$-relatively compact by Proposition 1.9.2, it follows that A(K) is $\sigma(\mu,\mu^*)$-relatively compact.

(ii) $\Longrightarrow$ (iii) Here we identify I with the transformation $A = [a_{ij}]$ where $A_{ii} = 1$, $i \geq 1$, and $a_{ij} = 0$ elsewhere.

(iii) $\Longrightarrow$ (i) First we establish the barreledness of $(\lambda,\tau(\lambda,\lambda^\beta))$. To do this let (μ,T) be an arbitrary FK-space with $\lambda \subset \mu$, and as usual, denote by I the identity map from λ into μ. If $x \in \lambda$, the set $A = \{x^{(n)}\} \cup \{x\}$ is $\tau(\lambda,\lambda^\beta)$-bounded. By (iii), A is $\sigma(\mu,\mu^*)$-relatively compact and so we find that $x^{(n)} \to x$ in $\sigma(\mu,\mu^*)$. Hence $\lambda \subset W_\mu$. By Theorem 4.1, (iv) $\Longrightarrow$ (i), the space λ is $\tau(\lambda,\lambda^\beta)$-barreled. Thus for any FK-space (μ,T) with $\lambda \subset \mu$ and for a matrix transformation A: $\lambda \to \mu$, we find that A is $\tau(\lambda,\lambda^\beta)$-T continuous [and therefore $\sigma(\lambda,\lambda^\beta)$-$\sigma(\mu,\mu^*)$ continuous] and I is $\tau(\lambda,\lambda^\beta)$-T continuous [and therefore $\sigma(\lambda,\lambda^\beta)$-$\sigma(\mu,\mu^*)$ continuous]. Also the space $(\lambda^\beta,\sigma(\lambda^\beta,\lambda))$ is quasicomplete and therefore sequentially complete.

Now from Proposition 4.5 and Theorem 1.3.11 it follows that the dual of the space λ, with respect to the projective topology S defined by the inclusion maps from λ into separable FK-spaces containing λ equipped with their weak topologies, is λ^β. In other words, $S = \sigma(\lambda,\lambda^\beta)$, and therefore every bounded set in $(\lambda,\tau(\lambda,\lambda^\beta))$ is weakly relatively compact by Theorem 1.3.10. Thus (i) is true by Propositions 1.9.2 and 1.9.3. □

5. TOPOLOGICAL PROPERTIES OF COORDINATE AND UNIT VECTORS

Throughout, let (λ, T) be a K-space, where T is a locally convex topology. All of the results that we have established so far depend upon the sequence $\{e^n\} \subset \lambda$ directly or indirectly. However, at no place have we imposed any condition on the sequence $\{e^n\}$ relative to the topology T. If the sequence $\{e^n\}$ is restricted relative to T in some manner, we would want to know the impact this restriction might have on the structure of the space λ. In this section we take up this problem in detail and investigate several of its solutions. A related problem concerning the topological behavior of the element e, in case $e \in \lambda$, is also dealt with. But for some deep results derived in this chapter, we could have discussed all these problems much earlier.

Wedge Spaces

An important class of spaces (λ, T), which finds interesting applications in Schauder basis theory and in summability theory, is the family of wedge spaces introduced in Ref. 15. Accordingly we have

DEFINITION 5.1 Let (λ, T) be a K-space. λ is said to be (i) a *wedge space* provided $e^n \to 0$ in T; (ii) a *weak wedge space* if $e^n \to 0$ in $\sigma(\lambda, \lambda^*)$; (iii) a *subsequence wedge space* if $e^{n_k} \to 0$ in T for some subsequence $\{n_k\}$ of $\{n\}$; and (iv) a *subsequence weak wedge space* in case there exists a subsequence $\{e^{n_k}\}$ of $\{e^n\}$ with $e^{n_k} \to 0$ in $\sigma(\lambda, \lambda^*)$.

Note: Most of the results of this section are due to Bennett, and if no reference is cited for a particular result it should be assumed that it has been taken from Ref. 15.

Let us begin with

THEOREM 5.2 An FK-space (λ, T) is a weak wedge space if and only if $\ell^1 \subset \lambda$ and the identity map $I: (\ell^1, \|\cdot\|) \to (\lambda, T)$ is weakly compact.

Proof. Let (λ, T) be a weak wedge space. Since $\{e^n\}$ is T-bounded, by Proposition 3.28, $\ell^1 \subset \lambda$. By hypothesis $\{f(e^n)\} \in c_0$; therefore $\{f(e^n)\} \in (\ell^1)^\beta$ for each $f \in \lambda^*$. Hence for all $x \in \ell^1$ and $f \in \lambda^*$, since I is continuous,

$$\langle x, \{f(e^n)\}\rangle = \langle I(x), f\rangle = \sum_{i \geq 1} x_i f(e^i)$$

Consequently I is $\sigma(\ell^1, c_0)$-$\sigma(\lambda, \lambda^*)$ continuous. By Theorem 1.7.12, the set $B = \{x : x \in \ell^1, \|x\| \leq 1\}$ is $\sigma(\ell^1, c_0)$-compact and hence B is $\sigma(\lambda, \lambda^*)$-compact.

Conversely, let $\lambda \supset \ell^1$ and $I: \ell^1 \to \lambda$ be weakly compact. Then $B = \{x : x \in \ell^1, \|x\| \leq 1\}$ is $\sigma(\lambda, \lambda^*)$-relatively compact. By Theorem 2.3,11, $e^n \to 0$ in $\sigma(\lambda, \lambda^*)$. □

We might ask if the statement of the preceding theorem is still valid in case we delete the words "weak" and "weakly." The answer is affirmative and is given in the next theorem, which also provides several other equivalent conditions for a K-space (λ, T) to be a wedge space. We need some preparation for this theorem.

Let $s = \{s_n\}$ denote throughout a strictly increasing sequence of non-negative integers with $s_1 = 0$. Let $\ell^\infty|s|$ designate the space defined by

$$\ell^\infty|s| = \left\{x : x \in \omega,\ \sup_n \sum_{i=s_n+1}^{s_{n+1}} |x_i| < \infty\right\}$$

Then $\ell^\infty|s|$ is a BK-space under the norm $\|\cdot\|_s$, where

$$\|x\|_s = \sup_n \sum_{i=s_n+1}^{s_{n+1}} |x_i| \qquad x \in \ell^\infty|s|$$

It is obvious that $\ell^\infty|s|$ is always normal and that $\ell^1 \subsetneq \ell^\infty|s| \subset \ell^\infty$.

LEMMA 5.3 Suppose $x^n \in c_0$, $n \geq 1$. Then we can choose an $x \in c_0$ such that

$$\lim_{i\to\infty} \frac{x_i^n}{x_i} = 0 \qquad \forall n \geq 1$$

Moreover,

$$x^\times \subset \bigcap_{n\geq 1} \{x^n\}^\times$$

Proof. It is easy to see that we can find a sequence $\{i_k : k = 0, 1, \ldots\} \subset \mathbb{N}$ so that

$$1 = i_0 < i_1 < \cdots$$

and

$$\max_{1\le n\le k} |x_i^n| < \frac{1}{4^k} \qquad i \ge i_k,\ k \ge 1$$

Define $x \in \omega$ by

$$x_i = \frac{1}{2^k} \qquad i_k \le i < i_{k+1},\ k \ge 1$$

Clearly $x \in c_0$, and for any fixed $n \ge 1$,

$$\left|\frac{x_i^n}{x_i}\right| < \frac{1}{2^k} \qquad \text{for } k \ge n,\ i_k \le i < i_{k+1}$$

Thus the first part is proved. The second part also follows from the preceding inequality. □

The next result is due to Garling [58, p. 1011].

PROPOSITION 5.4 Let A denote a subset of a K-space (λ,T) such that $A \subset S_\lambda$, A is coordinatewise bounded, and $x^{(n)} \to x$ uniformly in $x \in A$. Then any sequence $\{y^n\} \subset A$ has a Cauchy subsequence.

Proof. There exists a subsequence $\{u^n\}$ of $\{y^n\}$ such that $u_i^n \to u_i$ for each $i \ge 1$, where $u \in \omega$. Let $V \in \mathcal{B}$. There exists m in $\mathbb{N}$ such that

$$u^n - (u^n)^{(m)} \in \frac{1}{3} V \qquad \forall n \ge 1$$

For each $n \ge 1$, $(u^n)^{(m)} \in \lambda_m$, the m-dimensional subspace of λ generated by $e^1, \ldots, e^m$. Since $u_i^n \to u_i$ for each $i \ge 1$, $\{(u^n)^{(m)}\}$ converges to $u^{(m)}$ in λ_m, and so $\{(u^n)^{(m)}\}$ is Cauchy in λ_m. Hence there exists p in $\mathbb{N}$ such that

$$(u^n)^{(m)} - (u^k)^m \in \frac{1}{3} V \qquad \forall n,k \ge p$$

Thus

$$\begin{aligned} u^n - u^k &= u^n - (u^n)^{(m)} - u^k + (u^k)^{(m)} + (u^n)^{(m)} - (u^k)^{(m)} \\ &\in \frac{1}{3} V + \frac{1}{3} V + \frac{1}{3} V \subset V \qquad \text{for all } n,k \ge p \end{aligned}$$

Hence $\{u^n\}$ is Cauchy in (λ,T). □

We are now ready to state the theorem promised earlier.

THEOREM 5.5 Let (λ,T) be an FK-space. Then the following statements are equivalent:

(i) (λ,T) is a wedge space.

(ii) $x^\times \subset \lambda$ for some $x \in c_0$.

(iii) λ contains a scarce copy $S(\ell^\infty,r)$ of ℓ^∞, and the identity map $I: (s(\ell^\infty,r),\|\cdot\|_\infty) \to (\lambda,T)$ is compact.

(iv) λ contains a scarce copy $S(m_0,r)$ of m_0, and the identity map $I: (s(m_0,r),\|\cdot\|_\infty) \to (\lambda,T)$ is compact.

(v) λ contains $\ell^\infty|s|$ for some s, and the identity map $I: (\ell^\infty|s|,\|\cdot\|_s) \to (\lambda,T)$ is compact.

(vi) $\ell^1 \subset \lambda$, and the identity map $I: (\ell^1,\|\cdot\|) \to (\lambda,T)$ is compact.

Proof. (i) $\Longrightarrow$ (ii) T is generated by $\{p_n\}$, say. Let $x^n \in c_0$ be defined by $x_i^n = p_n(e^i)$. Suppose

$$y \in \bigcap_{n\geq 1} \{x^n\}^\times \quad \Longrightarrow \quad \sum_{i\geq 1} |x_i^n y_i| < \infty \qquad \forall n \geq 1$$

Thus $\Sigma_{i\geq 1}\, p_n(y_i e^i) < \infty$ for every $n \geq 1$, and from Proposition 3.2.1, $\Sigma_{i\geq 1}\, y_i e^i$ converges in (λ,T) to, say z, or $y^{(n)} \to z$. Hence $y_i^{(n)} \to z_i$ for each $i \geq 1$; also, we always have $y_i^{(n)} \to y_i$ for each $i \geq 1$. Consequently $y = z$; that is

$$\bigcap_{n\geq 1} \{x^n\}^\times \subset \lambda$$

Choosing x as in Lemma 5.3, (ii) follows.

(ii) $\Longrightarrow$ (iii) Choose $x \in c_0$ with $x^\times \subset \lambda$. Let $i_0 = 0$ and $\{i_k : k \geq 1\}$ denote a strictly increasing sequence satisfying

$$|x_i| < \frac{1}{2^k} \qquad i \geq i_k;\ k \geq 1$$

Define $\{r_i\}$ by

$$r_i = k + 1 \qquad \text{for } i_k < i \leq i_{k+1},\ k = 0, 1, \ldots$$

Hence, for $y \in s(\ell^\infty,r)$,

$$\sum_{i=i_k+1}^{i_{k+1}} |y_i| \leq \sum_{i=1}^{i_{k+1}} |y_i| \leq C_{i_{k+1}}(y)\|y\|_\infty \leq (k + 1)\|y\|_\infty$$

and so

$$\sum_{i=i_k+1}^{i_{k+1}} |x_i y_i| \le \frac{k+1}{2^k} \|y\|_\infty \quad \Longrightarrow \quad y \in x^\times$$

Hence $s(\ell^\infty, r) \subset x^\times \subset \lambda$, giving $S(\ell^\infty, r) \subset x^\times \subset \lambda$. The space $x^\times$ is an FK-space under the topology S given by the set of seminorms

$$y \to |y_i| \qquad i \ge 1 \qquad \text{and} \qquad y \to \sum_{i\ge 1} |x_i y_i|$$

Let now $A \subset s(\ell^\infty, r)$ be such that $\|y\|_\infty \le M$ for all $y \in A$. For $i_k < n \le i_{k+1}$ and $y \in A$,

$$\sum_{i\ge n+1} |x_i y_i| \le \sum_{j\ge k} \sum_{i=i_j+1}^{i_{j+1}} |x_i y_i| \le M \sum_{j\ge k} \frac{j+1}{2^j}$$

Hence $y^{(n)} \to y$ in $(x^\times, S)$ uniformly on A. Since $x^\times \subset \lambda$, by Proposition 3.1,

$$y^{(n)} \to y \qquad \text{in T}$$

uniformly in $y \in A$. Applying Proposition 5.4 we find that A is T-relatively compact.

(iii) $\Longrightarrow$ (iv) This is immediate.

(iv) $\Longrightarrow$ (i) The set $A = \{e^n\}$ is a bounded subset of $(s(m_0, r), \|\cdot\|_\infty)$. Hence A is T-relatively compact in λ. Using Theorem 2.3.10, we find that $e^n \to 0$ in T, since $e_i^n \to 0$ for each $i \ge 1$ in the T-closure of A.

(ii) $\Longrightarrow$ (v) Let $x \in c_0$ be such that $x^\times \subset \lambda$. Assume $s_1 = 0$ and s_2, s_3, ..., strictly increasing so that

$$|x_i| < \frac{1}{2^k} \qquad i \ge s_k;\ k \ge 2$$

Let $y \in \ell^\infty|s|$. Suppose $m, n \in \mathbb{N}$, $m \le n$. Then

$$\sum_{i=s_m+1}^{s_{n+1}} |x_i y_i| \le \sum_{k=m}^{n} \frac{1}{2^k} \sum_{i=s_k+1}^{s_{k+1}} |y_i| \le \|y\|_s \sum_{k=m}^{n} \frac{1}{2^k}$$

$$\Longrightarrow \quad y \in x^\times \quad \Longrightarrow \quad \ell^\infty|s| \subset \lambda$$

For the rest of the part we proceed as in (ii) $\Longrightarrow$ (iii) above.

(v) $\Longrightarrow$ (vi) Since $\ell^1 \subset \ell^\infty|s|$ is always true, and by Proposition 3.1, the identity map from ℓ^1 into $\ell^\infty|s|$ is continuous, (vi) readily follows from (v).

(vi) $\Rightarrow$ (i) Proceed as in (iv) $\Rightarrow$ (i). □

Further restriction of (λ,T) in the preceding theorem leads to more equivalent conditions, as shown in

THEOREM 5.6 Let (λ,T) be a separable FK-space; then the following conditions are equivalent:

(i) (λ,T) is a wedge space.

(ii), (iii), (iv), (v), (vi) Same as in Theorem 5.5, (ii)-(vi).

(vii) λ contains $S(\ell^\infty,r)$ for some r.

(viii) λ contains $S(m_0,r)$ for some r.

(ix) $\ell^\infty|s| \subset \lambda$ for some s.

The following result is not only useful in the proof of this theorem but also provides a set of wedge spaces.

PROPOSITION 5.7 If λ is any of the spaces $\ell^\infty|s|$, $S(\ell^\infty,r)$, or $S(m_0,r)$, then $(\lambda,\tau(\lambda,\lambda^\times))$ is a wedge space.

Proof. Let $\lambda = \ell^\infty|s|$, where $0 = s_1 < s_2 < \cdots$. Suppose $(\lambda,\tau(\lambda,\lambda^\times))$ is not a wedge space. Then for some $\tau(\lambda,\lambda^\times)$-neighborhood V of zero and an increasing sequence $\{i_k\} \subset \mathbb{N}$,

$$e^{i_k} \notin V \qquad k \geq 1$$

By choosing a subsequence of $\{i_k\}$ if necessary, we may suppose $s_1 < i_1 \leq s_2 < i_2 \leq s_3 < \cdots$, that is, $i_k \in (s_k,s_{k+1}]$, $k \geq 1$. Let $x \in \omega$ be taken so that

$$x_i = \begin{cases} 1 & \text{if } i = i_k,\ k \geq 1 \\ 0 & \text{elsewhere} \end{cases}$$

Then $x \in \lambda$, $\|x\|_s = 1$. Since λ is normal, by Theorem 2.8.3,

$$\sum_{k\geq 1} e^{i_k} = x$$

where the convergence of the series is taken relative to $\tau(\lambda,\lambda^\times)$. Thus

$$e^{i_k} \in V$$

for all sufficiently large k. This contradiction proves the wedge character of $(\lambda,\tau(\lambda,\lambda^\times))$, $\lambda = \ell^\infty|s|$. Similarly we can prove that the other spaces are wedge spaces; in the case of $S(m_0,r)$ we apply Theorem 2.1 instead of Theorem 2.8.3. □

Proof of Theorem 5.6. In view of the foregoing theorem, it suffices to show that (vii) ⟹ (viii) ⟹ (ix) ⟹ (i). Since (vii) ⟹ (viii) is straightforward, we need only prove that (viii) ⟹ (ix) ⟹ (i). If we can show that (viii) ⟹ (i) and (ix) ⟹ (i), our result will follow.

(ix) ⟹ (i) For the sake of notational convenience, let us write $\mu = \ell^\infty|s| \subset \lambda$. It is obvious that μ is monotone and so $\mu^\times$ is $\sigma(\mu^\times,\mu)$-sequentially complete (cf. Proposition 2.2). The identity map I: $(\mu,\tau(\mu,\mu^\times)) \to (\lambda,T)$ clearly has closed graph (apply the K-property to both spaces), so that an application of Theorem 1.10.18 yields the continuity of I. Proposition 5.7 then proves (i). The result (viii) ⟹ (i) follows similarly. □

So far we have given examples of wedge spaces that are monotone spaces. For nonmonotone spaces we have

PROPOSITION 5.8 The space $(bs,\tau(bs,bv_0))$ is a wedge space.

Proof. We shall prove something more than what is required. Indeed, we show that $(\ell^\infty,\tau(\ell^\infty,\ell^1))$ is topologically isomorphic to $(bs,\tau(bs,bv_0))$ and deduce the required result. Consider the surjection F: $\omega \to \omega$ given by $F(x) = \{x_1, x_1 + x_2, x_1 + x_2 + x_3, \ldots\}$. Then $F^{-1}(x) = \{x_1, x_2 - x_1, x_3 - x_2, \ldots\}$. One readily verifies that F^{-1} maps ℓ^∞ onto bs. For an arbitrary y in bv_0, define $u \in \ell^1$ by $u_i = y_i - y_{i+1}$, $i \geq 1$. Hence for x in ℓ^∞,

$$\langle F^{-1}(x),y\rangle = \sum_{i\geq 1} (x_i - x_{i-1})y_i = \sum_{i\geq 1} (y_i - y_{i+1})x_i$$

$$= \sum_{i\geq 1} u_i x_i = \langle x,u\rangle$$

Thus F^{-1}: $(\ell^\infty,\sigma(\ell^\infty,\ell^1)) \to (bs,\sigma(bs,bv_0))$ is continuous and so F^{-1} is

$\tau(\ell^\infty,\ell^1)$-$\tau(bs,bv_0)$ continuous (cf. Proposition 1.12.3). Similarly we can prove that F: $(bs,\tau(bs,bv_0)) \to (\ell^\infty,\tau(\ell^\infty,\ell^1))$ is continuous. Now $F^{-1}(e - e^{(n)}) = e^{n+1}$, and since $e^{(n)} \to e$ in $\tau(\ell^\infty,\ell^1)$ by Theorem 2.8.3, $e^{n+1} \to 0$ in $\tau(bs,\tau(bs,bv_0))$. □

The above result yields

PROPOSITION 5.9 If (λ,T) is a separable FK-space with $bs \subset \lambda$, then (λ,T) is a wedge space.

Proof. The map F: $\ell^1 \to bv_0$ defined by

$$F(x) = \left\{ \sum_{i \geq n} x_i \right\}$$

is clearly a surjection. Let $x \in \ell^1$ and $y \in bs$ be arbitrarily chosen. Define $u \in \ell^\infty$ by $u_n = \Sigma_{i=1}^n y_i$. Then

$$\begin{aligned} \langle F(x),y\rangle &= y_1 \sum_{i\geq 1} x_i + \cdots + y_n \sum_{i\geq n} x_i + \cdots \\ &= y_1x_1 + (y_1 + y_2)x_2 + \cdots = \langle x,u\rangle \end{aligned}$$

Hence F is $\sigma(\ell^1,\ell^\infty)$-$\sigma(bv_0,bs)$ continuous. Similarly the map F^{-1}: $bv_0 \to \ell^1$, $F^{-1}(x) = \{x_1 - x_2, x_2 - x_3, \ldots\}$ is $\sigma(bv_0,bs)$-$\sigma(\ell^1,\ell^\infty)$ continuous. Making use of Proposition 2.5.3 for $\lambda = \ell^\infty$, we conclude that bv_0 is $\sigma(bv_0,bs)$-sequentially complete. The graph of the identity map I: $(bs,\tau(bs,bv_0)) \to (\lambda,T)$ is clearly closed, and so from Theorem 1.10.18, I is $\tau(bs,bv_0)$-T continuous. Finally, it remains only to apply Proposition 5.8 to get the required result. □

Concerning subsequence wedge spaces, we have

PROPOSITION 5.10 Let (λ,T) be a K-space such that $\lambda \subsetneq c_0$. If some $x \in \lambda \sim c_0$ has the AK property, then (λ,T) is a subsequence wedge space.

Proof. The sequence $\{x^{(n)}\}$ is Cauchy in (λ,T) and so for any T-continuous seminorm p on λ,

$$|x_n|p(e^n) = p(x^{(n)} - x^{(n-1)}) \to 0$$

as $n \to \infty$. Since $x \notin c_0$, there exists a subsequence $\{n_k\}$ such that $\inf\{|x_{n_k}| : k \geq 1\} > 0$. Therefore $e^{n_k} \not\to 0$ in T as $k \to \infty$. □

The rest of this subsection is independent of Ref. 15.

Having considered the notions of wedge and subsequence wedge spaces, one naturally would be interested in knowing those spaces which are not subsequence wedge spaces; for instance, consider the spaces c_0, ℓ^1, and ℓ_∞ endowed with their natural norms. Thus in the direction opposite to subsequence wedge spaces, we have

DEFINITION 5.11 Let λ be a sequence space equipped with a locally convex topology T. Then λ is called (i) a *regular space* if $\{e^n\}$ is T-regular; and (ii) a *weak regular space* if $\{e^n\}$ is $\sigma(\lambda,\lambda^*)$-regular.

The following is a special case of a more general result given in Ref. 115.

PROPOSITION 5.12 Let (λ,T) be a sequence space, T being a locally convex topology. Consider the statements:

(i) λ is T-regular.

(ii) Whenever $\Sigma_{i\geq 1} \alpha_i e^i$ converges in (λ,T), then $\alpha \in c_0$.

(iii) Whenever $\Sigma_{i\geq 1} \alpha_i e^i$ converges in (λ,T), then $\alpha \in \ell^\infty$.

Then (i) $\Rightarrow$ (ii) $\Rightarrow$ (iii). If (λ,T) is a Fréchet space, then conditions (i) through (iii) are equivalent.

Proof. (i) $\Rightarrow$ (ii) Suppose for some $\alpha \in \omega$,

$$T\text{-}\lim_{n\to\infty} \sum_{i=1}^{n} \alpha_i e^i = x \qquad x \in \lambda$$

and let $\alpha \notin c_0$. Hence there exists a subsequence $\{\alpha_{n_k}\}$ of α such that $\inf\{|\alpha_{n_k}| : k \geq 1\} > 0$. If p is any T-continuous seminorm on λ, then

$$|\alpha_n| p(e^n) = p\left(\sum_{i=1}^{n} \alpha_i e^i - \sum_{i=1}^{n-1} \alpha_i e^i\right) \to 0 \qquad \text{as } n \to \infty$$

$$\Rightarrow \quad |\alpha_{n_k}| p(e^{n_k}) \to 0 \qquad \text{as } k \to \infty$$

$$\Rightarrow \quad p(e^{n_k}) \to 0 \qquad \text{as } k \to \infty$$

As p is arbitrary, we find $e^{n_k} \to 0$ in T as $k \to \infty$. This contradiction proves (ii).

(ii) $\Longrightarrow$ (iii) Obvious.

(iii) $\Longrightarrow$ (i) We may suppose that T is generated by $\{p_k\}$ with $p_1 \le p_2 \le \cdots$. Assume (i) is not true. Then for each $k \ge 1$, we find an e^{n_k} such that

$$p_k(e^{n_k}) \le 2^{-2k}$$

Define $\alpha \in \omega$ by

$$\alpha_i = \begin{cases} 2^k & i = n_k,\ k \ge 1 \\ 0 & i \ne n_k,\ k \ge 1 \end{cases}$$

For any $j \ge 1$,

$$\sum_{i\ge1} p_j(\alpha_i e^i) = \sum_{k\ge1} p_j(\alpha_{n_k} e^{n_k}) < \infty$$

Therefore $\Sigma_{i\ge1}\, \alpha_i e^i$ converges absolutely relative to T. By Proposition 3.2.1, $\Sigma_{i\ge1}\, \alpha_i e^i$ converges in (λ,T). By (iii), $\alpha \in \ell^\infty$. However, this is not true and hence (i) follows. □

There is a simpler characterization of weak regular spaces when they are placed in duality with their Köthe duals.

PROPOSITION 5.13 The space $(\lambda,\tau(\lambda,\lambda^\times))$ is weak regular if and only if $\ell^\infty \subset \lambda^\times$.

Proof. If $\ell^\infty \subset \lambda^\times$, then $e \in \lambda^\times$. Observe that

$$e^n \notin \{x : x \in \lambda,\ q_e(x) < 1\} \qquad \forall n \ge 1$$

and so $\{e^n\}$ is $\sigma(\lambda,\lambda^\times)$-regular.

On the other hand, let $\{e^n\}$ be $\sigma(\lambda,\lambda^\times)$-regular. Choose $y \in \ell^\infty$ and $x \in \lambda$ arbitrarily. Now there exist $\varepsilon > 0$ and $u \in \lambda^\times$ such that $q_u(e^n) \ge \varepsilon$, $n \ge 1$. If $M = \sup_i |y_i|$, then

$$\sum_{i\ge1} |x_i y_i| \le \frac{M}{\varepsilon} \sum_{i\ge1} |x_i u_i| < \infty$$

and so $y \in \lambda^\times$. □

We close this subsection with the following three exercises on wedge spaces.

EXERCISE 5.14 An FK-space containing a wedge FK-space is a wedge space. A closed subspace, containing ϕ, of a wedge FK-space is a wedge FK-space. A countable intersection of wedge FK-spaces is a wedge FK-space. Verify these statements.

EXERCISE 5.15 Let $x \in \omega$. Then show that the space $x^{\times} = \{y \in \omega : \Sigma_{i\geq 1} |x_i y_i| < \infty\}$ when topologized by the seminorms

$$y \to |y_j| \qquad j \geq 1 \qquad \text{and} \qquad y \to \sum_{j\geq 1} |x_j y_j|$$

where $y \in x^{\times}$, is a wedge FK-space if and only if $x \in c_0$. Hence deduce that the intersection of all wedge FK-spaces and also of all weak wedge FK-spaces is ℓ^1.

EXERCISE 5.16 If λ is a wedge FK-space and μ is a separable FK-space such that $\lambda \cap \ell^{\infty} \subset \mu$, then μ is a wedge space.

Conull Spaces

Conull spaces were introduced by Snyder [238] to study matrix transformations; they are indeed special types of wedge spaces possessing the element e.

DEFINITION 5.17 A locally convex sequence space (λ, T) with $e \in \lambda$ is said to be *conull* (resp. *strongly conull*) provided $e \in W_\lambda$ (resp. $e \in S_\lambda$).

Clearly we have the following implication diagram:

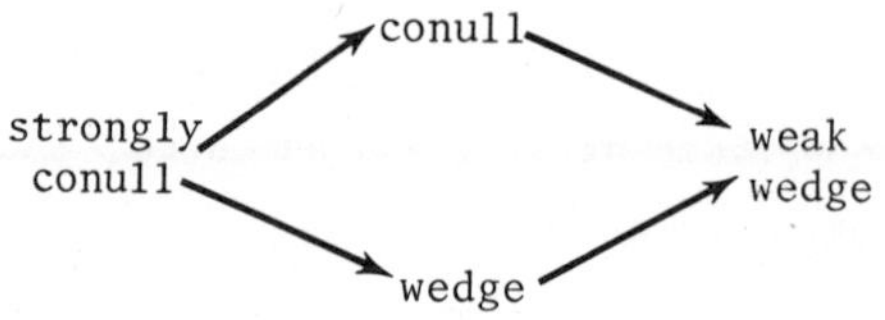

The following characterization of strongly conull spaces is due to Bennett [15].

THEOREM 5.18 Let (λ,T) be an FK-space. Then the following statements are equivalent, where F is the map defined in Proposition 5.8.

(i) (λ,T) is strongly conull.

(ii) $F[x^\times] = \{y \in \omega : \Sigma_{j\geq 1} |y_j - y_{j-1}||x_j| < \infty, y_0 = 0\} \subset \lambda$ for some $x \in c_0$.

(iii) $F[\ell^\infty|s|] = \{y \in \omega : \sup_n \Sigma_{i=s_n+1}^{s_{n+1}} |y_i - y_{i-1}| < \infty, y_0 = 0\} \subset \lambda$ for some s, and the identity map $I: (F[\ell^\infty|s|], \|\cdot\|^s) \to (\lambda,T)$ is compact, where for $y \in F(\ell^\infty|s|)$,

$$\|y\|^s = \sup_n \sum_{i=s_n+1}^{s_{n+1}} |y_i - y_{i-1}| \qquad y_0 = 0$$

(iv) $bv \subset \lambda$, and the identity map $I: (bv,\|\cdot\|) \to (\lambda,T)$ is compact.

Proof. (i) $\Rightarrow$ (ii) Consider the space $F^{-1}[\lambda]$ equipped with the FK-topology S given by the seminorms q_k, $q_k(y) = p_k(F(y))$, where $\{p_k\}$ is the generating sequence of seminorms for T. Observe that $q_k(e^{n+1}) = p_k(e - e^{(n)})$ and thus $(F^{-1}[\lambda],S)$ is a wedge space. By Theorem 5.5, (i) $\Rightarrow$ (ii), there exists $x \in c_0$ with $x^\times \subset F^{-1}[\lambda]$, that is, $F[x^\times] \subset \lambda$.

(ii) $\Rightarrow$ (iii) We have $x^\times \subset F^{-1}[\lambda]$ for some $x \in c_0$. As noted above, $F^{-1}[\lambda]$ is an FK-space under the topology S. Using Theorem 5.5, (ii) $\Rightarrow$ (v), we find that $\ell^\infty|s| \subset F^{-1}[\lambda]$ for some suitable s, and the identity map $I_s: (\ell^\infty|s|,\|\cdot\|_s) \to (F^{-1}[\lambda],S)$ is compact. Hence $F[\ell^\infty|s|] \subset \lambda$ and $I = F \circ I_s \circ F^{-1}$. If A is bounded in $F[\ell^\infty|s|]$, then $F^{-1}[A]$ is bounded in $\ell^\infty|s|$ and so $I_s[F^{-1}[A]]$ is relatively compact in $F^{-1}[\lambda]$. Observe that $F: F^{-1}[\lambda] \to \lambda$ is continuous [for y in $F^{-1}[\lambda]$, $q_k(y) = p_k(F(y))$] and this proves (iii).

(iii) $\Rightarrow$ (iv) Since $bv \subset F[\ell^\infty|s|]$, we get $bv \subset \lambda$. If A is bounded in bv, then $\|y\|^s < \infty$ uniformly in $y \in A$, that is, A is bounded in $F[\ell^\infty|s|]$. Now apply (iii).

(iv) $\Rightarrow$ (i) This follows as in Theorem 5.5, (iv) $\Rightarrow$ (i), replacing e^n by $e - e^{(n)}$, since $\{e - e^{(n)} : n \geq 1\}$ is bounded in bv. □

For conull FK-spaces, we have (Ref. 15)

THEOREM 5.19 An FK-space (λ,T) is conull if and only if $bv \subset \lambda$ and the identity map $I: (bv,\|\cdot\|) \to (\lambda,T)$ is weakly compact.

Proof. Consider the FK-space $(F^{-1}(\lambda),S)$ defined in the proof of Theorem 5.18, (i) $\Rightarrow$ (ii). It is easily verified that (λ,T) is conull if and only if $(F^{-1}(\lambda),S)$ is a weak wedge space [indeed, $F: (F^{-1}(\lambda),S) \to (\lambda,T)$ is a topological isomorphism, and therefore it is so relative to the weak topologies of $F^{-1}(\lambda)$ and λ, from Proposition 1.12.3]. Now the result follows by applying Theorem 5.2 to the space $(F^{-1}(\lambda),S)$. □

EXERCISE 5.20 Let (λ,S) and (μ,T) be FK-spaces with $\lambda \subset \mu$. Show that (i) if (λ,S) is conull, then (μ,T) is also conull and (ii) if (μ,T) is conull and λ is T-closed, then (λ,S) is conull. [Hint: Use the Hahn-Banach theorem; cf. Ref. 238 also.]

EXERCISE 5.21 Let (λ,T) be an FK-space with $c \subset \lambda$ (Snyder [238, p. 378] calls such spaces *conservative spaces*). If λ is $\sigma(\lambda,\lambda^*)$-sequentially complete, show that (λ,T) is conull. [Hint: Each $f \in \lambda^*$ is also in c^*; thus $\{f(e - e^{(n)})\}$ is Cauchy; cf. Ref. 238 also.]

EXERCISE 5.22 Prove that the intersection of all strongly conull FK-spaces (and also of all conull FK-spaces) is bv.

6. MATRIX TRANSFORMATIONS

Broadly speaking, researchers have followed two major directions in the study of matrix transformations. One of them is to obtain the precise form of an infinite matrix $A = [a_{ij}]$ which carries a sequence space λ into another sequence space μ. In other words, one can investigate necessary and sufficient conditions to be imposed on the a_{ij}'s so that $\lambda \subset \mu_A$. The other aspect of the study is to unfold various topological properties of the space μ_A, especially when $\mu = c$.

The purpose of this section is to provide at length some general theorems on the former aspect of the theory; our treatment of the second part will not be in such great detail.

Specific Transformations

It is not only natural but also advantageous to investigate the analytical forms of infinite matrices carrying one sequence space into another. One of the most important practical applications of these analytical forms is to signal theory, wherein various signals emanating from one source and converted into different signals by the receiver can be represented by matrices. Moreover, the precise forms of these matrix transformations are convenient tools in many offshoots of functional analysis. For instance, they have proved to be extremely useful for calculating diameters of different sets in the theory of approximative dimensions--a branch closely related to the theory of nuclear spaces (cf. Hutton [96]).

Transformations Related to Simple Sequence Spaces

There are several known theorems concerning the analytical forms of the matrices transforming one of the familiar sequence spaces (e.g., c, c_0, ℓ^p, ℓ^∞) into another; for example, one can look into Ref. 245 for several such classical results. As we have pointed out earlier, the spaces of analytic or entire sequences play a very prominent role in several branches of analysis and functional analysis; consequently a good deal of attention was directed to obtaining specific forms of infinite matrices converting one of the analytic spaces into another; see for instance, Refs. 22, 196, 197, 198, 55, 99, 255, 256, 257, 80, and numerous references cited therein. Quite recently, Jacob [100] discovered a common feature of these analytic spaces, namely the simple character of a sequence space (Chap. 2, Sec. 5) responsible for these previously known matrix transformations. This particular property helped him establish a unified theory of matrix transformations acting on such spaces, which includes some of the results on matrix transformations cited at the beginning of this paragraph.

Unless stated otherwise, we follow Ref. 100 for the rest of this subsection. We write (λ,μ) for the *collection of all matrix transformations* $A: \lambda \to \mu$. Let us begin with

THEOREM 6.1 Let λ be a normal simple sequence space and A an infinite matrix. Then the following statements are equivalent:

(i) A is in $(\lambda^\times,\ell^\infty)$.

(ii) $A^\perp$ is in (ℓ^1,λ).

(iii) $\{a^i\} \subset \lambda$ and is $\sigma(\lambda,\lambda^\times)$-bounded, where $a^i = \{a_{ij} : j \geq 1\}$, the ith row of A.

(iv) $|a_{ij}| \leq y_j$ for all $i \geq 1$ and $j \geq 1$, where $y = \{y_j\} \in \lambda$.

Proof. Let us observe that λ is perfect (cf. Exercise 2.5.12) and hence (i) and (ii) are equivalent, by Proposition 3.3. If (ii) holds, then for each $n \geq 1$, $(A^{\perp}(e^n))_j = \Sigma_{i\geq 1} a_{ji}e_i^n = a_{jn}$ and so $\{a_{ij} : j \geq 1\} \in \lambda$ for each $i \geq 1$. If $u \in \lambda^{\times}$ then for some $M > 0$,

$$\sup_i |(Au)_i| \leq M$$

$$\Longrightarrow \left|\sum_{j\geq 1} a_{ij}u_j\right| \leq M \qquad \forall i \geq 1$$

$$\Longrightarrow q_u(a^i) \leq M \qquad \forall i \geq 1$$

Hence (iii) follows. Since λ is simple and normal, (iii) clearly implies (iv). Finally, suppose (iv) is true. Let $u \in \lambda^{\times}$ and suppose

$$M = \sum_{j\geq 1} |y_j u_j|$$

Then for each $i \geq 1$,

$$\sum_{j\geq 1} |a_{ij}u_j| \leq M$$

and so $A(u)$ exists; moreover $|(A(u))_i| \leq M$ for each $i \geq 1$, i.e., $A(u) \in \ell^{\infty}$. Thus (iv) $\Longrightarrow$ (i). □

As a corollary we derive the following result proved earlier by Rao [197, p. 166], Hahn [85, p. 7], and Tonne [255, p. 667].

PROPOSITION 6.2 Let $0 \leq r < \infty$ and $A = [a_{ij}]$ be an infinite matrix. Then the following statements are equivalent:

(i) A is in $(\Pi_{1/r}, \ell^{\infty})$.

(ii) $A^{\perp}$ is in (ℓ^1, d_r).

(iii) There exist numbers R and α with $0 < R < 1/r$, $\alpha > 0$, such that $|a_{ij}| \leq \alpha R^j$ for all $i,j \geq 1$.

Proof. By Exercises 2.2.10 (ii) and 2.6.28, the space d_r is perfect and simple. For the remaining arguments apply Theorem 6.1(i)-(iii) and Proposition 2.6.27. □

THEOREM 6.3 Let λ be a normal simple sequence space and $A = [a_{ij}]$ an infinite matrix. Then the following statements are equivalent:

(i) A is in $(\lambda^{\times}, c)$.

(ii) The sequence $\{a^i\} \in \lambda$ and is $\sigma(\lambda, \lambda^{\times})$-convergent in λ.

(iii) $\{a_{ij} : i \geq 1\} \in c$ for each $j \geq 1$, and there is a $y = \{y_j\} \in \lambda$ such that $|a_{ij}| \leq y_j$, $i,j \geq 1$.

Proof. (i) $\Rightarrow$ (ii) By Proposition 3.3(i), $A^{\perp} \in (c^{\times},\lambda)$. Hence $\{(A^{\perp}(e^n))_j\} = \{a_{jn} : j \geq 1\} \in \lambda$, or $a^i \in \lambda$, $a^i = \{a_{ij} : j \geq 1\}$. If $u \in \lambda^{\times}$, then by (i), $\{(A(u))_i\} \in c$; that is,

$$\sup_i \left|\sum_{j\geq 1} a_{ij}u_j\right| < \infty$$

and so $\{a^i\}$ is $\sigma(\lambda,\lambda^{\times})$-bounded. Now $\{a_{ij} : i \geq 1\} \in c$ for each $j \geq 1$, and so $\{a^i\}$ is coordinatewise convergent. Using Theorem 2.5.10, we get the $\sigma(\lambda,\lambda^{\times})$-convergence of $\{a^i\}$.

(ii) $\Rightarrow$ (iii) Since $e^j \in \lambda^{\times}$,

$$\langle a^i,e^j\rangle \xrightarrow{i} \langle a,e^j\rangle \qquad \forall j \geq 1$$

$$\Rightarrow \quad a_{ij} \xrightarrow{i} a_j \qquad \forall j \geq 1$$

where $a \in \lambda$ and is the $\sigma(\lambda,\lambda^{\times})$-limit of $\{a^i\}$. Hence $\{a_{ij} : i \geq 1\} \in c$ for every $j \geq 1$. Further, $\{a^i\}$ is $\sigma(\lambda,\lambda^{\times})$-bounded in λ, and since λ is simple, we get the last part of (iii).

(iii) $\Rightarrow$ (i) Let $u \in \lambda^{\times}$ and $\varepsilon > 0$. There exists J in $\mathbb{N}$ such that

$$\sum_{j\geq J+1} |y_j u_j| < \frac{\varepsilon}{4}$$

Also, for each $i \geq 1$,

$$\sum_{j\geq 1} |a_{ij}u_j| \leq \sum_{j\geq 1} |y_j u_j| < \infty$$

and so for $i \geq 1$,

$$(A(u))_i = \sum_{j\geq 1} a_{ij}u_j$$

exists. Since $\{a_{ij} : i \geq 1\} \in c$ for each $j \geq 1$, we can find an $N \equiv N(J,\varepsilon)$ such that

$$\left|\sum_{j=1}^{J} (a_{mj} - a_{nj})u_j\right| < \frac{\varepsilon}{2} \qquad \forall m,n \geq N$$

Therefore

$$\left|\sum_{j\geq 1} (a_{mj} - a_{nj})u_j\right| < \frac{\varepsilon}{2} + 2 \sum_{j\geq J+1} |u_j y_j| < \varepsilon \qquad \forall m,n \geq N$$

thereby forcing $\{(\Sigma_{j\geq 1} a_{ij}u_j)_i\}$ to be Cauchy in $\mathbb{K}$. Hence (i) follows.

As a corollary of Theorem 6.3, we get the following result proved in Ref. 196, Theorem III, p. 172 and Ref. 255, Theorem 2, p. 667.

PROPOSITION 6.4 Let $0 \leq r < \infty$ and $A = [a_{ij}]$ be an infinite matrix. Then the following statements are equivalent:

(i) A is in $(\Pi_{1/r}, c)$.

(ii) $\{a_{ij} : i \geq 1\} \in c$ for $j \geq 1$ and there exist numbers R and α with $0 < R < 1/r$, $\alpha > 0$, such that $|a_{ij}| \leq \alpha R^j$ for all $i,j \geq 1$.

Proof. Let $\lambda = d_r$ in the preceding theorem, (i) $\Longleftrightarrow$ (iii), and proceed as in Proposition 6.3. □

PROPOSITION 6.5 Let λ be a normal simple sequence space and $A = [a_{ij}]$ an infinite matrix. Then the following are equivalent:

(i) A is in $(\lambda^\times, c_0)$.

(ii) $a^i \in \lambda$ for $i \geq 1$ and $a^i \to 0$ in $\sigma(\lambda,\lambda^\times)$, where $a^i = \{a_{ij} : j \geq 1\}$.

(iii) $\{a_{ij} : i \geq 1\} \in c_0$ for $j \geq 1$ and there is a $y = \{y_j\} \in \lambda$ such that $|a_{ij}| \leq y_j$ for all $i,j \geq 1$.

Proof. (i) $\Longrightarrow$ (ii) Following the proof of Theorem 6.3, (i) $\Longrightarrow$ (ii), we find that $a^i \in \lambda$ and $\{a_{ij} : i \geq 1\} \in c_0$ for $j \geq 1$; moreover $\{a^i\}$ is $\sigma(\lambda,\lambda^\times)$-convergent. Necessarily this limit has to be zero ($a^i_j \to 0$ as $i \to \infty$ for each $j \geq 1$).

For the other parts we follow the corresponding implications of Theorem 6.3. □

Next we have

THEOREM 6.6 Let λ and μ be two normal sequence spaces. Assume μ to be simple also. If $A = [a_{ij}]$ is an infinite matrix, then the following statements are equivalent:

(i) A is in (λ, μ).

(ii) $A^\perp$ is in $(\mu^\times, \lambda^\times)$.

(iii) For each $x \in \lambda$, there exists $y \in \mu$ such that

$$\sum_{j\geq 1} |a_{ij}x_j| \leq y_i \qquad \forall i \geq 1$$

Proof. Observe that μ is perfect by Exercise 2.5.12, and hence Proposition 3.3 immediately yields the equivalence of (i) and (ii). To complete the proof we need establish (i) $\Longrightarrow$ (iii) and (iii) $\Longrightarrow$ (i).

(i) $\Longrightarrow$ (iii) Let $x \in \lambda$ and consider

$$K_x = \{u : u \in \omega, \ |u_i| = |x_i|, \ i \geq 1\}$$

Then $K_x \subset \{x\}^N$, and so by Exercise 2.8.23, K_x is $\sigma(\lambda,\lambda^\times)$-bounded. From Proposition 3.2, $A[K_x]$ is $\sigma(\mu,\mu^\times)$-bounded. By virtue of the fact that μ is normal and simple, we can choose a $y \in \mu$ such that

$$\Big|\sum_{j\geq 1} a_{ij}u_j\Big| \leq y_i \qquad \forall i \geq 1 \text{ and } u \in K_x \tag{*}$$

For any given $u \in K_x$, choose $\{\alpha_j^i\} \subset \mathbb{K}$ such that $|\alpha_j^i| = 1$ for each $j \geq 1$ and $\alpha_j^i a_{ij}u_j = |a_{ij}u_j|$, $j \geq 1$. Since $\{\alpha_j^i u_j\} \in K_x$, by (*) we have

$$\sum_{j\geq 1} |a_{ij}u_j| = \Big|\sum_{j\geq 1} a_{ij}\alpha_j^i u_j\Big| \leq y_i$$

and we are through with (iii).

(iii) $\Longrightarrow$ (i) Let $x \in \lambda$. Then

$$|(A(x))_i| \leq y_i \qquad \forall i \geq 1$$

Since $y \in \mu$, μ being normal, $\{(A(x))_i\} \in \mu$. □

Theorem 6.6 leads to the following results, the second and third having been proved in Ref. 255, p. 667, and in Ref. 22, p. 36, respectively.

PROPOSITION 6.7 Let λ be a normal simple sequence space and $A = [a_{ij}]$ an infinite matrix; then (i) $\Longleftrightarrow$ (ii) $\Longleftrightarrow$ (iii) where

(i) $A \in (\lambda^\times, \ell^1)$.

(ii) $A^{\perp} \in (\ell^\infty, \lambda)$.

(iii) There exists $y \in \lambda$ such that

$$\sum_{i\geq 1} |a_{ij}| \leq y_j \qquad \forall j \geq 1$$

Proof. As shown in Theorem 6.5, we have the equivalence of (i) and (ii).

(ii) $\Longrightarrow$ (iii) Since $e \in \ell^\infty$, we follow the proof of Theorem 6.6, (ii) $\Longrightarrow$ (iii), with the roles of i and j interchanged.

(iii) $\Longrightarrow$ (i) Let $x \in \lambda^\times$. Choose a $y \in \lambda$ satisfying the inequality in (iii). Then

$$\sum_{i\geq 1} |(A(x))_i| \leq \sum_{i\geq 1} \sum_{j\geq 1} |a_{ij}||x_j|$$

$$= \sum_{j\geq 1} \sum_{i\geq 1} |a_{ij}||x_j| < \infty$$

where we have followed the usual laws for change of limits in double infinite series; see, for instance, Ref. 220, p. 143. □

PROPOSITION 6.8 Suppose $0 \leq r < \infty$ and $A = [a_{ij}]$ is an infinite matrix. Then the following are equivalent:

(i) $A \in (\Pi_{1/r}, \ell^1)$.

(ii) There exist numbers R and α with $0 < R < 1/r$, $\alpha > 0$, such that

$$\sum_{i\geq 1} |a_{ij}| \leq \alpha R^j \qquad \forall j \geq 1$$

Proof. Let $\lambda = d_r$ in Proposition 6.7, (i) $\Longleftrightarrow$ (iii), and observe that $\{\alpha R^j\} \in \lambda$. □

PROPOSITION 6.9 Suppose $0 \leq r < \infty$ and $0 \leq s < \infty$, and $A = [a_{ij}]$ is an infinite matrix. Then the following are equivalent:

(i) $A \in (\Pi_{1/r}, \Pi_{1/s})$.

(ii) $A^\perp \in (d_s, d_r)$.

(iii) For each α with $0 < \alpha < 1/s$, there exist β and R such that $0 < R < 1/r$, $\beta > 0$, and

$$\sum_{i\geq 1} |a_{ij}|\alpha^i \leq \beta R^j \qquad \forall j \geq 1$$

Proof. In view of Proposition 3.3, it is sufficient to establish (ii) $\Longleftrightarrow$ (iii).

(ii) $\Longrightarrow$ (iii) By Theorem 6.6, (i) $\Longrightarrow$ (iii), to each $x \in d_s$ there exists $y \in d_r$ such that

$$\sum_{i\geq 1} |a_{ij}x_i| \leq y_j \qquad \forall j \geq 1$$

In particular, choosing $x_i = \alpha^i$ $(0 < \alpha < 1/s)$ we find that

$$\sum_{i\geq 1} |a_{ij}|\alpha^i \leq y_j \qquad \forall j \geq 1$$

Since $y \in d_r$, there exist $\beta > 0$ and R with $0 < R < 1/r$ such that $y_j \leq \beta R^j$, $j \geq 1$. Hence (iii) follows.

(iii) $\Longrightarrow$ (ii) Suppose $x \in d_s$. Then for some $k > 0$ and α with $0 < \alpha < 1/s$, $|x_i| \leq k\alpha^i$ for $i \geq 1$. Hence

$$\sum_{i\geq 1} |a_{ij}||x_j| \leq k\beta R^j \qquad \forall j \geq 1$$

Consequently $A^{\perp}(x) \in d_r$. □

An immediate application of Proposition 6.6 is the following result given in Ref. 135, p. 11.

PROPOSITION 6.10 Let $A = [a_{ij}]$ be an infinite matrix. Then $A \in (\ell^1, \ell^1)$ if and only if there exists $M > 0$ such that

$$\sup_{j\geq 1} \sum_{i\geq 1} |a_{ij}| \leq M$$

Proof. Put $\lambda = \ell^{\infty}$ in Proposition 6.7. □

Further Remarks on Analytic Sequence Spaces

Let us note that condition (ii) of Proposition 6.4 can be stated equivalently as

PROPOSITION 6.11 There is R, $0 < R < 1/r$, such that A is a continuous matrix transformation from $(\Pi_{1/r}, p_R)$ to $(c, \|\cdot\|)$, where

$$p_R(x) = \sum_{j\geq 1} |x_j|R^n \qquad x \in \Pi_{1/r}$$

Proof. Indeed, if $x \in \Pi_{1/r}$, then by Proposition 6.4(ii),

$$|(A(x))_i| \leq \sum_{j\geq 1} |a_{ij}||x_j| \leq \alpha \sum_{j\geq 1} |x_j||R^j| < \infty$$

$$\Longrightarrow \quad \|A(x)\| \leq \alpha p_R(x) \qquad \forall x \text{ in } \Pi_{1/r} \tag{*}$$

and so Proposition 6.11 follows. Assume now that Proposition 6.11 is true. Then clearly $\{a_{ij} : i \geq 1\} \in c$ for each $j \geq 1$. Moreover, the given continuity of A implies a relation of the form (*) for some $\alpha > 0$ and an R with $0 < R < 1/r$. Putting $x = e^n$ in (*) we get

$$|(A(e^n))_i| \leq \alpha R^n \qquad \forall i \geq 1,\ n \geq 1$$

or

$$|a_{ij}| \leq \alpha R^j \qquad \forall i,j \geq 1$$

and so we get (ii) of Proposition 6.4. □

Similarly we can show that Proposition 6.11 with c replaced by ℓ^∞ is equivalent to (iii) of Proposition 6.2.

The foregoing discussion thus completes the proof of the following result, which incidentally also covers Theorem 2 [equivalence of (1), (2), and (4)] of Tonne [256, p. 386].

PROPOSITION 6.12 Let $0 \leq r < \infty$ and $A = [a_{ij}]$ be an infinite matrix. Then the following statements are equivalent:

(i) $A \in (\Pi_{1/r}, c)$ [resp. $(\Pi_{1/r}, \ell^\infty)$].

(ii) If $x^n \to 0$ in $\Pi_{1/r}$ then $A(x^n) \to 0$ in c (resp. ℓ^∞).

(iii) There is R, $0 < R < 1/r$, such that A is a continuous matrix transformation from $(\Pi_{1/r}, p_R)$ to $(c, \|\cdot\|)$ [resp. $(\ell^\infty, \|\cdot\|)$].

Note: Let us remind the reader that $\Pi_{1/r}$ is equipped with its natural locally convex topology T generated by the family of seminorms $\{p_R : 0 < R < 1/r\}$. It is well known that $(\Pi_{1/r}, T)$ is a Fréchet space (see for instance Refs. 10 and 126).

Next we note that condition (iii) of Proposition 6.8 can be restated as

PROPOSITION 6.13 For each α with $0 < \alpha < 1/s$ there exist $\beta > 0$ and R, $0 < R < 1/r$, such that

$$p_\alpha(A(x)) \leq \beta p_R(x) \qquad \forall x \in \Pi_{1/r}$$

Proof. Indeed, (iii) of Proposition 6.9 implies that $A(x) \in \Pi_{1/s}$ for each $x \in \Pi_{1/r}$; moreover

$$p_\alpha(A(x)) = \sum_{i\geq 1} |(A(x))_i|\alpha^i \leq \sum_{i\geq 1}\left(\sum_{j\geq 1} |a_{ij}||x_j|\right)\alpha^i$$

$$= \sum_{j\geq 1}\left(\sum_{i\geq 1} |a_{ij}|\alpha^i\right)|x_j| \leq \beta p_R(x)$$

and so Proposition 6.13 follows. We can now easily dispose of the other implication as well. □

We have thus proved the following result, which also includes Theorem 1 of Ref. 256.

PROPOSITION 6.14 Let $0 \leq r < \infty$, $0 \leq s < \infty$, and $A = [a_{ij}]$ be an infinite matrix. Then the following are equivalent:

(i) $A \in (\Pi_{1/r}, \Pi_{1/s})$.
(ii) If $x^n \to 0$ in $\Pi_{1/r}$ then $A(x^n) \to 0$ in $\Pi_{1/s}$.
(iii) For each α with $0 < \alpha < 1/s$, there exist $\beta > 0$ and R, $0 < R < 1/r$, such that A is a continuous matrix transformation from $(\Pi_{1/r}, p_R)$ to $(\Pi_{1/s}, p_\alpha)$.

Note: Let us note that since $(\Pi_{1/r}, T)$ is an AK-FK space which is also monotone, it follows from Proposition 2.3.2 that $\lambda^\times = \lambda^*$. Consequently, Proposition 6.12 (resp. Proposition 6.14) follows by combining Proposition 3.2, Proposition 1.13.3, and Proposition 6.4 (resp. Proposition 6.8).

Dual of an Entire Sequence Space

Let us now turn our attention to matrix transformations from the space d (dual of δ) into itself. Heller [88] was the first to give a characterization of such transformations; subsequently Raphael [200] gave an alternative proof of this result. Later on, Tonne [257] found a number of conditions equivalent to the aforementioned characterization due to Heller. The next result, which we derive with the help of Theorem 6.5, includes the characterization of an infinite matrix mapping d into itself mentioned above. We first require some terminology. For $p > 0$, let X_p denote the subspace of d consisting of those $x \in d$ for which $\|x\|_p \equiv \sup\{p^n|x_n| : n \geq 1\} < \infty$; observe that $e^n \in X_p$ for each $n \geq 1$ and $p > 0$, and moreover,

X_p is a BK-space (Ref. 200, p. 123). Now we have the desired

PROPOSITION 6.15 Let $A = [a_{ij}]$ be an infinite matrix; then the following statements are equivalent:

(i) $A \in (d,d)$.

(ii) $A^{\perp} \in (\delta,\delta)$.

(iii) For every $x \in d$, there exists $y \in d$ such that

$$\sum_{j\geq 1} |a_{ij}||x_j| \leq y_i \qquad \forall i \geq 1$$

(iv) For every $x \in d$, there exists $y \in d$ such that

$$|a_{ij}||x_j| \leq y_i \qquad \text{for } i,j \geq 1$$

(v) For every $\alpha > 0$, there exists $\beta > 0$ such that

$$|a_{ij}| \leq \frac{\alpha^j}{\beta^i} \qquad \forall i,j \geq 1$$

(vi) For every $p > 0$, there exists $q > 0$ such that $A(x) \in X_q$ for all x in X_p, and $\|A(x)\|_q \leq M\|x\|_p$ where $M > 0$ and depends upon p.

Proof. (i) $\Longleftrightarrow$ (ii) Obvious.

(ii) $\Longrightarrow$ (iii) This follows from Theorem 6.6.

(iii) $\Longrightarrow$ (iv) This is immediate.

(iv) $\Longrightarrow$ (v) For given α, define $x \in d$ by $x_i = \alpha^{-i}$. Hence there is a $y \in d$ such that

$$|a_{ij}| \leq \frac{\alpha^j}{\beta^i} \qquad \forall i,j \geq 1$$

where $1/\beta = \sup\{y_i^{1/i}\}$.

(v) $\Longrightarrow$ (i) Let $x \in d$. Hence for some $\gamma > 0$, $|x_i| \leq \gamma^i$, $i \geq 1$. Choose $\alpha > 0$ with $\alpha\gamma < 1$. By (v) there corresponds $\beta > 0$ such that

$$|a_{ij}| \leq \frac{\alpha^j}{\beta^i} \qquad \forall i,j \geq 1$$

Hence

$$|(A(x))_i| \leq \sum_{j\geq 1} \frac{\alpha^j}{\beta^i} \gamma^j = \frac{\alpha\gamma}{1 - \alpha\gamma} \frac{1}{\beta^i} \qquad \forall i \geq 1$$

which implies that $A(x) \in d$.

(v) $\Longrightarrow$ (vi) Let $p > 0$ be chosen arbitrarily and let $x \in X_p$. Then

$$\|x\|_p = \sup_j \{p^j |x_j|\} < \infty$$

Choose $\alpha > 0$ such that $\alpha/p < 1$. In view of (v) we can select a $q > 0$ so that $|a_{ij}| \le \alpha^j/q^i$ for all $i,j \ge 1$. Thus

$$|(A(x))_i| \le \|x\|_p \sum_{j\ge 1} \left(\frac{\alpha}{p}\right)^j \frac{1}{q^i} = \frac{M\|x\|_p}{q^i} \qquad M = \frac{\alpha}{p-\alpha}$$

$$\Longrightarrow \quad \|A(x)\|_q \le M\|x\|_p$$

(vi) $\Longrightarrow$ (v) Put $x = e^j$ in (vi). Then

$$\sup_i\{|(A(e^j))_i|q^i\} \le M \sup_n\{p^n e^j_j\} \qquad \forall j \ge 1$$

or

$$|a_{ij}|q^i \le Mp^j \qquad \forall i,j \ge 1$$

and so (v) follows. □

Transformations Related to FK-spaces

In this subsection we consider only those matrix transformations $A\colon \lambda \to \mu$, where λ is one of the familiar sequence spaces $(\ell^1, bv_0, bv, \ell^\infty)$ and μ is an FK-space which is not necessarily simple. Let us begin with the following result due to Bennett [14, p. 19].

THEOREM 6.16 Let $A = [a_{ij}]$ be an infinite matrix and (λ,T) an FK-space. Then the following two conditions are equivalent:

(i) $A \in (\ell^1,\lambda)$.

(ii) $a^j \equiv \{a_{ij} : i \ge 1\} \in \lambda$ for $j \ge 1$, and $\{a^j\}$ is T-bounded.

Proof. (i) $\Longrightarrow$ (ii) We have $\ell^1 \subset \lambda_A$ and therefore $\{e^n\}$ is bounded in λ_A, by Proposition 3.28. From Theorem 3.7, the set $\{A(e^n) : n \ge 1\}$ is T-bounded and this implies (ii).

(ii) $\Longrightarrow$ (i) In view of Proposition 3.28, it suffices to show that $\{e^n\}$ is bounded in λ_A relative to the topology mentioned in Theorem 3.7. Since λ is a K-space, for each $i \ge 1$ there exists $K_i > 0$ such that

$$q_i(e^n) = |a_{in}| \le K_i \qquad \forall n \ge 1$$

Further, for each $i \geq 1$ there exists $M_i > 0$ such that

$$(r_i \circ A)(e^j) = r_i(a^j) \leq M_i \qquad \forall j \geq 1$$

Consequently $\{e^j\}$ is bounded in λ_A. □

Remark: In case $\lambda = c$ or ℓ^p $(1 \leq p \leq \infty)$ the above theorem provides results proved earlier by Hahn [85], Cohen and Dunford [30], and Knopp and Lorentz [135].

Note: If $\lambda = \ell^p$, Sargent [224, Theorem 2] obtained Theorem 6.16 by replacing ℓ^1 by the BK-space $n(\phi)$, a space closely related to ℓ^1. We might like to know if Theorem 6.16 remains valid in general when ℓ^1 is replaced by $n(\phi)$.

The next result, which includes Theorem XI of Ref. 85 and Theorem 1 of Ref. 171, is again due to Bennett [14, p. 20].

THEOREM 6.17 Let (λ,T) be an FK-space and $A = [a_{ij}]$ an infinite matrix. Then the following two statements are equivalent:

(i) $A \in (bv_0,\lambda)$.

(ii) $a^j \equiv \{a_{ij} : i \geq 1\} \in \lambda$ for $j \geq 1$, and $\{\Sigma_{j=1}^n a^j\}$ is T-bounded.

Proof. (i) $\Longrightarrow$ (ii) We have $bv_0 \subset \lambda_A$ and so from Proposition 3.29 and Theorem 3.7, $\{A(e^{(n)})\}$ is T-bounded. Since $A(e^{(n)}) = \Sigma_{j=1}^n a^j$, (ii) is thus proved.

(ii) $\Longrightarrow$ (i) On account of Proposition 3.29, it is sufficient to prove that $\{e^{(n)}\}$ is bounded in λ_A (cf. Theorem 3.7 for the topology on λ_A and other relevant notions). Since λ is a K-space, there exists $N_i > 0$ for each $i \geq 1$ such that

$$\sup_{p\geq 1}\left|\sum_{j=1}^{p} a_{ij}\right| \leq N_i$$

$$\Longrightarrow \quad q_i(e^{(n)}) = \sup_{1\leq m\leq n}\left|\sum_{j=1}^{m} a_{ij}\right| \leq N_i$$

for all $n \geq 1$. Also,

$$\sup_{n\geq 1} (r_i \circ A)(e^{(n)}) = \sup_{n\geq 1} r_i\left(\sum_{j=1}^{n} a^j\right) < \infty$$

for each $i \geq 1$. Hence (i) follows. □

Finally we give a result characterizing an infinite matrix carrying ℓ^∞ into ℓ^p $(1 \leq p \leq \infty)$. This result, which makes use of sophisticated tools from the theory of sequence spaces and improves upon earlier results of Lorentz [106, Lemma 1], Mehdi [172] (see also Ref. 224, Theorem D), Peyerimhoff [186, Theorem 1], and Zeller [271, p. 344], is due to Bennett and Kalton [18, p. 520].

THEOREM 6.18 Let $1 \leq p \leq \infty$ and $A = [a_{ij}]$ be an infinite matrix. Then the following statements are equivalent:

(i) $A \in (\ell^\infty, \ell^p)$.

(ii) $\sup_{J\subset \mathbb{N}} \Sigma_{i\geq 1} |\Sigma_{j\in J} a_{ij}|^p < \infty$.

(iii) $\Sigma_{i\geq 1} |\Sigma_{j\in J} a_{ij}|^p < \infty$ for each $J \subset \mathbb{N}$.

Proof. (i) $\Longrightarrow$ (ii) We have $\ell^\infty \subset \ell^p_A$. By Theorem 3.7, the map $A: \ell^p_A \to \ell^p$ is continuous. Hence by Proposition 3.1, the map $A: \ell^\infty \to \ell^p$ is continuous. If S is the set of all sequences whose coordinates are zeros and/or ones, then S is bounded in ℓ^∞, and so

$$\sup\{\|A(x)\|_p : x \in S\} < \infty$$

For any $J \subset \mathbb{N}$, the sequence $x = \{x_j\}$ defined by

$$x_j = \begin{cases} 1 & j \in J \\ 0 & j \notin J \end{cases}$$

is in S, and so

$$(A(x))_i = \sum_{j\in J} a_{ij}$$

Therefore (ii) follows.

(ii) $\Longrightarrow$ (iii) Obvious.

(iii) $\Longrightarrow$ (i) Let $x \in m_0$. Then we can find disjoint subsets J_r $(1 \leq r \leq n)$ and a finite set $\{\alpha_1, \ldots, \alpha_n\}$ of scalars such that $x_j = \alpha_r$, $j \in J_r$ $(1 \leq r \leq n)$. Therefore, using (iii), we have

$$\sum_{i\geq 1} |(A(x))_i|^p = \sum_{i\geq 1} \left|\sum_{j\geq 1} a_{ij}x_j\right|^p$$

$$= \sum_{i\geq 1} \left|\sum_{r=1}^{n} \sum_{j\in J_r} a_{ij}x_j\right|^p < \infty$$

$$\Longrightarrow \quad A(x) \in \ell^p \quad \Longrightarrow \quad x \in \ell^p_A$$

Hence $m_0 \subset \ell^p_A$. By Theorem 6.27, ℓ^p_A is separable, and consequently Proposition 3.34 implies that $\ell^\infty \subset \ell^p_A$, that is, $A \in (\ell^\infty, \ell^p)$. □

Note: For other results on the characterization of matrix transformations, see Section 7.

Diagonal Transformations

If $A = [a_{ij}]$ is any infinite matrix, then we write D_A for $[a_{ij}]$ with $a_{ij} = 0$ for $i \neq j$; thus $D_A = [\delta_{ij}a_{ij}]$. From any sequence $x = \{x_i\}$ we can construct an infinite matrix D_x defined by $[a_{ij}]$ where $a_{ii} = x_i$, $i \geq 1$, and $a_{ij} = 0$ when $i \neq j$; in other words, $D_x = [\delta_{ij}x_i]$. If $x \in \omega$ and A is an infinite matrix, we use the symbol xA to mean D_xA. Thus $D_xA = [x_ia_{ij}]$. Similarly $Ay = [a_{ij}y_j]$.

To begin with we consider the following problem. If $A = [a_{ij}]$ takes a sequence space λ into another sequence space μ, then where does D_A take λ? This problem was motivated by the following result of Peyerimhoff [186, Corollary (a)] and Pelczynski and Szlenk [184, Corollary 1], which runs as follows:

PROPOSITION 6.19 If A is an infinite matrix $[a_{ij}]$ with $A \in (\ell^\infty, \ell^1)$, then $D_A \in (\ell^\infty, \ell^1)$.

Proof. We need equivalently prove that

$$\sum_{i\geq 1} |a_{ii}| < \infty$$

since

$$\sum_{i\geq 1} |(D_A(x))_i| = \sum_{i\geq 1} |a_{ii}||x_i| \qquad x \in \ell^\infty$$

As proved in Theorem 6.18, (i) $\Rightarrow$ (ii), the map $A: \ell^\infty \to \ell^1$ is continuous. If B is the set of all sequences formed by 0, 1, and -1, then B is a bounded subset of ℓ^∞ and therefore we can find a constant $K > 0$ such that

$$\sup\left\{\sum_{i\geq 1}\left|\sum_{j\geq 1} a_{ij}x_j\right| : x \in B\right\} \leq K$$

Define *Rademacher functions* on [0,1] as follows (Refs. 63, 190, 236).

$$r_j(t) = \text{sign } \sin 2^j \pi t \qquad j \geq 1,\ t \in [0,1]$$

That is,

$$r_j(t) = \begin{cases} (-1)^k & t \in \left(\frac{k}{2^j}, \frac{k+1}{2^j}\right),\ k = 0, 1, \ldots, 2^j - 1 \\ 0 & t = \frac{k}{2^j},\ k = 0, 1, \ldots, 2^j \end{cases}$$

Thus for each $t \in [0,1]$, the sequence $\{r_j(t)\} \in B$. Hence

$$\sum_{i\geq 1}\left|\sum_{j\geq 1} a_{ij}r_j(t)\right| \leq K \qquad \forall t \in [0,1] \tag{*}$$

Now by Khintchin's inequality (cf. Ref. 104, p. 131; see also Ref. 190, p. 43), we have

$$\left(\sum_{j=1}^{n} a_{ij}^2\right)^{1/2} \leq 8 \int_0^1 \left|\sum_{j=1}^{n} a_{ij}r_j(t)\right| dt \qquad \forall n \geq 1$$

Since $\{a_{ij} : j \geq 1\} \in \ell^1$, applying the Lebesgue dominated convergence theorem (cf. Ref. 246, p. 262), we get

$$\left(\sum_{j\geq 1} a_{ij}^2\right)^{1/2} \leq 8 \int_0^1 \left|\sum_{j\geq 1} a_{ij}r_j(t)\right| dt$$

Integrating the inequality (*) over the interval [0,1], it follows

$$\sum_{i\geq 1}\left(\sum_{j\geq 1} a_{ij}^2\right)^{1/2} \leq 8 \sum_{i\geq 1} \int_0^1 \left|\sum_{j\geq 1} a_{ij}r_j(t)\right| dt$$

$$= 8 \int_0^1 \sum_{i\geq 1}\left|\sum_{j\geq 1} a_{ij}r_j(t)\right| dt \leq 8K$$

Since $\sup_{j\geq 1} |a_{ij}| \leq (\Sigma_{j\geq 1} a_{ij}^2)^{1/2}$, we conclude

$$\sum_{i\geq 1} |a_{ii}| \leq \sum_{i\geq 1} \sup_{j\geq 1} |a_{ij}| \leq 8K. \qquad \square$$

After Tong [254, Theorem 2.1] we have the following answer to the question raised at the beginning of this subsection.

PROPOSITION 6.20 Let λ and μ be two sequence spaces such that λ is monotone. If $A = [a_{ij}]$ is an infinite matrix with $A \in (\lambda, \mu)$, then $D_A \in (\lambda, \mu^{\times\times})$; in particular, if μ is also perfect, then $A \in (\lambda, \mu)$ implies that $D_A \in (\lambda, \mu)$.

Proof. We follow Ref. 18 for the proof. Let $B = yAx = [y_i a_{ij} x_j]$, where $x \in \lambda$ and $y \in \mu^{\times}$. Then $B \in (m_0, \ell^1)$. Indeed, if $\alpha \in m_0$, then

$$(B(\alpha))_i = \sum_{j \geq 1} y_i a_{ij} x_j \alpha_j = \sum_{j \geq 1} y_i a_{ij} u_j$$

where $u = \{u_j\} \in \lambda$ (λ is monotone). Hence

$$(B(\alpha))_i = y_i (A(u))_i$$

As $\{(A(u))_i\} \in \mu$ and $\{y_i\} \in \mu^{\times}$, we find

$$\sum_{i \geq 1} |(B(\alpha))_i| < \infty$$

and so $B \in (m_0, \ell^1)$, that is, $m_0 \subset \ell^1_B$. Thus, from Proposition 3.34, $\ell^\infty \subset \ell^1_B$, i.e., $B \in (\ell^\infty, \ell^1)$. By Proposition 6.19, $D_B = [\delta_{ij} y_i a_{ij} x_j] \in (m_0, \ell^1)$, and so $yD_A x \in (m_0, \ell^1)$ for each $x \in \lambda$ and $y \in \mu^{\times}$. Now let $z \in \lambda$; then $z = \alpha x$ where $\alpha \in m_0$ and $x \in \lambda$, since

$$\lambda = \bigcup_{x \in \lambda} m_0 \cdot x$$

So

$$(D_A(z))_i = a_{ii} \alpha_i x_i$$

Choose any $y \in \mu^{\times}$; then

$$\sum_{i \geq 1} |y_i (D_A(z))_i| = \sum_{i \geq 1} |y_i a_{ii} \alpha_i x_i|$$

$$= \sum_{i \geq 1} |((yD_A x)(\alpha))_i| < \infty$$

and so $D_A(z) \in \mu^{\times\times}$. □

The following result, stated in Ref. 18, p. 521, contains Proposition 6.19.

PROPOSITION 6.21 Let $A = [a_{ij}]$ be an infinite matrix such that $A \in (\ell^p, \ell^q)$, where $p > q \geq 1$. Then

$$\sum_{i\geq 1} |a_{ii}|^{pq/(p-q)} < \infty$$

Proof. By the preceding result, $D_A \in (\ell^p, \ell^q)$. Define r by $1/r + 1/q = 1$ and let

$$m = \frac{pq}{p - q} \qquad \text{and} \qquad n = \frac{pr}{p + r} > 1$$

Then $1/m + 1/n = 1$. Now for each x in ℓ^p,

$$\sum_{i\geq 1} |a_{ii}x_i|^q < \infty$$

and so

$$\sum_{i\geq 1} |a_{ii}x_iy_i| < \infty \qquad \forall x \in \ell^p,\ y \in \ell^r$$

$$\Longrightarrow \quad \{a_{ii}\} \in (\ell^p\ell^r)^\times \tag{*}$$

Next, we show that $\ell^p\ell^r = \ell^n$. Indeed, let $u = \{x_iy_i\} \in \ell^p\ell^r$ where $x \in \ell^p$ and $y \in \ell^r$. Then

$$\sum_{i\geq 1} |u_i|^n = \sum_{i\geq 1} |x_i|^{pr/(p+r)}|y_i|^{pr/(p+r)}$$

$$\leq \left\{\sum_{i\geq 1} [|x_i|^{pr/(p+r)}]^{(p+r)/r}\right\}^{r/(p+r)}$$

$$\times \left\{\sum_{i\geq 1} [|y_i|^{pr/(p+r)}]^{(p+r)/p}\right\}^{p/(p+r)} < \infty$$

Thus $\ell^p\ell^r \subset \ell^n$. Now let $u \in \ell^n$; then

$$\sum_{i\geq 1} |u_i|^{pr/(p+r)} < \infty$$

Define x and y by

$$x_i = u_i^{r/(p+r)} \quad \text{and} \quad y_i = u_i^{p/(p+r)} \quad i \geq 1$$

Then $x \in \ell^p$, $y \in \ell^r$, and so $u \in \ell^p \ell^r$, that is, $\ell^n \subset \ell^p \ell^r$. In view of (*) and the above equality we conclude that

$$\{a_{ii}\} \subset (\ell^n)^\times = \ell^m$$

and this completes the desired result. □

Composition of Transformations

A class of matrices when composed with diagonal matrices formed by the elements of the spaces μ and $\lambda^\times$, λ and μ being two sequence spaces, gives rise to matrix transformations from λ to μ. Such a composition of matrices is useful in characterizing nuclear operators from λ or $\lambda^\times$ to μ or $\mu^\times$ (cf. Ref. 44, p. 212). Our intent in this subsection is to describe this composition in detail; we follow Ref. 44 for all three results given below.

Let

$$\mathcal{A}_M = \{A = [a_{ij}] : |a_{ij}| \leq 1 \text{ for all } i,j \geq 1\}$$

and consider the following collections of matrices:

$$\mu\mathcal{A}_M = \{D_y A : y \in \mu,\ A \in \mathcal{A}_M\}$$

$$\mathcal{A}_M\lambda = \{AD_x : A \in \mathcal{A}_M,\ x \in \lambda\}$$

$$\mu\mathcal{A}_M\lambda = \{D_y A D_x : y \in \mu,\ A \in \mathcal{A}_M,\ x \in \lambda\}$$

Further, let

$$\sum(\lambda,\mu) = \left\{A : A \in (\lambda,\mu),\ \sum_{j\geq 1} |a_{ij}x_j| < \infty,\ \forall x \text{ in } \lambda\right\}$$

Clearly, if λ is monotone then $\Sigma(\lambda,\mu) = (\lambda,\mu)$.

PROPOSITION 6.22 Let λ and μ be two sequence spaces such that μ is normal. Then

$$\mu\mathcal{A}_M\lambda^\times \subset \Sigma(\lambda,\mu)$$

Proof. Let $B \in \mu\mathcal{A}_M\lambda^\times$. Then $B = [b_{ij}]$ with $b_{ij} = y_i a_{ij} u_j$, where $y \in \mu$, $A = [a_{ij}] \in \mathcal{A}_M$ and $u \in \lambda^\times$. If $x \in \lambda$, we find that

$$\sum_{j\geq 1} |b_{ij}x_j| \leq |y_i| \sum_{j\geq 1} |u_jx_j| < \infty \qquad \forall i \geq 1$$

giving $B \in \Sigma\ (\lambda,\mu)$. □

PROPOSITION 6.23 Let λ and μ be two sequence spaces, μ being normal. Define Φ: $\mu \cdot \lambda^\times \equiv \{D_xD_y : x \in \mu,\ y \in \lambda^\times\} \to \mu A_M\lambda^\times$ by $\Phi(D_xD_y) = D_xID_y$, where $I = [a_{ij}] \in A_M$ with $a_{ij} = 1$, $i = j$, and $a_{ij} = 0$, $i \neq j$ $(i,j \geq 1)$. Then $\mu \cdot \lambda^\times$ can be identified under Φ with the family of diagonal matrices of $\mu A_M\lambda^\times$.

Proof. Let $\Phi(D_xD_y) = \Phi(D_uD_v)$. Then $x_iy_i = u_iv_i$ for all $i \geq 1$ and so $D_xD_y = D_{xy} = D_{uv} = D_uD_v$, showing Φ to be one-one. To complete the proof, suppose $A = [a_{ij}] \in \mu A_M\lambda^\times$, where $a_{ij} = 0$, $i \neq j$ $(i,j \geq 1)$. We can write $a_{ij} = y_ib_{ij}u_j$ with $\{y_i\} \in \mu$, $[b_{ij}] \in A_M$ and $\{u_j\} \in \lambda^\times$. Put $v_i = b_{ii}u_i$. Then $A = D_{yv} = D_yID_v$. Since $v \in \lambda^\times$, $\Phi(D_yD_v) = A$. □

DEFINITION 6.24 Suppose λ and μ are sequence spaces and $A: \lambda \to \mu$ is a linear operator. A is said to be *normally bounded* provided there exists an $\eta(\lambda,\lambda^\times)$-neighborhood V of $0 \in \lambda$ such that $(A[V])^\circ$ is an $\eta(\mu^\times,\mu)$-neighborhood of $0 \in \mu^\times$, or equivalently, $A[V] \subset \{y\}^N$ for some $y \in \mu$.

THEOREM 6.25 Let λ and μ be two normal sequence spaces. Then $\mu A_M\lambda^\times$ consists precisely of those matrix transformations in $\Sigma\ (\lambda,\mu)$ which are normally bounded.

Proof. Let $\Sigma_1\ (\lambda,\mu)$ denote those members of $\Sigma\ (\lambda,\mu)$ which are normally bounded. We shall prove that $\mu A_M\lambda^\times = \Sigma_1\ (\lambda,\mu)$.

Suppose $A \in \mu A_M\lambda^\times$. Then $A \in \Sigma\ (\lambda,\mu)$ by Proposition 6.22. Now $A = D_y[a_{ij}]D_u$, that is,

$$A = [y_ia_{ij}u_j]$$

where $y \in \mu$, $[a_{ij}] \in A_M$, and $u \in \lambda^\times$. Suppose $V = \{x : x \in \lambda,\ p_u(x) \leq 1\}$. Hence for x in V,

$$|(A(x))_i| = \left|\sum_{j\geq 1} y_ia_{ij}u_jx_j\right| \leq |y_i|p_u(x) \leq |y_i| \qquad i \geq 1$$

Therefore, $A(x) \in \{y\}^N$ and so $A \in \Sigma_1\ (\lambda,\mu)$.

On the other hand, let $A = [a_{ij}] \in \Sigma_1(\lambda,\mu)$. Then there exist $y \in \mu$, $y \geq 0$, and $u \in \lambda^{\times}$, $u \geq 0$, such that

$$A[V] \subset \{y\}^N$$

where

$$V = \{x : x \in \lambda,\ p_u(x) \leq 1\} = (\{u\}^N)^\circ$$

Define $z \in \omega$ by

$$z_i = \begin{cases} 0 & \text{if } y_i = 0 \\ \frac{1}{y_i} & \text{if } y_i \neq 0 \end{cases}$$

Then $zA \equiv D_z A = [z_i a_{ij}]$, and for x in V,

$$|(D_z A(x))_i| = |z_i||(A(x))_i| \leq |z_i||y_i| \leq 1 \qquad \forall i \geq 1$$

Thus for all x in V and $i \geq 1$,

$$\left|\sum_{j\geq 1} z_i a_{ij} x_j\right| \leq 1 \implies \{z_i a_{ij}\}_j \in V^\circ \qquad \forall i \geq 1$$

But $V^\circ = (\{u\}^N)^{\circ\circ} = \{u\}^N$, and consequently

$$|z_i a_{ij}| \leq |u_j| \qquad \forall i,j \geq 1 \tag{*}$$

Define $w \in \omega$ by

$$w_i = \begin{cases} 0 & \text{if } u_i = 0 \\ \frac{1}{u_i} & \text{if } u_i \neq 0 \end{cases}$$

Using (*) we obtain

$$|z_i a_{ij} w_j| \leq 1 \qquad \forall i,j \geq 1$$

and hence $B = D_z A D_w = [z_i a_{ij} w_j] \in \mathcal{A}_M$. So we find that

$$E = D_y D_z A D_w D_u = D_y B D_u \in \mu \mathcal{A}_M \lambda^{\times}$$

We next show that $A = E$ and this will complete the proof.

What we essentially want to prove is that

$$y_i z_i a_{ij} w_j u_j = a_{ij} \qquad \forall i,j \geq 1$$

and this is accomplished for four different cases.

Case 1. If $y_i \neq 0$ and $u_j \neq 0$ $(i,j \geq 1)$ then clearly

$$y_i z_i a_{ij} w_j u_j = a_{ij} \qquad \forall i,j \geq 1$$

Case 2. Suppose for some index i_0, $y_{i_0} \neq 0$, and for some index j_0, $u_{j_0} = 0$. Let $a_{i_0 j_0} \neq 0$. Consider $\alpha \in \phi$, where

$$\alpha = \frac{1 + y_{i_0}}{a_{i_0 j_0}} e^{j_0}$$

Then $p_u(\alpha) = 0$ and so $\alpha \in V$. But

$$(A(\alpha))_{i_0} = \sum_{j\geq 1} a_{i_0 j} \alpha_j = 1 + y_{i_0} > y_{i_0} \quad \Longrightarrow \quad A(\alpha) \notin \{y\}^N$$

This contradiction forces $a_{i_0 j_0} = 0$ and we conclude

$$y_i z_i a_{ij} w_j u_j = a_{ij}$$

whenever $y_i \neq 0$ and $u_j = 0$.

Case 3. Suppose now $y_{i_0} = 0$, $u_{j_0} \neq 0$, and $a_{i_0 j_0} \neq 0$. Choose $\delta > 0$ with $\delta u_{j_0} < 1$, and put

$$\alpha = \delta e^{j_0}$$

Then $p_u(\alpha) = |\alpha_{j_0} u_{j_0}| = \delta u_{j_0} < 1 \quad \Longrightarrow \quad \alpha \in V$. But

$$|(A(\alpha))_{i_0}| = |a_{i_0 j_0} \alpha_{j_0}| > 0 = y_{i_0} \quad \Longrightarrow \quad A(\alpha) \notin \{y\}^N$$

Hence, as before,

$$y_i z_i a_{ij} w_j u_j = a_{ij}$$

whenever $y_i = 0$ and $u_j \neq 0$.

Case 4. Finally, assume that $y_{i_0} = 0 = u_{j_0}$ and $a_{i_0 j_0} \neq 0$. Let $\delta > 0$ and put $\alpha = \delta e^{j_0}$. Then $p_u(\alpha) = 0$, that is, $\alpha \in V$. But

$$|(A(\alpha))_{i_0}| = \delta |a_{i_0 j_0}| > 0 = y_{i_0} \quad \Longrightarrow \quad A(\alpha) \notin \{y\}^N$$

Consequently

$$y_i z_i a_{ij} w_j u_j = a_{ij}$$

whenever $y_i = 0$, $u_j = 0$.

Thus in all cases $y_i z_i a_{ij} w_j u_j = a_{ij}$ for $i,j \geq 1$. □

Summability Domains

In earlier parts of this section we laid down conditions on an infinite matrix $A = [a_{ij}]$ for it to transform a sequence space λ into another sequence space μ. The following question arises: If we are given an infinite matrix A and a sequence space μ, then what sort of subsets λ of ω are transformed into μ? In other words, we are interested in those subsets λ of ω such that $\lambda \subset \mu_A$. Of course, corresponding to a given choice of μ, the form of the required λ depends upon the nature of A, and in this direction we have some specific answers contained in Theorems 6.6, 6.16, and 6.17. Since $\mu_A \subset \mu_A$, in particular we would like to have a characterization of μ_A, possibly in terms of known sequence spaces or in terms of the properties of μ. This seems to be a very difficult problem indeed, and remains still open. However, we do have some results which have a bearing on the foregoing problem, namely, the properties of μ_A related to similar properties of μ. The first fundamental result in this direction is due to Zeller [270] as mentioned earlier, namely, Theorem 3.7 when μ is an FK-space. Recently Bennett [13, 15] has given a few more general results which are equally interesting and useful, and we follow him for the rest of this section.

To avoid repetition, throughout the remaining part of this section we use the notation A and $\mu \equiv (\mu,T)$, respectively, for an infinite matrix $[a_{ij}]$ and an FK-space whose topology T is generated by the increasing sequence $\{r_i\}$ of T-continuous seminorms on μ.

The Characterization Theorem for μ_A

The following useful characterization of μ_A as a closed subspace of a certain product space is due to Bennett [13, p. 194].

THEOREM 6.26 For each A and μ as described above, the space μ_A is topologically isomorphic to a closed subspace of the product space Ω with

$$\Omega = \omega \times \prod_{i\geq 1} (c)_i \times \mu$$

where Ω is endowed with its product topology P.

Proof. Define $\psi\colon \mu_A \to \Omega$ by

$$\psi(x) = \left(x, \left\{\sum_{j=1}^{n} a_{1j}x_j\right\}, \left\{\sum_{j=1}^{n} a_{2j}x_j\right\}, \ldots, A(x)\right)$$

which is well defined since

$$\lim_{n\to\infty} \sum_{j=1}^{n} a_{ij}x_j$$

exists and is equal to $(A(x))_i$ for each $i \geq 1$. Clearly ψ is 1-1 and onto a linear subspace Ω_1 of Ω, $\Omega_1 = \{\psi(x) : x \in \mu_A\}$. If the net $x^\alpha \to 0$ in μ_A, by Theorem 3.7,

$$x_i^\alpha \to 0$$

$$\sup_n \left|\sum_{j=1}^{n} a_{ij}x_j^\alpha\right| = q_i(x^\alpha) \to 0 \qquad \forall i \geq 1$$

$$A(x^\alpha) \to 0 \qquad \text{in } (\mu,T)$$

Therefore $\psi(x^\alpha) \to 0$ in Ω_1 relative to $P|\Omega_1$. Similarly it follows that $\psi^{-1}(\hat{x}^\alpha) \to 0$ whenever $\hat{x}^\alpha \to 0$ in $(\Omega_1,P|\Omega_1)$. This establishes that ψ is a topological isomorphism from (μ_A,S) onto $(\Omega_1,P|\Omega_1)$, S being the natural topology on μ_A defined in Theorem 3.7. Since μ_A is S-complete, Ω_1 is a closed subspace of (Ω,P). □

We deduce

THEOREM 6.27 Let A be an infinite matrix and (μ,T) be a separable FK-space. Then (μ_A,S) is a separable FK-space.

Proof. On account of Theorem 3.7, we need show that (μ_A,S) is separable. From Proposition 1.4.13, the space (Ω,P) is a separable metrizable space. Hence from Proposition 1.4.11, $(\Omega_1,P|\Omega_1)$ is separable, and thus by Theorem 6.26, (μ_A,S) is separable. □

THEOREM 6.28 Let A be an infinite matrix and (μ,T) an FK-space such that μ^* is $\beta(\mu^*,\mu)$-separable. Then μ_A^* is $\beta(\mu_A^*,\mu_A)$-separable.

Proof. By Proposition 1.7.17(ii), Ω^* is $\beta(\Omega^*,\Omega)$-separable. Hence by the first part of this proposition, Ω_1^* is $\beta(\Omega_1^*,\Omega_1)$-separable. Finally, use Theorem 6.26 to obtain the desired conclusion. □

EXERCISE 6.29 For a row-finite matrix A, show that μ_A is topologically isomorphic to a closed subspace of the product $\omega \times \mu$. Hence deduce that if μ is Montel or reflexive, so is the space μ_A; also show that the equivalence of weak and strong convergence in μ implies the same in μ_A. [Hint: For the first part, see the note following Theorem 3.7 and the proof of Theorem 6.26. For the rest, use Proposition 1.3.8 also.]

Wedge and Conull Properties of μ_A

If (μ,T) is an FK-space, then μ_A is also an FK-space and hence the results of Section 5, namely Theorems 5.2, 5.5, 5.6, 5.18, and 5.19 are applicable to the space μ_A. Our aim in this section is to give additional conditions equivalent to the above properties, which μ_A is likely to possess because of its association with A. For brevity let us write r^i and k^j, respectively, for the ith row and jth column of A. We begin with (Ref. 15, p. 66)

THEOREM 6.30 The following conditions are equivalent:

(i) μ_A is a wedge space.

(ii) $\ell^1 \subset \mu_A$, $r^i \in c_0$, $\forall i \geq 1$, and the mapping A: $\ell^1 \to \mu$ is compact.

(iii) $k^j \in \mu$, $\forall j \geq 1$, and $k^j \to 0$ as $j \to \infty$ in μ.

Proof. (i) $\Longrightarrow$ (ii) From Theorem 5.5, (i) $\Longrightarrow$ (vi), $\ell^1 \subset \mu_A$ and the inclusion mapping I: $\ell^1 \to \mu_A$ is compact. Also, A: $\mu_A \to \mu$ is continuous, by Theorem 3.7. Hence $A(e^j) \to 0$ as $j \to \infty$ in (μ,T), which is a K-space. Therefore $(A(e^j))_i \to 0$ as $j \to \infty$, $\forall i \geq 1$. But $(A(e^j))_i = a_{ij}$, $\forall i,j \geq 1$. Therefore $r^i \in c_0$ for each $i \geq 1$. Further, if B is bounded in ℓ^1, $I(B) = B$ is relatively compact in μ_A and therefore A(B) is relatively compact.

(ii) $\Longrightarrow$ (iii) Obviously $k^j = A(e^j) \in \lambda$, $\forall j \geq 1$. As the sequence $\{e^j\}$ is bounded in ℓ^1, it follows from Theorem 2.3.11 and $r^i \in c_0$, $\forall i \geq 1$, that $k^j \to 0$ in λ.

(iii) $\Rightarrow$ (i) Using the notation of Theorem 3.7 for the seminorms generating the topology of μ_A, we have for fixed $i \geq 1$,

$$p_i(e^m) = 0 \qquad \text{for all } m > i$$

$$q_i(e^m) = |a_{im}| = |k_i^m| \qquad \forall m \geq 1$$

and $(r_i \circ A)(e^m) = r_i(k^m)$, $\forall m \geq 1$. Since $k^m \to 0$ in μ which is a K-space, $(r_i \circ A)(e^m)$ and $q_i(e^m)$ tend to zero as $m \to \infty$. Hence μ_A is a wedge space. □

Remark: If μ is separable, then μ_A is also separable, by Theorem 6.27, whence the conditions of Theorem 5.5 for the space μ_A become equivalent to the conditions (ii) and (iii) of the above result.

Concerning the weak wedge character of the space μ_A, we have (Ref. 15, p. 66)

THEOREM 6.31 The following conditions are equivalent:

(i) μ_A is a weak wedge space.

(ii) $\ell^1 \subset \mu_A$, $r^i \in c_0$, $\forall i \geq 1$, and the mapping A: $\ell^1 \to \mu$ is weakly compact.

(iii) $k^j \in \mu$, $\forall j \geq 1$, and $k^j \to 0$ in $\sigma(\mu,\mu^*)$.

Proof. (i) $\Rightarrow$ (ii) From Theorem 5.2, $\ell^1 \subset \mu_A$ and the inclusion mapping I: $\ell^1 \to \mu_A$ is weakly compact. Also, A: $\mu_A \to \mu$ is weakly continuous, by Theorem 3.7 and Proposition 1.12.2. Thus A: $\ell^1 \to \mu$, where $A = A \circ I$, is weakly compact.

(ii) $\Rightarrow$ (iii) Proceed as in the proof of (ii) $\Rightarrow$ (iii) of Theorem 6.30.

(iii) $\Rightarrow$ (i) Follows from Theorem 6.26. □

Remark: In Theorems 6.30 and 6.31, it is necessary to assume that $r^i \in c_0$, $i \geq 1$, for otherwise we have

EXAMPLE 6.32 Let $\mu = \omega$ and $A = [a_{ij}]$, where $a_{ij} = 1$ for all $i,j \geq 1$. Clearly $r^i \notin c_0$ for any $i \geq 1$. Also, the map A: $\ell^1 \to \omega$, where for $x \in \ell^1$,

$$Ax = \left\{ \sum_{j\geq 1} x_j, \sum_{j\geq 1} x_j, \ldots \right\}$$

is clearly continuous, and therefore compact by Exercise 2.6.4. It can be easily verified that $\omega_A = cs$, which is not even a weak wedge space.

The following theorem due to Bennett [15] completely solves the problem raised by Sember in Ref. 232 of how to characterize the conullity of μ_A containing bv for an arbitrary FK-space μ. It includes his results for bv_A (Ref. 229) and c_A (Ref. 230) as particular cases, and is an improvement of his later results (Ref. 231).

THEOREM 6.33 The following conditions are equivalent:

(i) μ_A is (conull) strongly conull.

(ii) $bv \subset \mu_A$ and the mapping $A\colon bv \to \mu$ is (weakly) compact.

(iii) $k^j \in \mu$, $\forall j \geq 1$, and $\{\alpha^n : n \geq 1\}$, where $\alpha^n = \{\Sigma_{j=1}^n a_{ij} : i \geq 1\}$, (weakly) converges in μ.

Proof. The proof is analogous to those of preceding theorems, except that in proving (i) $\Longrightarrow$ (ii), we make use of Theorems 5.18 and 5.19 instead of Theorems 5.5 and 5.2. □

The restriction on the FK-space (μ,T) leads to

THEOREM 6.34 Let (μ,T) be an FK-space in which T- and $\sigma(\mu,\mu^*)$-convergent sequences are the same and let A be an infinite matrix. Then

(i) μ_A is a wedge space if and only if μ_A is a weak wedge space.

(ii) μ_A is conull if and only if μ_A is strongly conull.

Proof. (i) If μ_A is a weak wedge space, then from Theorem 6.31, (i) $\Longrightarrow$ (ii), $\ell^1 \subset \mu_A$, $r^i \in c_0$, $i \geq 1$, and $A\colon \ell^1 \to \mu$ is weakly compact. By hypothesis any weakly relatively compact set in μ is T-relatively compact and hence $A\colon \ell^1 \to \mu$ is compact. Now apply Theorem 6.30, (ii) $\Longrightarrow$ (i).

(ii) To prove this proceed as in (i) and use Theorem 6.33, (i) $\Longleftrightarrow$ (ii). □

THEOREM 6.35 Let (μ,T) be a reflexive FK-space and A an infinite matrix. Then the following conditions are equivalent:

(i) μ_A is a weak wedge (conull) space.

(ii) $\ell^1 \subset \mu_A$ and $r^i \in c_0$, $i \geq 1$ ($bv \subset \mu_A$).

Proof. (i) $\Rightarrow$ (ii) Follows from Theorem 6.31, (i) $\Rightarrow$ (ii) [Theorem 6.33, (i) $\Rightarrow$ (ii)].

(ii) $\Rightarrow$ (i) It is sufficient to show that the mapping A: $\ell^1 \to \mu$ (A: $\ell^1 \to bv$) is weakly compact. Let B be a bounded set in ℓ^1 (bv). Then B is bounded in μ_A by Proposition 3.1. As A: $\mu_A \to \mu$ is continuous (cf. Theorem 3.7), A (B) is bounded in μ and therefore weakly relatively compact by Proposition 1.9.2. □

THEOREM 6.36 Let (μ,T) be a Montel FK-space and A an infinite matrix. Then the following conditions are equivalent:

(i) μ_A is a weak wedge (conull) space.
(ii) μ_A is a wedge (strongly conull) space.
(iii) $\ell^1 \subset \mu_A$ and $r^i \in c_0$, $i \geq 1$ ($bv \subset \mu_A$).

Proof. (i) $\Rightarrow$ (ii) We have from Theorem 6.31, (i) $\Rightarrow$ (ii) [Theorem 6.33, (i) $\Rightarrow$ (ii)] that $\ell^1 \subset \mu_A$, $r^i \in c_0$, $i \geq 1$ ($bv \subset \mu_A$), and A: $\ell^1 \to \mu$ (A: $bv \to \mu$) is weakly compact. Now in (μ,T), weakly compact sets, being weakly bounded and therefore T-bounded, are T-relatively compact. Hence A is compact and (ii) follows from Theorem 6.30, (ii) $\Rightarrow$ (i) [Theorem 6.33, (ii) $\Rightarrow$ (i)].

(ii) $\Rightarrow$ (iii) Immediate from Theorem 6.30, (i) $\Rightarrow$ (ii) [Theorem 6.33, (i) $\Rightarrow$ (ii)].

(iii) $\Rightarrow$ (i) This follows from Theorem 6.35, (ii) $\Rightarrow$ (i), as Montel spaces are always reflexive (cf. Proposition 1.9.5). □

EXERCISE 6.37 (i) Show that a reflexive FK-space (μ,T) is a weak wedge space if and only if $\ell^1 \subset \mu$, and is conull if and only if $bv \subset \mu$. (ii) A Montel FK-space (μ,T) is a wedge space if and only if $\ell^1 \subset \mu$, and strongly conull if and only if $bv \subset \mu$. [Hint: Use Theorems 6.35 and 6.36, respectively, for (i) and (ii), where A is the identity matrix.]

7. NUCLEAR SEQUENCE SPACES

Nuclearity is comparatively a very rich property of locally convex spaces; indeed a nuclear l.c. TVS behaves somewhat like a finite dimensional space. One of the most important applications of nuclearity in the theory of bases is that a Fréchet space with a Schauder base is nuclear if and only if every base is absolute (Refs. 173 and 266). [This aspect of the study will be dealt with in our forthcoming work (Ref. 125).] Also, nuclear spaces find numerous applications in the theory of distributions, especially in characterizing bilinear functionals (kernel theorem, see Ref. 62) and also in the spectral resolution of self-adjoint operators (Ref. 62, Chapter 4). Above all, nuclearity of a space has penetrating impact on the structure of its locally convex topology. Nuclear spaces enjoy a very prominent place among all locally convex spaces, having a number of extremely important properties.

Our concern here is to obtain concrete characterizations of those spaces which are nuclear by means of the components comprising a particular locally convex space. Under the circumstances we restrict ourselves to a specific class of spaces, namely, the sequence spaces which are the subject of our present study, and characterize their nuclearity. However, the general problem of characterizing nuclearity of a sequence space seems to be very difficult; we consider those spaces which include the spaces of analytic sequences and study their nuclear behavior. We also incorporate a few results involving the Schwartz character of these spaces. At the end of this section we include a few applications to matrix transformations.

Sequence Spaces Generated by Power Sets

Throughout we shall write a sequence x as $\{x_0, x_1, x_2, \ldots\}$ instead of the usual notation $\{x_1, x_2, \ldots\}$. Unless stated otherwise, we write P for a subset of ω satisfying the following conditions:

(i) Each $\alpha \in P$ is ≥ 0.

(ii) For each $n \geq 0$ there is an α in P with $\alpha_n > 0$.

(iii) For each α in P one can choose a β in P such that $\alpha_n \leq \beta_n$, $n \geq 0$.

DEFINITION 7.1 The set P satisfying (i) through (iii) is called a *Köthe set* or a *system of steps* or a *power set*. The sequence space

$$\Lambda(P) = \left\{x \in \omega : p_\rho(x) \equiv \sum_{n\geq 0} |x_n|\rho_n < \infty,\ \forall\rho \in P\right\}$$

is called a *Köthe power space*.

Note: We shall assume from now on that the space $\Lambda(P)$ is equipped with its natural locally convex topology T generated by the family $D = \{p_\sigma : \sigma \in P\}$ of seminorms on $\Lambda(P)$.

It is this space $(\Lambda(P),T)$ with varying P with which we shall be mostly concerned in the rest of this section. Fenske and Schock [51] considered a generalization of the space $\Lambda(P)$. After them, let us consider the sequence space $\Lambda^q(P)$ of order q $(1 \leq q \leq \infty)$ defined below.

$$\Lambda^q(P) = \left\{x \in \omega : p_\rho^q(x) \equiv \left\{\sum_{n\geq 0} |x_n|^q \rho_n\right\}^{1/q} < \infty, \ \forall \rho \in P\right\} \qquad 1 \leq q \leq \infty$$

and for $q = \infty$,

$$\Lambda^\infty(P) = \{x \in \omega : p_\rho^\infty(x) \equiv \sup_{n\geq 0} |x_n|\rho_n < \infty, \ \forall \rho \in P\}$$

We find that $\Lambda(P) = \Lambda^1(P)$. It will be assumed from now on that the space $\Lambda^q(P)$ is equipped with its natural locally convex topology T generated by $\{p_\sigma^q : \sigma \in P\}$ where $1 \leq q \leq \infty$. Let us recall the function ϕ introduced in Section 13 of Chapter 1. In another paper (Ref. 52), Fenske and Schock consider the following generalization of the space $\Lambda^q(P)$, namely, the space $\Lambda_\phi(P)$, where

$$\Lambda_\phi(P) = \left\{x \in \omega : p_\rho^\phi(x) \equiv \sum_{n\geq 0} \phi(|x_n|\rho_n) < \infty, \ \forall \rho \in P\right\}$$

As before, we equip this space with the topology generated by $\{p_\sigma^\phi : \sigma \in P\}$.

Note: Several results for the space $\Lambda(P)$ have been generalized to the space $\Lambda^q(P)$ or $\Lambda_\phi(P)$ by Fenske, Rosenberger, and Schock (cf. papers referred to earlier in this section as well as in Section 13 of Chapter 1). However, we shall not go into the details of these results.

DEFINITION 7.2 A power set P satisfying the following additional two conditions is called a *power set of infinite* (resp. *finite*) type.

(i) Each $a \in P$ is $\gg 0$ and nondecreasing (resp. nonincreasing).

(ii) For each $a \in P$ there exists $b \in P$ such that $a_n^2 \leq b_n$ (resp. $a_n \leq b_n^2$) for $n \geq 0$.

DEFINITION 7.3 If P is a power set of infinite (resp. finite) type, the corresponding Köthe power space is called a G_∞ (resp. G_1)*-space* or a *smooth sequence space* of *infinite* (resp. *finite*) *type*. We usually denote this space by $\Lambda_\infty(P)$ [resp. $\Lambda_1(P)$]. Further, if $\alpha \in \omega$ satisfies the relation $0 = \alpha_0 \leq \alpha_1 \leq \cdots \leq \alpha_n \to \infty$, the G_∞ (resp. G_1)-space $\Lambda_\infty(P)$ [resp.

$\Lambda_1(P)]$ generated by $P = \{\{k^{\alpha_n} : n \ge 0\} : k \ge 1\}$ [resp. $\{\{(1 - 1/k^{\alpha_n}) : n \ge 0\} : k \ge 2\}$] is denoted by $\Lambda_\infty(\alpha)$ [resp. $\Lambda_1(\alpha)$], where k is an integer.

EXERCISE 7.4 Let $\alpha \in \omega$ satisfy the relation $0 = \alpha_0 \le \alpha_1 \le \cdots \le \alpha_n \to \infty$ with n. Define P_1 and P_2 by

$$P_1 = \{\{\rho^{\alpha_n}\} : 0 < \rho < \infty\} \qquad P_2 = \{\{\rho^{\alpha_n}\} : 0 < \rho < 1\}$$

Show that $\Lambda(P_1) = \Lambda_\infty(\alpha)$ and $\Lambda(P_2) = \Lambda_1(\alpha)$. If in addition α satisfies the condition that for some $\rho > 1$,

$$\sum_{n\ge0} \rho^{-\alpha_n} < \infty$$

prove that (Ref. 194, p. 162)

$$\Lambda_\infty(\alpha) = \{x \in \omega : |x_n|^{1/\alpha_n} \to 0\}$$

In particular, if $\alpha = \{n\}$, show that $\Lambda_\infty(\alpha) = \delta$ [here $P_1 = \{\{\rho^n\} : 0 < \rho < \infty\}$, $\Lambda(P_1) = \Lambda_\infty(\alpha) = \delta$].

Estimation of Diameters in Sequence Spaces

Let us begin with a more general situation.

PROPOSITION 7.5 Let λ be an arbitrary sequence space equipped with its normal topology $\eta(\lambda,\lambda^\times)$. Let $u,v \in \lambda^\times$ with $u,v > 0$ and $p_u \le p_v$. Define $U_u = \{x : x \in \lambda, p_u(x) \le 1\}$ and similarly define U_v. Then, if $\alpha \in \omega$ is defined by

$$\alpha_n = \begin{cases} \dfrac{u_n}{v_n} & v_n \ne 0 \\ 0 & \text{otherwise} \end{cases}$$

we have

$$\inf_{i\le n} \alpha_i \le \delta_n(U_v,U_u) \le \sup_{i\ge n} \alpha_i$$

where the left-hand inequality is valid for $u \gg 0$.

Proof. Because of the earlier change in notation, $e^0 = \{1, 0, 0, \ldots\}$, $e^1 = \{0, 1, 0, 0, \ldots\}$, and so on. Let L_n be the subspace of λ with $L_n = \operatorname{sp}\{e^0, \ldots, e^{n-1}\}$. For $x \in U_v$, and $x^{(n)} = \Sigma_{i=0}^{n-1} x_i e^i$,

$$p_u(x - x^{(n)}) = \sum_{i\geq n} |x_i u_i| \leq \sup_{i\geq n} \left\{\frac{u_i}{v_i}\right\} \sum_{i\geq n} |x_i v_i| \leq \sup_{i\geq n} \alpha_i$$

$$\Longrightarrow \quad x \in (\sup_{i\geq n} \alpha_i) U_u + L_n \quad \Longrightarrow \quad \delta_n(U_v, U_u) \leq \sup_{i\geq n} \alpha_i$$

On the other hand, consider the normed space (λ, p_u) and let

$$x \in (\inf_{i\leq n} \alpha_i)(U_u \cap L_{n+1})$$

Then

$$\begin{aligned} p_v(x) &= \sum_{i\geq 0} |x_i v_i| = \sum_{i=0}^{n} |x_i v_i| \\ &= (\inf_{i\leq n} \alpha_i) \sum_{i=0}^{n} |y_i v_i| \qquad y \in U_u \\ &= (\inf_{i\leq n} \alpha_i) \sum_{i=0}^{n} |y_i u_i| \alpha_i^{-1} \leq 1 \end{aligned}$$

$$\Longrightarrow \quad (\inf_{i\leq n} \alpha_i)(U_u \cap L_{n+1}) \subset U_v$$

Now observe that U_v is bounded in (λ, p_u); indeed, for $x \in U_v$,

$$p_u(x) = \sum_{i\geq 0} |u_i x_i| \leq \sum_{i\geq 0} |v_i x_i| \leq 1$$

Therefore from Proposition 1.13.5,

$$\delta_n(U_v, U_u) \geq \inf_{i\leq n} \alpha_i$$

and thus we obtain the result. □

Note: Proposition 7.5 includes, in particular, the results of Mitiagin [173, p. 75] and Terzioğlu [247; (1), p. 79, and (2), p. 80]. The next result, whose derivation depends upon the preceding proposition, includes another theorem proved in Ref. 247; (3), p. 80.

PROPOSITION 7.6 Let λ, u, and v be as in Proposition 7.7, where we do not suppose that $u >> 0$. Then $\delta_n(U_v,U_u) \to 0$ if and only if $u_n/v_n \to 0$ as $n \to \infty$, where $u_n/v_n = 0$ if $v_n = 0$ and $0/0 = 0$.

Proof. Suppose $u_n/v_n \to 0$ and so $\alpha_n \to 0$. By the right-hand inequality in Proposition 7.5, we find that $\delta_n(U_v,U_u) \to 0$.

Let now $\delta_n(U_v,U_u) \to 0$. Define a linear map $F: \lambda \to \ell^1$ by $F(x) = ux$. Since $\|F(x)\|_1 = p_u(x)$, F is $\eta(\lambda,\lambda^\times)$-$\|\cdot\|_1$ continuous. It is clear that $F[U_u] \subset U_1 = \{x : x \in \ell^1, \|x\|_1 \le 1\}$; hence from Propositions 1.13.2(iii) and 1.13.6,

$$\delta_n(F[U_v]) = \delta_n(F[U_v], U_1) \to 0$$

Using Proposition 1.13.3 we find that $F[U_v]$ is compact in ℓ^1 (use Propositions 1.2.9 and 1.2.13).

Let $x^m = \alpha_m e^m$, $m \ge 0$. Then $x^m \in F[U_v]$ since $e^m/v_m \in U_v$ for $v_m \ne 0$. Hence by Proposition 2.6.11, $\alpha_m \to 0$ as $m \to \infty$. □

PROPOSITION 7.7 Let λ be a sequence space equipped with its normal topology $\eta(\lambda,\lambda^\times)$. Suppose $u,v \in \lambda^\times$ with $u \le v$ and $u,v > 0$, and let

$$\lim_{n\to\infty} \delta_n(U_v,U_u) = 0$$

Suppose $J = \{i : i \in \mathbb{N}, i \ge 0 \text{ and } u_i \ne 0\}$. If J is infinite, then there exists a permutation σ of J, say $\sigma(J) = \{n_0, n_1, \ldots, n_k, \ldots\}$, so that

$$\alpha_{n_k} = \delta_k(U_v,U_u) \qquad \forall k \ge 1$$

If J is finite and has k elements, then

$$\delta_n(U_v,U_u) = 0 \qquad n \ge k$$

Proof. Consider first the case when J has k elements and suppose $K = \mathbb{N} \sim J$. Further, let us write M_u for the kernel of p_u and $L_u = \mathrm{sp}\{e^i : i \in J\}$. Now (cf. beginning of Chapter 2)

$$x = \bar{x}_J + \bar{x}_K \qquad \bar{x}_J \in L_u,\ \bar{x}_K \in M_u$$

and this representation is unique; moreover

$$p_u(x - \bar{x}_J) = 0$$

Hence, for any $\varepsilon > 0$,

$$U_v \subset \varepsilon U_u + L_u \implies \delta_k(U_v, U_u) = 0 \implies \delta_n(U_v, U_u) = 0 \qquad n \geq k$$

by Proposition 1.13.2.

Let us consider the case when J is infinite. The sequence $\{\alpha_n\}$ tends to 0 by Proposition 7.6. Hence there exists a permutation σ of J such that

$$\alpha_{\sigma(m)} \leq \alpha_{\sigma(n)} \qquad \text{for } m,n \in J,\ m \geq n$$

Let us write $\sigma(J) = \{n_0, n_1, \ldots, n_k, \ldots\}$.

Define L_k as $\mathrm{sp}\{e^i : i = n_0, \ldots, n_{k-1}\}$. Then L_k is a k-dimensional subspace of λ. Let $x \in U_v$ and $x^{(k)} \in L_k$; then

$$p_u(x - x^{(k)}) = \sum_{i \geq k} |x_{n_i}| u_{n_i} \leq \alpha_{n_k} \sum_{i \geq k} |x_{n_i}| v_{n_i} \leq \alpha_{n_k}$$

$$\implies U_v \subset \alpha_{n_k} U_u + L_k \implies \delta_k(U_v, U_u) \leq \alpha_{n_k}$$

Define the linear operator $F\colon \lambda \to \ell^1$ by $F(x) = ux$ and suppose L_{k+1} is the subspace of ℓ^1 generated by $e^{n_0}, \ldots, e^{n_k}$. For y in the set $U_1 \cap L_{k+1}$, we have

$$\sum_{i=0}^{k} |y_{n_i}| \frac{v_{n_i}}{u_{n_i}} \leq \frac{1}{\alpha_{n_k}} \implies p_v\left(\alpha_{n_k} \frac{y}{u}\right) \leq 1$$

$$\implies \alpha_{n_k} y \in uU_v = F[U_v]$$

$$\implies \alpha_{n_k}(U_1 \cap L_{k+1}) \subset F[U_v]$$

By Proposition 1.13.5,

$$\alpha_{n_k} \leq \delta_k(F[U_v], U_1) \leq \delta_k(U_v, U_u)$$

and so we get the required equality. □

Characterization of Nuclear and Schwartz Spaces

The preceding results lead to the following two characterization theorems, which we shall call the *Schock-Terzioğlu criterion* and the *Grothendieck-Pietsch criterion*, respectively.

THEOREM 7.8 A sequence space $(\lambda,\eta(\lambda,\lambda^{\times}))$ is a Schwartz space if and only if to each $u \in \lambda^{\times}$, $u > 0$, there corresponds a $v \in \lambda^{\times}$, $v > 0$, such that $u \le v$ and $\{u_n/v_n\} \in c_0$.

Proof. By Proposition 2.4.3, $\eta(\lambda,\lambda^{\times}) = \eta_p(\lambda,\lambda^{\times})$ and so we may replace η by η_p in the statement of the theorem. If $(\lambda,\eta_p(\lambda,\lambda^{\times}))$ is Schwartz, then by Theorem 1.13.16, to every u in $\lambda^{\times}$, $u > 0$, there corresponds a $v \in \lambda^{\times}$, $u \le v$ (or $U_v \prec U_u$), such that

$$\lim_{n\to\infty} \delta_n(U_v,U_u) = 0$$

Thus, by Proposition 7.6, $\{u_n/v_n\} \in c_0$. Another application of Proposition 7.6 leads to the desired converse. □

Note: Theorem 7.8 is mentioned in Ref. 250, p. 4.

THEOREM 7.9 A sequence space $(\lambda,\eta(\lambda,\lambda^{\times}))$ is nuclear if and only if to each $u \in \lambda^{\times}$, $u > 0$, there corresponds a $v \in \lambda^{\times}$, $u \le v$, such that $\{u_n/v_n\} \in \ell^1$.

Proof. As in the preceding theorem we replace η by η_p. Suppose first that $(\lambda,\eta_p(\lambda,\lambda^{\times}))$ is nuclear. Hence by Theorem 1.13.15, to each $u \in \lambda^{\times}$, $u > 0$, there corresponds a $v \in \lambda^{\times}$, $u \le v$ (that is, $U_v \subset U_u$), such that

$$\sum_{n\ge 0} \delta_n(U_v,U_u) < \infty$$

Hence $\delta_n(U_v,U_u) \to 0$ and so from Proposition 7.7,

$$\sum_{k\ge 0} \alpha_{n_k} < \infty$$

That is, $\{\alpha_n\} \in \ell^1$. The converse follows similarly. □

Remarks: For the space $(\Lambda(P),T)$ where P is an arbitrary power set, the following results characterize its Schwartz property and nuclearity (Ref. 226, p. 16; Ref. 247, (4), p. 81, and Ref. 51, p. 17; Ref. 190, p. 98).

THEOREM 7.10 The space $(\Lambda(P),T)$ is a Schwartz space if and only if for each $u \in P$ there exists a $v \in P$ with $u \le v$ such that $\{u_n/v_n\} \in c_0$.

THEOREM 7.11 The space $(\Lambda(P),T)$ is nuclear if and only if to every $u \in P$ there corresponds a $v \in P$ with $u \leq v$ such that $\{u_n/v_n\} \in \ell^1$.

Although the proofs of the last two theorems are identical with the corresponding proofs of Theorems 7.8 and 7.9, Theorems 7.8 and 7.10 (and also Theorems 7.9 and 7.11) are independent of each other. However, under special circumstances, one can deduce Theorem 7.8 (resp. Theorem 7.9) from Theorem 7.10 (resp. Theorem 7.11) and vice versa. Indeed, if λ is perfect and P is taken to be the set of all $u \in \lambda^{\times}$ with $u > 0$, then Theorem 7.8 (resp. Theorem 7.9) can be deduced from Theorem 7.10 (resp. Theorem 7.11). On the other hand, for countable power sets P, Theorem 7.10 (resp. Theorem 7.11) follows from Theorem 7.8 (resp. Theorem 7.9), for the space $(\Lambda(P),T)$ then becomes a Fréchet space possessing the AK-property, which ultimately forces $\eta(\Lambda(P),\Lambda(P)^{\times})$ to be equal to T.

Schwartz Property and Nuclearity of G_∞*-Spaces*

The following result, with minor modifications in the proof, is due to Terzioğlu.

PROPOSITION 7.12 A G_∞-space $(\Lambda(P),T)$ is Schwartz (res. nuclear) if and only if there exists a $u \in P$ such that $\{1/u_n\} \in c_0$ (resp. $\{1/u_n\} \in \ell^1$).

Proof. *Schwartz Property* If the given space is Schwartz, then by Theorem 7.10, to every $a \in P$ there corresponds a $u \in P$ such that $\{a_n/u_n\} \in c_0$. Using Definition 7.2(i) we find that

$$\frac{a_0}{u_n} \leq \frac{a_n}{u_n} \qquad \Longrightarrow \qquad \left\{\frac{1}{u_n}\right\} \in c_0$$

Conversely, let there be a $u \in P$ with $\{1/u_n\} \in c_0$. Choose an arbitrary $a \in P$. In view of (iii) above Definition 7.1 and Definition 7.2 (ii), we can find, respectively, b and d in P such that $b_n \geq \max\{a_n,u_n\}$ and $a_n^2 \leq d_n$ for $n = 0, 1, 2, \ldots$. Let $g \in P$ with $g_n \geq \max\{b_n,d_n\}$. Hence

$$\frac{a_n}{g_n} \leq \frac{\sqrt{d_n}}{g_n} \leq \frac{1}{\sqrt{g_n}} \leq \frac{1}{\sqrt{b_n}} \leq \frac{1}{\sqrt{u_n}} \to 0 \qquad \text{as } n \to \infty$$

Hence $\{a_n/g_n\} \in c_0$, and so Theorem 7.10 yields the Schwartz property of $(\Lambda(P),T)$.

Nuclearity If $(\Lambda(P),T)$ is nuclear then for each $a \in P$ we find a u in P with $\{a_n/u_n\} \in \ell^1$. As $a_0 \le a_n$ for all $n \ge 0$, we have $\{1/u_n\} \in \ell^1$.

On the other hand, let $\{1/u_n\} \in \ell^1$ for some $u \in P$. Let $a \in P$. We can determine $b \in P$ with $b_n \ge \max\{u_n, a_n\}$. Hence $\{1/b_n\} \in \ell^1$. We can find another $g \in P$ such that $b_n^2 \le g_n$ for $n \ge 0$. Therefore

$$\frac{a_n}{g_n} \le \frac{b_n}{g_n} \le \frac{1}{b_n} \qquad n \ge 0$$

Hence $\{a_n/g_n\} \in \ell^1$ and consequently the nuclearity of $(\Lambda(P),T)$ follows by application of Theorem 7.11. □

There is another characterization of nuclearity for the G_∞-space $\Lambda(P)$ contained in Ref. 251, p. 498.

PROPOSITION 7.13 A G_∞-space $(\Lambda(P),T)$ is nuclear if and only if for every $k \ge 1$ there exist $u \in P$ and $M > 0$ such that $(n + 1)^k \le Mu_n$ for all $n \ge 0$.

Proof. The sufficiency part is immediate from Proposition 7.13. Let $(\Lambda(P),T)$ be nuclear so that there is a $u \in P$ with $\{1/u_n\} \in \ell^1$. Here each member of P is nondecreasing; consequently

$$(n + 1)\frac{1}{u_n} \le \sum_{i=0}^{n} \frac{1}{u_i} \le \sum_{i\ge 0} \frac{1}{u_i} = M$$

(say). Thus $(n + 1) \le Mu_n$ for all $n \ge 0$. For the given choice of k, we can find a $v \in P$ so that

$$(u_n)^{2^k} \le v_n \qquad n \ge 0$$

$$\Longrightarrow \quad (n + 1)^k \le M^{2^k} v_n \qquad n \ge 0$$

and this completes the necessity part. □

EXERCISE 7.14 (i) If a G_∞-space $(\Lambda(P),T)$ is not Schwartz, prove that $\Lambda(P) = \ell^1$; and (ii) prove that the G_∞-space $\Lambda_\infty(\alpha)$ is always a Schwartz space.

EXERCISE 7.15 Prove that the G_∞-space $\Lambda_\infty(\alpha)$ is nuclear if and only if for some r, $0 < r < 1$, $\Sigma_{n\ge 0}\, r^{\alpha_n} < \infty$.

Schwartz Property and Nuclearity of G_1*-Spaces*

To begin with, let us prove the following (Ref. 247, p. 89)

PROPOSITION 7.16 A G_1-space $(\Lambda(P),T)$ is Schwartz if and only if $P \subset c_0$.

Proof. Let $P \subset c_0$ and $u \in P$. From Definition 7.2(ii), we can determine a $v \in P$ with $u_n \le v_n^2$, $n \ge 0$. Hence $u_n/v_n \le v_n \to 0$ and so $\{u_n/v_n\} \in c_0$. Thus $\Lambda(P)$ is Schwartz by Theorem 7.10.

Conversely, let $\Lambda(P)$ be Schwartz and assume $u \in P$. We can find a $v \in P$ with $\{u_n/v_n\} \in c_0$. Now using Definition 7.2(i),

$$\frac{u_n}{v_0} \le \frac{u_n}{v_n} \qquad \Longrightarrow \qquad u \in c_0$$

Hence $P \subset c_0$. □

EXERCISE 7.17 Prove that every G_1-space $\Lambda_1(\alpha)$ is Schwartz.

Our next result on the characterization of nuclearity of the G_1-space $\Lambda(P)$ requires the notion of rapidly decreasing sequences (cf. Ref. 23).

DEFINITION 7.18 An $x \in \omega$ is called *rapidly decreasing* provided $\{n^k x_n\} \in \ell^\infty$ for $k = 1, 2, \ldots$.

Note: Unless specified otherwise, the collection of all rapidly decreasing sequences will be *hereafter denoted* by S. If $\alpha_n = \ln(n + 1)$, $n \ge 0$, and $P = \{\{k^{\alpha_n}\} : k \ge 1\}$, the G_∞-space $\Lambda_\infty(\alpha)$ is S; also, if $P = \{\{(n + 1)^k\} : k \ge 1\}$, we again find that $\Lambda(P) = S$ [here $\Lambda(P)$ is a G_∞-space].

We also need (cf. Lemmas 1 and 2 of Ref. 11, p. 139; see also Ref. 252, p. 2)

PROPOSITION 7.19 A decreasing sequence α with $\alpha_n > 0$ is rapidly decreasing if and only if

$$\sum_{n\ge0} \alpha_n^\gamma < \infty$$

for every real number $\gamma > 0$.

Proof. Let α be rapidly decreasing and $\gamma > 0$ be a given real number. Then we can find an integer k with $\gamma k > 1$ and a constant $M > 0$ such that $n^k \alpha_n \le M$ for each $n \ge 1$. Hence

$$\sum_{n\ge0} \alpha_n^\gamma = \alpha_0^\gamma + \sum_{n\ge1} \alpha_n^\gamma \le \alpha_0^\gamma + \sum_{n\ge1} \frac{M^\gamma}{n^{\gamma k}} < \infty$$

Conversely, if k is a given positive integer, choose $\gamma = 1/k$. As α is decreasing, the inequality

$$n\alpha_n^\gamma \le \sum_{m=1}^{n} \alpha_m^\gamma \le \sum_{m\ge0} \alpha_m^\gamma = M$$

implies $n^k \alpha_n \le M^k$ for all $n \ge 0$. □

Next we have (Ref. 247, p. 90; cf. also Ref. 252, p. 3)

PROPOSITION 7.20 For a G_1-space $(\Lambda(P),T)$ the following statements are equivalent:

(i) $(\Lambda(P),T)$ is nuclear.

(ii) $P \subset S$.

(iii) $P \subset \ell^1$.

Proof. (i) ⟹ (ii) Let $a \in P$ and r be any positive number. We can determine an even integer m with $mr \ge 1$. By Definition 7.2(ii), we can determine a member $b \in P$ such that

$$a_n^r \le b_n^{mr} \qquad \forall n \ge 0$$

Using Theorem 7.11, we find $\alpha \in \ell^1$ and $g \in P$ such that $b_n \le \alpha_n g_n$, $n \ge 0$. Therefore

$$a_n^r \le \alpha_n^{mr} g_n^{mr} \le \alpha_n^{mr} g_0^{mr}$$

$$\Longrightarrow \quad \sum_{n\ge0} a_n^r < \infty$$

and so by Proposition 7.19, $a \in S$, i.e., $P \subset S$.

(ii) ⟹ (iii) Trivial.

(iii) ⟹ (i) Let $a \in P$. There exists $b \in P$ with $a_n \le b_n^2$, $n \ge 0$. Hence $a_n/b_n \le b_n$. But $b \in \ell^1$; therefore $\{a_n/b_n\} \in \ell^1$. □

Note: The proof (i) $\Longrightarrow$ (ii) is comparatively much shorter than that in Ref. 247.

EXERCISE 7.21 Prove that the G_1-space $\Lambda_1(\alpha)$ is nuclear if and only if for each r, $0 < r < 1$, $\{r^{\alpha_n}\} \in \ell^1$.

EXAMPLE 7.22 Let $\{i_n\}$ be a sequence of integers defined by $i_0 = 0$, $i_n = 1! + 2! + \cdots + n!$, $n \geq 1$. Define $\{\alpha_n\}$ by

$$\alpha_0 = 1 \qquad \alpha_1 = 1 \qquad \alpha_i = n \qquad \text{and} \qquad i_{n-1} + 1 \leq i \leq i_n \qquad n \geq 1$$

Then

$$\sum_{i \geq 0} q^{\alpha_i} = q^{\alpha_0} + q^{\alpha_1} + \sum_{n \geq 2} \sum_{i=i_{n-1}+1}^{i_n} q^{\alpha_i} = q^{\alpha_0} + \sum_{n \geq 1} n! q^n$$

Consequently $\Sigma_{i \geq 0} q^{\alpha_i}$ converges only when $q = 0$. Hence from Exercises 7.15 and 7.21, the spaces $\Lambda_\infty(\alpha)$ and $\Lambda_1(\alpha)$ are nonnuclear; however, both of them are Schwartz spaces.

Comments on Generalizations of Nuclearity

In earlier subsections we have given a rigorous characterization of the nuclearity property and the Schwartz property of a class of sequence spaces. There are closely related topics which we have not touched upon so far. For instance, we have (i) diametrical dimensions of sequence spaces, (ii) impact of Schauder bases on the nuclearity and Schwartz property of sequence spaces and vice versa, (iii) structure theorems of nuclear and Schwartz spaces, (iv) nuclear and Schwartz maps. Indeed, our projected plan prevents us from discussing these topics here. For the same reason, it would not be possible to consider another important development concerning the subject matter of this section, namely, the study of strongly (*stark*) nuclear spaces or S-nuclear spaces and their generalization to $\Lambda(\alpha)$- and $\Lambda(P)$-nuclearity.

The different spaces mentioned in the foregoing paragraph are special cases of λ-nuclearity defined in Chapter 1. Although a good account of λ-nuclearity is to be found in Ref. 45, a number of deep results parallel to the usual nuclearity are still left unexplored, and probably investigators are aware of several constraints restricting them from going ahead in this direction. Therefore the aim has been to study λ-nuclearity with special conditions.

It was Martineau [165] who introduced the class of S-nuclear spaces, which were rediscovered by Brudovskii [23,24]. Brudovskii's statement characterizing S-nuclearity was corrected by Köthe [141 (5), p. 293] (cf. also Ref. 142). Ramanujan [194] and Spuhler [240] considered the notion of $\Lambda(\alpha)$-nuclearity where $\Lambda(\alpha)$ is a nuclear power series space of infinite type, and it was extended by Dubinsky and Ramanujan [45] to $\Lambda_\infty(\alpha)$-nuclearity. Terzioğlu [251] further generalized the concept of $\Lambda_\infty(\alpha)$-nuclearity to $\Lambda(P)$-nuclearity where $\Lambda(P)$ is an arbitrary G_∞-space. Thus Terzioğlu's results are most general in the direction of Λ-nuclearity.

Another generalization of ℓ^1-nuclearity (that is, nuclearity) to p-nuclearity was considered by Fenske and Schock who (Ref. 51, p. 17) extended the well-known Grothendieck-Pietsch criterion to p-nuclearity; in a different paper (Ref. 52) they also studied the ϕ-nuclearity of spaces. In Ref. 209, p. 12, Rosenberger introduced the concept of ℓ_ϕ-nuclear operators (i.e., ℓ_ϕ-nuclear maps) and using this definition he (Ref. 210) gave an interesting extension of the nuclearity concept in terms of ϕ-nuclearity which he developed further in Ref. 211.

Matrix Transformations in Nuclear Spaces

We continue here the study of matrix transformations initiated in Section 6. Let us begin with the following result which is more general than a similar result due to Jacob [100]. All sequences considered hereafter are defined over $\mathbb{N}$.

THEOREM 7.23 Let λ be a normal sequence space such that $\lambda^\times$ is simple, μ a perfect sequence space such that $(\mu,\eta(\mu,\mu^\times))$ is nuclear, and $A = [a_{ij}]$ is an infinite matrix. Then the following statements are equivalent:

(i) $A \in (\lambda,\mu)$.

(ii) $A^\perp \in (\mu^\times,\lambda^\times)$.

(iii) For each $x \in \mu^\times$ there corresponds an element $y \in \lambda^\times$ such that

$$|a_{ij}x_i| \le y_j \qquad \forall i,j \ge 1$$

Proof. (i) $\Longrightarrow$ (ii) This follows from Proposition 3.3.

(ii) $\Longrightarrow$ (iii) This is a consequence of Theorem 6.6.

(iii) $\Longrightarrow$ (i) The condition (iii) guarantees the existence of $(A(x))_i$ for each $x \in \lambda$ and $i \geq 1$. Let now $x \in \lambda$ and $u \in \mu^\times$. The nuclearity of $(\mu,\eta(\mu,\mu^\times))$ yields an element $v \in \mu^\times$, $v \geq 0$, and an $\alpha \in \ell^1$ such that $|u_n| = \alpha_n v_n$, $n \geq 1$ (cf. Theorem 7.9). From (iii), we find an element $y \in \lambda^\times$ such that

$$|a_{ij}v_i| \leq y_j \qquad \forall i,j \geq 1$$

Hence

$$\begin{aligned}\sum_{i\geq 1} |(A(x))_i u_i| &\leq \sum_{i\geq 1}\sum_{j\geq 1} |a_{ij}x_j||u_i| \\ &\leq \sum_{i\geq 1} \alpha_i \sum_{j\geq 1} |a_{ij}v_i x_j| < \infty\end{aligned}$$

Thus $A(x) \in \mu^{\times\times} = \mu$. □

By Theorem 7.11, the space $\Pi_{1/r}$ $(0 \leq r < \infty)$ is nuclear relative to its natural locally convex topology generated by the power set $P = \{\{\rho^n\} : 0 < \rho < 1/r\}$; moreover $\Pi^\times_{1/r} = d_r$. With these observations we have the following result, which in particular includes the theorems of Fricke and Powell [55, p. 255] and Rao [196, p. 172].

PROPOSITION 7.24 Let $A = [a_{ij}]$ be an infinite matrix. Suppose r and s satisfy the inequalities $0 \leq r < \infty$ and $0 \leq s < \infty$. Then the following statements are equivalent:

(i) $A \in (\Pi_{1/s},\Pi_{1/r})$.

(ii) $A^\perp \in (d_r,d_s)$.

(iii) For each α, $0 < \alpha < 1/r$, there exist $\beta > 0$ and R with $0 < R < 1/r$ such that

$$|a_{ij}|\alpha^i \leq \beta R^j \qquad \forall i,j \geq 1$$

Proof. (i) $\Longrightarrow$ (ii) This results from Proposition 3.3.

(ii) $\Longrightarrow$ (iii) Let $x = \{\alpha^i\} \in d_r$. By Theorem 7.23 we find $y \in d_s$ such that

$$|a_{ij}|\alpha^i \leq y_j \qquad \forall i,j \geq 1$$

Since $\limsup_{j\to\infty} y_j^{1/j} < 1/s$, there exist $\beta > 0$ and R, $0 < R < 1/s$, such that

$$y_j < \beta R^j \qquad j \geq 1$$

and so we obtain (iii).

(iii) $\Rightarrow$ (ii) Let $x \in d_r$. We can choose α and γ with $0 < \alpha < \gamma < 1/r$, and R, $0 < R < 1/s$, such that

$$|x_i| < \alpha^i$$

and

$$|a_{ij}|\gamma^i \leq \beta R^j \qquad \forall i,j \geq 1$$

Hence

$$|(A^{\perp}(x))_j| \leq \sum_{i\geq 1} |a_{ij}||x_i| < \beta \sum_{i\geq 1} R^j \left(\frac{\alpha}{\gamma}\right)^i < \infty$$

Moreover,

$$\limsup_{j\to\infty} |(A^{\perp}(x))_j|^{1/j} \leq R < \frac{1}{r}$$

Hence $A^{\perp}(x) \in d_s$. □

We now come to a result of Rao whose proof here is comparatively much shorter than that given in Ref. 197, p. 163. Of course, our proof makes use of Theorem 7.23.

PROPOSITION 7.25 For an infinite matrix $A = [a_{ij}]$, the following statements are equivalent:

(i) $A \in (\ell^1, \delta)$.

(ii) $A^{\perp} \in (d, \ell^{\infty})$.

(iii) For every α, $0 < \alpha < \infty$, there exists an element $y \in \ell^{\infty}$ such that

$$|a_{ij}|\alpha^i \leq y_j \qquad \forall i,j \geq 1$$

(iv) $|a_{ij}|^{1/i} \to 0$ as $i \to \infty$ uniformly in $j \geq 1$.

Proof. (i) $\Longleftrightarrow$ (ii) follow from Proposition 3.3.

(ii) $\Rightarrow$ (iii) For any α with $0 < \alpha < \infty$, $\{\alpha^i\} \in d$. Hence (iii) follows from Theorem 7.23, (ii) $\Rightarrow$ (iii).

(iii) $\Rightarrow$ (iv) Let $\varepsilon > 0$ be chosen arbitrarily. By (iii) there exists $y \in \ell^\infty$ such that

$$|a_{ij}| \le \varepsilon^i y_j \qquad \forall i,j \ge 1$$

$$\Rightarrow \quad |a_{ij}| \le \|y\|\varepsilon^i \qquad \forall i,j \ge 1$$

Hence $|a_{ij}|^{1/i} \to 0$ as $i \to \infty$ uniformly in $j \ge 1$. □

8. ORLICZ AND MODULAR SEQUENCE SPACES

The study of Orlicz and Lorentz sequence spaces was initiated with a certain specific purpose in Banach space theory. Indeed, Lindberg [150,151] got interested in Orlicz spaces in connection with finding Banach spaces with symmetric Schauder bases having complementary subspaces isomorphic to c_0 or ℓ^p $(1 \le p < \infty)$. Subsequently Lindenstrauss and Tzafriri studied these Orlicz sequence spaces in more detail, and solved many important and interesting structural problems in Banach spaces [152-154]. In the meantime, Woo [267] generalized the concept of Orlicz sequence spaces to modular sequence spaces and this led him to sharpen some of the results of Lindberg and of Lindenstrauss and Tzafriri; he carried this study further in Ref. 268. The Orlicz sequence spaces are the special cases of Orlicz spaces introduced in Ref. 179 and extensively studied in Ref. 145. Orlicz spaces find a number of useful applications in the theory of nonlinear integral equations. Whereas the Orlicz sequence spaces are the generalizations of ℓ^p-spaces, the L^p-spaces find themselves enveloped in Orlicz spaces.

The purpose of this section is to acquaint the reader with the elements of these sequence spaces, especially their structural features and AK-characteristics. For deeper results in Orlicz and modular sequence spaces, one may consult Refs. 155, 156, and 267, and several references given therein. We shall not study either of these topics extensively here.

Orlicz Sequence Spaces

One of the obvious generalizations of the function $M(x) = x^p$ which plays a prominent role in the construction of the ℓ^p-spaces is the one given in

DEFINITION 8.1 An *Orlicz function* is a function $M: [0,\infty) \to [0,\infty)$ which is continuous, nondecreasing, and convex, with $M(0) = 0$, $M(x) > 0$ for $x > 0$, and $M(x) \to \infty$ as $x \to \infty$.

An Orlicz function M can always be represented (see Ref. 145, p. 5; cf. also Ref. 112 for a more general representation theorem in this direction) in the following integral form:

$$M(x) = \int_0^x p(t)\, dt$$

where p, known as the *kernel* of M, is right-differentiable for $t \geq 0$, $p(0) = 0$, $p(t) > 0$ for $t > 0$, p is nondecreasing, and $p(t) \to \infty$ as $t \to \infty$.

Note: An Orlicz function is sometimes referred to as an O-*function* as well.

Consider the kernel p(t) associated with an Orlicz function M(t), and let

$$q(s) = \sup\{t : p(t) \leq s\}$$

Then q possesses the same properties as the function p. Suppose now

$$N(x) = \int_0^x q(s)\, ds$$

Then N is an Orlicz function. The functions M and N are called *mutually complementary* O-*functions* (or *mutually complementary Orlicz functions*).

The following result on complementary O-functions is quoted from Ref. 145, p. 12.

PROPOSITION 8.2 Let M and N be mutually complementary functions. Then we have (*Young's inequality*)

(i) For $x,y \geq 0$, $xy \leq M(x) + N(y)$.

We also have

(ii) For $x \geq 0$, $xp(x) = M(x) + N(p(x))$.

Also, $M(\alpha x) < \alpha M(x)$ for $x \geq 0$ and $0 < \alpha < 1$.

DEFINITION 8.3 For each O-function M, let $\tilde{\ell}_M$ be the collection of x in ω with

$$\delta(x;M) \equiv \sum_{i\geq 1} M(|x_i|) < \infty$$

Then $\tilde{\ell}_M$ is called the *Orlicz sequence class*.

DEFINITION 8.4 Let M and N be mutually complementary functions. The class ℓ_M defined by

$$\ell_M = \left\{x : x \in \omega, \sum_{i\geq 1} x_i y_i \text{ converges for all } y \in \tilde{\ell}_N\right\}$$

is called an *Orlicz sequence space*.

EXERCISE 8.5 Show that $\tilde{\ell}_M \subset \ell_M$.

PROPOSITION 8.6 For each $x \in \ell_M$,

$$\sup\left\{\left|\sum_{i\geq 1} x_i y_i\right| : \delta(y,N) \leq 1\right\} < \infty$$

Proof. Suppose the required result is not true. Then for each $n \geq 1$ there exists y^n with $\delta(y^n,N) \leq 1$ such that

$$\left|\sum_{i\geq 1} x_i y_i^n\right| > 2^n$$

Without loss of generality we may assume that $x, y^n >> 0$, $n \geq 1$. Since $B = \{y : \delta(y,N) \geq 1\}$ is bounded in ℓ^∞ [indeed, choose $\alpha_0 > 0$ with $(\alpha_0/2)q(\alpha_0/2) \geq 1$ and verify that $|y_i| \leq \alpha_0$ for all $i \geq 1$ and $y \in B$], we can define a sequence $z = \{z_i\}$, where

$$z_i = \sum_{n\geq 1} \frac{1}{2^n} y_i^n$$

By the convexity of N,

$$N\left(\sum_{n=1}^{m} \frac{1}{2^n} y_i^n\right) \leq \frac{1}{2}\left[N(y_i^1) + N\left(\frac{y_i^2}{2} + \cdots + \frac{y_i^m}{2^{m-1}}\right)\right] \leq \cdots \leq \sum_{n=1}^{m} \frac{1}{2^n} N(y_i^n)$$

and hence, using the continuity of N, we find that

$$\delta(z,N) \le \sum_{i\ge1} \sum_{n\ge1} \frac{1}{2^n} N(y_i^n) \le \sum_{n\ge1} \frac{1}{2^n} = 1$$

But for every $m \ge 1$,

$$\sum_{i\ge1} x_i z_i \ge \sum_{i\ge1} x_i \sum_{n=1}^{m} \frac{1}{2^n} y_i^n = \sum_{n=1}^{m} \sum_{i\ge1} \frac{x_i y_i^n}{2^n} \ge m$$

Therefore $\Sigma_{i\ge1} x_i z_i$ diverges and this implies that $x \notin \ell_M$, a contradiction. Hence the result. □

The preceding result allows us to introduce the function $\|x\|_M : \ell_M \to \mathbb{R}^+$, where

$$\|x\|_M = \sup\left\{ \left| \sum_{i\ge1} x_i y_i \right| : \delta(y,N) \le 1 \right\}$$

and we leave it to the reader to verify that $(\ell_M, \|\cdot\|_M)$ is a Banach space.

It is clear that $\phi \subset \ell_M$ and we conclude easily that $\|x^n\|_M \to 0$ implies that $x_i^n \to 0$ for each $i \ge 1$ [in proving this, observe that $\delta(e^i,N) \le 1$ if $N(1) \le 1$; otherwise $\delta(e^i/N(1),N) \le 1$]. Hence we have proved

PROPOSITION 8.7 $(\ell_M, \|\cdot\|_M)$ is a BK-space.

The space ℓ_M can also be made a BK-space under a different and equivalent norm $\|\cdot\|_{(M)}$ defined by

$$\|x\|_{(M)} = \inf\left\{ k > 0 : \sum_{i\ge1} M\left(\frac{|x_i|}{k}\right) \le 1 \right\}$$

Direct computation immediately leads to

PROPOSITION 8.8 We have, for x in ℓ_M, the inequality

$$\sum_{i\ge1} M\left(\frac{|x_i|}{\|x\|_{(M)}}\right) \le 1$$

Proposition 8.8 helps us conclude that for $x,y \in \ell_M$,

$$\sum_{i\geq 1} M\left(\frac{|x_i + y_i|}{\|x\|_{(M)} + \|y\|_{(M)}}\right) \leq 1$$

and consequently $\|x + y\|_{(M)} \leq \|x\|_{(M)} + \|y\|_{(M)}$. It is easy to see that

$$\|\alpha x\|_{(M)} = \inf\left\{k > 0 : \delta\left(\frac{\alpha x}{k};M\right) \leq 1\right\}$$

$$= \inf\left\{|\alpha|r > 0 : \delta\left(\frac{x}{r};M\right) \leq 1\right\} = |\alpha|\,\|x\|_{(M)}$$

THEOREM 8.9 For x in ℓ_M,

$$\|x\|_{(M)} \leq \|x\|_M \leq 2\|x\|_{(M)}$$

The proof requires a number of intermediate results.

PROPOSITION 8.10 Let $x \in \ell_M$ with $\|x\|_M \leq 1$. Then $y = \{p(|x_n|)\} \in \tilde{\ell}_N$ and $\delta(y;N) \leq 1$.

Proof. It is easily seen that for any z in $\tilde{\ell}_N$,

$$\left|\sum_{i\geq 1} x_i z_i\right| \leq \begin{cases} \|x\|_M & \text{if } \delta(z;N) \leq 1 \\ \delta(z;N)\|x\|_M & \text{if } \delta(z;N) > 1 \end{cases} \qquad (*)$$

Let now $x \in \ell_M$ with $\|x\|_M \leq 1$. Since $\phi \subset \ell_M$, $x^{(n)} \in \ell_M$ for $n \geq 1$. Observe that

$$\|x\|_M \geq \left|\sum_{i\geq 1} x_i y_i^{(n)}\right| = \left|\sum_{i\geq 1} x_i^{(n)} y_i\right| \qquad n \geq 1$$

for every $y \in \tilde{\ell}_N$ with $\delta(y;N) \leq 1$, and thus

$$\|x^{(n)}\|_M \leq \|x\|_M \leq 1$$

Since

$$\sum_{i=1}^{n} N(p(|x_i|)) = \sum_{i\geq 1} N(p(x_i^{(n)}))$$

we find that $\{p(|x_i^{(n)}|) : i \geq 1\} \in \tilde{\ell}_N$ for each $n \geq 1$.

Let $m \geq 1$ be an integer such that

$$\sum_{i=1}^{m} N(p(|x_i|)) > 1$$

Then

$$\sum_{i\geq 1} N(p(|x_i^{(m)}|)) > 1$$

By Proposition 8.2(ii),

$$\begin{aligned} N(p(|x_i^{(m)}|)) &< M(|x_i^{(m)}|) + N(p(|x_i^{(m)}|)) \\ &= |x_i^{(m)}|p(|x_i^{(m)}|) \qquad \forall i,m \geq 1 \end{aligned}$$

and so, by (*),

$$\sum_{i\geq 1} N(p(|x_i^{(m)}|)) \leq \|x^{(m)}\|_M \delta(\{p(|x_i^{(m)}|)\};N)$$

$$\Longrightarrow \quad \|x^{(m)}\|_M > 1$$

This contradiction implies that

$$\sum_{i=1}^{m} N(p(|x_i|)) \leq 1 \qquad \forall m \geq 1$$

Hence $\{p(|x_i|)\} \in \tilde{\ell}_N$ and $\delta(\{p(|x_i|)\};N) \leq 1$. □

PROPOSITION 8.11 Let $x \in \ell_M$ with $\|x\|_M \leq 1$. Then $x \in \tilde{\ell}_M$ and $\delta(x;M) \leq \|x\|_M$.

Proof. Let $y = \{p(|x_i|)/\text{sgn } x_i\}$. Then from Proposition 8.10, $y \in \tilde{\ell}_N$ and $\delta(y;N) \leq 1$. By Proposition 8.2,

$$\begin{aligned} \sum_{i\geq 1} M(|x_i|) &\leq \sum_{i\geq 1} M(|x_i|) + \sum_{i\geq 1} N(p(|x_i|)) \\ &= \sum_{i\geq 1} |x_i|p(|x_i|) = \Big|\sum_{i\geq 1} x_i y_i\Big| \leq \|x\|_M \end{aligned}$$

$$\Longrightarrow \quad \delta(x;M) \leq \|x\|_M \quad \square$$

Proposition 8.11 immediately yields

PROPOSITION 8.12 For $x \in \ell_M$,

$$\sum_{i\geq 1} M\left(\frac{|x_i|}{\|x\|_M}\right) \leq 1$$

Proof of Theorem 8.9. Using Proposition 8.12, we get

$$\|x\|_{(M)} \leq \|x\|_M$$

Let us observe that if $x \in \ell_M$ with $\|x\|_{(M)} \leq 1$, then $x \in \tilde{\ell}_M$ and $\delta(x;M) \leq 1$. Indeed,

$$\frac{1}{\|x\|_{(M)}} \sum_{i\geq 1} M(|x_i|) \leq \sum_{i\geq 1} M\left(\frac{|x_i|}{\|x\|_{(M)}}\right) \leq 1$$

by Proposition 8.8. Thus $x/\|x\|_{(M)} \in \tilde{\ell}_M$ with $\delta(x/\|x\|_{(M)};M) \leq 1$. We notice further that for an arbitrary $z \in \tilde{\ell}_M$,

$$\|z\|_M = \sup\left\{\left|\sum_{i\geq 1} z_i y_i\right| : \delta(y;N) \leq 1\right\} \leq 1 + \delta(z;M) \qquad (*)$$

The preceding inequality (*) can be deduced easily from Proposition 8.2(i). Hence

$$\left\|\frac{x}{\|x\|_{(M)}}\right\|_M \leq 1 + \sum_{i\geq 1} M\left(\frac{|x_i|}{\|x\|_{(M)}}\right) \leq 2$$

by Proposition 8.8. □

COROLLARY 8.13 $(\ell_M, \|\cdot\|_{(M)})$ is a BK-space.

EXERCISE 8.14 Prove that $\ell_M = \ell_M^1$ where ℓ_M^1 is the class of all $x \in \omega$ such that

$$\sum_{i\geq 1} M\left(\frac{|x_i|}{r}\right) < \infty$$

for some $r > 0$. [Hint: Use Proposition 8.12.]

In view of Exercise 8.14, it is natural to introduce the following definition after Gribanov [69].

DEFINITION 8.15 The subspace of ℓ_M consisting of those x in ℓ_M such that $\Sigma_{i\geq 1} M(|x_i|/k) < \infty$ for each $k > 0$ is denoted by h_M, M being an Orlicz function.

Note: Henceforth we shall abbreviate $\|\cdot\|_{(M)}$ as $\|\cdot\|$ provided it does not lead to any confusion. The topology of h_M is the one it inherits from $\|\cdot\|$. With these words we have (Ref. 151)

PROPOSITION 8.16 Let M be an Orlicz function. Then $(h_M, \|\cdot\|)$ is an AK-BK space.

Proof. We first prove that the space in question is an AK-space. Thus let $x \in h_M$. For each ε, $0 < \varepsilon < 1$, one can find an n_0 such that

$$\sum_{i\geq n_0} M\left(\frac{|x_i|}{\varepsilon}\right) \leq 1$$

Hence for $n \geq n_0$,

$$\|x - x^{(n)}\| = \inf\left\{k > 0 : \sum_{i\geq n+1} M\left(\frac{|x_i|}{k}\right) \leq 1\right\}$$

$$\leq \inf\left\{k > 0 : \sum_{i\geq n} M\left(\frac{|x_i|}{k}\right) \leq 1\right\} \varepsilon$$

Returning to the second part, it suffices to prove that h_M is closed in ℓ_M. Therefore let $\{x^n\}$ be a sequence in h_M such that $\|x^n - x\| \to 0$, where $x \in \ell_M$. To complete the proof we need show that $\Sigma_{i\geq 1} M(|x_i|/k) < \infty$ for every $k > 0$. To $k > 0$ there corresponds an m such that $\|x^m - x\| \leq k/2$, and so by the convexity of M,

$$\sum_{i\geq 1} M\left(\frac{|x_i|}{k}\right) = \sum_{i\geq 1} M\left(\frac{2|x_i^m| - 2(|x_i^m| - |x_i|)}{2k}\right)$$

$$\leq \frac{1}{2}\sum_{i\geq 1} M\left(\frac{2|x_i^m|}{k}\right) + \frac{1}{2}\sum_{i\geq 1} M\left(\frac{2|x_i^m - x_i|}{k}\right)$$

$$\leq \frac{1}{2}\sum_{i\geq 1} M\left(\frac{2|x_i^m|}{k}\right) + \frac{1}{2}\sum_{i\geq 1} M\left(\frac{|x_i^m - x_i|}{\|x^m - x\|}\right) < \infty$$

by Proposition 8.8. Thus $x \in h_m$. □

From the preceding proposition it is clear that ℓ_M is not in general an AK-space unless we restrict M further. Therefore, let us introduce

DEFINITION 8.17 An Orlicz function M is said to satisfy the Δ_2-*condition for small* x or *at* 0 if for each $k > 0$ there exist $R_k > 0$ and $x_k > 0$ such that

$$M(kx) \le R_k M(x) \qquad \forall x \in (0, x_k]$$

EXERCISE 8.18 Show that M in Definition 8.17 satisfies the Δ_2-condition if and only if

$$\limsup_{x \to 0} \frac{M(2x)}{M(x)} < \infty$$

We have now (cf. Ref. 69 also)

PROPOSITION 8.19 Let M be an Orlicz function. Then the following are equivalent:

(i) M satisfies the Δ_2-condition at 0.

(ii) $h_M = \ell_M$.

(iii) ℓ_M is an AK-space.

Proof. (i) $\Rightarrow$ (ii) We need prove that $\ell_M \subset h_M$. Let $x \in \ell_M$; then for $\rho > 0$,

$$\sum_{i \ge 1} M\left(\frac{|x_i|}{\rho}\right) < \infty \quad \Longrightarrow \quad M\left(\frac{|x_i|}{\rho}\right) \to 0 \qquad \text{as } i \to \infty \tag{*}$$

Choose an arbitrary $\eta > 0$. If $\rho \le \eta$, then $\Sigma_{i \ge 1} M(|x_i|/\eta) < \infty$. Let now $\eta < \rho$ and put $k = \rho/\eta$. One can determine $R \equiv R_k > 0$ and $r \equiv r_k > 0$ with

$$M(kx) \le RM(x) \qquad \forall x \text{ in } (0, r]$$

By (*) there exists an I in $\mathbb{N}$ such that

$$M\left(\frac{|x_i|}{\rho}\right) < \frac{1}{2}\, rp\left(\frac{r}{2}\right) \qquad \forall i \ge I$$

and the last inequality yields

$$\frac{|x_i|}{\rho} \le r \qquad \forall i \ge I \tag{**}$$

For otherwise, we can find $j > I$ with $|x_j|/\rho > r$, and thus

$$M\left(\frac{|x_j|}{\rho}\right) \geq \int_{r/2}^{|x_j|/\rho} p(t)\, dt > \frac{1}{2}\, rp\left(\frac{r}{2}\right)$$

This contradiction establishes (**). Using (**) one finds that

$$\sum_{i\geq I} M\left(\frac{|x_i|}{\eta}\right) \leq \sum_{i\geq I} M\left(\frac{|x_i|}{\rho}\right)$$

and hence $\Sigma_{i\geq 1} M(|x_i|/\eta) < \infty$ for every $\eta > 0$. Thus we have (ii).

(ii) $\Longrightarrow$ (iii) This follows from Proposition 8.16.

(iii) $\Longrightarrow$ (i) Suppose M does not satisfy the Δ_2-condition at 0. Then there exists a decreasing sequence $\{x_n\}$ with $x_n \to 0$ such that $M(2x_n)/M(x_n) > 2^{n+1}$ and $M(x_n) \leq 2^{-n}$ for every $n \geq 1$. One can choose integers α_n so that $2^{-(n+1)} < \alpha_n M(x_n) \leq 2^{-n}$ for $n \geq 1$. Hence

$$\sum_{n\geq 1} \alpha_n M(x_n) \leq 1 \qquad \alpha_n M(2x_n) > 1, \ \forall n \geq 1$$

For any $y \in \ell^\infty$, define $z \in \omega$ by

$$z_i = \begin{cases} x_1 y_1 & 1 \leq i \leq \alpha_1 \\ x_j y_j & \sum_{k=1}^{j} \alpha_k + 1 \leq i \leq \sum_{k=1}^{j+1} \alpha_k,\ j \geq 1 \end{cases}$$

Then

$$\sum_{i\geq 1} M\left(\frac{|z_i|}{\|y\|_\infty}\right) = \sum_{n\geq 1} \alpha_n M\left(\frac{x_n |y_n|}{\|y\|_\infty}\right) \leq 1 \tag{8.20}$$

and so $z \in \ell_M$. Thus we have the map $T\colon \ell^\infty \to \ell_M$, $T(y) = z$, and from (8.20), $\|T(y)\| \leq \|y\|_\infty$. Again, by Proposition 8.8, for $y \in \ell^\infty$,

$$\sum_{i\geq 1} M\left(\frac{|(T(y))_i|}{\|T(y)\|}\right) \leq 1$$

$$\Longrightarrow \quad \alpha_n M\left(\frac{x_n |y_n|}{\|T(y)\|}\right) \leq 1 \qquad \forall n \geq 1$$

If for some $m \geq 1$, $2\|T(y)\| < |y_m|$, then $2x_m < x_m|y_m|/\|T(y)\|$ and so

$$1 < \alpha_m M\left(\frac{x_m |y_m|}{\|T(y)\|}\right)$$

and this gives a contradiction. Hence $2^{-1}\|y\|_\infty \le \|T(y)\| \le \|y\|_\infty$ for $y \in \ell^\infty$. It is easily seen that $\|T(e) - \Sigma_{i=1}^n (T(e))_i e^i\| \to 0$ and so $\|e - e^{(n)}\|_\infty \to 0$, which is, however, absurd. □

EXERCISE 8.21 Show that an Orlicz function M satisfies the Δ_2-condition at 0 if and only if ℓ_M is separable.

Comparison of ℓ_M *with* ℓ^p $(1 \le p \le \infty)$

To be precise in comparing a given ℓ_M with one of the spaces ℓ_p $(1 \le p \le \infty)$, it would be advantageous to start with

DEFINITION 8.22 Two Orlicz functions M_1 and M_2 are said to be *equivalent* if there are positive constants α, β, and x_0 such that

$$M_1(\alpha x) \le M_2(x) \le M_1(\beta x) \tag{8.23}$$

for all x with $0 \le x \le x_0$.

And now we have the desired

PROPOSITION 8.24 Let M_1 and M_2 be two Orlicz functions. Then M_1 and M_2 are equivalent if and only if $\ell_{M_1} = \ell_{M_2}$ and the identity map $I: (\ell_{M_1}, \|\cdot\|_{M_1}) \to (\ell_{M_2}, \|\cdot\|_{M_2})$ is a topological isomorphism.

Proof. Let M_1 and M_2 be equivalent and satisfy (8.23). Suppose $x \in \ell_{M_2}$, then $\Sigma_{i\ge1} M_2(|x_i|/\rho) < \infty$ for some $\rho > 0$. Hence for some $k \ge 1$, $|x_i|/k\rho \le x_0$ for all $i \ge 1$. Therefore, $\Sigma_{i\ge1} M_1(\alpha|x_i|/k\rho) \le \Sigma_{i\ge1} M_2(|x_i|/\rho) < \infty$. Thus $\ell_{M_2} \subset \ell_{M_1}$. Similarly, $\ell_{M_1} \subset \ell_{M_2}$. Let us abbreviate here $\|\cdot\|_{M_1}$ and $\|\cdot\|_{M_2}$ by $\|\cdot\|_1$ and $\|\cdot\|_2$, respectively. For $x \in \ell_{M_2}$,

$$\sum_{i\ge1} M_2\left(\frac{|x_i|}{\|x\|_2}\right) \le 1$$

One can find $\gamma > 1$ with $(x_0/2)\gamma p_2(x_0/2) \ge 1$, where p_2 is the kernel associated with M_2. Hence

$$M_2\left(\frac{|x_i|}{\|x\|_2}\right) \le \gamma\ \frac{x_0}{2}\ p_2\left(\frac{x_0}{2}\right) \qquad \forall i \ge 1$$

$$\Longrightarrow \quad \frac{|x_i|}{\gamma\|x\|_2} \le x_0 \qquad \forall i \ge 1$$

Therefore

$$\sum_{i\ge1} M_1\left(\frac{\alpha|x_i|}{\gamma\|x\|_2}\right) < 1$$

and so $\|x\|_1 \le (\gamma/\alpha)\|x\|_2$. For the other inequality, choose γ_1 with $\gamma_1\beta > 1$ such that $\gamma_1\beta(x_0/2)p_1(x_0/2) \ge 1$. Hence, as before, $\|x\|_2 \le \beta\gamma_1\|x\|_1$. Thus

$$\alpha\gamma^{-1}\|x\|_1 \le \|x\|_2 \le \beta\gamma_1\|x\|_1$$

which establishes the topological isomorphism of I.

For the converse, assume that $\ell_{M_1} = \ell_{M_2}$ and that for no $x_0 > 0$ and $\alpha > 0$ is the inequality $M_1(x) \le M_2(\alpha x)$ satisfied for x in $(0,x_0]$. Hence we can find a monotonically decreasing sequence $\{x_n\}$, $x_n \to 0$, such that $M_1(x_n) > M_2(2^n n x_n)$ where $n \ge 1$. One can select a sequence of integers k_n with

$$\frac{1}{2^{n+1}} < k_n M_1(x_n) \le \frac{1}{2^n} \qquad \forall n \ge 1$$

Define y in ω by

$$y = (\underbrace{2x_1,\ldots,2x_1}_{k_1\text{ times}},\ldots,\underbrace{2^n n x_n,\ldots,2^n n x_n}_{k_n\text{ times}},\ldots)$$

Then

$$\sum_{n\ge1} M_2(y_n) = \sum_{n\ge1} k_n M_2(2^n n x_n) \le \sum_{n\ge1} \frac{1}{2^n} < \infty$$

Hence $y \in \ell_{M_2}$ and so $y \in \ell_{M_1}$. On the other hand, for $\alpha \ge 1$, choose m in $\mathbb{N}$ such that $m \ge \alpha$. Then

$$\sum_{n\ge1} M_1\left(\frac{y_n}{\alpha}\right) = \sum_{n\ge1} k_n M_1\left(\frac{2^n n x_n}{\alpha}\right) \ge \sum_{n\ge1} 2^n k_n M_1\left(\frac{n x_n}{\alpha}\right)$$

$$\ge \sum_{n\ge m} 2^n k_n M_1(x_n) = \infty$$

giving thus that y is not in ℓ_{M_1}. Hence M_1 and M_2 are equivalent. □

Remark: From the preceding proposition it follows that the behavior of M outside a neighborhood of 0 is irrelevant to the definition of ℓ_M. In fact, let M be an Orlicz function in $[0,\infty)$ and define

$$M_1(x) = \begin{cases} M(x) & 0 \le x \le x_0 \\ \dfrac{x}{x_0} M(x_0) & x > x_0 \end{cases}$$

Then M_1 is an Orlicz function in $[0,\infty)$ and $\ell_{M_1} = \ell_M$.

As far as the comparison of M with that of ℓ^p $(1 \le p \le \infty)$ is concerned, we have the following result of Lindberg [151].

PROPOSITION 8.25 Let M be an Orlicz function and p the corresponding kernel. Then

(i) ℓ_M is topologically isomorphic to ℓ^1 if and only if $p(0) = a > 0$.

(ii) If $p(x) = 0$ for all x in $[0,x_0]$ where x_0 is some positive number, then ℓ_M is topologically isomorphic to ℓ^∞ and h_M is topologically isomorphic to c_0.

Proof. (i) Note that ℓ^1 is generated by the function $M_1(x) = x$. If ℓ_M is topologically isomorphic to ℓ^1, we find $Ax \le M(x) \le Bx$ for $0 \le x \le x_0$, where A, B, and x_0 are some positive constants. For sufficiently small $x > 0$ (and of course $x < x_0$), $Ax \le M(x) \le xp(x)$, and so

$$p(0) = \lim_{x\to 0^+} p(x) \ge A > 0$$

Let now $p(0) = a > 0$. For $x > 0$,

$$M(x) \le xp(x) \qquad M(x) \ge xp(0)$$

$$\Longrightarrow \quad \lim_{x\to 0^+} \frac{M(x)}{x} = a > 0$$

and so we have constants $A,B > 0$ with $Ax \le M(x) \le Bx$ for $0 \le x \le x_0$. Thus

ℓ_M is topologically isomorphic to the space generated by $M_1(x) = x$, i.e., ℓ^1.

(ii) Let $p(x) = 0$ for $0 \le x \le x_0$. If $u \in \ell^\infty$, one can find a $k > 0$ such that $|u_i|/k \le x_0$ for $i \ge 1$, and so $\Sigma_{i\ge1} M(|u_i|/k) < \infty$, giving thus $u \in \ell^\infty$ if and only if $u \in \ell_M$ (cf. the proof of Proposition 8.24 for the converse inclusion). One can easily determine an x_1 with $M(x_1) \ge 1$. Let $u \in \ell^\infty$ and $\alpha = \|u\|_\infty > 0$. For every ε, $0 < \varepsilon < \alpha$, we can determine u_j with $|u_j| > \alpha - \varepsilon$ and so $\Sigma_{i\ge1} M(|u_i|x_1/\alpha) \ge M((\alpha - \varepsilon)x_1/\alpha)$. As M is continuous, we find $\Sigma_{i\ge1} M(|u_i|x_1/\alpha) \ge 1$, and so $\|u\|_\infty \le x_1\|u\|$, for otherwise $\Sigma_{i\ge1} M(|u_i|/\|u\|) > 1$ (cf. Proposition 8.8). Further,

$$\sum_{i\ge1} M\left(\frac{|u_i|x_0}{\alpha}\right) = 0$$

and it follows that $\|u\| \le (1/x_0)\|u\|_\infty$. Thus the identity map $I: (\ell_M, \|\cdot\|) \to (\ell^\infty, \|\cdot\|)$ is a topological isomorphism.

For the remaining part, let us observe that if $u \in h_M$, then for any $\varepsilon > 0$,

$$|u_i| \le \varepsilon x_1$$

for all sufficiently large i, where x_1 is some positive number with $p(x_1) > 0$. Hence $u \in c_0$. Let $u \in c_0$. Then for any $k > 0$, $|u_i|/k < (1/2)x_0$ for all sufficiently large i. Thus

$$\sum_{i\ge1} M\left(\frac{|u_i|}{k}\right) < \infty \qquad \forall k > 0$$

giving $u \in h_M$. Hence $h_M = c_0$ and we are done. □

EXERCISE 8.26 Let M be an Orlicz function. Show that ℓ_M is topologically isomorphic to ℓ^p $(1 \le p < \infty)$ if and only if M is equivalent to M_p, $M_p(x) = x^p$.

Duals of h_M *and* ℓ_M

The pleasant condition under which we would like to determine the dual of ℓ_M is that ℓ_M should be an AK-space. However, this amounts to finding the dual of h_M, and in this direction we have the following:

PROPOSITION 8.27 Let M and N be mutually complementary O-functions. Then $h_M^\beta = \ell_N$ and hence $h_M^* = \ell_N$.

Proof. Let $y \in \ell_N$ and so $\Sigma_{i\geq 1} N(|y_i|/r) < \infty$ for some $r > 0$. Take any x in h_M. Now $|x_i y_i| \leq M(|rx_i|) + N(|y_i|/r)$. Hence $\Sigma_{i\geq 1} x_i y_i$ converges and $y \in h_M^\beta$. On the other hand, suppose $y \in h_M^\beta$. Using Definition 8.4, we find $h_M^\beta \subset \ell_N$. Thus $h_M^\beta = \ell_N$. The last part is disposed of by using Propositions 2.3.9 and 9.16. □

COROLLARY 8.28 $h_M^\times = h_M^\beta = h_M^\gamma = h_M^* = \ell_N$.

Proof. Indeed, h_M is normal. □

EXERCISE 8.29 If M and N are mutually complementary O-functions satisfying the Δ_2-condition at 0, show that ℓ_M is perfect.

Remarks on Orlicz Sequence Spaces

In the preceding paragraphs we have presented the elementary properties of ℓ_M; however, there are many striking results related to the structure of ℓ_M, and of course based on our preceding basic background, which would equally occupy the attention of vector space pathologists but are outside the scope of this book. For instance, if M is an Orlicz function, set

$$a_M = \liminf_{x\to 0} \frac{xM'(x)}{M(x)} \qquad b_M = \limsup_{x\to 0} \frac{xM'(x)}{M(x)}$$

Then one has (Ref. 151, p. 129; cf. also Ref. 156, p. 148)

PROPOSITION 8.30 Let ℓ_M be separable. Then ℓ_M is reflexive if and only if $1 < a_M \leq b_M < \infty$.

For the following result, one may look into Ref. 152, p. 382.

THEOREM 8.31 Every Orlicz sequence space ℓ_M contains a subspace isomorphic to ℓ^p for some $p \geq 1$.

Many deeper results on Orlicz sequence spaces can be found in Ref. 156.

OK-*Spaces*

Lindenstrauss and Tzafriri [154, p. 369] pointed out a possible generalization of the space ℓ_M to the case when M is an Orlicz function that does not satisfy the convexity condition. This problem was picked up recently by Kalton [110] who succeeded in finding many interesting features distinguishing these two theories of sequence spaces. In the next few pages we present some results relevant to the topological structure of this generalized version of ℓ_M.

To begin with let us introduce the definition of a K-*function* E which is an Orlicz function but is not convex. Motivated by Exercise 8.14, we *define* ℓ^E (resp. h^E) to be the space of all x in ω for which $\Sigma_{i\geq 1} E(|x_i|/r) < \infty$ for some (resp. all) $r > 0$. We shall call ℓ^E an OK-*space*. If x and y are in ℓ^E, then for some $r_1, r_2 > 0$,

$$\sum_{i\geq 1} E\left(\frac{|x_i|}{r_1}\right) < \infty \qquad \text{and} \qquad \sum_{i\geq 1} E\left(\frac{|y_i|}{r_2}\right) < \infty$$

Let $r = 2 \max\{r_1, r_2\}$. Then

$$\sum_{i\geq 1} E\left(\frac{|x_i + y_i|}{r}\right) \leq \sum_{i\geq 1} E\left(\frac{2|x_i|}{r}\right) + \sum_{i\geq 1} E\left(\frac{2y_i}{r}\right)$$

giving $x + y \in \ell^E$. If $\alpha \in \mathbb{K}$, we can find j in $\mathbb{N}$ so that $|\alpha|/2^j < 1/r_1$; thus $\alpha x \in \ell^E$. Therefore ℓ^E is a vector space over $\mathbb{K}$.

We now define a linear topology on ℓ^E. For each $\varepsilon > 0$, let

$$B(\varepsilon) \equiv B_E(\varepsilon) = \{x \in \omega : \Sigma_{i\geq 1} E(|x_i|) \leq \varepsilon\}$$

and consider the family $\mathcal{B} = \{rB(\varepsilon) : r, \varepsilon > 0\}$. One immediately verifies that each member of $\mathcal{B}$ is balanced. We next verify that each member $rB(\varepsilon)$ of $\mathcal{B}$ is absorbing. Indeed, if x is in ℓ^E, we can find $\alpha > 0$ with $\Sigma_{i\geq 1} E(|x_i|/\alpha r) < \infty$, and so for some m in $\mathbb{N}$,

$$\sum_{i\geq m+1} E\left(\frac{|x_i|}{\alpha r}\right) < \frac{\varepsilon}{2}$$

Choose $\alpha_1, \ldots, \alpha_m$ such that

$$E\left(\frac{|x_1|}{r\alpha_1}\right) < \frac{\varepsilon}{2}, \ \ldots, \ E\left(\frac{|x_m|}{r\alpha_m}\right) < \frac{\varepsilon}{2m}$$

If $\beta = \max\{\alpha, \alpha\alpha_1, \ldots, \alpha\alpha_m\}$, then

$$\sum_{i\geq 1} E\left(\frac{|x_i|}{r\beta}\right) \leq \sum_{i=1}^{m} E\left(\frac{|x_i|}{r\alpha\alpha_i}\right) + \sum_{i\geq m+1} E\left(\frac{|x_i|}{r\alpha}\right) < \frac{\varepsilon}{2} + \frac{\varepsilon}{2} = \varepsilon$$

Hence $x \in \beta r B(\varepsilon)$. Further, we claim that

$$\frac{r}{2} B\left(\frac{\varepsilon}{2}\right) + \frac{r}{2} B\left(\frac{\varepsilon}{2}\right) \subset rB(\varepsilon)$$

For, if $x,y \in (r/2)B(\varepsilon/2)$, then

$$\sum_{i\geq 1} E\left(\frac{|x_i + y_i|}{r}\right) \leq \sum_{i\geq 1} E\left(\frac{2|x_i|}{r}\right) + \sum_{i\geq 1} E\left(\frac{2|y_i|}{r}\right) \leq \frac{\varepsilon}{2} + \frac{\varepsilon}{2} = \varepsilon$$

Thus $x + y \in rB(\varepsilon)$.

Summing up the preceding discussion and using Proposition 1.2.3, we find that $\mathcal{B}$ generates a (Hausdorff) linear topology T_E on ℓ^E. Restricting each ε and r in the family $\mathcal{B}$ to be rational, we easily find that T_E is metrizable (cf. Definition 1.4.2). From the monotonocity and continuity, there directly follows the K-character of T_E [that is, (ℓ^E, T_E) is a K-space] which in turn yields the completeness of (ℓ^E, T_E). The preceding discussion in this subsection finally leads to the following:

PROPOSITION 8.32 For an OK-function E, the space (ℓ^E, T_E) is a Fréchet K-space (cf. Definition 2.3.3).

We shall be interested only in those spaces ℓ^E which are AK-spaces, and this is indeed achieved by assuming E to satisfy the Δ_2-condition at 0 (cf. Definition 8.17). In view of the remark following the proof of Proposition 8.24, we may regard a K-function E as satisfying the Δ_2-condition at 0 if and only if to every $\alpha > 0$, we have

$$K_{E,\alpha} = \sup_{0<x<\infty} \frac{E(\alpha x)}{E(x)} < \infty \tag{8.33}$$

The condition in (8.33) is usually called the *Δ_2-condition on* $\mathbb{R}$ satisfied by E.

PROPOSITION 8.34 If E is a K-function satisfying the Δ_2-condition on $\mathbb{R}$, then $h^E = \ell^E$, and (ℓ^E, T_E) is an AK-Fréchet K-space.

Proof. Let us first note that $h^E = \ell^E$; in fact, if $x \in \ell^E$, then for some $\alpha > 0$, $\Sigma_{i\geq 1} E(|x_i|/\alpha) < \infty$. Choose an arbitrary $\beta > 0$. Hence

$$\sum_{i\geq 1} E\left(\frac{|x_i|}{\beta}\right) = \sum_{i\geq 1} E\left(\frac{|x_i|}{\alpha}\right) \cdot \frac{E(\alpha y_i/\beta)}{E(y_i)} \qquad y_i = \frac{|x_i|}{\alpha}$$

$$\leq K_{E,\alpha/\beta} \sum_{i\geq 1} E\left(\frac{|x_i|}{\alpha}\right) < \infty$$

Therefore $x \in h^E$ and so $h^E = \ell^E$.

Let $x \in \ell^E$, $r > 0$, and $\varepsilon > 0$ be arbitrarily chosen. From the inequality

$$\sum_{i\geq 1} E\left(\frac{|x_i|}{r}\right) < \infty$$

we conclude the existence of an integer n_0 such that

$$\sum_{i\geq n+1} E\left(\frac{|x_i|}{r}\right) \leq \varepsilon \qquad \forall n \geq n_0$$

This in turn implies that $x^{(n)} - x \in rB(\varepsilon)$ for all $n \geq n_0$. The arbitrary character of r and $\varepsilon > 0$ implies that $x^{(n)} \to x$ in T_E. Now apply Proposition 8.32. □

Note: Sometimes it will be convenient to talk about T_E in terms of the pseudonorms which generate this topology. For each r and $\varepsilon > 0$, let

$$p_{r,\varepsilon}(x) = \inf\{\alpha > 0 : x \in \alpha r B(\varepsilon)\}$$

Clearly $p_{r,\varepsilon}(\beta x) = |\beta| p_{r,\varepsilon}(x)$ and $p_{r,\varepsilon}(x + y) \leq p_{s,\delta}(x) + p_{s,\delta}(y)$ for all x,y in ℓ^E and β in $\mathbb{K}$, where $s = r/2$ and $\delta = \varepsilon/2$. Hence the family $D_{T_E} = \{p_{r,\varepsilon} : r,\varepsilon > 0\}$ of pseudonorms on ℓ^E generates the topology T_E.

In case E satisfies the Δ_2-condition on $\mathbb{R}$, the family $\{p_\varepsilon : \varepsilon > 0\}$ of pseudonorms on ℓ^E defined by

$$p_\varepsilon(x) = \inf\left\{\alpha > 0 : \sum_{i\geq 1} E\left(\frac{|x_i|}{\alpha}\right) \leq \varepsilon\right\}$$

also generates a linear topology T'_E on ℓ^E such that $T'_E \approx T_E$. Indeed, for x in ℓ^E (E satisfies the Δ_2-condition on $\mathbb{R}$),

$$p_{r,\varepsilon}(x) = \inf\{\alpha > 0 : x \in \alpha r B(\varepsilon)\}$$

$$= \frac{1}{r} \inf\left\{\alpha r > 0 : \sum_{i\geq 1} E\left(\frac{|x_i|}{\alpha r}\right) \leq \varepsilon\right\}$$

$$= \frac{1}{r} \inf\left\{\beta : \sum_{i\geq 1} E\left(\frac{|x_i|}{\beta}\right) \leq \varepsilon\right\}$$

Hence

$$p_{r,\varepsilon}(x) = \frac{1}{r} p_\varepsilon(x) \qquad x \in \ell^E$$

To prepare for the final result of this subsection, let us associate a function $\hat{E}$ to each K-function E as follows:

$$\hat{E}(x) = \inf\left\{\frac{1}{n} \sum_{i=1}^{n} E(x_i) : 0 \leq x_i \leq 1, \frac{1}{n} \sum_{i=1}^{n} x_i = x\right\} \qquad 0 \leq x \leq 1$$

and

$$\hat{E}(x) = E(x) \qquad x > 1$$

It is clear that $\hat{E}$ is convex in $[0,1]$ and satisfies all those properties which E does on $\mathbb{R}$. Besides, $\hat{E}$ is equivalent to an Orlicz function and so $\ell_{\hat{E}}$ is a Banach space. Observe that $\hat{E}(x) \leq E(x)$ for all $x \geq 0$. Further, if G is any K-function with G convex on $[0,1]$ and $G(x) \leq E(x)$, $x \geq 0$, then $G(x) \leq \hat{E}(x)$ for all $x \geq 0$.

Let us now pass on to the last and main result of this subsection, which is interesting in itself and is related to the Mackey topology of ℓ^E. We have (Ref. 110, p. 256)

THEOREM 8.35 Let E be a K-function satisfying the Δ_2-condition at 0. Then $\tau(\ell^E, (\ell^E)^*)$ is equivalent to the topology on ℓ^E induced by the topology of $\ell_{\hat{E}}$.

Proof. For convenience, let us assume temporarily that $\ell^E = X$ and $\ell_{\hat{E}} = Y$; also suppose that T_1 is the topology on X generated by E while T_2 is the topology on X induced by $\tau(Y,Y^*)$, the norm topology on Y generated by $\hat{E}$.

If $X_1^* = (X,T_1)^*$ and $X_2^* = (X,T_2)^*$ (for notation, cf. the note following Proposition 1.6.2), then from $\hat{E}(x) \leq E(x)$ we find that $X_2^* \subset X_1^*$; hence $\tau(X,X_2^*) \subset \tau(X,X_1^*)$. But $Y^* \subset X_2^*$; therefore $\tau(X,Y^*) \subset \tau(X,X_1^*)$. Since

$\tau(X,Y^*) = \tau(Y,Y^*)|X$, we finally conclude that the norm topology on ℓ^E induced by $\hat{E}$ is weaker than the Mackey topology $\tau(\ell^E,(\ell^E)^*)$.

To prove the converse, let us consider any $p \in D_\tau$, $\tau \equiv \tau(\ell^E,(\ell^E)^*)$ (for notation, see the discussion preceding Definition 1.2.8). By Proposition 1.8.8, p is continuous on ℓ^E relative to T_1. To get the required conclusion, we need show that p is continuous on ℓ^E relative to the topology T_2. The proof of this fact is broken into several steps.

(I) We first show that there exists α, $0 < \alpha \le E(1)$, such that for x in ℓ^E

$$\sum_{i\ge 1} E(|x_i|) \le \alpha \quad \Longrightarrow \quad p(x) \le 1 \tag{*}$$

Indeed, by the continuity of p on (ℓ^E,T_1) we can find ε and $\beta > 0$ such that

$$\sum_{i\ge 1} E\left(\frac{|x_i|}{\beta}\right) \le \varepsilon \quad \Longrightarrow \quad p(x) \le 1 \qquad x \in \ell^E$$

If $\beta \ge 1$, then $\Sigma_{i\ge 1} E(|x_i|) \le \varepsilon$ implies that $\Sigma_{i\ge 1} E(|x_i|/\beta) \le \varepsilon$ and so $p(x) \le 1$, and we get (*) with $\alpha = \varepsilon$. If $\beta < 1$, then using (8.33) we find that whenever $\Sigma_{i\ge 1} E(|x_i|) \le \varepsilon/K_{E,\beta}$, then $\Sigma_{i\ge 1} E(|x_i|/\beta) \le \varepsilon$, and so $p(x) \le 1$, and this once again yields (*). Thus

$$\sum_{i\ge 1} E(|x_i|) \le \min\left\{\varepsilon, \frac{\varepsilon}{K_{E,\beta}}\right\} \quad \Longrightarrow \quad p(x) \le 1$$

which gives the statement in (*) in both of the cases.

(II) Using (I) we next establish that for x in ℓ^E, $\sup |x_n| \le 1$,

$$p(x) \le \frac{2+\gamma}{\alpha} \sum_{i\ge 1} E(|x_i|) + 1 \tag{**}$$

where γ is some positive constant. In fact, the boundedness of $\{e^n\}$ in ℓ^E gives rise to a constant γ such that $p(e^n) \le \gamma$ for $n \ge 1$.

Let $x \in \ell^E$ with $\sup |x_n| \le 1$. Suppose $J = \{i \in \mathbb{N} : E(|x_i|) > \alpha\}$ and put $L = \mathbb{N} \sim J$. Then

$$\alpha|J| \le \sum_{i\in J} E(|x_i|) < \infty$$

$|J|$ being the measure of J, and it follows that J is finite. Also

$$p\left(\sum_{i\in j} x_i e^i\right) \le \gamma|J| \le \frac{\gamma}{\alpha} \sum_{i\ge 1} E(|x_i|)$$

Choose m in $\mathbb{N}$ so that the sets $\sigma_1, \ldots, \sigma_{m+1}$ divide L into a finite number of parts such that

$$\frac{1}{2}\alpha \le \sum_{i\in\sigma_j} E(|x_i|) \le \alpha \qquad j = 1, 2, \ldots, m$$

and

$$0 \le \sum_{i\in\sigma_{m+1}} E(|x_i|) < \frac{1}{2}\alpha$$

Then

$$\frac{1}{2} m\alpha \le \sum_{j=1}^{m} \sum_{i\in\sigma_j} E(|x_i|) \le \sum_{i\ge 1} E(|x_i|)$$

Also, using (*), we have

$$p\left(\sum_{i\in\sigma_j} x_i e^i\right) \le 1 \qquad j = 1, \ldots, m + 1$$

Hence

$$p\left(\sum_{i\in L} x_i e^i\right) = p\left(\sum_{j=1}^{m+1} \sum_{i\in\sigma_j} x_i e^i\right) \le m + 1 \le \frac{2}{\alpha} \sum_{i\ge 1} E(|x_i|) + 1$$

Thus (cf. Proposition 8.34)

$$\begin{aligned} p(x) &= p\left(\sum_{i\ge 1} x_i e^i\right) \\ &\le p\left(\sum_{i\in J} x_i e^i\right) + p\left(\sum_{i\in L} x_i e^i\right) \\ &\le \frac{\gamma}{\alpha} \sum_{i\ge 1} E(|x_i|) + \frac{2}{\alpha} \sum_{i\ge 1} E(|x_i|) + 1 \end{aligned}$$

and so (**) is proved.

(III) Here we show that whenever $x \in \phi$, with $\Sigma_{i\ge 1} \hat{E}(|x_i|) \le \alpha$, then $p(x) \le 2\gamma + 5$. So, let x be the sequence just described. Since $\alpha \le E(1)$, $|x_i| \le 1$ for each $i \ge 1$; also observe that $x_i = 0$ except for a finite number of indices i. Therefore, for a sufficiently large positive integer N, one may choose sequences $\{y_i^k\}$, $k = 1, \ldots, N$, with $0 \le y_i^k \le 1$, such that

$$\frac{1}{N}(y_i^1 + \cdots + y_i^N) = |x_i|$$

and

$$\frac{1}{N}\sum_{k=1}^{N} E(y_i^k) \leq \hat{E}(|x_i|) + \frac{\alpha}{2^i}$$

where $y_i^k = 0$ $(1 \leq k \leq N)$ provided $x_i = 0$. Hence

$$\frac{1}{N}\sum_{i\geq 1}\sum_{k=1}^{N} E(y_i^k) \leq \sum_{i\geq 1} \hat{E}(|x_i|) + \alpha \leq 2\alpha$$

Define $z^k \in \phi$ by

$$z_i^k = (\operatorname{sgn} x_i)y_i^k \qquad 1 \leq k \leq N,\ i \geq 1$$

Then

$$\sum_{k=1}^{N} z_i^k = (\operatorname{sgn} x_i)\sum_{k=1}^{N} y_i^k = Nx_i$$

and so

$$x = \frac{1}{N}\sum_{k=1}^{N} z^k$$

Observe that $\sup_i |z_i^k| \leq 1$ for $1 \leq k \leq N$. Thus, by (**),

$$p(z^k) \leq \frac{\gamma + 2}{\alpha}\sum_{i\geq 1} E(|z_i^k|) + 1 = \frac{\gamma + 2}{\alpha}\sum_{i\geq 1} E(y_i^k) + 1$$

Hence

$$p(x) \leq \frac{1}{N}\frac{\gamma + 2}{\alpha}\sum_{k=1}^{N}\sum_{i\geq 1} E(y_i^k) + 1 \leq 2\gamma + 5$$

(IV) Finally it is shown that whenever $x \in \ell^E$ with $\Sigma_{i\geq 1}\hat{E}(|x_i|) \leq \alpha$, then $p(x) \leq 2\gamma + 5$. Indeed, for any x in ℓ^E, $p(x^{(n)}) \to p(x)$. Now for x in ℓ^E with $\Sigma_{i\geq 1}\hat{E}(|x_i|) \leq \alpha$,

$$\sum_{i\geq 1} \hat{E}(|x_i^{(n)}|) = \sum_{i=1}^{n} \hat{E}(|x_i|) \leq \sum_{i\geq 1} \hat{E}(|x_i|) \leq \alpha$$

Consequently $p(x^{(n)}) \leq 2\gamma + 5$ [cf. (III)]. Letting $n \to \infty$, we obtain $p(x) \leq 2\gamma + 5$.

From (IV) we find that

$$p(x) \le \frac{2\gamma + 5}{\alpha} \|x\|_{(\hat{E})} \qquad \forall x \text{ in } \ell^E$$

and this proves the continuity of p on (ℓ^E, T_2). □

Modular Sequence Spaces

Another generalization of Orlicz sequence spaces is due to Woo [267]. Let $\{M_n\}$ be a sequence of Orlicz functions. Define the vector space $\ell\{M_n\}$ by

$$\ell\{M_n\} = \left\{x \in \omega : \sum_{n\ge1} M_n\left(\frac{|x_n|}{r}\right) < \infty \text{ for some } r > 0\right\}$$

and equip this space with the norm $\|\cdot\|$, where

$$\|x\| = \inf\left\{r > 0 : \sum_{n\ge1} M_n\left(\frac{|x_n|}{r}\right) \le 1\right\}$$

The space $(\ell\{M_n\}, \|\cdot\|)$, or simply $\ell\{M_n\}$, is a Banach space and is called a *modular sequence space*. The space $\ell\{M_n\}$ also generalizes the concept of *modulared sequence space* introduced earlier by Nakano [176], who considered the space $\ell\{M_n\}$ when $M_n(x) = x^{\alpha_n}$, where $1 \le \alpha_n < \infty$ for $n \ge 1$. All those results on Orlicz sequence spaces that we have mentioned in the preceding paragraphs can be generalized to modular sequence spaces provided we carefully handle the generalized notions of equivalence and the Δ_2-condition at 0; this has been achieved by Woo [267], and according to him we have

DEFINITION 8.36 Two sequences $\{M_n\}$ and $\{N_n\}$ of Orlicz functions are said to be m-*equivalent* provided $\ell\{M_n\} = \ell\{N_n\}$.

DEFINITION 8.37 A sequence $\{M_n\}$ of Orlicz functions is said to satisfy the *uniform* Δ_2-condition at 0 provided there exist $p \ge 1$ and n_0 in $\mathbb{N}$ such that for all x, $0 < x < 1$, and $n \ge n_0$, we have $xM_n'(x)/M_n(x) \le p$.

Let us recall the *space* $h\{M_n\}$, that is, the space of all those x in ω such that

$$\sum_{n\ge1} M_n\left(\frac{|x_n|}{r}\right) < \infty \qquad \forall r > 0$$

In what follows we suppose that $M_n(1) = 1$ for all $n \geq 1$. At this stage we do not wish to go into the details of several results on modular sequence spaces whose corresponding analogs in Orlicz sequence spaces have been given earlier, except for the following analog of Proposition 8.19 (cf. Ref. 267, p. 281).

PROPOSITION 8.38 For a sequence $\{M_n\}$ of Orlicz functions, the following statements are equivalent:

(i) $\ell\{M_n\} = \ell\{N_n\}$ where $\{N_n\}$ is a sequence of Orlicz functions satisfying the uniform Δ_2-condition at 0.

(ii) $\ell\{M_n\} = h\{M_n\}$.

(iii) $(\ell\{M_n\}, \|\cdot\|)$ is an AK-space, where for x in $\ell\{M_n\}$,

$$\|x\| = \inf\left\{r > 0 : \sum_{n\geq 1} M_n\left(\frac{|x_n|}{r}\right) \leq 1\right\}$$

Proof. The proof is not a direct imitation of the corresponding result in Orlicz sequence spaces.

(i) $\Longrightarrow$ (ii) We first show that $\ell\{N_n\} = h\{N_n\}$ and for that purpose let $\Sigma_{n\geq 1} N_n(|x_n|/r) < \infty$ for some $r > 0$. Choose $k < r$ with $k > 0$. By the Δ_2-condition on $\{N_n\}$ we have $p \geq 1$ and n_0 as required in Definition 8.37. Since $1 < p/(p - 1)$, choose α_0 with $1 < \alpha_0 < p/(p - 1)$. If $\alpha = r/k$, let us consider two cases: (a) when $1 < \alpha \leq \alpha_0$ and (b) when $\alpha > \alpha_0$.

Case (a) For $n \geq n_0$ and $0 < x < 1/\alpha$,

$$N_n(\alpha x) - N_n(x) = (\alpha - 1)xN_n'(\theta_n)$$

$$\leq (\alpha - 1)xN_n(\theta_n) \cdot \frac{p}{\theta_n} \leq \frac{(\alpha - 1)pN_n(\alpha x)}{\alpha}$$

where $x \leq \theta_n \leq \alpha x$, $n \geq n_0$. Thus

$$N_n(\alpha x) \leq K(p,\alpha)N_n(x)$$

where $n \geq n_0$, $0 < x < 1/\alpha$, $K(p,\alpha) > 1$, and $\alpha \leq \alpha_0$.

Case (b) Let m be the smallest integer with $\alpha_0^m \geq \alpha$. Hence, for $0 < x < (1/\alpha_0)\alpha_0^{-m}$ and $n \geq n_0$,

$$N_n(\alpha x) \leq N_n(\alpha_0^m x) = N_n(\alpha_0 \cdot \alpha_0^{m-1}x) \leq K(p,\alpha_0)N_n(\alpha_0^{m-1}x)$$

by case (a). Proceeding in this way m - 1 times more we find that

$$N_n(\alpha x) \le [K(p,\alpha_0)]^m N_n(x)$$

valid for $n \ge n_0$ and $0 < x < \alpha_0^{-m-1}$.

Thus, using cases (a) and (b), we have n_0, $f(\alpha)$, and $e(\alpha)$ such that

$$N_n(\alpha x) \le e(\alpha)N_n(x) \qquad \forall n \ge n_0;\ 0 < x < f(\alpha)$$

Next observe that $\Sigma_{n\ge1} N_n(|x_n|/r) < \infty$ implies that $|x_n|/r \to 0$ (indeed, the Δ_2-condition on $\{N_n\}$ yields the inequality $N_n(x) \ge x^p$ for $0 \le x < 1$ and $n \ge n_0$; see Ref. 267, p. 280) and so $|x_n|/r < f(\alpha)$ eventually in n and there follows the desired inequality, namely,

$$\sum_{n\ge1} N_n\left(\frac{|x_n|}{k}\right) < \infty$$

If $k \ge r$, the preceding inequality follows trivially, and thus $\ell\{N_n\} = h\{N_n\}$. This finishes the proof of (ii).

(ii) $\Longrightarrow$ (iii) As in Proposition 8.16.

(iii) $\Longrightarrow$ (i) First of all we claim the existence of positive numbers $p, n_0 \in \mathbb{N}$ and $\alpha \in (0,1)$ such that $xM_n'(x)/M_n(x) \le p$ for $0 \le x \le \alpha$ and $n \ge n_0$. Suppose this is false; accordingly, we may introduce the double sequence $\{x_{mn}\}$ as follows:

$$x_{mn} = \sup\{x : 0 \le x \le 2^{-m},\ xM_n'(x) \ge 2^m M_n(x)\}$$

It is easily seen (indeed, make use of the continuity of M_n and monotonic increasing character of M_n') that $x_{mn} M_n'(x_{mn}) \ge 2^m M_n(x_{mn})$ for $m,n \ge 1$. We next assert the existence of an m in $\mathbb{N}$ such that $\Sigma_{n\ge1} M_n(x_{mn}) < \infty$. Otherwise, one can find $p_1 < p_2 < \cdots < p_m < \cdots \to \infty$ with

$$2^{-m} \le \sum_{n=p_m+1}^{p_{m+1}} M_n(x_{mn}) \qquad m \ge 1$$

Since $x_{mn} < 1$, $M_n(x_{mn})/x_{mn} \le M_n(1)/1$ and so $M_n(x_{mn}) \le x_{mn} \Longrightarrow M_n(x_{mn}) < 2 \cdot 2^{-m}$ for all $m,n \le 1$. Hence $\{p_n\}$ can be chosen so that

$$\sum_{n=p_m+1}^{p_{m+1}} M_n(x_{mn}) \le 2 \cdot 2^{-m} \qquad \forall m \ge 1$$

Now

$$M_n(2x_{mn}) \ge M_n'(x_{mn}) \int_{x_{mn}}^{2x_{mn}} dt \ge 2^m M_n(x_{mn})$$

Let us put

$$y_m = \sum_{n=p_m+1}^{p_{m+1}} x_{mn} e^n \qquad m \ge 1$$

and define $T: \ell^\infty \to \ell\{M_n\}$ by $T(\alpha) = \Sigma_{m\ge1} \alpha_m y_m = \{\alpha_1 x_{1(p_1+1)}, \ldots, \alpha_1 x_{1p_2}; \alpha_2 x_{2(p_2+1)}, \ldots, \alpha_2 x_{2p_3}; \alpha_3 x_{3(p_3+1)}, \ldots, \alpha_3 x_{3p_4}; \ldots\}$. To see that $T(\alpha)$ does belong to $\ell\{M_n\}$, let us observe that

$$\sum_{m\ge1} \sum_{n=p_m+1}^{p_{m+1}} M_n\left(\frac{|\alpha_m| x_{mn}}{2\|\alpha\|_\infty}\right) \le \sum_{m\ge1} \sum_{n=p_m+1}^{p_{m+1}} M_n\left(\frac{1}{2} x_{mn}\right) \le \sum_{m\ge1} \frac{1}{2} \cdot 2 \cdot 2^{-m} = 1$$

which also gives $\|T(\alpha)\| \le 2\|\alpha\|_\infty$. Next we assert that given $\alpha \in \ell^\infty$, for no $m \ge 1$ is the inequality $2\|T(\alpha)\| < |\alpha_m|$ true. For otherwise, one gets some k in $\mathbb{N}$ such that

$$\sum_{m\ge1} \sum_{n=p_m+1}^{p_{m+1}} M_n\left(\frac{|\alpha_m| x_{mn}}{\|T(\alpha)\|}\right) > \sum_{n=p_k+1}^{p_{k+1}} M_n(2x_{kn}) \ge \sum_{n=p_k+1}^{p_{k+1}} 2^k M_n(x_{kn}) \ge 1$$

and from this we conclude that $\|T(\alpha)\| > \|T(\alpha)\|$. Hence we conclude that $2^{-1}\|\alpha\|_\infty \le \|T(\alpha)\| \le 2\|\alpha\|_\infty$ for every $\alpha \in \ell^\infty$. However, this conclusion deprives $\ell\{M_n\}$ of its AK-character, and so $\Sigma_{n\ge1} M_n(x_{mn}) < \infty$ for some m in $\mathbb{N}$. Choose $y_n > x_{mn}$ such that $M_n(y_n) = M_n(x_{mn}) + 2^{-n}$ and then define N_n by

$$N_n(x) = \begin{cases} M_n(x) & \text{for } x \ge y_n \\ \dfrac{xM_n(y_n)}{y_n} & \text{for } x \le y_n \end{cases}$$

Clearly each N_n is an Orlicz function, and for all $n \ge 1$, $xN_n'(x)/N_n(x) \le 2^m$, valid for all x with $0 \le x \le 2^{-m}$. It is not difficult to conclude that $\inf_n M_n(2^{-m}) > 0$ (for otherwise, $\ell\{M_n\}$ will have a subspace isomorphic to ℓ^∞) and thus $\inf_n N_n(2^{-m}) > 0$. Finally, observe that $\ell\{M_n\} = \ell\{N_n\}$ where $\{N_n\}$ satisfies the uniform Δ_2-condition at 0. □

9. LORENTZ SEQUENCE SPACES

These spaces are the special cases of Lorentz spaces, which Lorentz [159] introduced for solving some problems related to harmonic analysis and interpolation theory; for further work on Lorentz spaces and their applications, we refer to several sources cited in Ref. 27, p. 234. Lorentz sequence spaces which are perfect symmetric spaces probably were first introduced by Sargent in Ref. 224. However, a more systematic development was carried out almost simultaneously by Garling [57] and Ruckle [216], the former having given comparatively a more comprehensive and general treatment of these sequence spaces, which he extended in Ref. 60. Since then these spaces have occupied the attention of a number of mathematicians who explored their applications to the theory of symmetric and subsymmetric Schauder bases in Banach spaces and some other closely related topics; see Refs. 7, 8, 25, 26, 27, and 28 (cf. also Ref. 156).

As we shall recognize a little later, a special case of the class of Lorentz sequence spaces has already been touched upon (Section 5, Chapter 2); our purpose in this last section is to study these spaces in full generality and consequently examine their AK-BK character. Our approach to the proofs of the results on this topic is not only different but also more general than what we have given earlier. Essentially we follow Refs. 57 and 60 for the rest of this section.

DEFINITION 9.1 Let $1 \le p < \infty$ and $x \in c_0$, $x \notin \ell^1$, with $x >> 0$ and $1 = x_1 \ge x_2 \ge \cdots$. The sequence space $d(x,p)$, where

$$d(x,p) = \{y \in c_0 : \sup\{\Sigma_{n\ge1} x_n|y_{\sigma(n)}|^p : \sigma \in \Pi\} < \infty\}$$

is called a *Lorentz sequence space of order* p.

Note: For $p = 1$, $d(x,p) = x^\delta$ (cf. Proposition 2.5.25) and so $d(x,1)$ is an AK-BK symmetric sequence space under the norm $\|\cdot;1\|$ where for $y \in d(x,1)$,

$$\|y;1\| = \sup\{\Sigma_{n\ge1} x_n|y_{\sigma(n)}| : \sigma \in \Pi\}$$

As mentioned earlier we shall pay considerable attention to exploring the AK-BK properties of the space $d(x,p)$ equipped with its natural norm $\|\cdot;p\|$, where for $y \in d(x,p)$,

$$\|y;p\|^p = \sup\{\Sigma_{n\ge1} x_n|y_{\sigma(n)}|^p : \sigma \in \Pi\}$$

and this is indeed achieved via a unified approach to a general construction of perfect sequence spaces equipped with a certain locally convex topology.

A Method of Constructing a Topology

We follow Ref. 57 for this subsection. Let Q be a family {A} with $A \subset \omega$ satisfying the following conditions:

(i) Q is directed by set theoretic inclusion.

(ii) $\sup\{|x_n| : x \in A\} < \infty$ for each A in Q and n in $\mathbb{N}$.

(iii) For each n in $\mathbb{N}$, there corresponds A in Q with x in A such that $x_n \neq 0$.

DEFINITION 9.2 We introduce *spaces* λ_Q and *seminorms* p_A on λ_Q as follows:

$$\lambda_Q = \{x \in \omega : \sup\{\Sigma_{n\geq 1} |a_n x_n| : a \in A\} < \infty, \forall A \text{ in } Q\}$$

For A in Q and x in λ_Q,

$$p_A(x) = \sup\{\Sigma_{n\geq 1} |a_n x_n| : a \in A\}$$

It is clear that λ_Q is normal and contains ϕ, $p_A \leq p_B$ for $A \subset B$, and $\{p_A : A \in Q\}$ generates a Hausdorff locally normal locally convex topology T_Q on λ_Q. In case we do not mention any specific topology on λ_Q it will be assumed that it is endowed with T_Q.

For A in Q, let

$$\kappa_A = \{x \in \omega : \sup\{\Sigma_{n\geq 1} |a_n x_n| : a \in A\} < \infty\}$$

and for x in κ_A, let

$$t_A(x) = \sup\{\Sigma_{n\geq 1} |a_n x_n| : a \in A\}$$

Then

$$\lambda_Q = \cap \{\kappa_A : A \in Q\} \qquad p_A = t_A|\lambda_Q$$

and so T_Q is the projective topology for which the injections $i_A: \lambda_Q \to \kappa_A$ are continuous.

It is, however, convenient to express each κ_A as the direct sum of its two subspaces. So let $A \in Q$ and define

$$I_A = \{n : \sup\{|a_n| : a \in A\} > 0\}$$

$$J_A = \mathbb{N} \sim I_A = \{n : a_n = 0, \forall a \text{ in } A\}$$

By Exercise 2.8.8,

$$\kappa_A = (\overline{\kappa_A})_{I_A} \oplus (\overline{\kappa_A})_{J_A} = \pi_A \oplus \bar{\omega}_{J_A}$$

where

$$\pi_A = \kappa_A \cap \bar{\omega}_{I_A}$$

PROPOSITION 9.3 (π_A, t_A) is a Banach space and hence (λ_Q, T_Q) is complete.

Proof. The proof of this result is routine and so is omitted. □

Let $\nu_A = \pi_A^\times$. Then $\nu_A = ((\overline{\kappa_A})_{I_A})^\times = \overline{(\kappa_A)_{I_A}^\times} = \kappa_A^\times \cap \bar{\omega}_{I_A}$. Let us remind the reader of the straightforward observation contained in

PROPOSITION 9.4 Each y in ν_A defines a member of π_A^*.

Proof. Let

$$f_y^{(n)}(x) = \sum_{i=1}^{n} x_i y_i \qquad f_y(x) = \sum_{i\geq 1} x_i y_i \qquad x \in \pi_A$$

An application of Theorem 1.10.3 immediately yields the membership of f_y in π_A^*. □

PROPOSITION 9.5 Let $A \in Q$ and let B be the unit closed ball of π_A. Then $\pi_B = \nu_A$.

Proof. If $y \in \nu_A$, by Proposition 9.4 there corresponds $K_y > 0$ such that

$$\left|\sum_{i\geq 1} x_i y_i\right| \leq K_y \qquad \forall x \text{ in } B$$

$$\Longrightarrow \qquad \sum_{i\geq 1} |x_i y_i| \leq K_y \qquad \forall x \text{ in } B$$

and so $y \in \pi_B$, giving $\nu_A \subset \pi_B$. Conversely, for y in π_B,

$$\sum_{i\geq 1} |x_i y_i| \leq M_y < \infty \qquad M_y > 0$$

for any x in π_A with $t_A(x) \leq 1$, and thus $y \in \pi_A^\times$. □

PROPOSITION 9.6 For A in Q, κ_A is a perfect sequence space.

Proof. Invoking both the notation and conclusion of the preceding proposition, we find that

$$\nu_B = \pi_B^\times = \nu_A^\times = (\overline{(\kappa_A^\times)_{I_A}})^\times = \overline{(\kappa_A^{\times\times})_{I_A}} = \kappa_A^{\times\times} \cap \bar{\omega}_{I_A}$$

Denote by C the closed unit ball of π_B. Clearly, for a in A,

$$\sup\{\Sigma_{i\geq 1} |x_i a_i| : x \in B\} \leq 1$$

and so $A \subset C$. If $x \in \nu_B$, it follows that (cf. proof of Proposition 9.5)

$$\sup\{\Sigma_{i\geq 1} |c_i x_i| : c \in C\} < \infty$$

$$\Longrightarrow \quad \sup\{\Sigma_{i\geq 1} |a_i x_i| : a \in A\} < \infty$$

Therefore $x \in \pi_A$ and so $\kappa_A \cap \bar{\omega}_{I_A} = \kappa_A^{\times\times} \cap \bar{\omega}_{I_A}$. Now

$$\kappa_A = \pi_A \oplus \bar{\omega}_{J_A} \quad \Longrightarrow \quad \kappa_A^\times = \pi_A^\times \oplus \bar{\omega}_{J_A}^\times = \nu_A \oplus \bar{\omega}_{J_A}^\times$$

$$\Longrightarrow \quad \kappa_A^{\times\times} = \nu_A^\times \oplus \bar{\omega}_{J_A}^{\times\times} = \kappa_A^{\times\times} \cap \bar{\omega}_{I_A} \oplus \bar{\omega}_{J_A}^{\times\times}$$

$$= \kappa_A \cap \bar{\omega}_{I_A} \oplus \bar{\omega}_{J_A}^{\times\times} = \pi_A \oplus \bar{\omega}_{J_A}$$

Thus $\kappa_A^{\times\times} = \kappa_A$. □

EXERCISE 9.7 Show that λ_Q is perfect. [Hint: $\lambda_Q = \cap \{\kappa_A : A \in Q\}$.]

Construction of Symmetric Perfect Spaces

To see that the results of the preceding subsection can be applied to certain concrete spaces with which we are concerned, let $Q = \{A : A \subset \ell^\infty$, $A \neq \emptyset$, and if $0 \in A$ then A contains an $x \neq 0\}$.

DEFINITION 9.8

(i) $\mu_Q = \{x \in \omega : \sup\{\Sigma_{i\geq 1} |a_i x_{\sigma(i)}| : a \in A, \sigma \in \Pi\} < \infty, \forall A \text{ in } Q\}$.

(ii) For x in μ_Q and A in Q,

$$\|x\|_A = \sup\left\{\sum_{i\geq 1} |a_i x_{\sigma(i)}| : a \in A, \sigma \in \Pi\right\}$$

Note: If Q consists of just one element A, then we write μ_A for μ_Q.

For A in Q, let $A(\Pi) = \{a_\sigma : a \in A, \sigma \in \Pi\}$ and let us take $Q^* \equiv Q(\Pi) = \{A(\Pi) : A \in Q\}$. Since each A in Q is bounded in ℓ^∞, it follows that Q^* satisfies (i), (ii), and (iii) of the preceding subsection. Also,

$$\sum_{i\geq 1} |a_i x_{\sigma(i)}| = \sum_{i\geq 1} |x_i a_{\sigma^{-1}(i)}| \qquad \sigma \in \Pi$$

and thus $\mu_Q = \lambda_{Q^*}$. We are now in a position to state and prove one of the main results (cf. Ref. 57, p. 93) of this section, namely,

THEOREM 9.9 The space $\mu_Q = \lambda_{Q^*}$ is a symmetric perfect sequence space such that $\ell^1 \subset \mu_Q \subset \ell^\infty$; moreover, this space equipped with the family of norms $\{\|\cdot\|_A : A \in Q\}$ is a complete locally convex space.

Proof. By Exercise 9.7, μ_Q is perfect; it is clearly symmetric. Observe that $A(\Pi)$ is bounded for each A in Q and so $\ell^1 \subset \mu_Q$. Let $x \in \mu_Q$ but $x \notin \ell^\infty$. For each $n \geq 1$ there exists k_n ($k_n < k_{n+1}$) such that $|x_{k_n}| \geq n$; accordingly there exists $\{\sigma_n\} \subset \Pi$ with $|x_{\sigma_n(k)}| \geq n$. Choose a in A with $a_k \neq 0$. Hence

$$\sup\left\{\sum_{i\geq 1} |a_i x_{\sigma(i)}| : a \in A, \sigma \in \Pi\right\} \geq \sup_n |a_k x_{\sigma_n(k)}| = \infty$$

which contradicts the membership of x in μ_Q. Thus $\mu_Q \subset \ell^\infty$. The last part follows from Proposition 9.3. □

EXERCISE 9.10 Show that (i) the mapping $x \to x_\sigma$ ($x \in \mu_Q$, $\sigma \in \Pi$) is a homeomorphism, (ii) the inclusion map $\ell^1 \to \mu_Q$ is continuous, and (iii) the inclusion map $\mu_Q \to \ell^\infty$ is continuous. [Hints: (i) $\|x\|_A = \|x_\sigma\|_A$; (ii) $\|x\|_A \leq \sup\{\|a\|_\infty : a \in A(\Pi)\}\|x\|_1$; and (iii) choose $a \in A$, $a_k \neq 0$, and $\{\sigma_n\} \subset \Pi$ with $\sigma_n(k) = n$; thus $\|x\|_A \geq |a_k|\|x\|_\infty$.]

Remark: In general $\ell^1 \subset \mu_Q \subset \ell^\infty$, and so it is natural to inquire as to when $\mu_Q = \ell^1$ or ℓ^∞. An answer to this problem is contained in (cf. Ref. 57)

PROPOSITION 9.11 (i) If $\cup \{A : A \in Q\} \not\subset c_0$, then $\mu_Q = \ell^1$ and the identity map is a topological isomorphism. (ii) $\mu_Q = \ell^\infty$ if and only if $\cup \{A : A \in Q\} \subset \ell^1$ and each $A \in Q$ is bounded in ℓ^1; under these conditions, the identity map $\mu_Q \to \ell^\infty$ is a topological isomorphism.

Proof. (i) Choose a in $A \in Q$ with $a \notin c_0$. Hence for some $\varepsilon > 0$, $|a_{n_i}| > \varepsilon$, $i \geq 1$, where $n_1 < n_2 < \cdots$. Choose $\sigma_k \in \Pi$ such that $\sigma_k(i) = n_i$ $(1 \leq i \leq k)$. Then for $k \geq 1$,

$$\varepsilon \sum_{i=1}^{k} |x_i| \leq \sum_{i=1}^{k} |a_{n_i}||x_i| \leq \sum_{i\geq 1} |a_i||x_{\sigma_k^{-1}(i)}| \leq \|x\|_A$$

and so $x \in \ell^1$, and $\varepsilon\|x\|_1 \leq \|x\|_A$. This combined with Exercise 9.10(ii) (see especially the hint) yields (i).

(ii) Let the condition on Q be satisfied. Assume $x \in \ell^\infty$. Then

$$\sup_{a \in A} \sum_{i\geq 1} |a_i x_{\sigma(i)}| \leq \|x\|_\infty \sup_{a \in A} \sum_{i \geq 1} |a_i| < \infty$$

and so $\ell^\infty \subset \mu_Q \Longrightarrow \mu_Q = \ell^\infty$. On the other hand, if for some $A \in Q$,

$$\sup_{a \in A} \sum_{i\geq 1} |a_i| = \infty$$

then $e \notin \mu_Q = \ell^\infty$, which is absurd. Finally, let us note that

$$\|x\|_A \leq (\sup_{a\in A} \sum_{i\geq 1} |a_i|)\|x\|_\infty \qquad x \in \mu_Q$$

Now combine the inequality with Exercise 9.10(iii) (see especially the hint). □

A Special Case of μ_Q

To achieve the goal of this section, let us further narrow down the class Q. Indeed, throughout this subsection, let us assume that

$$\cup \{A : A \in Q\} \subset c_0 \qquad \text{and} \qquad \mu_Q \neq \ell^\infty$$

In particular this implies that

$$\ell^1 \subset \mu_Q \subset c_0$$

(cf. Proposition 2.5.20).

PROPOSITION 9.12 For x in μ_Q,

$$\|x\|_A = \|x'\|_A = \|\hat{x}\|_A$$

where x' and $\hat{x}$ are the sequences introduced respectively in Definitions 2.5.22 and 2.5.26.

Proof. In view of Proposition 2.5.23 and Exercise 2.5.27, x' and $\hat{x}$ belong to μ_Q.

Given $\varepsilon > 0$, there exist a in A, ρ in Π, and n in $\mathbb{N}$ such that

$$\|x'\|_A - \varepsilon < \sum_{i=1}^{n} |a_i x'_{\rho(i)}|$$

Clearly there exists σ in Π with $x_{\sigma(i)} = x'_{\rho(i)}$ for $1 \le i \le n$, giving

$$\|x'\|_A - \varepsilon \le \sum_{i=1}^{n} |a_i x_{\sigma(i)}| \le \|x\|_A$$

$$\Longrightarrow \quad \|x'\|_A \le \|x\|_A$$

Similarly $\|x\|_A \le \|x'\|_A$. Since $\hat{x} = |x'|_\sigma$ (cf. note before Exercise 2.5.27) for some σ in Π, it follows that $\|x'\|_A = \|\hat{x}\|_A$. □

The following result (Ref. 57) generalizes Theorem 2.5.28.

THEOREM 9.13 We have

(i) $\mu_Q = \{x \in c_0 : \sup\{\Sigma_{i\ge 1} \hat{a}_i \hat{x}_i : a \in A\} < \infty, \forall A \text{ in } Q\}$.

(ii) $\|x\|_A = \sup\{\Sigma_{i\ge 1} \hat{a}_i \hat{x}_i : a \in A\}$, $x \in \mu_Q$.

Proof. Let $x \in \mu_Q$. In view of Proposition 9.12, it is sufficient to prove that $\|\hat{x}\|_A = \sup\{\Sigma_{i\ge 1} \hat{a}_i \hat{x}_i : a \in A\}$ for each A in Q. Let $\varepsilon > 0$. Then there exist b in A, σ in Π, and n in $\mathbb{N}$ with

$$\|\hat{x}\|_A - \varepsilon \le \sum_{i=1}^{n} \hat{x}_i |b_{\sigma(i)}|$$

Put $J = \{\sigma(1), \ldots, \sigma(n)\}$, and choose ρ in Π so that $\rho(J) = J$ and $|b_{\rho\sigma(i)}| \le |b_{\rho\sigma(i-1)}|$ for $2 \le i \le n$. Then

$$\sum_{i=1}^{n} \hat{x}_i |b_{\sigma(i)}| \le \sum_{i=1}^{n} \hat{x}_i |b_{\rho\sigma(i)}| \le \sum_{i=1}^{n} \hat{x}_i \hat{b}_i \le \sup_{a\in A} \sum_{i\ge 1} \hat{x}_i \hat{a}_i$$

$$\Longrightarrow \quad \|\hat{x}\|_A \le \sup_{a\in A} \sum_{i\ge 1} \hat{x}_i \hat{a}_i \tag{*}$$

To prove the reverse inequality, suppose that $\sup\{\Sigma_{i\ge 1} \hat{x}_i \hat{a}_i : a \in A\} < \infty$ for each A in Q, otherwise there is nothing to prove. Hence from (*), $x \in \mu_Q$. For $\varepsilon > 0$, there exist b in A and n in $\mathbb{N}$ with

$$\sup_{a\in A} \sum_{i\ge 1} \hat{x}_i \hat{a}_i - \varepsilon \le \sum_{i=1}^{n} \hat{x}_i \hat{b}_i$$

One can find σ in Π with $|b_{\sigma(i)}| = \hat{b}_i$, $1 \le i \le n$, and thus

$$\sup_{a\in A} \sum_{i\ge 1} \hat{x}_i \hat{a}_i - \varepsilon \le \|x\|_A = \|\hat{x}\|_A$$

Finally, if for some A in Q, $\sup\{\Sigma_{i\ge 1} \hat{x}_i \hat{a}_i : a \in A\} = \infty$, then $\sup\{\Sigma_{i\ge 1} \hat{x}_i |a_{\sigma(i)}| : a \in A, \sigma \in \Pi\} = \infty$, i.e., $\|x\|_A = \|\hat{x}\|_A = \infty$ and so $x \notin \mu_Q$. □

AK-property of μ_Q

Let us recall the space μ_Q of Definition 9.8. Although the main result of this subsection is obtained under restriction on μ_Q, the following two propositions are comparatively general in nature; once again we follow Ref. 57 for the rest of this subsection.

PROPOSITION 9.14 Let $x \in \mu_Q$ and $\sigma \in P$, where P is the semigroup of all injective mappings of $\mathbb{N}$ into itself. If $x^{(n)} \to x$, then $x_\sigma^{(n)} \to x_\sigma$ as $n \to \infty$.

Proof. Given $\varepsilon > 0$ and A in Q, we determine N in $\mathbb{N}$ such that $\|x^{(n)} - x\|_A \le \varepsilon$ for $n \ge N$. Let $M > \max\{m : \sigma(m) \le N\}$. If $p > q \ge M$, choose ρ in Π with $\rho(i) = \sigma(i)$, $1 \le i \le p$. Hence, for a in A,

$$\sum_{i=1}^{p} |(x_\sigma - x_\sigma^{(q)})_i a_i| = \sum_{i=q+1}^{p} |a_i x_{\sigma(i)}| = \sum_{i=q+1}^{p} |a_i x_{\rho(i)}|$$

$$\le \sum_{i\ge N+1} |x_i a_{\rho^{-1}(i)}| \le \|x - x^{(N)}\|_A \le \varepsilon$$

Since p can be chosen as large as we please and $a \in A$ is arbitrary, we get

$$\|x_\sigma - x_\sigma^{(q)}\|_A \le \varepsilon \qquad \forall q \ge M$$

Thus $x_\sigma^{(q)} \to x_\sigma$ as $q \to \infty$. □

EXERCISE 9.15 Let $x \in \mu_Q$ and $\sigma \in \Pi$. Show that $x^{(n)} \to x$ if and only if $x_\sigma^{(n)} \to x_\sigma$.

PROPOSITION 9.16 Let $x \in \mu_Q$. Then $x^{(n)} \to x$ if and only if $x'^{(n)} \to x'$.

Proof. Let $x^{(n)} \to x$. Now $x' = x_\sigma$ for some σ in P where $\sigma(1) < \sigma(2) < \cdots$. Now apply Proposition 9.14 to get $x'^{(n)} \to x'$. Conversely, for $\varepsilon > 0$ and A in Q there corresponds an N with $\|x'^{(n)} - x'\|_A \le \varepsilon$ for all $n \ge N$. Let σ be as before with $x' = x_\sigma$. If $p > q > \sigma(N + 1)$, choose N_1 such that $\sigma(N_1) \ge p$. Clearly $N < N_1$. Now choose ρ in Π such that $\rho(i) = \sigma(i)$ for $N \le i \le N_1$. Thus, for a in A,

$$\sum_{i=q+1}^{p} |x_i a_i| \le \sum_{i=\rho(N+1)}^{\rho(N_1)} |x_i a_i| = \sum_{i=N+1}^{N_1} |x_i' a_{\rho(i)}| \le \|x' - x'^{(N)}\|_A$$

Therefore, $\|x - x^{(q)}\|_A \le \varepsilon$ for $q > \sigma(N + 1)$. □

THEOREM 9.17 Let $\mu_Q \subset c_0$. If $x \in \mu_Q$, then $x^{(n)} \to x$ if and only if $\hat{x}^{(n)} \to \hat{x}$.

Proof. Since $x \in c_0$, $\hat{x}$ is well defined and $\hat{x} = |x'|_\sigma$ for some σ in Π. Now

$$\hat{x}^{(n)} - \hat{x} = |x'^{(n)}|_\sigma - |x'|_\sigma \to 0 \quad \Longleftrightarrow \quad |x'^{(n)}| \to |x'|$$

by Exercise 9.15. From Proposition 9.16, $|x'^{(n)}| \to |x'| \Longleftrightarrow |x^{(n)}| \to |x|$. However, $|x^{(n)}| \to |x| \Longleftrightarrow x^{(n)} \to x$. □

The following is a more general result and answers in the affirmative the converse of the problem contained in Proposition 2.4.19 for a class of normal sequence spaces (cf. Ref. 57).

THEOREM 9.18 Let $Q = \{A_n : n \geq 1\}$ and $x \in \lambda_Q$. Then $x^{(n)} \to x$ in T_Q if and only if there exists y in λ_Q such that $x_i/y_i \to 0$ as $i \to \infty$ in $I_x = \{i : x_i \neq 0\}$.

Proof. Observe that T_Q is locally normal (cf. the remark following Definition 2.3.21) and so the sufficiency part follows from Proposition 2.4.19.

For necessity, assume without loss of generality that $A_1 \subset A_2 \subset \cdots$. Let us write p_i for p_{A_i}, $i \geq 1$. Since $x^{(n)} \to x$, we find a sequence $\{m_i\}$ from $\mathbb{N}$ such that $p_i(x - x^{(m_i)}) \leq 1/4^i$. Define $y \in \omega$ by

$$y_i = \begin{cases} x_i & 1 \leq i \leq m_1 \\ 2^k x_i & m_k < i \leq m_{k+1},\ k \geq 1 \end{cases}$$

Then $x_i/y_i \to 0$ as $i \to \infty$ in I_x. Now take an arbitrary A_j and let $a \in A_j$. Then

$$\sum_{i\geq 1} |a_i y_i| = \sum_{i=1}^{m_j} |a_i y_i| + \sum_{k\geq j} \sum_{i=m_k+1}^{m_{k+1}} |a_i y_i|$$

$$\leq 2^j \sum_{i=1}^{m_j} |a_i x_i| + \sum_{k\geq j} 2^k \sum_{i=m_k+1}^{m_{k+1}} |a_i x_i|$$

$$\leq 2^j p_j(x) + \sum_{k\geq j} 2^k p_k(x - x^{(m_k)})$$

$$\Longrightarrow \quad \sum_{i\geq 1} |a_i y_i| \leq 2^j p_j(x) + 2^{-j+1} \qquad \text{for all } a \text{ in } A_j$$

Therefore $y \in \kappa_{A_j}$ for every $j \geq 1$. Thus $y \in \lambda_Q$. □

For the subspaces μ_Q contained in c_0, we have the following variation of Theorem 9.18, namely (cf. Ref. 57),

THEOREM 9.19 Let $\mu_Q \subset c_0$ and $x \in \mu_Q$. If for some y in μ_Q, $\hat{x}_i/\hat{y}_i \to 0$ as $i \to \infty$, then $x^{(n)} \to x$ in μ_Q. The converse is also true provided Q is finite or countable.

Proof. Let $\hat{x}_i/\hat{y}_i \to 0$ for some y in μ_Q. From Proposition 2.4.19, $\hat{x}^{(n)} \to \hat{x}$ in μ_Q. Theorem 9.17 now yields $x^{(n)} \to x$ in μ_Q.

Conversely, let Q be finite or countable and $x^{(n)} \to x$ in μ_Q. Then $\hat{x}^{(n)} \to \hat{x}$ (Theorem 9.17). Using Theorem 9.18, we find the existence of y in μ_Q such that $\hat{x}_i/y_i \to 0$ as $i \to \infty$. Let us note that we can choose $y >> 0$. Let $\sigma \in \Pi$ be such that $\hat{y} = y_\sigma$. Now let $\varepsilon > 0$ and $\hat{x}_i/y_i < \varepsilon$ for $i \geq n_0$. Set $n_1 = \max\{\sigma^{-1}(i) : 1 \leq i \leq n_0\}$. Then $i > n_1$ implies that $\sigma(i) > n_0$.

Choose $i > n_1$ arbitrarily and let $\sigma(i) \leq i$. Hence

$$\frac{\hat{x}_i}{\hat{y}_i} = \frac{\hat{x}_i}{y_{\sigma(i)}} \leq \frac{\hat{x}_{\sigma(i)}}{y_{\sigma(i)}} < \varepsilon$$

from above.

Choose $i > n_1$ arbitrarily and let $\sigma(i) > i$. We can choose $j > i$ with $n_0 < \sigma(j) \leq i$. Then

$$\frac{\hat{x}_i}{\hat{y}_i} \leq \frac{\hat{x}_{\sigma(j)}}{\hat{y}_j} = \frac{\hat{x}_{\sigma(j)}}{y_{\sigma(j)}} < \varepsilon$$

Thus, in any case $\hat{x}_i/\hat{y}_i < \varepsilon$ for $i > n_1$. Therefore $\hat{x}_i/\hat{y}_i \to 0$ as $i \to \infty$. □

The Space d(x,p)

Let us now return to the basic theme of this section, namely, the exploration of AK-BK properties of the space d(x,p). We need confine our attention to the case when $1 < p < \infty$, the case $p = 1$ having already been dealt with in Section 5, Chapter 2. To begin with, let us express d(x,p) in a different form convenient in applications. For a normal symmetric sequence space λ, let

$$\lambda^{\wedge} = \{x : x \in \lambda,\ x = \hat{x}\}$$

In the definition of d(x,p), observe that $x \in c_0^{\wedge}$ and that $x \notin \ell^1$. It is readily checked that

$$d(x,p) = \left\{y : y \in c_0,\ \sum_{i\geq 1} x_i \hat{y}_i^p < \infty\right\}$$

Let $b \in \omega$ be defined by $b_i = x_i^{1/p}$. Suppose $M_q = (\ell^q)^{\wedge} \cap B_q$, B_q being the closed unit ball of ℓ^q, where $p^{-1} + q^{-1} = 1$, $p > 1$. Then $d(x,p) = \mu(x,p)$, where

$$\mu(x,p) = \left\{y : y \in c_0,\ \sup_{z\in M_q} \sum_{i\geq 1} \hat{y}_i z_i b_i < \infty\right\}$$

Indeed, let $y \in d(x,p)$. For z in M_q, we use Hölder's inequality to get

$$\sum_{i\geq 1} \hat{y}_i z_i b_i \leq \left\{\sum_{i\geq 1} (\hat{y}_i b_i)^p\right\}^{1/p} \left\{\sum_{i\geq 1} z_i^q\right\}^{1/q} \leq \left[\sum_{i\geq 1} x_i \hat{y}_i^p\right]^{1/p}$$

$$\Longrightarrow \quad y \in \mu(x,p)$$

Hence $d(x,p) \subset \mu(x,p)$. Suppose $y \in \mu(x,p)$. Then

$$\sum_{i\geq 1} x_i \hat{y}_i^p = \sum_{i\geq 1} \hat{y}_i b_i z_i \qquad z_i = (b_i \hat{y}_i)^{p-1}$$

$$= \|z\|_q \sum_{i\geq 1} \hat{y}_i b_i \left(\frac{z_i}{\|z\|_q}\right)$$

$$\leq \|z\|_q \sup_{u\in M_q} \sum_{i\geq 1} \hat{y}_i u_i b_i$$

$$\Longrightarrow \quad \sum_{i\geq 1} x_i \hat{y}_i^p \leq \left\{\sum_{i\geq 1} b_i^p \hat{y}_i^p\right\}^{1/q} \sup_{u\in M_q} \sum_{i\geq 1} \hat{y}_i u_i b_i$$

$$\Longrightarrow \quad \left\{\sum_{i\geq 1} x_i \hat{y}_i^p\right\}^{1/p} \leq \sup_{u\in M_q} \sum_{i\geq 1} \hat{y}_i u_i b_i < \infty$$

Therefore $y \in d(x,p)$, and so

$$d(x,p) = \mu(x,p)$$

If $A = \{\{z_i b_i\} : z \in M_q\}$, it follows that $d(x,p) = \mu_A$ (cf. Theorem 9.13) and for y in $d(x,p)$,

$$\|y;p\| = \left\{\sum_{i\geq 1} x_i \hat{y}_i^p\right\}^{1/p} = \sup_{z\in A} \sum_{i\geq 1} \hat{y}_i z_i = \|y\|_A$$

We can now conveniently state and prove the basic result of this subsection, namely,

THEOREM 9.20 The space $(d(x,p), \|\cdot;p\|)$ is an AK-BK perfect symmetric sequence space.

Proof. We need only observe that

$$d(x,p) = \mu_A \qquad \text{and} \qquad \|\cdot;p\| = \|\cdot\|_A$$

where $A = \{zx^{1/p} : z \in M_q\}$, $x^{1/p} = \{x_i^{1/p}\}$. The K-ness of $d(x,p)$ is virtually immediate, while the Banach character of the space in question follows from Theorem 9.9. The same theorem also gives rise to the perfect and symmetric characters of $d(x,p)$.

Now employing the same technique as in the proof of the last part of Theorem 2.5.28, we derive easily that $\|\hat{y}^{(n)} - \hat{y}; p\| \to 0$ as $n \to \infty$, and therefore $\hat{y}^{(n)} \to \hat{y}$ in $(\mu_A, \|\cdot\|_A)$. Using Theorem 9.17, we get $y^{(n)} \to y$ in $(\mu_A, \|\cdot\|_A)$ and this in turn implies that $y^{(n)} \to y$ in $(d(x,p), \|\cdot;p\|)$. □

Dual of d(x,p)

From Theorem 9.20 and Propositions 2.2.7 and 2.3.9, we conclude that $d(x,p)^* = d(x,p)^\zeta$ where $\zeta = \alpha, \beta, \gamma$, or δ. In this subsection we obtain the form of either of the duals of the space d(x,p); we follow Ref. 60 for the rest of this subsection. Indeed, we introduce a sequence space which shall ultimately be identified with $d(x,p)^\times$. Let us now define the space $\nu(x,p)$ as follows.

DEFINITION 9.21 Let $1 < p < \infty$ and M_q be as before, $p^{-1} + q^{-1} = 1$. Then we have

$$\nu(x,p) = \left\{ z : z \in c_0,\ \sup_n \left(\frac{\sum_{i=1}^n \hat{z}_i}{\sum_{i=1}^n k_i b_i} \right) < \infty, \text{ for some } k \text{ in } M_q \right\}$$

where x is as in Definition 9.1 and $b_i = x_i^{1/p}$.

PROPOSITION 9.22 $\nu(x,p)$ is a linear space. For each z in $\nu(x,p)$, let

$$\|z;x,p\| = \inf_{k \in M_q} \sup_n \left(\frac{\sum_{i=1}^n \hat{z}_i}{\sum_{i=1}^n k_i b_i} \right)$$

Then $(\nu(x,p), \|\cdot;x,p\|)$ is a BK-space and the closed unit disk D of $\nu(x,p)$ is $\sigma(\omega,\phi)|\nu(x,p)$-compact.

Proof. It is immediate that if $y \in \nu(x,p)$ and $\alpha \in \mathbb{K}$ then αy is in $\nu(x,p)$ and $\|\alpha y;x,p\| = |\alpha|\,\|y;x,p\|$. Let y and z be in $\nu(x,p)$ and $\varepsilon > 0$. There exist r and s in M_q such that

$$\sum_{i=1}^n \hat{y}_i < (\|y;x,p\| + \varepsilon) \sum_{i=1}^n r_i b_i \qquad \sum_{i=1}^n \hat{z}_i < (\|z;x,p\| + \varepsilon) \sum_{i=1}^n s_i b_i$$

Put

$$t = (\|y;x,p\| + \|z;x,p\| + 2\varepsilon)^{-1}[(\|y;x,p\| + \varepsilon)r + (\|z;x,p\| + \varepsilon)s]$$

Then $t \in M_q$. If $u = y + z$ then $\hat{u}_i \leq \hat{y}_i + \hat{z}_i$. Thus writing $A = \|y;x,p\| + \varepsilon$, $B = \|z;x,p\| + \varepsilon$, and $\alpha = A + B$, we find

$$\sum_{i=1}^{n} b_i t_i \geq \frac{1}{\alpha}\left(A \sum_{i=1}^{n} b_i r_i + B \sum_{i=1}^{n} b_i s_i\right)$$

$$\geq \frac{1}{\alpha}\left(\sum_{i=1}^{n} \hat{y}_i + \sum_{i=1}^{n} \hat{z}_i\right) \geq \frac{1}{\alpha} \sum_{i=1}^{n} \hat{u}_i$$

Since $n \geq 1$ is arbitrary, one concludes that

$$\|y + z;x,p\| = \|u;x,p\| \leq \|y;x,p\| + \|z;x,p\| + 2\varepsilon$$

and therefore $(\nu(x,p),\|\cdot;x,p\|)$ is a normed space. Now for each $i \geq 1$, $|y_i| \leq \hat{y}_1 \leq b_1\|y;x,p\|$; consequently, each map $y \to y_i$ is $\|\cdot;x,p\|$-continuous. Thus the space $(\nu(x,p),\|\cdot;x,p\|)$ is a K-space.

We now come to the other part of the result. Let us first of all observe that D is $\sigma(\omega,\phi)|\nu(x,p)$-bounded and so it is $\sigma(\omega,\phi)|\nu(x,p)$-relatively compact. Denote by $\bar{D}$ the $\sigma(\omega,\phi)|\nu(x,p)$-closure of D and suppose $y \in \bar{D}$. Since $\bar{D}$ is closed in the metric space $(\omega,\sigma(\omega,\phi))$, there exists a sequence $\{y^j\}$ in D such that $y_i^j \to y_i$ as $j \to \infty$ for each $i \geq 1$. Also,

$$\hat{y}_i \leq \limsup_{j\to\infty} \hat{y}_i^j \qquad i \geq 1$$

Next, to each $\varepsilon > 0$, there exists for each j a k^j in M_q with

$$\sum_{i=1}^{n} \hat{y}_i^j < (1 + \varepsilon) \sum_{i=1}^{n} k_i^j b_i \qquad \forall n \geq 1$$

Let us further observe that the closed unit disk in ℓ^q is $\sigma(\ell^q,\ell^p)$-compact. We may suppose that $\{k^j\}$ or a subsequence of $\{k^j\}$ converges to an element k of M_q in the topology $\sigma(\omega,\phi)|\ell^q$. Therefore

$$\sum_{i=1}^{n} \hat{y}_i \leq \limsup_{j\to\infty} \sum_{i=1}^{n} \hat{y}_i^j \leq (1 + \varepsilon) \limsup_{j\to\infty} \sum_{i=1}^{n} k_i^j b_i$$

$$= (1 + \varepsilon) \sum_{i=1}^{n} k_i b_i \qquad \forall n \geq 1$$

Hence $y \in \nu(x,p)$ and $\|y;x,p\| \le 1 + \varepsilon$, thus showing D to be $\sigma(\omega,\phi)|\nu(x,p)$-compact. From this one also concludes that αD is, for every $\alpha > 0$, $\sigma(\omega,\phi)|\nu(x,p)$-complete. An application of Proposition 1.2.15 now forces $\nu(x,p)$ to be complete under the norm $\|\cdot;x,p\|$. □

To prove the AK-ness of $\nu(x,p)$, let us introduce another space $\pi(x,p)$ in the following

DEFINITION 9.23 Let x, b, p, and q be as in Definition 9.21. Then we have

$$\pi(x,p) = \left\{ z : z \in c_0 \text{ with } \frac{\sum_{i=1}^n \hat{z}_i}{\sum_{i=1}^n k_i b_i} \to 0 \text{ as } n \to \infty, \text{ for some k in } M_q \right\}$$

PROPOSITION 9.24 We have $\nu(x,p) = \pi(x,p)$ and $(\nu(x,p),\|\cdot;x,p\|)$ is an AK-BK space.

Proof. It suffices to show that $\nu = \pi$ and the space in question possesses the AK-property. Clearly $\pi(x,p) \subset \nu(x,p)$. Let $z \in \nu(x,p)$ and $k \in M_q$ be such that

$$\sup_n \left(\frac{\sum_{i=1}^n \hat{z}_i}{\sum_{i=1}^n k_i b_i} \right) = \alpha < \infty$$

Case (i) Let $z \in \ell^1$. Since $x \notin \ell^1$, therefore $b \notin \ell^p$, and so for some $a \in B_q$,

$$\sum_{i\ge1} b_i |a_i| = \infty$$

We can determine σ in Π with $\hat{a} = |a_\sigma|$ and $\Sigma_{i\ge1} b_i |a_{\sigma(i)}| = \infty$. Put $k' = \hat{a}$; then $k' \in M_q$ and $\Sigma_{i\ge1} k'_i b_i = \infty$. As $\Sigma_{i\ge1} \hat{z}_i < \infty$, we find that

$$\frac{\sum_{i=1}^n \hat{z}_i}{\sum_{i=1}^n k'_i b_i} \to 0 \qquad \text{as } n \to \infty$$

Case (ii) Let $z \notin \ell^1$. Since $\Sigma_{i=1}^n k_i b_i > (1/\alpha) \Sigma_{i=1}^n \hat{z}_i$, we have $\Sigma_{i\geq 1} k_i b_i = \infty$. By Theorem 9.19, there exists k' in M_q such that $k_i/k'_i \to 0$ as $i \to \infty$. Let now $\varepsilon > 0$; then we find N in $\mathbb{N}$ with $k_i < \varepsilon k'_i$ for $i > N$. For simplicity, put $\phi(n) = \Sigma_{i=1}^n k_i b_i$. Then, for $n > N$,

$$\frac{\sum_{i=1}^n \hat{z}_i}{\sum_{i=1}^n k'_i b_i} < \frac{\varepsilon\alpha\phi(n)}{\phi(n) - \phi(N)} \to \varepsilon\alpha \qquad \text{as } n \to \infty$$

Therefore

$$\frac{\sum_{i=1}^n \hat{z}_i}{\sum_{i=1}^n k'_i b_i} \to 0 \qquad \text{as } n \to \infty$$

The preceding considerations yield, for each $\varepsilon > 0$, a positive integer n_0 such that (whether $z \in \ell^1$ or $\notin \ell^1$)

$$\frac{\sum_{i=1}^n \hat{z}_i}{\sum_{i=1}^n k'_i b_i} \leq \varepsilon \qquad \text{for } n \geq n_0 \tag{*}$$

where $k' \in M_q$. Also, $|z_i| \leq n_0^{-1} k'_1 b_1 \varepsilon$ for $i \geq i_0$. Choose $j \geq i_0$ and let $f = z - z^{(j)}$. Hence, for $n \leq n_0$,

$$\sum_{i=1}^n \hat{f}_i \leq n n_0^{-1} k'_1 b_1 \varepsilon \leq \varepsilon \sum_{i=1}^n k'_i b_i$$

and for $n > n_0$,

$$\sum_{i=1}^n \hat{f}_i \leq \sum_{i=1}^n \hat{z}_i \leq \varepsilon \sum_{i=1}^n k'_i b_i$$

[cf. (*) above]. Therefore $\|z - z^{(j)}; x, p\| \leq \varepsilon$ for $j \geq i_0$. □

We require one more result before we come to the final theorem of this final section.

PROPOSITION 9.25 We have $\nu(x,p)^{\times} = \mu(x,p)$.

Proof. Since $b \notin \ell^p$, there exists $k \in M_q$ [cf. case (i) of the preceding proof] such that $\Sigma_{i\geq 1} k_i b_i = \infty$. If $f_i = k_i b_i$, then $f = \hat{f} \notin \ell^1$; but $f \in \nu(x,p)$. Hence $\ell^1 \subset \nu(x,p) \not\subset \ell^1$, and therefore $\ell^{\infty} \not\subset \nu(x,p)^{\times}$. By Exercise 2.5.19 and Proposition 2.5.20, we thus obtain $\nu(x,p)^{\times} \subset c_0$. Let us denote by $\|\cdot;x,p\|^*$ the dual norm on $\nu(x,p)^* = \nu(x,p)^{\times}$ [since $(\nu(x,p), \|\cdot;x,p\|)$ is an AK-BK space].

Let $u \in \mu(x,p)$. To show that $u \in \nu(x,p)^{\times}$, suppose $v \in \nu(x,p)$ and $\varepsilon > 0$ are arbitrary. There exists $k \in M_q$ such that

$$\sum_{i=1}^{n} \hat{v}_i \leq (\|v;x,p\| + \varepsilon) \sum_{i=1}^{n} k_i b_i \qquad \forall n \geq 1$$

Set $s_n = \Sigma_{i=1}^{n} \hat{v}_i$, $t_n = \Sigma_{i=1}^{n} k_i b_i$. Then

$$\begin{aligned}
\sum_{i=1}^{n} |u_i v_i| \leq \sum_{i=1}^{n} \hat{u}_i \hat{v}_i &= \sum_{i=1}^{n-1} (\hat{u}_i - \hat{u}_{i+1}) s_i + s_n \hat{u}_n \\
&\leq (\|v;x,p\| + \varepsilon) \left[\sum_{i=1}^{n-1} (\hat{u}_i - \hat{u}_{i+1}) t_i + t_n \hat{u}_n \right] \\
&= (\|v;x,p\| + \varepsilon) \sum_{i=1}^{n} \hat{u}_i k_i b_i \\
&\leq (\|v;x,p\| + \varepsilon) \left(\sum_{i=1}^{n} x_i \hat{u}_i^p \right)^{1/p} \left(\sum_{i=1}^{n} k_i^q \right)^{1/q}
\end{aligned}$$

$$\Longrightarrow \quad \sum_{i\geq 1} |u_i v_i| \leq (\|v;x,p\| + \varepsilon) \|u;p\| \tag{*}$$

Hence $u \in \nu(x,p)^{\times}$ and $\mu(x,p) \subset \nu(x,p)^{\times}$.

Conversely, let $u \in \nu(x,p)^{\times}$. By Exercise 2.5.19, $\hat{u} \in \nu(x,p)^{\times}$. Observe that if $y \in \nu(x,p)$, then $|y|$, y_{σ}, and $\{\alpha_i y_i\}$ are in $\nu(x,p)$, where $|\alpha_i| = 1$, $i \geq 1$, and $\sigma \in \Pi$; and $\|y;x,p\| = \||y|;x,p\| = \|y_{\sigma};x,p\| = \|\{\alpha_i y_i\};x,p\| = \|\hat{y};x,p\|$. Hence, for u in $\nu(x,p)^{\times}$,

$$\begin{aligned}
|\hat{u}(y)| &= \left| \sum_{i\geq 1} \hat{u}_i y_i \right| = \left| \sum_{i\geq 1} |u_{\sigma(i)}| y_i \right| \\
&= \left| \sum_{j\geq 1} |u_j| y_{\sigma^{-1}(j)} \right| = \left| \sum_{j\geq 1} u_j (\alpha_j y_{\sigma^{-1}(j)}) \right|
\end{aligned}$$

and so $|\hat{u}(y)| \le \|u;x,p\|^*\|y;x,p\|$. Hence $\|\hat{u};x,p\|^* \le \|u;x,p\|^*$. Similarly, $|u(y)| \le \hat{u}(\hat{y}) \le \|\hat{u};x,p\|^*\|\hat{y};x,p\|$, giving thus, $\|u;x,p\|^* \le \|\hat{u};x,p\|^*$. Therefore

$$\|\hat{u};x,p\|^* = \|u;x,p\|^* \qquad u \in \nu(x,p)^\times$$

If $k \in \ell^q$, $\{\hat{k}_i b_i\} \in \nu(x,p)$ and $\|\{\hat{k}_i b_i\};x,p\| \le \|k\|_q$. Thus

$$\sum_{i\ge1} \hat{u}_i(k_i b_i) = |\hat{u}(kb)| \le \|u;x,p\|^*\|k\|_q \qquad (**)$$

and as the above inequality is true for any k in ℓ^q, we find that $\hat{u}b \in (\ell^q)^\times = \ell^p$ and that

$$\|\hat{u}b\|_p = \left[\sum_{i\ge1} (\hat{u}_i b_i)^p\right]^{1/p} = \left(\sum_{i\ge1} x_i \hat{u}_i^p\right)^{1/p} = \|u;p\|$$

Therefore $u \in \mu(x,p)$ and $\nu(x,p)^\times \subset \mu(x,p)$. □

PROPOSITION 9.26 For u in $\mu(x,p) = \nu(x,p)^\times$,

$$\|u;p\| = \|u;x,p\|^*$$

Proof. From (*) above,

$$|u(v)| \le \|v;x,p\|\|u;p\|$$

$$\Longrightarrow \quad \|u;x,p\|^* \le \|u;p\|$$

Making use of the second definition of $\|\cdot;p\|$ in terms of supremum and the above inequality (**), we conclude that

$$\|u;p\| \le \|u;x,p\|^*$$

Therefore we get $\|u;p\| = \|u;x,p\|^*$. □

The main result that we promised in the beginning of this subsection can now be stated:

THEOREM 9.27 The space $d(x,p)^*$ is isometrically isomorphic to $\nu(x,p)$.

Proof. As remarked earlier $d(x,p)^* = \mu(x,p)^\times$. The closed unit disk C^{**} of $d(x,p)^*$ is $\sigma(d(x,p)^*, d(x,p))$-compact, that is, C^{**} is $\sigma(\nu(x,p)^{\times\times}, \mu(x,p))$-compact. Hence the closed unit disk C of $\nu(x,p)$ is $\sigma(\nu(x,p), \mu(x,p))$-compact, i.e., C is $\sigma(\nu(x,p),\nu(x,p)^*)$-compact. Thus, by Proposition 1.9.3, $(\nu(x,p),\|\cdot;x,p\|)$ is reflexive; in other words, $\nu(x,p)$ is isometrically isomorphic to $\nu(x,p)^{**} = \mu(x,p)^* = d(x,p)^*$. □

COROLLARY 9.28 The spaces $d(x,p)$ and $\nu(x,p)$ are reflexive spaces.

Remark: There is another natural characterization of $\nu(x,p)$ depending upon tensor product techniques and the interested reader may refer to its original version in Ref. 60, p. 607.

Comparison of $d(x,p)$ *and* $d(x,p)^{\times}$ *with* ℓ^p

The spaces $d(x,p)$ and $d(x,p)^{\times}$ are not in general topologically isomorphic to the spaces ℓ^r $(1 \le r \le \infty)$. Indeed, we have already observed the truth of this statement for $p = 1$ in the remark following Exercise 2.5.36; however, in view of Corollary 9.28, these spaces when $1 < p < \infty$ cannot be isomorphic to ℓ^1 and ℓ^{∞}. Indeed, we have the following example in support of this statement.

EXAMPLE 9.29 Consider $d(x,p)$ when $x = \{1/n\}$. Suppose $d(x,p)^{\times}$ is topologically isomorphic to ℓ^r under the map $F\colon d(x,p)^{\times} \to \ell^r$, where it is clear now that $1 < r < \infty$. Since $d(x,p) \subset c_0$, $e^n \to 0$ in $\sigma(d(x,p)^{\times}, d(x,p))$. Let $F(e^n) = y^n$ $(n \ge 1)$. By Proposition 1.12.2, $y^n \to 0$ in $\sigma(\ell^r, \ell^s)$, where $r^{-1} + s^{-1} = 1$. Thus, by a result from Ref. 12, p. 200, there exists a subsequence $\{y^{n_j}\}$ of $\{y^n\}$ such that

$$\left\| \sum_{j=1}^{N} y^{n_j} \right\|_r \le AN^{1/r} \qquad A > 0$$

for all large N. Hence

$$\left\| \sum_{j=1}^{N} e^{n_j}; x,p \right\| \le BN^{1/r} \qquad B > 0$$

for all large N. If $k \in M_q$ and $m \in \mathbb{N}$, then by the Hölder inequality,

$$\sum_{i=1}^{m} k_i b_i \le \left(\sum_{i=1}^{m} k_i^q \right)^{1/q} \left(\sum_{i=1}^{m} \frac{1}{i} \right)^{1/p} \le \left(\sum_{i=1}^{m} \frac{1}{i} \right)^{1/p}$$

Thus

$$\left\| \sum_{j=1}^{N} e^{n_j}; x,p \right\| \ge \frac{N}{\left(\sum_{i=1}^{N} \frac{1}{i}\right)^{1/p}} \sim \frac{N}{(\ln N)^{1/p}}$$

$$\Rightarrow \quad \frac{\left\| \sum_{j=1}^{N} e^{n_j};x,p \right\|}{N^{1/r}} \to \infty \qquad \text{as } N \to \infty$$

The contradiction arrived at thus disposes of the required conclusion.

REFERENCES

1. A. Alexiewicz. On sequences of operations (II), Studia Math. 11(1950), 200-236.
2. --- On the two-norm convergence, Studia Math. 14(1954), 49-56.
3. A. Alexiewicz and Z. Semadeni. Linear functionals on two norm spaces, Studia Math. 17(1958), 121-140.
4. --- The two-norm spaces and their conjugate spaces, Studia Math. 18(1959), 275-293.
5. --- Some properties of two-norm spaces and a characterization of reflexivity of Banach spaces, Studia Math. 19(1960), 115-132.
6. H. S. Allen. Projective convergence and limit in sequence spaces, Proc. London Math. Soc. 48(2) (1943-45), 310-338.
7. Z. Altshuler. Uniform convexity in Lorentz sequence spaces (preprint).
8. Z. Altshuler, P. G. Casazza, and B. L. Lin. On symmetric basic sequences in Lorentz sequence spaces, Israel Jour. Math. 15(1973), 140-155.
9. I. Amemiya and Y. Kōmura. Über nichtvollständige Montel Räume, Math. Ann. 177(1968), 273-277.
10. M. G. Arsove. Proper bases and linear homeomorphisms in the space of analytic functions, Math. Ann. 135(1958), 235-243.
11. M. G. Arsove and R. E. Edwards. Generalized bases in topological linear spaces, Studia Math. 19(1960), 95-113.
12. S. Banach. Théorie des opérations linéaires, Warsaw, 1932.
13. G. Bennett. A representation theorem for summability domains, Proc. London Math. Soc. 24(3) (1972), 193-203.
14. --- Some inclusion theorems for sequence spaces, Pacific Jour. Math. 46(1) (1973), 17-30.
15. --- A new class of sequence spaces with applications in summability theory, Jour. reine angew. Math. 266(1974), 49-75.
16. G. Bennett and N. J. Kalton. FK-spaces containing c_0, Duke Math. Jour. 39(3) (1972), 561-582.
17. --- Addendum to "FK-spaces containing c_0," Duke Math. Jour. 39(4) (1972), 819-821.

18. G. Bennett and N. J. Kalton. Inclusion theorems for K-spaces, Canadian Jour. Math. 25(3) (1973), 511-524.

19. C. Bessaga, A. Pełczynski, and S. Rolewicz. Some properties of the space (s), Colloq. Math. 7 (1959), 45-51.

20. N. Bourbaki. Espaces vectoriels topologiques, No. 1229, Hermann, Paris, 1964.

21. --- Espaces vectoriels topologiques, No. 1189, Hermann, Paris, 1966.

22. H. I. Brown. Entire methods of summation, Compo. Math. 21(1969), 35-42.

23. V. S. Brudoveskii. s-type mappings of locally convex spaces, Soviet Math. Dokl. 9(1968), 572-574.

24. --- Associated nuclear topology of type s, and strongly nuclear spaces, Soviet Math. Dokl. 9(1968), 61-63.

25. J. R. Calder and J. B. Hill. A collection of sequence spaces, Trans. Amer. Math. Soc. 152(1970), 107-118.

26. P. G. Casazza and B. L. Lin. On symmetric basic sequences in Lorentz sequence spaces II, Israel Jour. Math. 17(1974), 191-218.

27. --- On Lorentz sequence spaces, Bull. Acad. Sinica 2(1974), 233-240.

28. --- Some geometric properties of Lorentz sequence spaces (preprint).

29. H. R. Chillingworth. Generalized "dual" sequence spaces, Nederl. Akad. Wetensch. Indag. Math. 20(1958), 307-315.

30. L. W. Cohen and N. Dunford. Transformations on sequence spaces, Duke Math. Jour. 3(1937), 689-701.

31. J. B. Conway. The inadequacy of sequences, Amer. Math. Monthly 76(1969), 68-69.

32. T. A. Cook. A Study of Schauder Decompositions, Semireflexivity and Weakly Equicontinuous Schauder Bases in Locally Convex Spaces, Dissertation, Florida State University, 1970.

33. T. A. Cook and W. H. Ruckle. Absolute Schauder bases for C(X) with the compact-open topology, Proc. Amer. Math. Soc. 59(1976), 111-114.

34. R. G. Cooke. Infinite Matrices and Sequence Spaces, MacMillan, London, 1950.

35. --- Linear Operators, MacMillan, London, 1953.

36. M. M. Day. Normed Linear Spaces, Springer-Verlag, Berlin, 1973.

37. N. De Grande-De Kimpe. Generalized sequence spaces, Bull. Soc. Math. Belgique 23(1971), 123-166.

38. --- Locally convex spaces for which $\Lambda(E) = \Lambda[E]$ and the Dvoretzky-Rogers theorem, Compo. Math. 35(1977), 139-145.

39. M. De Wilde. Espaces de fonctions à valuers dans un espace linéaire à semi-normes, Ext. des Mem. Socs. Roy. Sci. Liège. 12(1966).

40. M. De Wilde and C. Houet. On increasing sequences of absolutely convex sets in locally convex spaces, Math. Ann. 192(1972), 257-261.

41. J. Dieudonné. On biorthogonal systems, Michigan Math. Jour. 2(1) (1953), 7-20.

42. J. Dieudonné and L. Schwartz. La dualité dans les espaces (F) et (LF), Ann. Inst. Four. Grenoble 1(1950), 61-101.

43. E. Dubinsky. Perfect Fréchet spaces, Math. Ann. 174(1967), 186-194.

44. E. Dubinsky and G. Crofts. Nuclear maps in sequence spaces, Duke Math. Jour. 36(1969), 207-214.

45. E. Dubinsky and M. S. Ramanujan. On λ-Nuclearity, Mem. Amer. Math. Soc. No. 128, Providence, Rhode Island, 1972.

46. E. Dubinsky and J. R. Retherford. Bases in compatible topologies, Studia Math. 28(1967), 221-226.

47. J. Dugundji. Topology, Prentice Hall, Englewood Cliffs, New Jersey, 1975.

48. N. Dunford and J. T. Schwartz. Linear Operators, Part I, Interscience, New York, 1966.

49. A. Dvoretzky. On series in linear topological spaces, Israel Jour. Math. 1(1963), 37-47.

50. A. Dvoretzky and C. A. Rogers. Absolute and unconditional convergence in linear normed spaces, Proc. Nat. Acad. Sci., U.S.A. 36(1950), 192-197.

51. G. Fenske and E. Schock. Über die diametrale Dimension von lokalkonvexen Räumen, BMBW-G.M.D., Bonn Nr. 10 (1969), 13-22.

52. --- Nuklearität und lokale Konvexitat von Folgenraumen, Math. Nachr. 45(1970), 327-335.

53. G. Fichtenholz. Sur les fonctionnelles linéaires, continues an sens generalise, Recueil Math. 4(1938), 193-214.

54. D. H. Fremlin. On Köthe Spaces, Dissertation, Cambridge University, 1966.

55. G. Fricke and R. E. Powell. A theorem on entire methods of summation, Comp. Math. 22(1970), 253-259.

56. D. J. H. Garling. The β- and γ-duality, Proc. Cambridge Philos. Soc. 63(1967), 963-981.

57. --- On symmetric sequence spaces, Proc. London Math. Soc. 16(3) (1966), 85-106.

58. --- On topological sequence spaces, Proc. Cambridge Phil. Soc. 63 (1967), 997-1019.

59. --- On ideals of operators in Hilbert spaces, Proc. London Math. Soc. 17(2) (1967), 115-138.

60. --- A class of reflexive symmetric BK-spaces, Canadian Jour. Math. 21(1969), 602-608.

61. I. M. Gelfand. Abstrakte Funktionen und lineare Operatoren, Mat. Sb. (N.S.) 46(4) (1938), 235-286.

62. I. M. Gelfand and N. Ya. Vilenkin. Generalized Functions, Vol. 4, Academic Press, New York, 1964.

63. C. Goffman and G. Pedrick. First Course in Functional Analysis, Prentice-Hall, Englewood Cliffs, New Jersey, 1965.

64. H. F. Green. Convergence in sequence spaces, Proc. Edinburgh Math. Soc. 11(1958/59), 83-85.

65. D. A. Gregory. Vector-Valued Sequence Spaces, Dissertation, University of Michigan, Ann Arbor, 1967.

66. --- Some basic properties of vector sequence spaces, Jour. reine angew. Math. 237(1969), 26-38.

67. --- Hereditary properties of vector sequence spaces, Jour. reine angew. Math. 243(1970), 66-69.

68. D. A. Gregory and J. H. Shapiro. Non-convex linear topologies with the Hahn-Banach extension property, Proc. Amer. Math. Soc. 25(4) (1970), 902-905.

69. Y. Gribanov. On the theory of ℓ_M-spaces (Russian), Uc. Zap. Kazansk un-ta 117(1957), 62-65.

70. A. Grothendieck. Sur une notion de produit tensoriel topologique d'espaces vectoriels topologiques, et une classe remarquable d'espaces liées a cette notion, Comp. Rend. Paris 233(1951), 1556-1558.

71. --- Sur les applicationes linéaires faiblement compactes d'espaces (CK), Canadian Jour. Math. 5(1953), 129-173.

72. --- Résumé des résultats essentiels dans le théorie des produits tensoriels, topologiques et des espaces nucléaires, Ann. Inst. Fourier 4(1954), 73-112.

73. --- Produits tensoriels topologiques et espaces nucléaires, Mem. Amer. Math. Soc. No. 16, Providence, Rhode Island, 1955.

74. --- La théorie de Fredholm, Bull. Soc. Math. de France 84(1956), 319-384.

75. --- Sur certaines classes de suites dans les espaces de Banach et le théorème de Dvoretzky-Rogers, Bol. Soc. Math. Sao Paulo 8(1956).

76. --- Topological Vector Spaces, Gordon and Breach, New York, 1975.

77. M. Gupta. A Topological Study of the Spaces of Analytic Functions of Several Variables, Doctoral Dissertation, I.I.T., Kanpur, 1973.

78. --- On the class of entire functions of several complex variables having finite growth, Jour. Korean Math. Soc. 13(1) (1976), 19-25.

79. --- K-spaces and matrix transformations, Proc. Conf. Func. Anal., University of Delhi, April 1978.

80. M. Gupta and P. K. Kamthan. Infinite matrices and tensorial transformations [to appear in Acta Math. Viet. 5(1980)].

81. --- Quasi-regular orthogonal system of subspaces, Proc. Roy. Irish Acad. 80A(1) (1980), 79-83.

82. M. Gupta, P. K. Kamthan, and K. L. N. Rao. The generalized sequence spaces c, c_0, ℓ^1, and ℓ^∞ and their Köthe duals, Tamkang Jour. Math. 7(2) (1976), 175-178.

83. --- Generalized Köthe sequence spaces and decompositions, Ann. Math. Pura Appl., Ser. IV 113(1977), 287-301.

84. --- Duality in certain generalized Köthe sequence spaces, Bull. Inst. Math. Acad. Sinica 5(2) (1977), 285-298.

85. H. Hahn. Über Folgen linearer Operationen, Monat. für Math. 32(1922), 3-88.

86. P. R. Halmos. Measure Theory, D. Van Nostrand, Princeton, N.J., 1950.

87. J. K. Hampson and A. Wilansky. Sequences in locally convex spaces, Studia Math. 14(1973), 221-223.

88. I. Heller. Contribution to the theory of divergent series, Pacific Jour. Math. 2(1952), 153-177.

89. I. N. Herstein. Topics in Algebra, Blaisdell, New York, 1964.

90. E. Hewitt and K. Stromberg. Real and Abstract Analysis, Springer-Verlag, New York, 1965.

91. T. H. Hilderbrandt. On unconditional convergence in normed spaces, Bull. Amer. Math. Soc. 40(1940), 959-962.

92. J. Horváth. Topological Vector Spaces, Vol. I, Addison-Wesley, Don Mills, Ontario, 1966.

93. T. Husain. The Open and Closed Graph Theorems in Topological Vector Spaces, Clarendon Press, Oxford, 1965.

94. T. Husain and P. K. Kamthan. Spaces of entire functions represented by Dirichlet series, Collect. Math. 19(3) (1968), 203-216.

95. T. Husain and S. M. Khaleelulla. On the countably, σ- and sequentially barrelled spaces, Canadian Math. Bull. 18(3) (1975), 431-432.

96. C. Hutton. Approximation Numbers of Bounded Linear Operators, Dissertation, Louisiana State University, 1973.

97. D. H. Hyers. Pseudonormed linear spaces and abelian groups, Duke Math. Jour. 5(1939), 628-634.

98. V. G. Iyer. On the space of integral functions I, Jour. Indian Math. Soc. 12(2) (1948), 13-30.

99. R. T. Jacob, Jr. Some matrix transformations of analytic sequence spaces, Pacific Jour. Math. 59(1975), 487-491.

100. --- Matrix transformations involving simple sequence spaces, Pacific Jour. Math. 70(1) (1977), 179-187.

101. --- A class of sequence spaces (preprint).

102. R. C. James. Bases and reflexivity in Banach spaces, Ann. Math. 52(1950), 518-527.

103. G. J. O. Jameson. Some short proofs on subseries convergence, Amer. Math. Monthly 79(1) (1972), 53-55.

104. S. Kaczmarz and H. Steinhaus. Theorie der Orthogonalreihen, Warszawa-Lwów, 1935.

105. N. J. Kalton. A barrelled space without a basis, Proc. Amer. Math. Soc. 26(3) (1970), 465-466.

106. --- Subseries convergence in topological groups and vector spaces, Israel Jour. Math. 10(1971), 402-412.

107. --- Some forms of the closed graph theorems, Proc. Cambridge Phil. Soc. 70(1971), 401-408.

108. --- Mackey duals and almost shrinking bases, Proc. Cambridge Phil. Soc. 74(1973), 73-81.

109. N. J. Kalton. Basic sequences in F-spaces and their applications, Proc. Edinburgh Math. Soc. 19(Ser. II), Pt. 2(1974), 151-167.

110. --- Orlicz sequence spaces without local convexity, Proc. Cambridge Phil. Soc. 81(1977), 253-277.

111. N. J. Kalton and W. H. Ruckle. A series characterization of subspaces of $L_p(\mu)$ spaces, Bull. Amer. Math. Soc. 79(5) (1973), 1019-1022.

112. P. K. Kamthan. Convex functions and their applications, Rev. Fac. Sci. Univ. Istanbul, Ser. A 28 (1963), 71-78.

113. --- FK-spaces for entire Dirichlet series, Collect. Math. 20(1969), 271-280.

114. --- A note on the space of entire functions, Labdev Jour. Sci. Tech. 7-A(3) (1969), 144-145.

115. --- Normalized bases on topological vector spaces, Portuguese Math. 35 (to appear).

116. --- Various topologies on the space of entire functions, Labdev Jour. Sci. Tech. 9(A), No. 3-4 (1971), 143-151; also in Proc. Int. Conf. Topology, I.I.T., Kanpur, Oct. 1968, 1-12.

117. --- A study on the space of entire functions of several complex variables, Yokohama Math. Jour. 21(1) (1973), 17-20.

118. --- Kolmogorov's diameters and their applications, Proc. Conf. Func. Anal. and Appl. Seminar, AMU, Aligarh, 1977 (to appear in Bull. AMU, Vol. 6).

119. --- Montel spaces of entire functions (preprint).

120. P. K. Kamthan and S. K. S. Gautam. Characterization of bounded sets in the space of entire Dirichlet functions of finite order (R), Boll. U.M.I.(5), 13-A(1976), 568-575.

121. P. K. Kamthan and M. Gupta. Expansion of entire functions of several complex variables having finite growth, Trans. Amer. Math. Soc. 192(1974), 371-382.

122. --- Space of entire functions of several complex variables having finite order point, Math. Japonicae 20(1) (1975), 7-19.

123. --- Characterization of bases in topological vector spaces, Tamkang Jour. Math. 7(1) (1976), 51-55.

124. --- Schauder bases and sequential duals, Bull. Soc. Roy. Sci. Liège 46(5-8) (1977), 153-155.

125. --- Bases in Topological Vector Spaces and Applications (a monograph under preparation).

126. --- Analytic functions in bicylinders, Indian Jour. Pure Appl. Math. 5(12) (1974), 1119-1126.

127. --- Weak Schauder bases and completeness, Proc. Roy. Irish Acad. 78, Sect. A(1978), 51-54.

128. --- Several notions of absolute Schauder bases, Jour. reine angew. Math. 307/308(1979), 160-165.

129. --- Weak unconditional Cauchy series, Rendi. Circolo Mat. Palermo (to appear).

130. P. K. Kamthan and S. K. Ray. On decompositions of barrelled spaces, Colloq. Math. 34(1) (1975), 73-79.

131. P. K. Kamthan, M. Gupta, and P. K. Subramanian. Schauder Decompositions and Mixed Topologies (a monograph under preparation).

132. L. V. Kantorovich. Functional Analysis in Normed Spaces, McMillan, New York, 1964.

133. J. L. Kelley. General Topology, D. Van Nostrand, Princeton, 1963.

134. J. L. Kelley and I. Namioka. Linear Topological Spaces, D. Van Nostrand, Princeton, 1968.

135. K. Knopp and G. G. Lorentz. Beiträge zur absoluten Limitierung, Arch. Math. 2(1949), 10-18.

136. R. J. Knowles. The strongest locally convex topology consistent with a Schauder base, Bull. Soc. Roy. Sci. Liège 44(3-4) (1975), 165-168.

137. R. J. Knowles and T. A. Cook. Incomplete reflexive spaces without Schauder bases, Proc. Cambridge Phil. Soc. 74(1973), 83-86.

138. Y. Kōmura. Some examples on linear topological spaces, Math. Ann. 153(1964), 150-162.

139. G. Köthe. Neubegründung der Theorie der vollkommenen Räume, Math. Nachr. 4(1951), 70-80.

140. --- Topological Vector Spaces I, Springer-Verlag, Berlin-Heidelberg-New York, 1969.

141. --- Stark nukleare Folgenräume, Jour. Fac. Sci. Univ., Tokyo, Sec. I 17(1970), 291-296.

142. --- Nuclearity and sequence spaces, Address, Func. Anal. Conf., Liège (1970), 13-18.

143. G. Köthe and O. Toeplitz. Lineare Räume mit unendlich vielen Koordinaten und Ringe unendlicher Matrizen, Jour. reine angew. Math. 171 (1934), 193-226.

144. M. A. Krasnoselskii, M. G. Krein, and D. P. Milman. On the defect numbers of linear operators in Banach spaces and geometrical questions, Sb. Inst. Mat. Akad. Nauk. Ukr. S.S.R. 11(1948), 97-112.

145. M. A. Krasnoselskii and Y. B. Rutitsky. Convex Functions and Orlicz Spaces, Groningen, Netherlands, 1961.

146. V. Krishnamurthy. On the continuous endomorphisms in the spaces of certain classes of entire functions, Proc. Nat. Inst. Sci. (India), Pt. A 26(6) (1960), 642-655.

147. C. G. Lascarides. A study of certain sequence spaces of Maddox and a generalization of a theorem of Iyer, Pacific Jour. Math. 38(1971), 487-500.

148. I. E. Leonard. Banach sequence spaces, Jour. Math. Anal. Appl. 54(1) (1976), 245-265.

149. M. Levin and S. Saxon. A note on the inheritance properties of locally convex spaces by subspaces of countable co-dimension, Proc. Amer. Math. Soc. 29(1) (1971), 97-102.

150. K. Lindberg. Contractive Projections on Orlicz Sequence Spaces and Continuous Function Spaces, Ph.D. thesis, University of California, Berkeley, 1970.

151. K. Lindberg. On subspaces of Orlicz sequence spaces, Studia Math. 45(1973), 119-146.

152. J. Lindenstrauss and L. Tzafriri. On Orlicz sequence spaces, Israel Jour. Math. 10(3) (1971), 379-390.

153. --- On Orlicz sequence spaces II, Israel Jour. Math. 11(4) (1972), 355-379.

154. --- On Orlicz sequence spaces III, Israel Jour. Math. 14(4) (1973), 368-389.

155. --- Classical Banach Spaces, Lecture Notes in Math., Springer-Verlag, Berlin, 1973.

156. --- Classical Banach Spaces I, Sequence Spaces, Springer-Verlag, Berlin, 1977.

157. S. Lipschutz. Theory and Problems of General Topology, Schaum, New York, 1965.

158. R. H. Lohman and W. J. Stiles. On separability in linear topological spaces, Proc. Amer. Math. Soc. 42(1974), 236-237.

159. G. G. Lorentz. Some new functional spaces, Ann. Math. 51 (1950), 37-55.

160. --- Discrete theorems on methods of summability II, Canadian Jour. Math. 3(1951), 236-256.

161. G. W. Mackey. On infinite dimensional linear spaces, Trans. Amer. Math. Soc. 57(1945), 155-207.

162. M. Mahowald. Barrelled spaces and the closed graph theorem, Jour. London Math. Soc. 36(1961), 108-110.

163. A. I. Markushevich. Sur les bases dans l'espace des fonctions analytiques, Mat. Sb. (N.S.) 17(59) (1945), 211-259.

164. J. T. Marti. Introduction to the Theory of Bases, Springer-Verlag, Berlin, 1969.

165. A. Martineau. Sur une propriété universelle de l'espace des distributions, C.R. Acad. Sci. Paris 259(1964), 3162-3164.

166. C. W. McArthur. On a theorem of Orlicz and Pettis, Pacific Jour. Math. 22(1967), 297-302.

167. --- A convergence criterion with applications in locally convex spaces, Duke Math. Jour. 34(1967), 193-200.

168. --- Developments in Schauder basis theory, Bull. Amer. Math. Soc. 78(6) (1972), 877-908.

169. --- Equicontinuous projective topology (preprint)

170. C. W. McArthur and J. R. Retherford. Some applications of an inequality in locally convex spaces, Trans. Amer. Math. Soc. 137(1969), 115-123.

171. F. M. Mears. Absolute regularity and the Norlund means, Ann. Math. 38(1937), 549-601.

172. M. R. Mehdi. Linear transformations between the Banach spaces L_p and ℓ_p with applications to absolute summability, Ph.D. thesis, University of London, 1959.

173. B. S. Mitiagin. Approximative dimension and bases in nuclear spaces, Amer. Math. Soc.: Russian Math. Surveys 16(1961), 59-127.

174. B. S. Mitiagin and A. Pełczynski. Nuclear operators and approximative dimension, Proc. Int. Cong. Math., Moscow, 1966; Eng. Transl., AMS Transl. 70, 137-145.

175. M. A. Naimark. Normed Rings, P. Noordhoff N.V., Groningen, 1964.

176. H. Nakano. Modulared sequence spaces, Proc. Jap. Acad. 27(1951), reprinted in Semi-ordered Linear Spaces, Tokyo, 1955.

177. I. N. Natanson. Theory of Functions of a Real Variable, Vol. I, Frederick Ungar, New York, 1964.

178. W. Orlicz. Beiträge zur Theorie der Orthogonalentwicklungen II, Studia Math. 1(1929), 241-255.

179. --- Über eine gewisse Klasse von Räumen vom Typus B, Bull. Int. Acad. Pol. 8(1932), 207-220.

180. --- Linear operators in Saks spaces (I), Studia Math. 11(1950), 237-272.

181. --- Linear operators in Saks spaces (II), Studia Math. 15(1955), 1-25.

182. --- On the continuity of linear operators in Saks spaces with an application to the theory of summability, Studia Math. 16(1957), 69-73.

183. W. Orlicz and V. Pták. Some remarks on Saks spaces, Studia Math. 16(1957), 56-58.

184. A. Pełczynski and W. Szlenk. Sur l'injection naturelle de l'espace ℓ dans l'espace ℓ^p, Colloq. Math. 10 (1963), 313-323.

185. B. J. Pettis. On integration in vector spaces, Trans. Amer. Math. Soc. 44(1938), 277-304.

186. A. Peyerimhoff. Über ein Lemma von Herrn H. C. Chow, Jour. London Math. Soc. 32(1957), 33-36.

187. N. Phoung-Các. Sur les espaces parfaits de suites généralises, Math. Ann. 171(1967), 131-143.

188. --- On some spaces of vector valued sequences, Math. Zeit. 95(1967), 242-250.

189. A. Pietsch. Verallgemeinerte Vollkommene Folgenräume, Akademi-Verlag, East Berlin, 1962.

190. --- Nuclear Locally Convex Spaces, Springer-Verlag, Berlin-Heidelberg-New York, 1967.

191. --- Absolute p-summierende Abbildungen in normierten Raumen, Studia Math. 28 (1967), 333-353.

192. M. S. Ramanujan. Absolutely λ-summing operators, a symmetric sequence space, Math. Zeit. 114(1970), 187-193.

193. --- Generalized nuclear maps in normed linear spaces, Jour. reine angew. Math. 244(1970), 190-197.

194. --- Power series spaces $\Lambda(\alpha)$ and associated $\Lambda(\alpha)$-nuclearity, Math. Ann. 189(1970), 161-168.

195. M. S. Ramanujan and T. Terzioğlu. Diametral dimensions of cartesian products, stability of smooth sequence spaces and applications, Jour. reine angew. Math. 280(1976), 163-171.

196. K. C. Rao. Matrix transformations of some sequence spaces, Pacific Jour. Math. 31(1969), 171-174.

197. --- Matrix transformations of some sequence spaces II, Glasgow Jour. Math. 11(1970), 161-166.

198. --- Matrix transformations of some sequence spaces III, Boll. U.M.I. 5(4) (1972), 7-13.

199. K. L. N. Rao. Generalized Köthe Sequence Spaces, Dissertation, I.I.T., Kanpur, 1976.

200. L. A. Raphael. On a characterization of infinite complex matrices mapping the space of analytic sequences into itself, Pacific Jour. Math. 27(1) (1968), 123-126.

201. S. K. Ray. Decompositions of Topological Vector Spaces, Dissertation, I.I.T., Kanpur, 1974.

202. A. P. Robertson. On unconditional convergence in topological vector spaces, Proc. Roy. Soc. Edinburgh Sect. A (68(1969), 145-157.

203. --- Unconditional convergence and the Vitali-Hahn-Saks theorem, Bull. Soc. Math. France Memoire 31-32 (1972), 335-341.

204. A. P. Robertson and W. Robertson. Topological Vector Spaces, Cambridge University Press, Cambridge, 1964.

205. S. Rolewicz. On a certain class of linear metric spaces, Bull. Acad. Polonaise Sci. Cl. III 5(1957), 471-473.

206. --- On a generalization of the Dvoretzky-Rogers theorem, Colloq. Math. 8(1961), 103-106.

207. --- Metric Linear Spaces, Polish Sci. Pub., Warsaw, 1972.

208. S. Rolewicz and C. Ryll-Nardzewski. On unconditional convergence in topological vector spaces, Colloq. Math. 17(1967), 327-331.

209. B. Rosenberger. F-norm Ideale von Operatoren in normierten Räumen, BMBW-GMD-44, Inst. Angew. Math. Informatik, Universität Bonn, 1971, 1-40.

210. --- ϕ-nukleare Räume, Math. Nachr. 52(1972), 147-160.

211. --- Universal generators for varieties of nuclear spaces, Trans. Amer. Math. Soc. 184(1973), 275-290.

212. R. C. Rosier. Generalized Sequence Spaces, Dissertation, University of Maryland, 1970.

213. --- Dual spaces of certain vector valued sequence spaces, Pacific Jour. Math. 46(1973), 487-501.

214. --- Vector sequence spaces and the Dvoretzky-Rogers theorem (to appear).

215. W. Ruckle. The construction of sequence spaces that have Schauder bases, Canadian Jour. Math. 18(1966), 1281-1293.

216. --- Symmetric coordinate spaces and symmetric bases, Canadian Jour. Math. 19(1967), 828-838.

217. --- On the characterization of sequence spaces associated with Schauder bases, Studia Math. 28(1967), 279-288.

218. W. Ruckle. An abstract concept of the sum of a numerical series, Canadian Jour. Math. 22(4) (1970), 863-874.

219. --- Topologies on sequence spaces, Pacific Jour. Math. 42(1) (1972), 235-249.

220. W. Rudin. Principles of Mathematical Analysis, McGraw-Hill, New York, 1953.

221. --- Functional Analysis, McGraw-Hill, New York, 1973.

222. S. Saks. On some functionals, Trans. Amer. Math. Soc. 35(1933), 549-556.

223. --- Addition to the note on some functionals, Trans. Amer. Math. Soc. 35(1933), 965-970.

224. W. L. C. Sargent. Some sequence spaces related to the ℓ^p spaces, Jour. London Math. Soc. 35(1960), 161-171.

225. H. H. Schaeffer. Topological Vector Spaces, Springer-Verlag, New York-Heidelberg-Berlin, 1970.

226. E. Schock. Diametrale Dimension, approximative Dimension und Anwendungen, BMBW-GMD, Bonn, Nr. 43(1971), 1-48.

227. L. Schwartz. Functional Analysis, Courant Inst. Math. Sci., New York University, 1964.

228. G. Seever. Measures on F-spaces, Trans. Amer. Math. Soc. 133(1968), 267-280.

229. J. J. Sember. A note on conull FK-spaces and variation matrices, Math. Z. 108(1968), 1-6.

230. --- Summability matrices as compact like operators, Jour. London Math. Soc. 2(2) (1970), 530-534.

231. --- Variational FK-spaces and two-norm convergence, Math. Z. 119 (1971), 153-159.

232. --- Collection of Problems, Conference on Sequence Spaces and Summability, State University of New York, Albany, July 1969.

233. J. H. Shapiro. Linear Functionals on Non-Locally Convex Spaces, Dissertation, University of Michigan, East Lansing, 1969.

234. --- Examples of proper, closed weakly dense subspaces in locally convex F-spaces, Israel Jour. Math. 7(1969), 369-380.

235. I. Singer. Best Approximations in Normed Linear Spaces, Springer-Verlag, Berlin, 1970.

236. --- Bases in Banach Spaces I, Springer-Verlag, Heidelberg, 1970.

237. --- Some remarks on domination of sequences, Math. Ann. 184(1970), 113-132.

238. A. K. Snyder. Conull and coregular FK-spaces, Math. Z. 90(1965), 376-381.

239. A. K. Snyder and A. Wilansky. Inclusion theorems and semiconservative FK-spaces, Rocky Mountain Jour. Math. 2(4) (1972), 595-603.

240. P. Spuhler. Λ-Nukleare Räume, Inaugural Dissertation, Universität Frankfurt am Main, December 1970.

241. W. J. Stiles. Some properties of ℓ_p, $0 < p < 1$, Trans. Amer. Math. Soc. 149(1970), 405-415.

242. P. K. Subramanian. Two-norm spaces and decompositions of Banach spaces I, Studia Math. 43(1972), 179-194.

243. --- Two-norm spaces and quasi-reflexivity, Tamkang Jour. Math. 8(1), (1977), 17-28.

244. P. K. Subramanian and S. Rothman. Two-norm spaces and decompositions of Banach spaces II, Trans. Amer. Math. Soc. 181(1973), 313-327.

245. A. E. Taylor. Introduction to Functional Analysis, John Wiley, New York, 1958.

246. --- General Theory of Functions and Integration, Blaisdell, Waltham, Mass., 1965.

247. T. Terzioğlu. Die diametrale Dimension von lokalkonvexen Räumen, Collect. Math. 20(1) (1968), 49-99.

248. --- On Schwartz spaces, Math. Ann. 182(1969), 236-242.

249. --- A characterization of compact linear mappings, Arch. Math. 22(1971), 75-78.

250. --- Linear operators on nuclear spaces and their extension properties, Rev. Fac. Sci. Univ. Istanbul, Ser. A 37 (1972), 1-21.

251. --- Smooth sequence spaces and associated nuclearity, Proc. Amer. Math. Soc. 37(2) (1973), 497-504.

252. --- Nuclear and strongly nuclear sequence spaces, Rev. Fac. Sci. Univ. Istanbul, Ser. A 34 (1969), 1-5.

253. O. Toeplitz. Die linearen volkommenen Räume der Funktionentheorie, Commet. Math. Helv. 23(1949), 222-242.

254. A. E. Tong. Diagonal submatrices of matrix maps, Pacific Jour. Math. 32(1970), 551-559.

255. P. C. Tonne. Matrix transformations on the power series convergent on the unit disc, Jour. London Math. Soc. 4(2) (1972), 667-670.

256. --- Matrix representations for linear transformations on series analytic in the unit disc, Pacific Jour. Math. 44(1973), 385-392.

257. --- Matrix representations for linear transformations on analytic sequences, Pacific Jour. Math. 46(1973), 269-274.

258. P. Turpin. The spaces $\Lambda_\beta(E)$ and $\Lambda_\sigma(E)$ (preprint).

259. G. R. Walker. λ-Nuclear and λ-Summing Operators, Dissertation, Indiana University, 1975.

260. --- Compactness of λ-nuclear operators, Michigan Math. Jour. 23 (1976), 167-172.

261. J. H. Webb. Sequential convergence in locally convex spaces, Proc. Cambridge Phil. Soc. 64(1968), 341-364.

262. L. J. Weill. Unconditional Bases in Locally Convex Spaces, Dissertation, Florida State University, Florida, 1966.

263. --- Unconditional and shrinking bases in locally convex spaces, Pacific Jour. Math. 29(1969), 467-483.

264. A. Wilansky. Functional Analysis, Blaisdell, New York, 1964.

265. --- Topics in Functional Analysis, Lecture Notes No. 45, Springer-Verlag, Berlin, 1967.

266. W. Wojtynski. On conditional bases in non-nuclear Fréchet spaces, Studia Math. 35(1970), 77-96.

267. J. Y. T. Woo. On modular sequence spaces, Studia Math. 48(1973), 271-289.

268. --- On a class of universal modular sequence spaces, Israel Jour. Math. 20(1975), 193-215.

269. P. C. Woods. Banach-Steinhaus Spaces and Decomposition of Operators in Locally Convex Spaces, Dissertation, Florida State University, 1972.

270. K. Zeller. Allgemeine Eigenschaften von Limitierungsverfahren, Math. Z. 53(1951), 463-487.

271. --- Matrix Transformationen von Folgenräumen, Univ. Roma 1st Alta. Mat. Rend. Mate. e. Appl. (5)12 (1954), 340-346.

272. --- Theorie der Limitierungsverfahren, Springer-Verlag, Berlin, 1970.

273. P. L. Zelonka. Some Results about Hilbert Space Topologies Generalized to Topological Vector Spaces, MS Thesis, Queen's University, Kingston, Canada, 1970.

ABBREVIATIONS AND NOTATION

ABBREVIATIONS

NOTATION[†]

[†]Notation for norms, sequence spaces, topological spaces, and topologies is listed separately below.

SEQUENCE SPACES

SPACES

INDEX